Biochemical Actions of Hormones

VOLUME II

Contributors

R. W. BUTCHER

HECTOR F. DeLUCA

EUGENE R. DeSOMBRE

RALPH I. DORFMAN

JAMES J. FERGUSON, JR.

IRVING B. FRITZ

THOMAS D. GELEHRTER

ELWOOD V. JENSEN

GERALD LITWACK

MARK J. MELANCON, JR.

A. H. REDDI

G. A. ROBISON

SANFORD SINGER

E. W. SUTHERLAND

GORDON M. TOMKINS

ROGER W. TURKINGTON

H. G. WILLIAMS-ASHMAN

G. R. WYATT

Biochemical Actions of Hormones

Edited by GERALD LITWACK

Fels Research Institute
Temple University
School of Medicine
Philadelphia, Pennsylvania

VOLUME II

ACADEMIC PRESS   New York and London 1972

A Subsidiary of Harcourt Brace Jovanovich, Publishers

ACADEMIC PRESS, INC.
111 Fifth Avenue, New York, New York 10003

United Kingdom Edition published by
ACADEMIC PRESS, INC. (LONDON) LTD.
24/28 Oval Road, London NW1 7DD

LIBRARY OF CONGRESS CATALOG CARD NUMBER: 70-107567

PRINTED IN THE UNITED STATES OF AMERICA

Contents

1.   **The Present Status of Genetic Regulation by Hormones**

     Gordon M. Tomkins and Thomas D. Gelehrter

2.   **Cyclic AMP and Hormone Action**

     R. W. Butcher, G. A. Robison, and E. W. Sutherland

3.   **Multiple Hormonal Interactions. The Mammary Gland**

     Roger W. Turkington

8.   Androgenic Regulation of Tissue Growth and Function

H. G. Williams-Ashman and A. H. Reddi

9.   Mechanism of Action of Gonadotropins and Prolactin

Ralph I. Dorfman

10.   The Mechanism of Action of Adrenocorticotropic Hormone

James J. Ferguson, Jr.

11.   25-Hydroxycholecalciferol: A Hormonal Form of Vitamin D

Hector F. DeLuca and Mark J. Melancon, Jr.

12.   Insect Hormones

> *G. R. Wyatt*

List of Contributors

Numbers in parentheses indicate the pages on which the authors' contributions begin.

R. W. Butcher (21, 81), Department of Biochemistry, University of Massachusetts Medical School, Worcester, Massachusetts

Hector F. DeLuca (337), Department of Biochemistry, University of Wisconsin, Madison, Wisconsin

Eugene R. DeSombre (215), The Ben May Laboratory for Cancer Research, The University of Chicago, Chicago, Illinois

Ralph I. Dorfman (295), Syntex Research, Stanford Industrial Park, Palo Alto, California

James J. Ferguson, Jr. (317), Department of Biochemistry, School of Medicine, University of Pennsylvania, Philadelphia, Pennsylvania

Irving B. Fritz (165), Banting and Best Department of Medical Research, University of Toronto, Toronto, Canada

Thomas D. Gelehrter (1), Division of Medical Genetics, Department of Medicine and Pediatrics, Yale University School of Medicine, New Haven, Connecticut

Elwood V. Jensen (215), The Ben May Laboratory for Cancer Research, The University of Chicago, Chicago, Illinois

Gerald Litwack (113), Fels Research Institute, Temple University School of Medicine, Health Sciences Center, Philadelphia, Pennsylvania

Mark J. Melancon, Jr.* (337), Department of Biochemistry, University of Wisconsin, Madison, Wisconsin

A. H. Reddi (257), The Ben May Laboratory for Cancer Research and Department of Biochemistry, The University of Chicago, Chicago, Illinois

* Present address: Department of Pharmacy, University of Wisconsin, Milwaukee, Wisconsin.

G. A. Robison (21, 81), Departments of Pharmacology and Physiology, Vanderbilt University School of Medicine, Nashville, Tennessee

Sanford Singer (113), Fels Research Institute, Temple University School of Medicine, Health Sciences Center, Philadelphia, Pennsylvania

E. W. Sutherland (21, 81), Department of Physiology, Vanderbilt University School of Medicine, Nashville, Tennessee

Gordon M. Tomkins (1), Department of Biochemistry and Biophysics, University of California at San Francisco, San Francisco, California

Roger W. Turkington (55), Department of Medicine, University of Wisconsin, Madison, Wisconsin

H. G. Williams-Ashman (257), The Ben May Laboratory for Cancer Research and Department of Biochemistry, The University of Chicago, Chicago, Illinois

G. R. Wyatt (385), Department of Biology, Yale University, New Haven, Connecticut

Preface

This collection of papers by researchers in the field of hormone action surveys the significant developments in our progress toward understanding the primary effects of hormones in cellular receptors at the molecular level. During the last six years, there have been enormous developments in this field. The extent of progress is reflected in the size of this two-volume work. An advantage in having two volumes is the prompt publication in Volume I of those manuscripts completed at an early date, an important consideration in a rapidly expanding area of research.

Some informational overlap between contributions was unavoidable, but, hopefully, has been held to a minimum. It seemed more sensible to tolerate a small degree of redundancy than to tamper with cohesiveness. There are certain areas in which relatively little progress has been made. Accordingly, a few gaps in coverage will be evident, such as the absence of a contribution on intestinal hormones.

The coverage is broad enough to make this work useful as a modern reference text for the endocrinologist. In many cases, new data from the contributors' laboratories are presented. Thus, the purpose of these two volumes is to provide in one source an up-to-date survey of molecular and biochemical approaches bearing on the problem of hormone mechanism.

GERALD LITWACK

Contents of Volume I

CHAPTER 1

The Present Status of Genetic Regulation by Hormones

Gordon M. Tomkins and Thomas D. Gelehrter

I. SIMPLE AND COMPLEX REGULATION IN MICROORGANISMS

Even small bacterial viruses containing three genes control their development and function by very sophisticated means (Stavis and August, 1970). Therefore, before considering the detailed mechanisms of hormone action in multicellular eukaryotic organisms, it is of interest to consider some aspects of the basic biology of regulation in much simpler systems. Regulatory processes can be regarded as either "simple" or "complex": simple meaning that a biological effector (substrate, feedback inhibitor, etc.) influences only one or a very limited number of processes; and complex indicating that regulation of a variety of cellular processes are controlled by a common mechanism.

The first simple control mechanism to be understood was gene repression (Jacob and Monod, 1961), in which a specific negative regulatory protein (repressor) combines with a particular operator site on the DNA of the chromosome to block the transcription into RNA of the gene lying

1

distal to (and therefore under control of) the operator. Specific small molecules (inducers) can combine with the operator–repressor complex and cause its dissociation (Gilbert and Müller-Hill, 1966, 1967; Riggs and Bourgeois, 1968; Riggs *et al.*, 1968; Ohshima *et al.*, 1970; Ptashne, 1967), thereby permitting transcription of the previously repressed genes, provided, however, that an RNA polymerase molecule is correctly attached to the promotor site on the DNA so that transcription can be initiated.

Since the latter condition is fulfilled only under physiologically appropriate circumstances, the initiation of transcription by the polymerase is also under positive control (Hinkle and Chamberlin, 1970; Zillig *et al.*, 1970; H. Travers, 1971). In some bacterial operons, a single regulatory protein may both promote and repress gene transcription. Whichever activity of the regulatory protein is favored appears to be determined by the small effector molecule (e.g., arabinose) which induces the operon (Englesberg *et al.*, 1969). Gene expression therefore requires the organism to make two independent "decisions": to remove the repressor and to initiate transcription.

The termination of transcription at a specific site is also controlled. The factor ρ is needed to arrest the polymerase at a particular point on the chromosome of bacteriophage λ (Roberts, 1970; Maitra *et al.*, 1970), and it may be that whether transcription is actually terminated at that point or continues on to a further "stop signal" is determined by the product of another regulatory gene (Roberts, 1970). These simple mechanisms are summarized in Fig. 1.

Prokaryotes also regulate the translation of genetic information into amino acid sequence, although less is known about this process. For

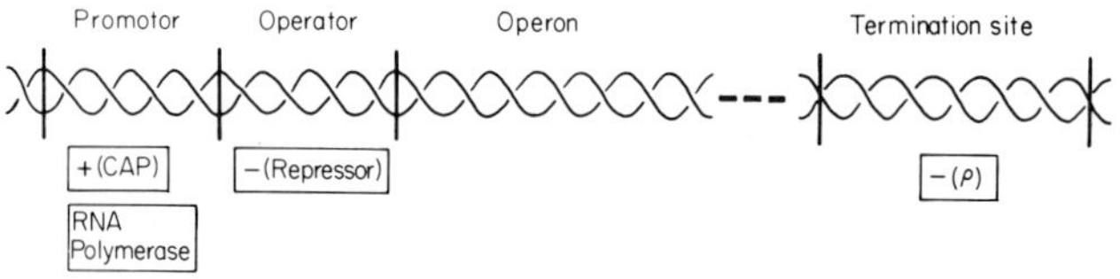

Fig. 1. "Simple" mechanisms controlling operator transcription. The figure illustrates a hypothetical operator with a promotor, operator, and termination site. A regulatory protein designated "+" is shown ready to attach to the promotor region which will then facilitate the interaction of the RNA polymerase with the DNA. "CAP" refers to the cAMP-binding protein of *E. coli* which is required, together with the cyclic nucleotide, for the expression of certain operons (see p. 4). The second protein designated "—" (for example, a repressor) is shown associating with the operator site. The attachment of repressor at this site will block the transcription of the operon by the RNA polymerase. A negative element designated "ρ," shown attaching to the termination site, prevents transcription from progressing beyond this point.

example, the coat proteins of the small RNA bacteriophages act as specific repressors of the translation of the polymerase cistron (Lodish and Robertson, 1969; Sugiyama, 1969). This mechanism, like repression of DNA transcription, depends on a specific protein blocking a unique site on a polynucleotide, except that in the case of the virus, the site is on a messenger RNA molecule rather than on DNA. Evidence for a different sort of regulatory mechanism comes from studies showing that ribosomes from virus-infected bacteria are unable to translate host–cell messenger RNA's but function normally with viral messengers (Hsu and Weiss, 1970). Alterations in the tertiary structure of the messenger itself may also control its own translation (Lodish and Robertson, 1969; Fukami and Imahori, 1971), and it has been proposed that the rate of messenger degradation is also regulated (Mosteller *et al.*, 1970). These mechanisms of control are summarized in Fig. 2.

Specific allosteric control of protein conformation is a widespread mechanism of biological regulation (Tomkins and Yielding, 1961; Monod *et al.*, 1965; Koshland *et al.*, 1966). Besides simply regulating enzyme activity, effectors may also influence the three-dimensional structure of certain proteins, modulate their intracellular degradation, and therefore their concentration (Schimke *et al.*, 1967).

In complex regulation, rather than a single process, an entire set or program of events is controlled by a single mediator. An example is the

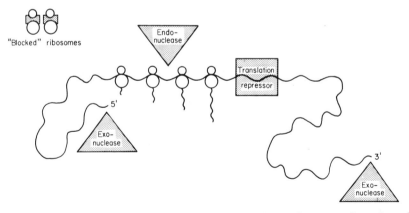

Fig. 2. Control of messenger RNA translation. The figure illustrates a hypothetical messenger RNA in the process of translation. Several untranslated areas of secondary structure are shown as loops. A specific translational repressor molecule is shown blocking the progress of ribosomes, and three types of nuclease are depicted attacking the messenger; an endonuclease and two exonucleases beginning messenger destruction at the 5' and 3' ends, respectively. In addition, several ribosomes are shown which are unable to attach to the messenger because they carry regulatory molecules which inhibit this process.

stringent response in bacteria controlled by the RC, or *rel* gene which governs the behavior of organisms starved for an essential amino acid (Stent and Brenner, 1961). Under conditions of amino acid deprivation, there follows:

1. Slowing of the synthesis of ribosomal and transfer RNA's with a relatively smaller effect on the formation of messenger RNA's (Lazzarini and Winslow, 1970; Primakoff and Berg, 1970).
2. Inhibition of the uptake of certain nucleic acid precursors, and their phosphorylation (Edlin and Neuhard, 1967; Nierlich, 1968).
3. Stimulation of the degradation of intracellular proteins (Goldberg, 1971) and of normally stable RNA (Lazzarini and Winslow, 1970).
4. Depression of glucose transport (Sokawa and Kaziro, 1969).

Several lines of evidence indicate that a common mechanism is responsible for all of these alterations. For example, all are restored to normal when the missing amino acid is supplied and none occur in organisms bearing mutation in the RC gene. Furthermore, chloramphenicol and certain other inhibitors of protein synthesis reverse several parameters of the stringent response (Pardee and Prestidge, 1956; Aronson and Spiegelman, 1961). Recent work (Cashel and Gallant, 1968, 1969; Cashel, 1969; Cashel and Kalbacher, 1970) has shown that a particular guanine-containing nucleotide, identified as 3'-pyrophosphorylguanosine 5'-pyrophosphate (ppGpp) rapidly accumulates in the bacterial cells under conditions of amino acid starvation. Its concentration is decreased by chloramphenicol. These observations suggest that ppGpp might somehow control the stringent response, and more direct evidence comes from experiments indicating that the enzymatic transcription of the ribosomal genes catalyzed by RNA polymerase and the factor ψR may be inhibited by ppGpp (A. Travers *et al.*, 1970).

Another complex regulatory program in bacteria is mediated by adenosine-3',5'-cyclic phosphate (cAMP) (Pastan and Perlman, 1971), the concentration of which increases when the organisms are deprived of glucose (Makman and Sutherland, 1965). The effector then adaptively promotes mRNA synthesis from genes whose products could relieve the carbohydrate deficiency. The mechanism of its action is still under active study, but the results to date show that cAMP promotes the attachment of a protein factor, CR or CAP, directly to the DNA (Riggs *et al.*, 1971). This observation, together with those showing that the cyclic nucleotide promotes mRNA synthesis from the operons under its control (Varmus *et al.*, 1970; Zubay *et al.*, 1970), suggests that cAMP and CAP direct the polymerase to the appropriate promotors. It should be recalled from our earlier discussion that transcription also requires an operon-specific inducer to remove the repressor.

The full implications of cAMP-mediated control in bacteria have not yet been explored, since the cyclic nucleotide may also control the translation of certain mRNA's (Pastan and Perlman, 1969). Furthermore, there are perhaps indications of even more complex interactions, since some processes may be controlled both by ppGpp and cAMP (Varmus *et al.*, 1970), and since another cyclic nucleotide cGMP, antagonizes the cAMP stimulation of the CAP–DNA association (Riggs *et al.*, 1971).

II. THE METABOLIC CODE

From this survey, we infer that specific metabolites (sugars, amino acids, etc.) influence only one or a few cellular processes, such as the function of a certain operon. On the other hand, mediators such as ppGpp and cAMP arise in response to more general environmental changes such as amino acid or carbon starvation and control an entire set of adaptive responses. We also note that complex mediators are not major metabolites themselves, but rather act as "symbols" for these substances, which act at much lower concentrations than the nutrients themselves. If this point of view is valid, we can regard the correspondence between a class of energy-yielding or structural molecules and a specific mediator as a metabolic code, similar to the genetic code in which a triplet of nucleic acid bases stands for an amino acid.

Using this logic, we might regard the hormones as having evolved by a further process of metabolic coding, in which an intracellular mediator such as cAMP become represented by intercellular effectors such as ACTH or TSH.

III. EVOLUTIONARY ORIGINS OF CELL–CELL INTERACTION

Hormones are chemical mediators of communication between different cells of the same organism. As such, they are part of a much larger universe of molecules which pass from cell to cell or from organism to organism by means of which complicated ecological systems are established and maintained (Whittaker and Feeny, 1971). In pursuing the question of the origins of hormone action on the molecular level, we can again find simpler models of intercellular interaction. Rather surprisingly, extensive communication exists between different types of prokaryotic cells, although the effect of one cell type on another tends to be deleterious rather than helpful. For example, the colicins secreted by one bacterium act specifically to poison, sometimes in an extremely sophisticated way, an "enemy" bacterium which presumably threatens the survival of the coliciogenic organism (Nomura, 1967). The colicins themselves are rather complicated molecules which interact with specific sites on the membrane of the receptor cells, a mechanism quite familiar to endocrinologists, although in a somewhat different context.

Chemical cooperation between cells also occurs in simple organisms. Hormones, secreted by one mating type of certain fungi, attract the opposite mating type, ultimately leading to genetic recombination. In at least one case, these primitive sex hormones are steroids (Barksdale, 1969).

A more familiar example of metabolic cooperation between single cells leading temporarily to metazoan morphology is the role of cyclic AMP in the slime mold (*Dictyostelium discoideum*). As long as the individual cells (myxamoeba) are well nourished, they exist as independent, free-living organisms. However, under starvation conditions, they secrete cyclic AMP which causes the aggregation of a large number of individual cells (Konijn *et al.*, 1967). Then, under the further influence of cyclic AMP, the aggregates ("slugs") move about presumably in "search" of nutriment. If their quest is successful, the multicellular slug disaggregates to form individual cells. However, if no food source is found, the organism sporulates, an activity which requires complex differentiation of the newly formed slug. The negative limb of a feedback loop is also found in the slime mold, since under certain circumstances these organisms also secrete the enzyme cyclic AMP phosphodiesterase, which catalyzes in the inactivation of the effector (Bonner, 1970). This organism illustrates the important biological principle that an effector (cyclic AMP) used in bacteria only for metabolic regulation can, in more complex cases, physically propel an organism to search for food.

Since adenyl cyclase in bacteria is an intracellular enzyme (Hirata and Hayaishi, 1967), sometime during evolution the cyclase must have become associated with the cell membrane, allowing it to be regulated by diffusible extracellular substances, giving rise to the present day hormone-modulated cyclase systems (Sutherland *et al.*, 1968). We might speculate that electrically excitable cells arose from hormone-producing progenitors, and that electrical "symbolism" ultimately became the dominant means of information transfer in sophisticated metazoan organisms, replacing the slower chemical mediators. Intermediates in this conversion can be seen in the neuroendocrine cells of primitive metazoa such as the coelenterates (Lentz, 1966). Thus, metabolic coding might have evolved toward the use of transient electronic configurations in the nervous system rather than the more stable molecular structures of the hormones as the principal symbolic means of regulation (Horridge, 1968).

IV. PLEIOTYPIC AND SPECIFIC CONTROL BY HORMONES

The existence and role of cAMP in both bacteria and mammals suggests that once a complex biological effector appears, the network of reactions it controls has considerable evolutionary stability. For example, in both bacteria and mammals, the cyclic nucleotide is an "indicator" of the nutritional states of the organism. When bacteria are deprived of glucose, cAMP promotes its production by overcoming catabolite repression (see above). Whereas in mammals, the nucleotide (via epinephrine and glucoagon) favors glucose production from glycogen in the liver (Sutherland *et al.*, 1965). The persistence of such regulatory patterns throughout evolution suggest a certain stability of the metabolic code. Apparently, once the basic symbolic association between a biological effector and a set of metabolic responses has been established, it tends to remain (with, of course, extensive elaboration) much as the codon assignments for the different amino acids have remained constant throughout evolution. The stability of the metabolic code might in fact be derived from the same sources as those suggested for the genetic code—that once a set of complex relationships is established in evolution, the minor changes which would be expected to occur with time are selected against, because the function of the entire program would be impaired. If this is true, paradoxically, the complex regulatory patterns may have a greater stability than simple circuits.

One such complex program which may have persisted is the stringent response to amino acid starvation (see above). When mammalian cells in culture are subjected to step-down conditions by removing serum from the medium or allowing them to grow to confluence, a set of processes is affected which strongly resembles the events in bacteria which follow when the organisms are deprived of an essential amino acid. The regulatory program in animal cells is referred to as the "pleiotypic" response, since it encompasses many different kinds of reactions (Hershko *et al.*,

1971). The processes identified with the pleiotypic response in mammalian cells are (1) inhibition of nucleic acid precursor, particularly uridine uptake; (2) inhibition of RNA synthesis; (3) inhibition of polysome formation and of protein synthesis; (4) inhibition of glucose transport; and (5) stimulation of intracellular protein breakdown.

The parameters of the pleiotypic response were initially defined by comparing growing with nongrowing cultured fibroblasts (Hershko *et al.*, 1971). It was found that all the elements of the response could be reversed when cells are exposed to the macromolecular factors in serum, or to insulin. These results suggested that the response can be reversed by the interaction of pleiotypic effector with the membranes of resting cells. It was also noted that malignantly transformed fibroblasts were relatively desensitized to the pleiotypic response. Thus, simian virus 40-transformed fibroblasts, under the same step-down conditions that initiate the response in untransformed cells, do not show the pleiotypic response seen with untransformed cells. In the same study (Hershko *et al.*, 1971), attention was called to the similarities between the actions of serum and insulin on cultured fibroblasts and the effects of other growth-promoting substances in a variety of specific target tissues. A number of hormones, including polypeptides, steroids, and thyroxin, as well as tissue-specific growth stimulators such as erythropoetin (Marks, 1971), nerve growth factor (Angeletti *et al.*, 1968), and phytohemagglutinin, may act as pleiotypic effectors in responsive cells. The pleiotypic control model proposes that a common set of reactions is affected in all these situations, and that this set of reactions strongly resembles the reactions under stringent control in bacteria. On the basis of these considerations, the hypothesis has been advanced that under resting conditions in a variety of cells, a pleiotypic mediator is formed which dampens cellular activity. Under appropriate stimulation, apparently involving specific membrane interactions, the concentration (or activity) of the mediator decreases, allowing the cell to prepare for active growth. In this model, malignancy is considered to be pleiotypic desensitization in which the membrane of the transformed cells cannot promote the formation of the mediator (Hershko *et al.*, 1971) (see Fig. 3).

On these grounds, the cellular response to a given hormone may be both pleiotypic and specific. The latter refers to the ability of a hormone in addition to its action as a pleiotypic effector, to alter the concentration of specific macromolecules as well. This dual action could account for observations that two different hormones may act as pleiotypic effectors, and yet stimulate the synthesis of different macromolecules in the same cell.

In the remainder of this chapter, we consider the specific aspect of the

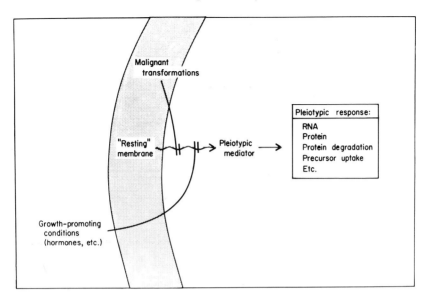

Fig. 3. Pleiotypic control. The cell membrane is illustrated to the left of the figure. In its "resting state" it promotes the production of the "pleiotypic mediator," which, in turn, regulates the processes under its control, illustrated to the right. Malignant transformation is shown as a membrane alteration which blocks the production of the mediator, as do the growth-promoting conditions such as the hormones (which are also illustrated as operating on the cell membrane).

action of the steroid hormones, in which the expression of only certain genes is controlled.

V. STEROID HORMONES AND GENE REGULATION

Steroid hormones like their biochemical precursors, the sterols, are found only in eukaryotic cells. In fungi, steroid hormones have been found which control the development of sexual organs and cause the attraction of sperm (Barksdale, 1969). In higher vertebrates, the major classes of steroid hormones—androgens, estrogens, progesterone, mineralcorticoids, and glucocorticoids—have multiple actions in sensitive tissues. The nature of the response depends on both the steroid hormone and the target cells; however, a single hormone may have quite different phenotypic effects on different tissues.

All the steroids are known to stimulate the synthesis of specific proteins. However, it may be difficult to determine which proteins are directly affected, and which only secondarily. Secondary effects could arise if the direct proteins are involved in the modulation of RNA, DNA, or protein synthesis or in rate-limiting metabolic reactions. For example, the estradiol induction of a specific uterine protein ("induced protein," IP) precedes the other changes subsequently brought about by the estrogens (Barnea and Gorski, 1970). Although the function of IP is unknown, its synthesis could represent a primary specific action of the hormone, the later events depending somehow on its presence. As an illustration of apparent diversity of function, the same adrenal glucocorticoid hormones induce the synthesis of specific proteins in liver (Knox et al., 1956) and in cultured hepatoma cells (Thompson et al., 1966), in nervous tissue such as brain (deVellis and Inglish, 1968) and chick embryo retina (Moscona and Piddington, 1967), in endocrine (pituitary) tumors (Bancroft et al., 1969), exocrine (pancreas) (Yalovsky et al., 1969), and eccrine (mammary gland) tissue (Juergens et al., 1965), and in HeLa cells (Cox and McLeod, 1962). Furthermore, these same hormones produce lipolysis in fat cells (Fain et al., 1965), inhibition of fibroblast growth (Ruhmann and Berliner, 1965), inhibition of neuronal discharge (Ruf and Steiner, 1967), inhibition of pituitary ACTH release (Arimura et al., 1969) and killing of lymphocytes (Gabourel and Aronow, 1962).

However, several lines of evidence suggest that these hormones have a limited type of specific reactivity. For example, studies with inhibitors of macromolecular synthesis suggest that specific enzyme inductions may be involved in the catabolic as well as anabolic effects of the steroids (Mosher et al., 1971). Furthermore, comparison studies with a variety of analogs suggest that the same steroids are effective in each of these systems, and with the same relative potency (Ringler, 1964). Similarly, the same steroids which inhibit some of the above actions inhibit the others, again with the same relative potency (Cox and Ruckenstein, 1971).

Since steroids are small nonpolar molecules, they are able to enter their target cells readily, rather than necessarily acting at the cell membranes as do the polypeptide hormones. Consistent with this view, adenyl cyclase and cyclic AMP do not appear to be involved in the actions of the steroid hormones. This seems well established in the case of the adrenal steroids (Granner et al., 1968), though there is still some controversy in the case of the sex steroids (Szego and Davis, 1969; Singhal et al., 1970).

Once in the cells, the steroids associate noncovalently with apparently specific macromolecules, the receptors. Specific binding proteins for estradiol (Jensen et al., 1971), progesterone (Sherman et al., 1970), dihydrotestosterone (Fang *et al.*, 1969), aldosterone (Fanestil and Edelman, 1966), cortisol (Munck and Brinck-Johnsen, 1968), and dexamethasone (Baxter and Tomkins, 1971), are found primarily in tissues responding strongly to a given hormone. It is of considerable interest that the general properties of the different steroid binding proteins are remarkably similar. They appear to be heat-labile, with sedimentation coefficients of 3–5 S at high ionic strength, but tend to aggregate at lower salt concentrations. Current data suggest that once the cytoplasmic receptors have bound their specific hormone, the steroid–receptor complex is transported to the nucleus. Various nuclear structures, such as DNA (King, 1971) or the chromosomal proteins (Bruchovsky and Wilson, 1968; Haussler *et al.*, 1968), have been identified as the site of binding. Whatever their ultimate destination, the structural and physiological similarity of the various steroid receptors, is consistent with the notion that all the steroids share common mechanisms of action.

The means by which steroids regulate the synthesis of specific proteins is not known, however. In large measure, our understanding is limited by the paucity of knowledge about the regulation of gene expression in eukaryotic organisms.

The genetic material, the direction of flow of genetic information, and the genetic code are the same in higher cells as in prokaryotes; the problems of adaptation posed to the two types of organisms are quite different, however. Furthermore, there are significant differences between microorganisms and higher animals with regard to the organization of the genetic material and to certain aspects of macromolecular synthesis. Mammalian cells contain at least one thousand times more DNA than bacteria, and it is packaged in highly organized chromosomes containing a variety of proteins as well as DNA (Hearst and Botchan, 1970). The chromosomes are in turn separated from the rest of the cell by the nuclear membrane. The DNA of higher organisms contains large portions of repetitive sequences whose special function, if any, remains unknown (Britten and Kohne, 1968), and in differentiated cells, large portions of the genome appear to be more or less permanently inactive (Hearst and Botchan, 1970).

In animal cells, the genome is transcribed into labile, large RNA molecules which are degraded without ever leaving the nucleus (Harris, 1964; (Attardi *et al.*, 1964). The function of this heterogeneous nuclear RNA is unknown; some of it may serve as a precursor to functional mRNA (Lindberg and Darnell, 1970) or even play an intranuclear regulatory role (Britten and Davidson, 1969). With few possible exceptions (Prescott *et al.*, 1971), heterogeneous, labile RNA has been found in all eukaryotes in which it has been sought, independent of species, tissue, state of differentiation, or rate of proliferation. Its existence suggests that regulation of gene transcription alone may not be sufficient to allow fine control of protein synthesis in animal cells and that some kind of modulation must occur after gene transcription.

The regulation of gene expression in higher organisms might be somewhat different than in bacteria, and could involve a number of steps in the processing of genetic information. These include the synthesis of mRNA (transcription); the selective stabilization of certain sequences of RNA within the nucleus; transport of such RNA to the cytoplasm; association of the RNA with ribosomes to make polysomal aggregates; the initiation, elongation, and termination of protein synthesis (translation); the release and folding of peptides; association of subunits; and finally, degradation of the final product.

Most ideas of how steroids regulate gene expression state that hormones stimulate synthesis of specific proteins by derepressing their corresponding genes directly to stimulate the synthesis of mRNA's for the affected proteins. The evidence for this view consists of the following kinds of observations.

1. The effects of various hormones are inhibited by prior treatment with inhibitors of DNA-dependent RNA synthesis.
2. Steroid hormones localize in the nucleus, and in some cases are said to bind to chromatin.
3. Chromatin isolated from hormone-treated tissues shows increased template activity in cell-free RNA synthesis (e.g., Hamilton, 1968).
4. Hormone administration causes increased rates of incorporation of labeled precursors into RNA and the apparent accumulation of new species of RNA molecules in treated tissues (see Tata, 1970, for references).
5. The insect hormone ecdysone causes puffing of specific loci on the polytene chromosomes, a change associated with the accumulation of newly synthesized RNA (Clever and Karlson, 1960).

Although these observations argue that steroid hormones cause the accumulation of RNA in treated tissues, they do not prove either that the hormones increase the rate of synthesis of RNA or that this is the mechanism by which they stimulate specific protein synthesis nor do they precisely identify the type of RNA accumulated. The inhibition of hormonal enzyme induction, for example, by actinomycin D (AMD) means only that the synthesis of some specific RNA is required for the process to occur, not that enhanced RNA synthesis is the mechanism by which it occurs.

Since an RNA species may accumulate either secondary to an increased rate of synthesis or to a decreased rate of degradation, and given the large amount of labile RNA in the nucleus, the latter mechanism becomes a significant and attractive possibility. Indeed, there is evidence that estradiol affects the kinds of RNA selectively protected and transported out of liver and uterine nuclei in the rabbit (Church and McCarthy, 1970).

An increased rate of precursor incorporation need not even signify a faster rate of macromolecular synthesis, but could be secondary to alterations in pool size or precursor penetration or activation. Increased RNA synthesis could result from changes in amount or activity of RNA polymerases, or to changes in RNA-synthesis-initiating factors.

Another important consideration is that an alteration in RNA synthesis may be causally unrelated to the hormone's specific effects on protein synthesis. In rat liver, for example, adrenal steroids increase the amounts of all classes of RNA, rather than supply the mRNA's for specific enzymes (Garren *et al.*, 1964a). In this case, in fact, the adrenal hormones could be active as pleiotypic effectors. More importantly, hormonal effects on RNA and specific protein synthesis can be dissociated in several experimental systems. In the newborn rat, administrations of glucocorticoids prior to the thirteenth day of life stimulates tyrosine aminotransferase (TAT) synthesis as in the adult, but has no effect on RNA synthesis (Barnabei *et al.*, 1966). In cultured hepatoma cells (Gelehrter and Tomkins, 1967) and in fetal liver in organ culture (Wicks, 1968), the hormonal induction of TAT is not associated with a change in overall RNA synthesis or turnover. And in transplanted lymphosarcoma, alanine aminotransferase activity is induced by glucocorticoids under conditions in which RNA synthesis is markedly reduced (Nichol and Rosen, 1964).

Finally, there is now evidence that steroid hormones enhance specific protein synthesis by regulating posttranscriptional steps in protein synthesis. This conclusion was first suggested by the observation of Garren *et al.* (1964b), that inhibitors of RNA synthesis paradoxically enhance the synthesis of tryptophan oxygenase in the livers of rats previously treated with cortisol. Since the intact animal is an enormously complex experimental system in which to study the primary cellular actions of the hormones, a major advance has been the development of simpler *in vitro* models. One such system that has proved particularly fruitful in the study of glucocorticoid induction of hepatic enzymes is the HTC cells, a line of rat hepatoma cells established in continuous culture by Thompson and co-workers (1966). HTC cells resemble normal liver cells in a number of morphological and biochemical characteristics, most notably in the induction of TAT by adrenal steroids (Tomkins *et al.*, 1966).

The addition of adrenal glucocorticoids to stationary or growing cultures of HTC cells results in a five- to fifteen fold increase in the rate of synthesis of TAT, which is maintained as long as the inducing steroid is present but declines rapidly if inducer is removed (Granner *et al.*, 1970). General protein synthesis is unaffected by the inducing steroids (Tomkins *et al.*, 1966), and the turnover of TAT is not altered under these conditions (Samuels and Tomkins, 1970).

The induction of TAT is prevented by concentrations of AMD which inhibit RNA synthesis by 85–95%, suggesting that RNA synthesis is necessary for induction to occur (Peterkofsky and Tomkins, 1967). Inhibitor studies also indicate that the amount of enzyme induction obtained is proportional to the amount of TAT-specific RNA which accumulates, and that this RNA can accumulate in the absence or protein synthesis. In striking contrast to the findings in intact rats, glucocorticoids do not stimulate the synthesis of total cellular RNA nor affect its turnover (Gelehrter and Tomkins, 1967). Direct analysis of HTC cell RNA by double-labeling techniques, however, has demonstrated the accumulation of small amounts of rapidly labeled, polysome-associated, nonribosomal RNA in steroid treated cells (Gelehrter and Tomkins, 1967).

Removal of the inducing steroid from fully induced cultures of HTC cells results in a prompt decline in the rate of TAT synthesis. However, when RNA synthesis is inhibited in fully induced cells by concentrations of AMD which completely prevent induction, TAT synthesis is maintained at the induced level for at least several hours (Tomkins *et al.*, 1970). Furthermore, once RNA synthesis is completely inhibited in induced cells, TAT synthesis becomes constitutive, i.e., enzyme synthesis continues at the elevated rate even if the inducer is removed. Thus, for this (and a number of other inducible enzymes), RNA synthesis is required both for induction and deinduction. In addition, the virtually complete inhibition of RNA synthesis by higher concentrations of AMD may cause a paradoxical increase in the rate of TAT synthesis (superinduction). The rate of degradation of TAT is unaffected under these conditions (Thompson *et al.*, 1970).

To explain these and other results, we have inferred the existence of a labile posttranscriptional repressor, which both inhibits messenger translation and enhances messenger degradation. The steroid–receptor complex (Baxter and Tomkins, 1971) is assumed to antagonize (either directly or indirectly) these actions of the repressor. Thus, according to this model, TAT synthesis is controlled by at least three genes—the structural gene for TAT, the regulatory gene coding for the repressor, and the gene for the receptor. On the basis of present evidence, the repressor could be either RNA or protein (Tomkins *et al.*, 1970), but in any case, it must be quite labile, and its synthesis is less sensitive to inhibition by AMD than is TAT induction. The repressor is assumed to interact in some way with the TAT message to inhibit its translation and promote its degradation.

The steroid–receptor complex either interacts directly with the repressor to antagonize its action, or else inhibit its synthesis or speeds its degradation. In the absence of active repressor (i.e., in the presence of inducing steroids) TAT message would be both stabilized and translated. Since TAT mRNA synthesis is continuous during the inducible phases of the cell cycle, the messenger concentration increases on induction. Since the inducer is normally required to antagonize the repressor, if the concentration or repressor is diminished (e.g., after its synthesis is inhibited by high concentrations of AMD), the inducer is no longer necessary to maintain TAT synthesis, which becomes constitutive. This model predicts that the rapid decline in the rate of TAT synthesis after removal of the inducer is secondary to the appearance of the repressor rather than to disappearance of the message, itself. Therefore, the capacity to synthesize TAT should be rescued by depleting the cells of repressor. In fact, inhibition of RNA synthesis by high concentrations of AMD at intervals after the removal of inducer does restore the elevated rate of synthesis as required by the model. Thus, in deinduced cells, there is a pool of repressed message which can be reactivated by inhibition of RNA synthesis (Tomkins *et al.*, 1969) (see Fig. 4). The general applicability of this model to the regulation of protein synthesis in higher organisms is supported by the many reports of proteins the synthesis of which are enhanced by AMD (see Tomkins *et al.*, 1969, for references).

Studies on TAT induction in synchronized cultures of HTC cells have also supported the model, as well as suggesting an inducer-independent transcriptional regulation of TAT synthesis. TAT can be synthesized throughout the cell cycle, but is steroid-inducible only during the latter two-thirds of G_1 and in the S phase (Martin and Tomkins, 1969). The model predicts that repressor is not made (and is therefore absent) during the noninducible phases of the cycle (G_2, M, and early G_1). Consequently TAT synthesis, once induced, should remain constitutive during these periods. Experimental evidence has been obtained showing that the repressor does indeed appear at the beginning of the inducible period and disappear at the end of the S phase (Martin *et al.*, 1969; Martin and Tomkins, 1970) whether or not steroid is present. The nature of this hormone-insensitive regulation is unknown, but it may control the transcription of both the structural and regulatory genes for TAT. The specificity of this mechanism is unclear, since most transcrip-

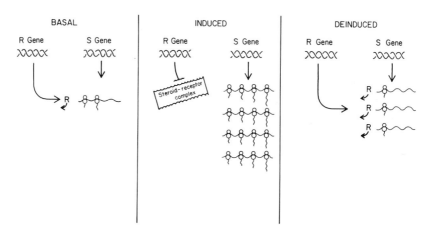

Fig. 4. Posttranscriptional regulation of specific gene expression. This model shows three states of the posttranscriptional control model for steroid hormone action. The basal state, left, depicts two genes, a structural and a regulatory gene, each of which is operating to produce its gene product. In the case of the structural gene, this product is the messenger RNA for the inducible enzyme. For the regulatory gene, the product is a labile posttranscriptional repressor (R) which both blocks messenger translation and promotes messenger degradation. In the induced state, shown in the middle, a steroid hormone has been added and has combined with its specific receptor. The steroid–receptor complex is depicted as blocking either the expression or action of the R gene product. This allows the accumulation of the messenger coded by the structural gene and more rapid translation of the messenger. The third state shown is "deinduction" in which the inducer has been removed. The translational repressor can once again function and is blocking the translation of the structural gene messenger. Ultimately, the repressed messenger will be degraded so that its concentration will become equal to that shown in the basal state.

tion is inhibited during mitosis. However, RNA synthesis resumes in G_1 and is active in G_2, suggesting that the steroid-insensitive transcription control over TAT synthesis may be relatively specific (Tomkins *et al.*, 1970).

We have also presented evidence for a posttranscriptional control of TAT synthesis mediated by nonsteroid effectors. The addition of either dialyzed serum (Gelehrter and Tomkins, 1969), or insulin (Gelehrter and Tomkins, 1970; Tomkins *et al.*, 1970) to cultures of HTC cells previously induced in the absence of serum results in a rapid two- to threefold further increase in the rate of TAT synthesis. This increase is not inhibited by concentrations of AMD, which completely inhibit steroid induction of TAT, arguing that the serum and insulin must act beyond DNA transcription.

However, the mechanism of the insulin effect clearly differs from that of glucocorticoids in that insulin does not cause the accumulation of TAT message nor the sustained induction of TAT. Furthermore the mechanism of insulin action on TAT appears not to be involved in the transport of sugars or amino acids, nor the mediation of cyclic AMP or adenyl cyclase. Since both serum and insulin also cause a modest increase in total protein synthesis and a shift in ribosome distribution toward polysomal aggregates, they may be functioning in HTC cells as pleiotypic effectors. This suggests that the translation of the TAT messenger may also be under control of the putative pleiotypic mediator. Preliminary experiments suggest that insulin acts at the cell surface as it does in other cells, since, as with other pleiotypic effects, Sepharose-bound insulin is as effective as free insulin.

In attempting to assess the role of hormones in gene regulation, a major hinderance to progress has been the inability to perform adequate genetic analyses. Unfortunately, no regulatory mutants for TAT have yet been discovered in HTC cells, but it is worth noting that viral-induced heterokaryons containing one HTC cell nucleus and one nucleus from cells which lack inducible TAT have in every case lacked inducible TAT, as assayed either enzymatically (Schneider and Weiss, 1971) or histochemically (Thompson and Gelehrter, 1971). This result is consistent with the presence of a steroid-insensitive repressor in the noninducible cell capable of repressing TAT synthesis directed by either parental genome. The increasing use of cell culture systems, and refinements in their genetic manipulation should soon allow a much greater understanding of hormones and gene action.

REFERENCES

Angeletti, P. U., Levi-Montalcini, R., and Calissano, P. (1968). *Advan. Enzymol.* **31**, 51.

Arimura, A., Bowers, C. Y., Schally, A. V., Saito, M., and Miller, M. C., III. (1969). *Endocrinology* **85**, 300.

Aronson, A. I., and Spiegelman, S. (1961). *Biochim. Biophys. Acta* **53**, 70.

Attardi, G., Parnas, H., Hwang, M., and Attardi, B. (1964). *J. Mol. Biol.* **20**, 145.

Bancroft, F. C., Levine, L., and Tashjian, A. H., Jr. (1969). *J. Cell Biol.* **43**, 432.

Barksdale, A. W. (1969). *Science* **166**, 831.

Barnabei, O., Romano, B., DiBitonto, G., Tomasi, V., and Sereni, F. (1966). *Arch. Biochem. Biophys.* **113**, 478.

Barnea, A., and Gorski, J. (1970). *Biochemistry* **9**, 1899.

Baxter, J. D., and Tomkins, G. M. (1971). *Proc. Natl. Acad. Sci. U. S.* **68**, 932.
Bonner, J. T. (1970). *Proc. Natl. Acad. Sci. U. S.* **65**, 110.
Britten, R. J., and Davidson, E. H. (1969). *Science* **165**, 349.
Britten, R. J., and Kohne, D. E. (1968). *Science* **161**, 529.
Bruchovsky, N., and Wilson, J. D. (1968). *J. Biol. Chem.* **243**, 5953.
Cashel, M. (1969). *J. Biol. Chem.* **244**, 3133.
Cashel, M., and Gallant, J. (1968). *J. Mol. Biol.* **34**, 317.
Cashel, M., and Gallant, J. (1969). *Nature* **221**, 838.
Cashel, M., and Kalbacher, B. (1970). *J. Biol. Chem.* **245**, 2309.
Church, R. B., and McCarthy, B. J. (1970). *Biochim. Biophys. Acta* **199**, 103.
Clever, U., and Karlson, P. (1960). *Exptl. Cell Res.* **20**, 623.
Cox, R. P., and McLeod, C. M. (1962). *J. Gen. Physiol.* **45**, 439.
Cox, R. P., and Ruckenstein, A. (1971). *J. Cellular Physiol.* **77**, 71.
deVellis, J., and Inglish, D. (1968). *J. Neurochem.* **15**, 1061.
Edlin, G., and Neuhard, J. (1967). *J. Mol. Biol.* **24**, 225.
Englesberg, E., Squires, C., and Meronk, F. (1969). *Proc. Natl. Acad. Sci. U. S.* **62**, 1100.
Fain, J. N., Kovacev, V. P., and Scow, R. O. (1965). *J. Biol. Chem.* **240**, 3522.
Fanestil, D. D., and Edelman, I. S. (1966). *Proc. Natl. Acad. Sci. U. S.* **56**, 872.
Fang, S., Anderson, K. M., and Liao, S. (1969). *J. Biol. Chem.* **244**, 6584.
Fukami, H., and Imahori, K. (1971). *Proc. Natl. Acad. Sci. U. S.* **68**, 570.
Gabourel, J. D., and Aronow, L. (1962). *J. Pharmacol. Exptl. Therap.* **136**, 213.
Garren, L. D., Howell, R. R., and Tomkins, G. M. (1964a). *J. Mol. Biol.* **9**, 100.
Garren, L. D., Howell, R. R., Tomkins, G. M., and Crocco, R. M. (1964b). *Proc. Natl. Acad. Sci. U. S.* **52**, 1121.
Gelehrter, T. D., and Tomkins, G. M. (1967). *J. Mol. Biol.* **29**, 59.
Gelehrter, T. D., and Tomkins, G. M. (1969). *Proc. Natl. Acad. Sci. U. S.* **64**, 723.
Gelehrter, T. D., and Tomkins, G. M. (1970). *Proc. Natl. Acad. Sci. U. S.* **66**, 390.
Gilbert, W., and Müller-Hill, B. (1966). *Proc. Natl. Acad. Sci. U. S.* **56**, 1891.
Gilbert, W., and Müller-Hill, B. (1967). *Proc. Natl. Acad. Sci. U. S.* **58**, 2415.
Goldberg, A. L. (1971). *Proc. Natl. Acad. Sci. U. S.* **68**, 362.
Granner, D. K., Chase, L., Aurbach, G. D., and Tomkins, G. M. (1968). *Science* **162**, 1018.
Granner, D. K., Thompson, E. B., and Tomkins, G. M. (1970). *J. Biol. Chem.* **245**, 1472.
Hamilton, T. H. (1968). *Science* **161**, 649.
Harris, H. (1964). *Nature* **202**, 249.
Haussler, M. R., Myrtle, J. F., and Norman, A. W. (1968). *J. Biol. Chem.* **243**, 4055.
Hearst, J. E., and Botchan, M. (1970). *Ann. Rev. Biochem.* **39**, 151.
Hershko, A., Mamont, P., Shields, R., and Tomkins, G. M. (1971). *Nature, New Biol.* **232**, 206.
Hinkle, D. C., and Chamberlin, M. (1970). *Cold Spring Harbor Symp. Quant. Biol.* **35**, 65.
Hirata, M., and Hayaishi, O. (1967). *Biochim. Biophys. Acta* **149**, 1.
Horridge, G. A. (1968). *In* "The Structure and Function of Nervous Tissue" (G. H. Bourne, ed.), Vol. I, pp. 1–31. Academic Press, New York.
Hsu, W., and Weiss, S. (1970). *Proc. Natl. Acad. Sci. U. S.* **64**, 345.
Jacob, F., and Monod, J. (1961). *J. Mol. Biol.* **3**, 318.
Jensen, E. V., Numata, M., Brecher, P. I., and DeSombre, E. R. (1971). *Biochem. Soc. Symp. (Cambridge, Engl.)* **32**, 133.

Juergens, W. G., Stockdale, F. E., Topper, Y. J., and Elias, J. J. (1965). *Proc. Natl. Acad. Sci. U. S.* **54**, 629.

King, R. (1971). "Schering Workshop on Steroid Receptors" (to be published).

Knox, W. E., Auerbach, V. H., and Lin, E. C. C. (1956). *Physiol. Rev.* **36**, 164.

Konijn, T. M., Van de Meene, J. G. C., Bonner, J. T., and Barkley, D. S. (1967). *Proc. Natl. Acad. Sci. U. S.* **58**, 1152.

Koshland, D. E., Jr., Némethy, G., and Filmer, D. (1966). *Biochemistry* **5**, 365.

Lazzarini, R. A., and Winslow, R. M. (1970). *Cold Spring Harbor Symp. Quant. Biol.* **35**, 383.

Lentz, T. L. (1966). "The Cell Biology of Hydra." Wiley, New York.

Lindberg, U., and Darnell, J. E. (1970). *Proc. Natl. Acad. Sci. U. S.* **65**, 1089.

Lodish, H. F., and Robertson, H. D. (1969). *Cold Spring Harbor Symp. Quant. Biol.* **34**, 655.

Maitra, U., Lockwood, A. H., Dubnoff, J. S., and Guha, A. (1970). *Cold Spring Harbor Symp. Quant. Biol.* **35**, 143.

Makman, R. S., and Sutherland, E. W. (1965). *J. Biol. Chem.* **240**, 1309.

Marks, P. A. (1971). *Harvey Lectures* (in press).

Martin, D. W., Jr., and Tomkins, G. M. (1969). *Proc. Natl. Acad. Sci. U. S.* **62**, 248.

Martin, D. W., Jr., and Tomkins, G. M. (1970). *Proc. Natl. Acad. Sci. U. S.* **65**, 1064.

Martin, D. W., Jr., Tomkins, G. M., and Bresler, M. (1969). *Proc. Natl. Acad. Sci. U. S.* **63**, 842.

Monod, J., Wyman, J., and Changeux, J. P. (1965). *J. Mol. Biol.* **12**, 88.

Moscona, A. A., and Piddington, R. (1967). *Science* **158**, 496.

Mosher, K. M., Young, D. A., and Munck, A. (1971). *J. Biol. Chem.* **246**, 654.

Mosteller, R. D., Rose, J. K., and Yanofsky, C. (1970). *Cold Spring Harbor Symp. Quant. Biol.* **35**, 461.

Munck, A., and Brinck-Johnsen, T. (1968). *J. Biol. Chem.* **243**, 5556.

Nichol, C. A., and Rosen, F. (1964). *In* "Actions of Hormones on Molecular Processes" (G. Litwack and D. Kritchevsky, eds.), pp. 234–256. Wiley, New York.

Nierlich, D. P. (1968). *Proc. Natl. Acad. Sci. U. S.* **60**, 1345.

Nomura, M. (1967). *Ann. Rev. Microbiol.* **21**, 257.

Ohshima, Y., Horiuchi, T., Iida, Y., and Kameyama, T. (1970). *Cold Spring Harbor Symp. Quant. Biol.* **35**, 425.

Pardee, A. B., and Prestidge, L. S. (1956). *J. Bacteriol.* **71**, 677.

Pastan, I., and Perlman, R. L. (1969). *J. Biol. Chem.* **244**, 2226.

Pastan, I., and Perlman, R. L. (1971). *Nature* **229**, 5.

Peterkofsky, B., and Tomkins, G. M. (1967). *J. Mol. Biol.* **30**, 49.

Prescott, D. M., Stevens, A. R., and Lauth, M. R. (1971). *Exptl. Cell Res.* **64**, 145.

Primakoff, P., and Berg, P. (1970). *Cold Spring Harbor Symp. Quant. Biol.* **35**, 391.

Ptashne, M. (1967). *Nature* **214**, 232.

Riggs, A. D., and Bourgeois, S. (1968). *J. Mol. Biol.* **34**, 361.

Riggs, A. D., Bourgeois, S., Newby, R. F., and Cohn, M. (1968). *J. Mol. Biol.* **34**, 365.

Riggs, A., Reiness, G., and Zubay, G. (1971). *Proc. Natl. Acad. Sci. U. S.* **68**, 1222.

Ringler, I. (1964). *Methods Hormone Res.* **3**, 227.

Roberts, J. W. (1970). *Cold Spring Harbor Symp. Quant. Biol.* **35**, 121.

Ruf, K., and Steiner, F. (1967). *Science* **156**, 667.

Ruhmann, A. G., and Berliner, D. L. (1965). *Endocrinology* **76**, 916.

Samuels, H. H., and Tomkins, G. M. (1970). *J. Mol. Biol.* **52**, 57.

Schimke, R. T., Sweeney, E. W., and Berlin, C. M. (1967). *J. Biol. Chem.* **240**, 322.

Schneider, J. A., and Weiss, M. C. (1971). *Proc. Natl. Acad. Sci. U. S.* **68**, 127.
Sherman, M. R., Corvol, P. L., and O'Malley, B. W. (1970). *J. Biol. Chem.* **245**, 6085.
Singhal, R. L., Vijayvargiya, R., and Ling, G. M. (1970). *Science* **168**, 261.
Sokawa, Y., and Kaziro, K. (1969). *Biochem. Biophys. Res. Commun.* **34**, 99.
Stavis, R. L., and August, J. T. (1970). *Ann. Rev. Biochem.* **39**, 527.
Stent, G. S., and Brenner, S. (1961). *Proc. Natl. Acad. Sci. U. S.* **47**, 2005.
Sugiyama, T. (1969). *Cold Spring Harbor Symp. Quant. Biol.* **34**, 687.
Sutherland, E. W., Øye, I., and Butcher, R. W. (1965). *Recent Progr. Hormone Res.* **21**, 623.
Sutherland, E. W., Robison, G. A., and Butcher, R. W. (1968). *Circulation* **37**, 279.
Szego, C. M., and Davis, J. S. (1969). *Mol. Pharmacol.* **5**, 470.
Tata, J. R. (1970). *In* "Biochemical Actions of Hormones" (G. Litwack, ed.), Vol. I, p. 89. Academic Press, New York.
Thompson, E. B., Tomkins, G. M., and Curran, J. F. (1966). *Proc. Natl. Acad. Sci. U. S.* **56**, 296.
Thompson, E. B., Granner, D. K., and Tomkins, G. M. (1970). *J. Mol. Biol.* **54**, 159.
Thompson, E. B., and Gelehrter, T. D. (1971). *Proc. Natl. Acad. Sci. U. S.* **68**, 2589.
Tomkins, G. M., and Yielding, K. L. (1961). *Cold Spring Harbor Symp. Quant. Biol.* **26**, 331.
Tomkins, G. M., Thompson, E. B., Hayashi, S., Gelehrter, T., Granner, D., and Peterkofsky, B. (1966). *Cold Spring Harbor Symp. Quant. Biol.* **31**, 349.
Tomkins, G. M., Gelehrter, T. D., Granner, D. K., Martin, D. W., Jr., Samuels, H. H., and Thompson, E. B. (1969). *Science* **166**, 1474.
Tomkins, G. M., Martin, D. W., Jr., Stellwagen, R. H., Baxter, J. D., Mamont, P., and Levinson, B. B. (1970). *Cold Spring Harbor Symp. Quant. Biol.* **35**, 635.
Travers, A., Kamen, R., and Cashel, M. (1970). *Cold Spring Harbor Symp. Quant. Biol.* **35**, 415.
Travers, H. (1971). *Nature* **229**, 69.
Varmus, H. E., Perlman, R., and Pastan, I. (1970). *J. Biol. Chem.* **245**, 2259.
Whittaker, R. H., and Feeny, P. P. (1971). *Science* **171**, 757.
Wicks, W. D. (1968). *J. Biol. Chem.* **243**, 900.
Yalovsky, U., Zelikson, R., and Kulka, R. G. (1969). *Federation European Biochem. Soc. Letters* **2**, 323.
Zillig, W., Zechel, K., Rabussay, D., Schachner, M., Sethi, V. S., Palm, P., Heil, A., and Seifert, W. (1970). *Cold Spring Harbor Symp. Quant. Biol.* **35**, 47.
Zubay, G., Schwartz, D., and Beckwith, J. (1970). *Cold Spring Harbor Symp. Quant. Biol.* **35**, 433.

CHAPTER 2

Cyclic AMP and Hormone Action

R. W. Butcher, G. A. Robison, and E. W. Sutherland

I. INTRODUCTION

It seems that wherever one may look in the world of motile living organisms, intracellular enzymatic processes are affected by extracellular influences. In bacteria, the availability of nutrients or the presence of

TABLE I

Some Hormone Actions Mediated by Changes in Cyclic AMP[a]

Hormone	Tissue	Effect[b]
Increased cyclic AMP levels		
Adrenocorticotropic hormone	Adrenal cortex	↑ Steroidogenesis
	Fat (rat)[c]	↑ Lipolysis
Luteinizing hormone	Corpus luteum, ovary, testis	↑ Steroidogenesis
	Fat	↑ Lipolysis
Catecholamines	Fat	↑ Lipolysis
	Liver	↑ Glycogenolysis, ↑ gluconeogenesis
	Skeletal muscle	↑ Glycogenolysis
	Heart	↑ Inotropic effect
	Salivary gland	↑ Amylase secretion
	Uterus	Relaxation
Glucagon	Liver	↑ Glycogenolysis, ↑ gluconeogenesis, ↑ induction of enzymes
	Fat	↑ Lipolysis
	Pancreatic β-cells	↑ Insulin release
	Heart	↑ Inotropic effect
Thyroid stimulating hormone	Thyroid	↑ Thyroid hormone release
	Fat	↑ Lipolysis
Melanocyte stimulating hormone	Dorsal frog skin	↑ Darkening
Parathyroid hormone	Kidney	↑ Phosphaturea
	Bone	↑ Ca^{2+} resorption
Vasopressin	Toad bladder, renal medulla	↑ Permeability
Hypothalamic releasing factors	Adenohypophysis	↑ Release of trophic hormones
Prostaglandins	Platelets	↓ Aggregation
	Thyroid	↑ Thyroid hormone release
	Adenohypophysis	↑ Release of trophic hormones
Decreased cyclic AMP levels		
Insulin	Fat	↓ Lipolysis
	Liver	↓ Glycogenolysis, gluconeogenesis
Prostaglandins	Fat	↓ Lipolysis
	Toad bladder	↓ Permeability
Catecholamines (α-adrenergic stimuli)	Frog skin	↓ Darkening
	Pancreas	↓ Insulin release
	Platelets	↓ Aggregation
Melatonin	Frog skin	↓ Darkening

noxious materials signal changes, and in multicellular organisms endocrine and/or nervous mechanisms come into play. In a remarkable number of cases, the transition from extracellular signal to intracellular action is provided by what is called a second messenger system (Fig. 1). The extracellular effector, in multicellular organisms a hormone or neurohumor, is transported to its target cell where it interacts with a component of the cell membrane, causing increased or decreased production of the second messenger. The only presently well defined second messenger is adenosine 3',5'-monophosphate (cyclic AMP). The hormone-sensitive enzyme system adenyl cyclase, which catalyzes its formation from ATP, is one key component of the cellular response to extracellular events. A second enzyme system, a family of cyclic nucleotide phosphodiesterases, inactivates cyclic AMP (at least in the sense of its role as a second messenger) by converting it to ordinary 5'-AMP. To date, these two systems were the only ones clearly recognized as

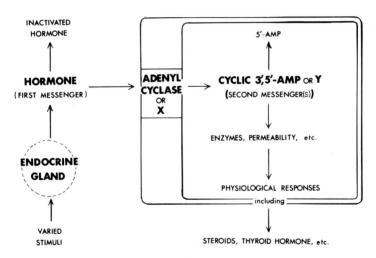

FIG. 1. The second messenger system.

Footnotes to Table I.

[a] References have been omitted in the interest of brevity, and the reader is referred to Robison et al. (1971) for a complete bibliography.

[b] Only the most prominent or thoroughly studied effects of hormones on their target tissues are listed. For example, in addition to stimulating steroidogenesis in the adrenal cortex, cyclic AMP also stimulated glucose oxidation, phosphorylase activation, ascorbate depletion, cholesterol ester hydrolysis and at least partially substituted for ACTH in the maintenance of adrenal weight and function in hypophysectomized animals.

[c] There is a striking species variation in the response of adipose tissues to hormones. Thus, not all species respond as shown in this table.

controlling intracellular levels of cyclic AMP, although it seems likely that others, e.g., the release of cyclic AMP from cells, may also be pertinent.

Once the level of the second messenger (i.e., cyclic AMP) is changed in a cell in response to an extracellular signal, the rates of those processes within the cell involving enzymes which are sensitive to changes in cyclic AMP levels will be altered. In other words, cells will respond to changes in cyclic AMP levels with whatever mechanisms they have available. Since it is well recognized that different cells have different enzymatic profiles, it is perhaps not surprising that cyclic AMP can mediate such a variety of physiological responses to hormones as those listed in Table I.

The specificity between the extracellular signal and the effector cell, at least in the case of hormones which act through increased cyclic AMP levels, appears to be determined by the molecular structures of the hormone and that part of the adenyl cyclase system with which the hormone interacts. Unfortunately, virtually nothing is known about the chemical structure of the adenyl cyclase system, but this kind of specificity has been demonstrated repeatedly in an operational sense, in that highly washed particulate preparations of adenyl cyclase from many tissues have shown exacting specificities for hormones.

It is our intention to present a rather generalized view of cyclic AMP and its role in nature in this chapter, with some emphasis on critical evaluation of methodologies and data with the hope that it might augment the more specific chapters which appear in this book. Our choices of references have been limited by the desire to be illustrative rather than comprehensive, and we trust that omission of any particular investigator's work will not be offensive.

II. DISCOVERY OF CYCLIC AMP

The experiments leading to the discovery of cyclic AMP have been reviewed in detail previously (Sutherland and Rall, 1960; Sutherland, 1962; Sutherland et al., 1965) and will be only briefly summarized here. It all began with the studies on the mechanism by which the catecholamines and glucagon stimulated glycogenolysis in the liver. The rate-limiting step between glycogen and glucose was found to be glycogen phosphorylase, and it was on the level of this enzyme that the hormones acted to stimulate the glycogenolytic mechanism (Fig. 2). Active and

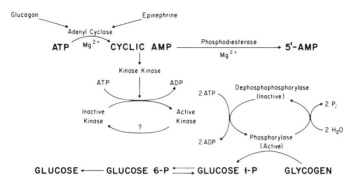

FIG. 2. Phosphorylase activation in liver.

inactive forms of phosphorylase were identified, and it became apparent that the hormones were altering the balance of the phosphorylase equilibrium toward the active form. Studies with highly purified active liver phosphorylase and the enzyme which reversibly inactivated it provided valuable information. Two moles of phosphate were released for each mole of phosphorylase which was inactivated, suggesting that the reverse reaction (activation) might involve phosphorylation. This proved to be the case, for an enzyme capable of activating dephospho-phosphorylase by phosphorylation at the expense of the terminal phosphates of 2 moles of ATP was identified and purified.

Studies with subcellular fractions of liver homogenates provided some very exciting results. Whole homogenates, fortified with Mg^{2+}, ATP, and inactive phosphorylase responded to the catecholamines and glucagon with very dramatic increases of phosphorylase activity. Conversely, although the four enzymes described above were soluble, supernatant fractions did not respond to the hormones. However, when washed particulate fractions were added to the liver supernatants, the effects of the hormones on phosphorylase activation were restored. Recombination experiments demonstrated that the particulate fractions elaborated a heat-stable factor synthesized from ATP, and that the hormones acted to increase the amount of the heat-stable factor. It was purified by ion exchange chromatography and found to contain adenine, ribose, and phosphate in the ratio 1:1:1. Further identification of the compound would have been very difficult because of the minute quantities produced by the particulate systems, and it was thus very fortunate that Lipkin and his co-workers (Cook *et al.*, 1957) had found a compound produced during barium hydroxide digestion of ATP which had similar properties. Both groups wrote to Dr. Leon Heppel asking for purified enzymes to assist in identifying their compounds, and he recognized the similarities in the tentative structures and suggested that samples might be exchanged. This was done, the two compounds were found to be identical, and large quantities of cyclic AMP were available by organic syntheses.

Very recently, additional components of the phosphorylase activation system have been identified. As depicted in Fig. 2, cyclic AMP in fact interacts with a "kinase kinase," which activates phosphorylase kinase, again by phosphorylation at the expense of the terminal phosphate of ATP. This enzyme is activated by cyclic AMP at very low concentrations and was discovered by Krebs and his co-workers (Walsh *et al.*, 1968). Like the cyclic AMP itself, cyclic AMP-activated protein kinases are found throughout nature (Walsh *et al.*, 1970; Greengard and Kuo, 1970) and may in fact be involved in a great many if not all of the actions of cyclic AMP on cellular processes.

III. COMPONENTS OF THE CYCLIC MECHANISM

A. CYCLIC AMP

Cyclic AMP has been identified almost without exception in the tissues of multicellular organisms which have been studied to date, in several unicellular organisms, and in a variety of mammalian body fluids. In general, in the absence of stimulation by exogenous hormones, intracellular concentrations of cyclic AMP have been of the order of 0.1–1.0 nmoles per gram of tissue (wet weight). Assuming an even distribution of cyclic AMP within the intracellular water, cyclic AMP concentrations would be between 1×10^{-7} and 1×10^{-6} M. By contrast, the concentration of ATP is about 5×10^{-3} M and ADP and 5′-AMP are only one order of magnitude lower. Therefore, cyclic AMP concentrations in cells are between $\frac{1}{1000}$ and $\frac{1}{10,000}$ of those of the other adenine nucleotides. The concentrations of cyclic AMP in plasma, cerebrospinal fluid, and gastric juice are of the order of 10^{-8} M, and in milk and urine about 10^{-6} M. The significance of cyclic AMP in these fluids is presently unclear.

While the concentration of cyclic AMP in cells in the absence of hormonal stimulation is relatively constant, the changes engendered by hormones are both dramatic and strikingly different from tissue to tissue. For example, the injection of ACTH into hypophysectomized rats so stimulated the cells of the adrenal cortex that intracellular cyclic AMP concentrations approached those of ATP (Grahame-Smith *et al.*,

1967). Similarly, glucagon is capable of increasing cyclic AMP levels in the isolated perfused rat liver by more than eightyfold (Robison *et al.*, 1967b). These very exaggerated cyclic AMP excursions are not likely to be of physiological significance, since the hormone concentrations required to produce them were far greater than are thought to occur physiologically. In addition, several systems in which cyclic AMP is known to play a role appear to be incapable of these very dramatic changes. For example, in isolated fat cells, maximal concentrations of lipolytic hormones increased cyclic AMP levels only three- to fivefold unless a phosphodiesterase inhibitor was present (Butcher *et al.*, 1968a).

Parenthetically, it should be noted that the changes in cyclic AMP levels required to maximally activate the responding systems which have thus far been studied are extremely small. An example of this is presented in Fig. 3, in which the rate of lipolysis in fat pads was plotted against the measured cyclic AMP levels. Although lipolysis was maximally stimulated when cyclic AMP levels were increased by only slightly over twofold, the cyclic AMP mechanisms continued to respond to increased stimulation in proportional fashion. This same sort of relationship has been found in a large number of systems, and in point of fact is probably predictable. The reasons for it are unclear, but in view

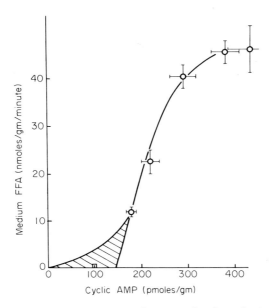

FIG. 3. The relationship between cyclic AMP levels and FFA release in rat epididymal fat pads (Butcher *et al.*, 1965).

of what is known about the mechanisms of action of cyclic AMP on activation systems—for example, the phosphorylase system (Fig. 2)—it is not surprising. The amplification built into such a system is obvious, and an arithmetic change in cyclic AMP levels can produce a much greater than arithmetic (perhaps logarithmic) change in the ultimate process being controlled.

B. Adenyl Cyclase

1. General Information

Although it is clear that many hormones work through changes in cyclic AMP levels and it is equally well established that they do so by activating the adenyl cyclase system, little is known about either the interaction of hormones and adenyl cyclase or even what adenyl cyclase actually is.

The mechanism of the adenyl cyclase reaction has not been established, although it is known that a divalent cation (Mg^{2+} or Mn^{2+}) is required and that pyrophosphate is formed stoichiometrically with cyclic AMP (Rall and Sutherland, 1962; Hirata and Hayaishi, 1967). Greengard et al. (1969) demonstrated that the reaction was reversible. Using highly purified preparations of adenyl cyclase from *Brevibacterium liquefaciens* incubated with cyclic AMP and PP_i in the presence of magnesium ions and pyruvate (a stimulator of this bacterial adenyl cyclase system), they found that a considerable amount of ATP was formed. While it seems highly unlikely that the reversibility of the reaction is of any physiological significance, since intracellular levels of pyrophosphate are low, the finding that reversal occurred was of interest because it provided evidence that the free energy of hydrolysis of the 3'-bond of cyclic AMP was even greater than that of the terminal phosphate of ATP.

Our ignorance of the nature of the adenyl cyclase system in higher animals stems from the fact that the enzyme system is particulate and extremely labile. Thus far, attempts to purify the system have largely been abortive, especially with intact sensitivity to hormones.

2. Distribution and Hormonal Sensitivity
of Adenyl Cyclase Systems

Adenyl cyclase is present in almost all tissues of the common laboratory mammals and in several other species, including man (Robison et al., 1971). In most hormone actions involving increased cyclic AMP levels (Table I), adenyl cyclase activation by relevant hormones has been demonstrated. Thus, while little is known about the exact mechanism of the adenyl cyclase system, a great deal is known about the operational specificity of the enzyme for hormones in mammals. The nucleated erythrocytes of birds (Davoren and Sutherland, 1963a) and frogs (Rosen and Rosen, 1969) contain adenyl cyclase activity, and in addition, the enzyme has been detected in a number of lower forms, even including unicellular organisms. Although adenyl cyclase is widely distributed throughout the animal kingdom, to date neither adenyl cyclase nor cyclic AMP have been reported in higher plants.

3. Intracellular Distribution

As was mentioned in Section II, the adenyl cyclase activity of liver and the other tissues studied during the experiments leading to the discovery of cyclic AMP was found to occur in the low speed or "nuclear" fraction which was shown by Neville (1960) to also contain fragments of cell membranes. Since adenyl cyclase could not be detected in preparations of canine erythrocytes but did occur in the nucleated erythrocytes of pigeons, the possibility that the principal locus of the enzyme was nuclear was considered. However, experiments with cell-free preparations of pigeon erythrocytes led to the conclusion that the methods of homogenization and fractionation employed had much to do with the sedimentation characteristics of adenyl cyclase (Davoren and Sutherland, 1963b). Briefly summarized, although under standard conditions adenyl cyclase was associated with fractions rich in DNA, centrifugation over 20% glycerol, or homogenization by passing erythrocytes through a small orifice under high pressure (which resulted in extensive fragmentation of the cell membranes with little damage to the nucleii) resulted in preparations in which DNA and adenyl cyclase were dissociated. After pressure homogenization, DNA was found primarily in the 600g precipitate, mitochondria (as judged by cytochrome oxidase content) in the 10,000g precipitate, and adenyl cyclase in the 78,000g precipitate. These data indicated that the adenyl cyclase systems of erythrocytes and rat liver were components of the cell membrane, and this has been more recently confirmed by other investigators (Pohl et al., 1969; Rosen and Rosen, 1969).

The membranes in the pressure-homogenized system of Davoren and Sutherland were shattered to fine debris, and were unresponsive to catecholamines. However Øye and Sutherland (1966) obtained preparations of epinephrine-sensitive adenyl cyclase activity in which only large pieces of membranes were visible by phase contrast microscopy. The adenyl cyclase activities of bird erythrocytes and liver were found to have specific densities of 1.18, as might be expected for membrane fractions.

Although these data strongly suggest a localization of the adenyl cyclase system to the cell membrane, they do not eliminate the possibility that the enzyme system may also occur in membrane constituents other than plasma membrane. Rabinowitz *et al.* (1965) found that most of the adenyl cyclase in homogenates of rabbit psoas muscle sedimented with the microsomal fraction, and preparations from other tissues may also contain some activity in this fraction (Sutherland *et al.*, 1962; Entman *et al.*, 1969; Hechter *et al.*, 1969). Perhaps some confusion has been engendered by the use of terms like "mitochondrial" or "microsomal" fractions to tissues other than liver. For example, adenyl cyclase was found to be distributed in the 8500 g and 78,000 g precipitates of homogenates of rat cerebral cortex (DeRobertis *et al.*, 1967). The 8500 g precipitate has been termed mitochondrial, but this is more an operational than a descriptive terminology, since upon subfractionation adenyl cyclase was found to be associated with fractions rich in nerve endings and in low concentration in the myelin and mitochondrial subfractions.

Data suggesting that the catalytic site of adenyl cyclase is located on the inside of the membrane was obtained by Øye and Sutherland (1966). Although exogenous ATP was hydrolyzed by ATPases, it was

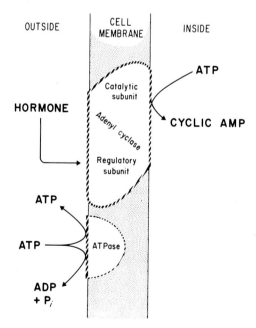

FIG. 4. The relationships among hormones, extracellular and intracellular ATP, and cyclic AMP in intact cells.

not converted to cyclic AMP. However, the erythrocytes were sensitive to activation by epinephrine and readily converted endogenous ATP to cyclic AMP. This was in sharp contradistinction to what was found with lysed red cells. In this system, exogenous ATP was required for cyclic AMP synthesis, and both epinephrine and sodium fluoride stimulated the enzyme. Another line of evidence for a localization of adenyl cyclase to the inside of the membrane was obtained in experiments with proteolytic enzymes. Incubation of intact erythrocytes with pepsin, trypsin, and bromelin decreased the ATPase activity somewhat without any significant change in the level of adenyl cyclase activity. By contrast, when hemolyzed cells were exposed to the proteolytic enzymes, both activities were abolished. The relationships suggested by these data are presented schematically in Fig. 4.

4. Purification and Properties

Attempts to obtain adenyl cyclase from the cells of multicellular organisms in a highly purified form have been unfruitful. Preparations containing adenyl cyclase have been washed in hypotonic solutions, frozen, washed again with hypotonic and hypertonic salt solutions, and then refrozen with good recovery of activity. Much of the activity in several tissues was solubilized or dispersed in a 1.8% Triton solution, after washing with 0.1% Triton, while concentrations of ATPase, pyrophosphatase, and phosphodiesterase relative to that of adenyl cyclase were lowered by these procedures. Levey (1970) recently reported solubilization of myocardial adenyl cyclase in the detergent Lubrol-PX, but aside from a better yield of adenyl cyclase in the detergent phase, the properties of this preparation were very little different from those reported by Sutherland *et al.* in 1962, in that all of the hormone response of the solubilized adenyl cyclase was abolished. However, to date no cyclase preparations have been obtained which were completely free of contaminating enzymes. In general, the net purification obtained in preparations of mammalian adenyl cyclase systems has been disappointingly small (only two- to threefold for brain, and fifteenfold for liver) (Sutherland *et al.*, 1962). In a few cases, more extensive purification has been reported but have been in fact more apparent than real. For example, Rosen and Rosen (1969) reported a two hundredfold increase in the specific activity of adenyl cyclase from amphibian erythrocyte preparations. However, since specific activity was expressed on the basis of protein, the purification may have been largely due to the effect of washing away hemoglobin.

Some preparations of brain adenyl cyclase have been lyophilized, and the dried powders extracted with dry ether in the cold with little or no loss of activity or hormone response (Sutherland et al., 1962). In general, particulate preparations of adenyl cyclase can be stored at −70°C for long periods without loss of activity after rapid freezing in hypotonic media. At higher temperatures, preparations from mammalian tissues deteriorate rapidly. In some cases, sulfhydryl reagents have been useful in maintaining adenyl cyclase activity, (e.g., Øye and Sutherland, 1966; Rosen and Rosen, 1969).

Much more effective purification of bacterial adenyl cyclase systems has been reported. Hirata and Hayaishi (1967) obtained a soluble adenyl cyclase from B. liquefaciens and purified the enzyme approximately two hundredfold. The enzyme was absolutely dependent upon pyruvate, which appeared to be an allosteric activator, but the enzyme was unaffected by fluoride. Thus, the bacterial enzyme was quite different from most known mammalian systems. Very recently, Tao and Huberman (1970) have reported the solubilization of a particulate adenyl cyclase system from Escherichia coli and approximately one hundredfold purification of the enzyme. It is unclear at this time how helpful studies with bacterial adenyl cyclases may be in determining the mechanism of action of hormones on the firmly particulate mammalian systems.

Adenyl cyclase preparations from most multicellular organisms are stimulated by fluoride ions (Rall and Sutherland, 1958; Sutherland et al., 1962). The mechanism of the stimulatory effect of fluoride is poorly understood. The optimal concentration of fluoride may vary from preparation to preparation, and it is generally found to be somewhere between 1 and 10 mM. It seems unlikely that fluoride ions are acting in the same way that hormones act. In general, the effects of fluoride ion are quantitatively greater than are those obtained with maximal concentrations of hormones, although a few exceptions exist. In addition, as mentioned previously, fluoride does not appear to stimulate the formation of cyclic AMP in intact cells.

The effects of cations have also been studied to some extent. Mn^{2+} can replace Mg^{2+} in at least some preparations (Sutherland et al., 1962), and in at least one case (fat cell ghosts) Mn^{2+} is more effective than Mg^{2+} in the presence of fluoride (Birnbaumer et al., 1969). Cu^{2+} and Zn^{2+} are strongly inhibitory, and Co^{2+} is also inhibitory to some extent (Sutherland et al., 1962; Birnbaumer et al., 1969). Ca^{2+} has been found to be inhibitory in some cases, although there is at least one hormone (ACTH) which seems to require calcium in order to effectively stimulate adenyl cyclase (Bär and Hechter, 1969b). Recently, Lefkowitz et al. (1970) reported that the binding of ACTH-^{125}I to adrenal adenyl cyclase preparations was unaffected by the addition of EGTA. However, the effect of ACTH on adenyl cyclase activation was markedly inhibited and high concentrations of calcium chloride-inhibited ACTH-^{125}I binding. In several systems, changes in Na^+ or K^+ have had little effect on the activities of adenyl cyclases, but Burke (1970) reported that 0.1 M K^+ stimulated and 0.1 M Na^+ inhibited the adenyl cyclase activity in cell-free preparations of thyroid when incubated with TSH. The pH optima for the formation of cyclic AMP in most preparations studied were between pH 7.2 and 8.2.

C. Phosphodiesterase

The initial studies of the cyclic nucleotide phosphodiesterase (PDase) were reported by Sutherland and Rall in 1958. The enzyme from dog heart was partially purified, and the reaction product was identified as 5'-AMP. Activation of PDase by Mg^{2+} and also inhibition by caffeine were reported. Further purification of the PDase was necessitated by problems involved with the assay of cyclic AMP in intact tissues. The phosphorylase assay system was known to be sensitive to activation or inhibition by substances found in tissues, including Ca^{2+}, glucose-1-phosphate, UDPG, and a number of unknown substances, and thus the availability of a specific and purified enzyme for the destruction of cyclic AMP was desirable. Although the PDase activity in extracts of brain was considerably higher than that in heart, the heart enzyme appeared to be a better candidate for purification because it was more amenable to fractionation and also because of the absence of interfering enzymes (Sutherland and Rall, 1958). Approximately 60% of the PDase activity in homogenates of beef heart was found to be associated with particulate fractions after low speed centrifugation (Butcher and Sutherland, 1962). The soluble PDase activity from beef heart was purified approximately 140-fold, while the activity associated with the particulate fractions was not elutable under a number of experimental conditions. However, at least in preliminary experiments, the particulate and soluble forms of the enzyme were enzymatically very similar.

The K_m of the purified enzyme was found to be about 1×10^{-4} M. It was inhibited by the methylxanthines, theophylline being about six times as potent as theobromine or caffeine, and the inhibition of the enzyme by theophylline appeared to be competitive. The PDase was inhibited by the protonated form of imidazole. The purified heart enzyme did not hydrolyze cyclic 2',3'-AMP, nor any of the straight chain nucleotides, nor did it have detectable effects on certain polynucleotides.

PDase activity was identified in several mammalian tissues and in preparations of lower phyla as well (Butcher and Sutherland, 1962). Until recently, there were very few other studies of the PDase. Drummond and Perrott-Yee (1961) reported the preparation of PDase from rabbit brain which had only slightly higher specific activity than the whole homogenate. Cheung (1967) studied rat brain PDase in greater detail but also reported no substantial purification. Nair (1966) reported the preparation of an enzyme from dog heart which was similar in specific activity and in most properties to the beef heart enzyme.

One of the more exciting reports dealing with the PDase was published by Brooker et al. (1968). As part of a report dealing with the assay of cyclic AMP by an isotope dilution method, they reported the presence of a second PDase activity in crude brain fractions with a K_m much lower than those found previously. Since that time, this sort of second activity has been reported in a number of systems, including adipose tissue (Loten and Sneyd, 1970; Beavo et al., 1971), amphibian erythrocytes (Rosen, 1970), and frog bladder epithelial cells and rat kidney (Jard and Bernard, 1970). Jard and Bernard also reported that they were able to prepare two forms of the PDase, one of molecular weight about 40,000, the other about 80,000, and that the high molecular weight form of the enzyme had a relatively low affinity for cyclic AMP and the lower molecular weight enzyme a higher affinity. Thompson and Appleman (1971) found a similar situation with rat brain PDase and in addition reported that only the high molecular weight fraction was active against cyclic GMP. They advanced the hypothesis that the high molecular weight form of the enzyme was actually a cyclic GMP diesterase.

The methylxanthines remained as the "standard" PDase inhibitors for a number of years, and they were widely used in studying the role of cyclic AMP in hormone actions. However, a number of more effective PDase inhibitors have appeared in the past few years. Cheung (1967) reported that ATP and other triphosphates were potent inhibitors of brain PDase. Nucleoside triphosphates at a final concentration of 3 mM produced inhibitions of from 75% (ATP) to 41% (TTP). He also found that citrate was an effective inhibitor of the PDase, producing 50% inhibition at 12 mM. Cheung suggested that the active form of the PDase was as a metalloenzyme complex, and that the nucleotides and citrate were acting as Mg^{2+} chelators. Another potentially very interesting inhibitor of the PDase found by Cheung was pyrophosphate.

Puromycin inhibited adipose tissue and skeletal muscle PDase (Appleman and Kemp, 1966), and very high concentrations of triiodothyronine inhibited adipose tissue PDase (Mandel and Kuehl, 1967). Several compounds of pharmacological interest have also been shown to be PDase inhibitors. For example, Senft (1968) and Moore (1968) have shown that diazoxide inhibits liver PDase, and quite recently papaverine was reported by Kukovetz and Pöch (1970) to inhibit purified heart PDase and PDase activity in homogenates of coronary arteries. Triner *et al.* (1970) reported that papaverine inhibited PDase activities in homogenates of rabbit aorta, rat uterus, and rat diaphragm. Both laboratories noted that papaverine was considerably more potent than theophylline. Interestingly, Beavo *et al.* (1971) found that papaverine, although a much more potent inhibitor of the PDase in cell-free preparations prepared from fat cells, stimulated neither lipolysis nor cyclic AMP accumulations in intact cells. However, they presented data suggesting that the ineffectiveness of papaverine on intact cells was due at least in part to binding to albumin in the incubation medium, and also perhaps to the localization of papaverine in the lipid phase of fat cells. Other compounds have also been developed, and because of the great potential therapeutic utility of PDase inhibitors—especially those with specificity for only certain tissues—it seems very likely that new and better agents will be developed in the near future.

While it seems very unlikely that the stimulation of the PDase by imidazole is of any physiological significance, it has been used by several workers in the studies of the possible participation of cyclic AMP in hormone actions, and in some cases it antagonized the effects of certain hormones. Cheung (1970) has reported the discovery and partial purification of a protein factor capable of stimulating PDase activity. While the physiological significance of this substance is unclear at this time, it is of great potential interest. Perhaps the single most exciting finding about the PDase, however, was reported by Loten and Sneyd (1970). They found that the PDase activity in isolated fat cells (as measured in homogenates) was very rapidly increased by short term incubation of the cells with low concentrations of insulin. The effect on the PDase activity was sufficient to account for the effect of insulin on decreasing cyclic AMP levels in fat cells, and may well have answered the question about the site of action of insulin, which has baffled us since 1966. Interestingly, Loten and Sneyd found that the effect of insulin was a dual one; the low K_m activity showed an increase in V_{max}, and the high K_m activity showed a decrease in K_m, but with no change in V_{max}.

Very little additional information about the PDase activity associated with particulate fractions has been published since 1962. Cheung and Salganicoff (1967) reported that brain PDase activity was mostly associated with microsomal fractions, and that considerable soluble activity was concentrated inside nerve endings. They also reported that Triton X-100 caused an activation of the enzyme, a process which was termed "unmasking of latent activity." DeRobertis *et al.* (1967) found that the PDase activity in rat brain homogenates was about 60% particulate. While the highest specific activity of PDase was found in the soluble fractions, the particulate activity was primarily found in fractions rich in nerve endings. After hyposmotic shock, about 50% of the activity associated with 11,500 g precipitates became soluble. Breckenridge and Johnston (1969) reported a thorough study of PDase activity in the rabbit central nervous system, in which they found that PDase activity was not uniquely associated with particular layers of the cerebral cortex or with specialized structures in the olfactory bulb.

PDase activity has been detected in unicellular organisms. Brana and Chytil (1966) reported the presence of the enzyme in *E. coli,* Chang (1968) in cellular slime molds, and Okabayashi and Ide (1970) in *Serratia marcescens.* The *E. coli* and slime mold enzymes were not inhibited by methylxanthines, while the preparation from *S. marcescens* was. Interestingly, the latter enzyme hydrolyzed pyrimidine 3',5'-monophosphates at considerable rates.

IV. ASSAYS

A. CYCLIC AMP

Perhaps the greatest impediment to progress in the cyclic AMP area has been the difficulty in developing really good assays for the compound. The vast number of techniques which have been reported support this contention, but by now there is such a variety of methods available, that except for their relative laboriousness and the inevitable problem of insufficient sensitivity, the situation is fairly attractive.

The liver phosphorylase activation system was the first assay for cyclic AMP to be reported (Rall and Sutherland, 1958) and with a few minor changes (Butcher *et al.,* 1965) it is still being used. Purified inactive liver phosphorylase and a crude liver supernatant containing the enzymes involved in the activation and inactivation of phosphorylase are incubated with magnesium, ATP, and other additives in the presence of known cyclic AMP standards (final concentrations 3.3×10^{-9} to 2×10^{-7} M) or suitably diluted unknowns. The rate of phosphorylase activation is accelerated by cyclic AMP in a concentration-dependent fashion, and the measurement of active phosphorylase accurately reflects the cyclic

AMP concentrations in unknowns. There are several problems inherent in this assay. First, as mentioned previously, it is subject to inhibition or activation by a variety of tissue constituents. Fortunately, this can be circumvented by use of ion exchange chromatography, purified PDase preparations, and the addition of crystalline cyclic AMP to extracts so that inhibitors might be detected. Second, the assay is extremely laborious. A number of enzymes and reagents have to be prepared and they must be appropriately balanced for the assay to reach optimal sensitivity. In addition, this system requires a great deal of attention just to keep it operating properly. The third problem with the assay is that it is indirect—i.e., with this system, the action of cyclic AMP is not being directly measured, but rather is the end result of a cascade of enzyme activations.

Krebs and his associates have developed an assay system based on the activation of skeletal muscle phosphorylase b (Posner *et al.*, 1964). This is a well defined and rather more easily produced system than the liver phosphorylase assay. Unfortunately, however, the muscle system is even more tedious than liver because of the very high concentrations of phosphorylase b which must be used.

The finding by Krebs and his co-workers that cyclic AMP does not activate phosphorylase b kinase directly, but rather interacts with a distinct protein which they have called kinase kinase has provided another assay system. Partially purified preparations of kinase kinase catalyze the phosphorylation of phosphorylase b kinase at the expense of the terminal phosphate of ATP, and this is stimulated by cyclic AMP. In addition, kinase kinase will phosphorylate casein, and an assay for cyclic AMP based upon the rate of ^{32}P incorporation (from $\gamma^{32}P$-ATP) into casein has been reported (Walsh *et al.*, 1968).

Breckenridge (1964) reported an assay which is based on fluorometric cycling techniques. In brief, cyclic AMP is separated from other adenine nucleotides and converted to 5'-AMP with purified phosphodiesterase. 5'-AMP is converted to ADP by the addition of a small amount of ATP and myokinase. Next, an ATP-generating system (phosphoenol pyruvate and pyruvate kinase) and an ATP-utilizing system (glucose, hexokinase, glucose-6-phosphate dehydrogenase, and $NADP^+$) are added. NADPH is generated at a rate dependent upon the amount of ATP originally present, and this of course is the sum of the cyclic AMP in the sample plus the ATP which was added to spark the myokinase reaction. This type of assay is extremely sensitive and direct, and can be set up with commercially available enzymes. However, the purification of cyclic AMP from the nucleotides and other interfering materials is difficult and tedious, and the problems of preparing reagents free of or very low in fluorescent materials are well recognized by anyone who has attempted to do so. Hardman et al. (1966) have used the cycling technique but generate inorganic phosphate (by hydrolyzing ATP to ADP + P_i with myosin ATPase and regenerating ATP with PEP and pyruvate kinase). Cyclic AMP is purified on Dowex-50 columns. Goldberg et al. (1969) have reported modifications of Breckenridge's assay, utilizing thin-layer chromatography to purify cyclic AMP.

Other methods have also appeared. Aurbach and Houston (1968) have reported a sensitive method involving the conversion of isolated cyclic AMP to 5'-AMP and then ATP, followed by measurement of ATP with a radioactive phosphate exchange reaction. Pauk and Reddy (1967) have developed a double isotope derivative dilution method which, although direct, is tedious and insensitive.

Kuo and DeRenzo (1969) and Humes et al. (1969) reported assays in which isolated fat cells were incubated with adenine-8-^{14}C, which presumably entered the cells. After incubation for 1–2 hours, the cells were washed and then exposed to hormones or other agents and the amount of radioactive cyclic AMP in the cells measured.

Brooker et al. (1968) reported the use of a crude phosphodiesterase preparation in an enzymatic radioisotope dilution method, which though somewhat lacking in sensitivity, is relatively less tedious than some of the other methods available. Johnson et al. (1970) reported a relatively simple and quite sensitive assay for cyclic AMP based on its conversion to ATP—as in the Breckenridge (1964) system—followed by measurement of the ATP formed by its luminescent reaction with firefly luciferase.

Steiner et al. (1969) developed a radioimmunoassay for cyclic AMP, and later (Steiner et al., 1970) for cyclic GMP, cyclic IMP, and cyclic UMP as well. These methods appear to be sensitive and can be used in a great many experimental situations once they are established.

Gilman (1970) reported a radioisotope binding assay using partially purified skeletal muscle phosphorylase b kinase kinase as the binding protein. This assay, although only recently reported, is sufficiently sensitive, reproducible, and relatively easy that it has already received widespread confirmation and is in use in a number of laboratories. A similar assay using a partially purified binding protein from the adrenal cortex has been reported by Walton and Garren (1970).

B. Adenyl Cyclase

Any of the systems capable of measuring cyclic AMP levels can be used to assay adenyl cyclase activity by measuring the cyclic AMP formed from ATP. However, since all of these methods are tedious, a number of assays in which radioactive ATP is used as a substrate with cell-free preparations have been reported, including Hirata and Hayaishi (1967), Krishna *et al.* (1968), Streeto and Reddy (1967), and Marsh (1970a), to name but a few. In general, these assays utilized column, thin-layer, or paper chromatography and in many cases barium–zinc precipitations of adenine nucleotides other than cyclic AMP to obtain the necessary purifications. It should be emphasized, however, that the purification procedures have to be very good, for the conversion of ATP to cyclic AMP is in most cases low (around 0.1%).

V. HORMONE ACTIONS MEDIATED BY INCREASED CYCLIC AMP LEVELS

A. STUDIES WITH CELL-FREE PREPARATIONS

These studies are of value for a variety of reasons, the most important of which is that the environments of the adenyl cyclase system can be simplified and thus better controlled than in intact cell systems. As mentioned previously, adenyl cyclase is found in the low speed centrifugal or nuclear fractions containing fragments of cell membranes in homogenates of most mammalian tissues. These preparations can be washed repeatedly, eliminating many small molecules and soluble enzymes, and in some cases they have been taken through additional purification steps with the retention of hormonal sensitivity, and the only additions which have to be made to such preparations in order to detect the effect of the hormone are ATP and Mg^{2+}. Of course, the ultimate goal remains a homogeneous preparation of adenyl cyclase, but to date it has not been possible to purify adenyl cyclase from mammalian sources extensively without destroying its sensitivity to hormonal stimulation. The sensitivity of adenyl cyclase systems to fluoride sometimes survives its ability to respond to hormones, but even this is extremely labile.

The lability of adenyl cyclase is a serious limitation to studies of broken cell preparations. However, once satisfactory preparations have been obtained, a number of useful experiments can be performed. Many preparations can be stored at $-70°C$ for long periods, and after thawing, can be used without any obvious alteration in the properties of the enzyme system. Portions of a given preparation treated and stored in this manner have yielded highly reproducible results. From a qualitative point of view, the response of a given adenyl cyclase system to hormones acting through the cyclic AMP mechanism has been extremely specific. As a note of caution, however, it should be pointed out that most tissues contain several types of cells. In other words, they are not homogeneous, and as such may contain several adenyl cyclase systems. As a result, where techniques for separating various cell types prior to homogenization are not available, the analysis of the experimental data may be complicated.

From a quantitative point of view, studies with cell-free preparations may be less than ideal. It is obvious that the adenyl cyclase system is in an altered environment because of dilution effects, the absence of endogenous inhibitors or activators, etc., and also because of the possible differences in the metabolism of the hormone under study (i.e., catabolism, tissue uptake, etc.). However, in those cases where structural analogs and/or competitive inhibitors are available, then the relative potencies of these agents on the adenyl cyclase system should be the same as their relative potencies in producing or inhibiting the physiological response of the intact tissue.

An example of the kinds of experiments which can be done with cell-free preparations came from the work of Murad *et al.* (1962), using extensively washed particulate fractions prepared from dog heart. The inotropic response of the canine heart is of the β-adrenergic type (i.e., the order of potencies of the catecholamines are L-isopropylarterenol > L-epinephrine > L-norepinephrine, and the response is blocked competitively by catecholamine analogs, e.g., dichloroisopropylarterenol and propranolol). As shown in Fig. 5, Murad *et al.* found that the same orders of potency obtained in the cell-free preparations from dog heart as were known to exist with the intact heart preparation. In addition, the effects of the catecholamines were antagonized competitively by β-adrenergic blocking agents, and Robison *et al.* (1967a) later extended these studies with other β-adrenergic blocking agents.

The adenyl cyclase activity of fat cells or fat cell ghosts prepared from the rat epididymal fat pad have been studied extensively with cell-free preparations as well. Birnbaumer and Rodbell (1969), Vaughan and Murad (1969), and Bär and Hechter (1969c) found that the catecholamines, ACTH, glucagon, and other polypeptide lipolytic hormones all stimulated fat cell adenyl cyclase. Earlier, the adenyl cyclase activity in homogenates of fat pads from fasted and refed rats was found to respond to the catecholamines with the characteristics of β-adrenergic responding systems, and to be blocked by β-adrenergic blockers (Butcher and Sutherland, 1967).

The above, of course, are painfully sketchy outlines of the kinds of

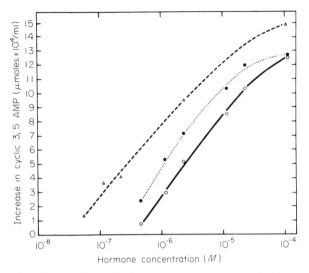

Fɪɢ. 5. The relation of catecholamine concentration to the formation of cyclic 3′,5′-AMP by dog heart adenyl cyclase. Hypotonic myocardial suspensions were incubated with tris buffer at pH 7.5, caffeine, albumin, magnesium sulfate, and ATP, and with and without catecholamine, for 12 minutes at 30°C. Each milliliter of incubation mixture contained particles derived from 51 mg of myocardium. The increase in the formation of cyclic 3′,5′-AMP in the presence of various concentrations of either ʟ-epinephrine (solid circles), ʟ-norepinephrine (open circles), or ʟ-isopropylarterenol (triangles) is plotted against the concentration of catecholamine. There was 7.7×10^{-4} μmole per milliliter of cyclic 3′,5′-AMP formed with no catecholamine added. (From Murad *et al.*, 1962.)

things that can be done with cell-free preparations, and the reader is referred to Table I for a more complete bibliography of such studies.

B. Studies with Intact Cell Preparations

While studies with cell-free preparations may provide a good deal of information unobtainable by other means, the results are not always directly applicable to events occurring in more highly organized systems. It is clear that the conditions used in the cell-free experiments are highly biased in that they are intentionally designed for maximal cyclic AMP accumulation. In addition, the control of cyclic AMP levels in intact cells involves more than the simple synthesis of the compound by the cyclase system and degradation by the phosphodiesterase. Rather, it seems probable that other factors, some known—e.g., the inhibition of phosphodiesterase by ATP, pyrophosphate, and other metabolites shown by Cheung (1967); excretion of cyclic AMP by the cell—and perhaps unknown factors, including sequestration, may be involved. Therefore, it is only by examining the levels of cyclic AMP in intact cell preparations that one can approximate the very complicated controls which pertain. In addition, if direct comparison of the effects of hormones on the physiological effect and changes in cyclic AMP levels are desired, in many cases there has been no alternative to intact cell preparations because the physiological effect of the hormones could not be elicited in the absence of cell structure. Examples of this are the inotropic effect on the heart, steroidogenesis in certain endocrine tissues, and lipolysis in the epididymal fat pad.

Many of the qualitative points which can be tested with broken cell preparations (e.g., relative potencies of analogs, inhibition by competitive antagonists) can also be studied with intact cell preparations. In addition, changes in cyclic AMP levels and the rate of the physiological process can be compared as functions of the concentration of the hormone needed to elicit the response and the time required for these changes to be manifested. It might be appropriate to mention that while the rate or magnitude of some cellular processes may be directly related to intracellular levels of cyclic AMP, in most cases the relationship appears to be more complex, as when a change in cyclic AMP acts as an activator to initiate a series of reactions. The more steps there are between an initial action of cyclic AMP and the response chosen for measurement, the greater may be the amplification, and thus, the more complex will the relationship between the two events appear. This may also make quantitative correlations at low levels of stimulation difficult, since the accuracies of the assays for cyclic AMP presently available leave much to be desired.

As with broken cell preparations, the possibility of complications arising from the heterogeneity of tissues should be considered. For example, intact fat pads contain cells which respond to prostaglandin E_1 (PGE_1) with increased levels of cyclic AMP. Conversely, fat cells themselves respond to PGE_1 with decreased cyclic AMP levels. As a result, the relationship of the antilipolytic effects of PGE_1 to its effects on the levels of cyclic AMP in adipose tissue were confusing until studies with relatively homogeneous preparations of isolated fat cells were carried out (Butcher and Baird, 1968). Indeed, it now appears that many and perhaps most tissues contain cells whose adenyl cyclases differ in their sensitivities to hormones. An example of this was provided by Chase and Aurbach (1968), who showed that vasopressin stimulated adenyl cyclase activity located primarily in cells from the renal medulla, while adenyl cyclase sensitive to parathyroid hormone was concentrated in the renal cortex. The situation in the kidney is further complicated by the fact that there are also epinephrine- and PGE_1-sensitive adenyl cyclases present. Thus, in the absence of homogeneous preparations, the degree of overlap of cell types may be such that the attempt to relate cyclic AMP levels in any specific physiological function may be difficult. In addition, it is manifest that measurements of cyclic AMP levels in heterogeneous systems without reference to physiological parameters are not really very informative.

Another complication encountered in intact cell preparations is that the levels of cyclic AMP in most tissues are subject to extremely rapid fluctuations, and in most cases the speed of tissue fixation becomes a highly critical factor. A good illustration of this was provided by Namm and Mayer (1968). They found that the effects of epinephrine on cyclic AMP levels in the heart were not detectable when pieces of tissue were removed by scissors and frozen by immersion in Freon at the temperature of liquid nitrogen, but were detectable when the hearts were clamped between aluminum blocks chilled to the temperature of liquid nitrogen. Parenthetically, it should be added that in no case have false positive effects of hormones on cyclic AMP levels been related to slow fixation. Rather, the problem has been one of loss of the increased cyclic AMP content of the tissue.

One of the more thoroughly studied systems using intact cell preparations is the effects of ACTH on the adrenal cortex of the rat (Grahame-Smith *et al.*, 1967), the physiological parameter under question being the increased rate of steroid hormone production and/or release in response to ACTH. Increases in adrenal cyclic AMP concentrations after ACTH administration occurred before increases in the rate of adrenal steroidogenesis in quartered rat adrenals *in vitro*. In hypophysectomized rats *in vivo*, increasing doses of ACTH produced increasing concentrations of adrenal cyclic AMP as steroidogenesis was progressively stimulated. At higher concentrations of ACTH (and hence higher intracellular cyclic AMP), the steroidogenic mechanism was operating at capacity, and although cyclic AMP levels continued to increase, no further increase in steroidogenesis could be elicited. In addition, adrenal concentrations of cyclic AMP remained elevated while the rate of steroidogenesis was maintained. Finally, the potency of analogs of ACTH in stimulating adrenal steroidogenesis was reflected in their potency in increasing adrenal cyclic AMP levels.

The lipolytic response of the rat epididymal fat pad is another system in which intact tissue studies were extensively employed. When fat pads were incubated for 20 minutes with low concentrations of epinephrine, cyclic AMP levels and the rate of lipolysis were proportionately increased (Butcher *et al.*, 1965). As the concentration of epinephrine was increased over maximal lipolytic levels, cyclic AMP continued to increase (see Fig. 3). Other hormones with lipolytic activity also increased cyclic AMP levels, while those without lipolytic activity did not (Butcher *et al.*, 1968a). β-Adrenergic blocking agents antagonized the effects of catecholamines on both cyclic AMP accumulation and on lipolysis, and as will be discussed in Section VI, insulin and the prostaglandins antagonized the effects of lipolytic hormones not only on lipolysis but also on cyclic AMP levels. Many of the hormone actions listed in Table I have also been studied using measurements of cyclic AMP levels in intact tissues (Robison *et al.*, 1971).

C. STUDIES WITH PHOSPHODIESTERASE INHIBITORS

The potentiation of hormone action(s) by a phosphodiesterase (PDase) inhibitor may in general be taken as reasonable presumptive evidence that the hormone acts by stimulating adenyl cyclase. By itself, this evidence is relatively weak for reasons to be discussed below, but this nevertheless represents an important criterion.

The major limitation of all these agents is that they are not very specific. In most cases, relatively high concentrations are required to inhibit the PDase, and at these concentrations the drugs often have other actions. These other effects might tend to promote the action of the hormone being studied, thus leading to a false positive insofar as this approach is regarded as a criterion, or as is more commonly the case, they might inhibit it, leading to a false negative. Order of potency studies might be helpful in distinguishing effects of PDase inhibition from effects resulting from some other action. For example, of the methylxanthines, theophylline has been found to be the most potent inhibitor of PDase from all mammalian tissues studied to date. This order of potency may not hold for all of the other actions of these drugs.

In the case of a negative result, to be able to eliminate the role from cyclic AMP in a particular hormone action, it should be established that it is really negative. Some of the actions of PDase inhibitors tend to oppose those of cyclic AMP. Examples of this include (for the methylxanthines at concentrations equal to or less than those required for PDase inhibition) stimulation of phosphorylase phosphatase (Sutherland, 1951) and glycogen synthetase phosphatase (DeWulf and Hers, 1968), inhibition of the release of cyclic AMP from avian erythrocytes (Davoren and Sutherland, 1963a), and inhibition of the rise in cyclic AMP caused by incubation with adenosine in guinea pig brain slices (Sattin and Rall, 1970). The presence of an active PDase in the tissue under study and sensitivity to the inhibitor being used should be established in cell-free preparations. It is clear that the properties of PDases, like those of many other enzymes, may differ from one tissue or species to another. To date, most of the PDases found in mammalian tissues have been susceptible to methylxanthine inhibition, but certain unicellular organisms contain PDases which are not affected by these compounds (Brana and Chytil, 1966; Chang, 1968).

A point to be considered in studies with PDase inhibitors is the concentration of the hormone. Obviously, when calls are maximally stimulated by a hormone, no matter how much the PDase may be inhibited, no enhancement of the physiological response would be expected to occur. Cyclic AMP levels may very well be enhanced, but if cyclic AMP is no longer rate-limiting (see Fig. 3), it would not be reflected by any increase in the rate of the physiological process. As a general rule, the most appropriate concentration of a hormone to use is the smallest concentration capable of eliciting a measurable and reproducible response. Under these conditions, the effects of hormones which stimulate adenyl cyclase would usually be increased in a clear cut and dramatic fashion by agents inhibiting the PDase.

In addition, it should be borne in mind that for the PDase inhibitors to produce a measurable response, there must be a finite level of adenyl cyclase activity. In some cases, especially in studies with isolated tissue or organ systems *in vitro*, PDase inhibitors may be capable of producing a response in the absence of added hormones. Variations occur from tissue to tissue, and of course may also vary with the experimental conditions.

D. Studies with Exogenous Cyclic AMP or Derivatives

In those cases where enough is known about the steps between the increase in cyclic AMP levels with physiological response being investigated, it may be possible to mimic the action of the hormones using broken cell preparations. However, this has been possible in only a few cases because of the complexity of the mechanisms responding to cyclic AMP. Therefore, it has been necessary to study the effects of exogenous cyclic AMP or derivatives of cyclic AMP on intact cell preparations. Most cells are relatively impermeable to phosphorylated compounds in general, and cyclic AMP is additionally subject to rapid hydrolysis by the PDase. Nevertheless, by the application of high concentrations of cyclic AMP, it has in several cases been possible to reproduce hormone effects in intact tissues. These experiments leave much to be desired, for at least in the terms of the second messenger hypothesis, cyclic AMP is an intracellular compound and little is known about the penetration of cyclic AMP into cells. In addition, nucleotides in general, especially in high concentrations, are toxic to cells (Green and Stoner, 1950). Thus, while this type of experiment is necessary, it is obvious that any attempt to draw mechanistic conclusions would be highly tenuous at best. Mention should be made of certain derivatives of cyclic AMP which have been used successfully. Dr. Theo Posternak of Geneva, Switzerland, as part of a collaborative project, synthesized a variety of mono- and diacylated derivatives of cyclic AMP. The most successful of these thus far has been N^6-2′-O-dibutyryl cyclic AMP, which has proved to be effective on some systems where exogenous cyclic AMP itself is either ineffective or much less effective. Such a situation has been reported by Babad et al. (1967) studying the rate of amylase secretion by the parotid gland, on lipolysis in adipose tissue (Butcher et al., 1965), on the adrenal glands (Imura et al., 1965; Bieck et al., 1969), thyroid slices (Pastan, 1966; Rodesch et al., 1969), bone (Vaes, 1968), smooth muscle, and in the isolated perfused heart (Kukovetz, 1968; Skelton et al., 1970). The reasons for the greater potency of the derivatives are not clear. There is no direct evidence that they penetrate cell membranes more readily than cyclic AMP, although this may occur and may in some cases be the explanation for their greater potency. It is also possible that they are more potent because they are more resistant to inactivation by the phosphodiesterase. This greater resistance to the action of the diesterases has been established in the case of the N^6-monoacyl derivatives and most likely applies to the 2′-O derivatives as well (Posternak et al., 1962; Henion et al., 1967; Moore et al., 1968).

Despite the difficulties attending studies with exogenous cyclic AMP, they are necessary if any cause–effect relationship is to be established. It's obvious that the first three experimental approaches cannot prove the role for cyclic AMP in the hormone action no matter how positive they may be, because of the possibility that effects on cyclic AMP and the physiological response under study may only be coincidental. Thus, while these experiments are undesirable from a number of points of view, they are still absolutely mandatory where cell-free preparations (with the physiological response intact) are unavailable.

E. Comments

Some of the hormone actions in which cyclic AMP has been implicated were listed in Table I. In a few cases all the criteria have been satisfied, in others they have been largely satisfied, and in others the evidence is only minimal. It is difficult to estimate the possibility of being misled by any single experimental approach, but where all four criteria have been satisfied, it would seem that the probability of cyclic AMP being involved in particular hormone response is very high.

VI. HORMONES ACTING VIA DECREASED INTRACELLULAR LEVELS OF CYCLIC AMP

A. INSULIN

The implication of cyclic AMP in the lipolytic actions of a number of hormones on adipose tissue suggested that the antilipolytic effect of insulin might be mediated by decreased cyclic AMP levels. The first suggestions that insulin might be acting to lower cyclic AMP levels were provided by Jungas and Ball (1963), who reported that insulin antagonized the lipolytic actions of low and moderate concentrations of epinephrine in fat pads incubated in the absence of glucose, where the effects of the insulin on glucose transport and hence reesterification might be minimized. In subsequent experiments, insulin did in fact cause decreases in cyclic AMP levels in fat pads incubated with epinephrine and caffeine. The effect of the insulin was very rapid, being evident within 5 minutes (the earliest time investigated), and was specific for native insulin. Statistically significant effects of insulin were detected with as little as 10 μU/ml (Butcher *et al.*, 1968a). Insulin antagonized the effects of polypeptide lipolytic hormones as well as the catecholamines (Butcher *et al.*, 1968a), and Sneyd *et al.* (1968) demonstrated that the effects of insulin on cyclic AMP levels were well correlated with its effects on lipolysis under conditions where cyclic AMP was the rate-limiting step on the lipolytic mechanism.

The mechanism by which insulin lowers cyclic AMP levels has in general resisted attempts at elucidation. This has been largely because effects of insulin have been undetectable in the absence of cell structure, and while the rate of turnover of cyclic AMP in intact cells is not known with any great certainty, it is in any event far too high to permit determination of the site of action of insulin in experiments with intact cells (Butcher *et al.*, 1968a; Butcher and Baird, 1968). Very recently, however, Loten and Sneyd (1970) have presented evidence indicating that insulin, when incubated with isolated fat cells, caused a very rapid and highly significant increase in PDase activity as measured in homogenates. Thus, the effect of insulin on cyclic AMP levels may provide fundamental information of two sorts—first, that some hormones may act through decreased cyclic AMP levels, and second, that they may do so by an effect on the PDase rather than on the adenyl cyclase system.

Effects of insulin on lowering cyclic AMP levels in liver have also been detected (Jefferson et al., 1968), and Craig et al. (1969) have demonstrated that insulin has a transient lowering effect on cyclic AMP levels in rat hemidiaphragms stimulated with epinephrine.

It seems highly unlikely that the effects of insulin on glucose transport in adipose tissue are mediated by decreased cyclic AMP levels, since conditions have been found in which insulin stimulates glucose transport despite elevated intracellular levels of cyclic AMP. However, there seems to be little doubt that the antilipolytic action of insulin on adipose tissue (as well as several other metabolic effects of insulin) involve decreased cyclic AMP levels, and Exton et al. (1970) have shown that all of the effects of insulin on liver may involve decreased cyclic AMP levels.

B. Prostaglandins

Steinberg et al. (1964) reported that prostaglandin E_1 (PGE_1) antagonized the effects of lipolytic hormones on both lipolysis and phosphorylase activation in rat epididymal fat pads. Their experiments suggested that PGE_1 might well be acting to lower cyclic AMP levels in fat pads, and such proved to be the case. However, the situation was quite complicated in intact fat pads because PGE_1 increased cyclic AMP levels in the absence of lipolytic hormones (Butcher and Sutherland, 1967). However, this increase in cyclic AMP levels was only an apparent one insofar as lipolysis was concerned, because it was occurring in cells other than adipocytes (Butcher et al., 1967; Butcher and Baird, 1968). In isolated fat cells, the effects of the prostaglandins were purely inhibitory. On the other hand, prostaglandins increase cyclic AMP levels in many systems, including platelets (Robison et al., 1969), thyroid (Zor et al., 1969a), corpus luteum (Marsh, 1970b), fetal bone (Chase and Aurbach, 1970), adenohypophysis (Zor et al., 1969b), and in lung, spleen, and diaphragm (Butcher and Baird, 1968). In those cases where cyclic AMP levels are increased in response to prostaglandins, the mechanism of action appears to involve an activation of adenyl cyclase. However, the site of action of PGE_1 in adipose tissue, where it decreases cyclic AMP levels, has not as yet been identified because the effect has not been elicitable in the absence of cell structure.

C. α-Adrenergic Stimuli

In 1967, we postulated that α-adrenergic agonists might be acting by lowering cyclic AMP levels, at least in those systems where they were oppositional to effects involving increased cyclic AMP levels (Robison *et al.*, 1967a). Since that time, α-adrenergic effects have been studied at the level of cyclic AMP in a number of systems, including pancreatic β-cells (Turtle and Kipnis, 1967), platelets (Robison *et al.*, 1969), dorsal frog skin (Abe *et al.*, 1969), and hamster white epididymal and brown adipose tissue (Hittelman and Butcher, 1971). In all these cases α-adrenergic stimuli have been associated with decreased cyclic AMP levels. While the site of action of α-adrenergic stimuli has not been identified as yet and the physiological significance of these decreases in cyclic AMP levels are unclear, it is interesting that thus far the data have been compatible with this hypothesis. A more complete discussion of this aspect of catecholamine action on cyclic AMP levels is presented in Chapter 4.

D. Comments

It would seem likely that other hormones may be found to act in association with decreased cyclic AMP levels, and it is already clear that certain drugs (e.g., the β-adrenergic blocking agents in systems involving the catecholamines, nicotinic acid, and certain analogs of the compound in adipose tissue, phenylisopropyladenosine in adipose tissue) do likewise. The same sorts of criteria applied to hormone actions involving increased cyclic AMP levels might be employed with those involving decreased levels, with certain reservations. For one thing, with many of these agents it has been extremely difficult to show effects in cell-free preparations, and in addition, in the absence of highly purified responding systems, it is difficult to show that removing cyclic AMP from the process will slow its rate. In any event, it is reasonable to speculate that mechanisms which involve decreased cyclic AMP may be as important biologically as those involving increased cyclic AMP levels.

VII. RESPONDING SYSTEMS

Until quite recently, studies on the mechanism of action of cyclic AMP were largely dependent on measuring external parameters (e.g., steroidogenesis, lipolysis). However, thanks to the elegant studies of Krebs and his co-workers (Walsh *et al.*, 1968, 1970; Corbin *et al.*, 1970), there is finally a considerable amount of evidence on how cyclic AMP acts, at least in certain systems (Fig. 2). That is, that cyclic AMP interacts— apparently in allosteric fashion—with phosphoprotein kinases. As a result of this interaction, the phosphorylation of secondary responding systems (e.g., phosphorylase b kinase or glycogen synthetase) is accelerated. In the case of the phosphorylase system, two enzymes are directly involved in the activation, in that after protein kinase activation by cyclic AMP, phosphorylase b kinase is phosphorylated at the expense of ATP, and this enzyme in turn catalyzes the phosphorylation of phosphorylase b. On the other hand, in the case of glycogen synthetase, a cyclic AMP-dependent protein kinase acts directly on the effector enzyme glycogen synthetase. Again, phosphorylation at the expense of ATP occurs, but in this case, conversion of the enzyme from its active to its inactive form results (Walsh et al., 1970).

Cyclic AMP-dependent protein kinases have been identified in a great many tissues (Kuo and Greengard, 1969) and appear to be involved in the mediation of several of the actions of cyclic AMP (Corbin et al., 1970; Huttenen et al., 1970; Gill and Garren, 1970; Langan, 1969). It has been proposed that all of the actions of cyclic AMP may well involve protein kinases (Greengard and Kuo, 1970). Unfortunately, in many cases, even the nature of the responding system is unclear; e.g., contractile or transport phenomena. Thus, while the notion that protein kinases are involved in all the actions of cyclic AMP is attractive and should be seriously considered, it remains in the realm of speculation.

In conclusion, it is obvious that we have only lightly touched on many aspects of the cyclic AMP system and have left out others. One new development which must be mentioned, albeit briefly, is the discovery of cyclic GMP in animal tissues, and the elucidation of some of the properties of the enzyme synthesizing and degrading it. (See chapter by J. G. Hardman in Robison et al., 1971.) While the role of cyclic GMP in control processes is unknown at present, it seems very likely that it is involved in the regulation of enzymatic activities.

REFERENCES

Abe, K., Robison, G. A., Liddle, G. W., Butcher, R. W., Nicholson, W., and Baird, C. E. (1969). Endocrinology 85, 674.
Appleman, M. M., and Kemp, R. G. (1966). Biochem. Biophys. Res. Commun. 24, 564.
Aurbach, G. D., and Houston, B. A. (1968). J. Biol. Chem. 243, 5935.
Babad, H., Ben-Zvi, R., Bdolah, A., and Schramm, M. (1967). European J. Biochem. 1, 96.
Bär, H.-P., and Hechter, O. (1969a). Biochem. Biophys. Res. Commun. 35, 686.

Bär, H. P., and Hechter, O. (1969b). *Proc. Natl. Acad. Sci. U. S.* **63**, 350.

Bär, H. P., and Hechter, O. (1969c). *Anal. Biochem.* **29**, 476.

Beavo, J. A., Rogers, N. L., Crofford, O. B., Baird, C. E., Hardman, J. G., Sutherland, E. W., and Newman, E. V. (1971). *Ann. N. Y. Acad. Sci.* (in press).

Bieck, P., Stock, K., and Westermann, E. (1969). *Arch. Pharmakol. Exptl. Pathol.* **263**, 387.

Birnbaumer, L., and Rodbell, M. (1969). *J. Biol. Chem.* **244**, 3477.

Birnbaumer, L., Pohl, S. L., and Rodbell, M. (1969). *J. Biol. Chem.* **244**, 3468.

Brana, H., and Chytil, F. (1966). *Folia Microbiol.* (*Prague*) **11**, 43.

Breckenridge, B. McL. (1964). *Proc. Natl. Acad. Sci. U. S.* **52**, 1580.

Breckenridge, B. McL., and Johnston, R. E. (1969). *J. Histochem. Cytochem.* **17**, 505.

Brooker, G., Thomas, L. J., Jr., and Appleman, M. M. (1968). *Biochemistry* **7**, 4177.

Burke, G. (1970). *Biochim. Biophy. Acta* **220**, 30.

Butcher, R. W., and Baird, C. E. (1968). *J. Biol. Chem.* **243**, 1713.

Butcher, R. W., and Sutherland, E. W. (1962). *J. Biol. Chem.* **237**, 1244.

Butcher, R. W., and Sutherland, E. W. (1967). *Ann. N. Y. Acad. Sci.* **139**, 849.

Butcher, R. W., Ho, R. J., Meng, H. C., and Sutherland, E. W. (1965). *J. Biol. Chem.* **240**, 4515.

Butcher, R. W., Pike, J. E., and Sutherland, E. W. (1967). *Proc. Nobel Symp., 2nd, 1966* p. 133. Interscience, New York.

Butcher, R. W., Baird, C. E., and Sutherland, E. W. (1968a). *J. Biol. Chem.* **243**, 1705.

Butcher, R. W., Robison, G. A., Hardman, J. G., and Sutherland, E. W. (1968b). *Advan. Enzyme Regulation* **6**, 357.

Chang, Y. Y. (1968). *Science* **160**, 57.

Chase, L. R., and Aurbach, G. D. (1968). *Science* **159**, 545.

Chase, L. R., and Aurbach, G. D. (1970). *J. Biol. Chem.* **245**, 1520.

Cheung, W. Y. (1967). *Biochemistry* **6**, 1079.

Cheung, W. Y. (1970). *Biochem. Biophys. Res. Commun.* **38**, 533.

Cheung, W. Y., and Salganicoff, L. (1967). *Nature* **214**, 90.

Cook, W. H., Lipkin, D., and Markham, R. (1957). *J. Am. Chem. Soc.* **79**, 3607.

Corbin, J. D., Reimann, E. M., Walsh, D. A., and Krebs, E. G. (1970). *J. Biol. Chem.* **245**, 4849.

Craig, J. W., Rall, T. W., and Larner, J. (1969). *Biochim. Biophys. Acta* **177**, 213.

Davoren, P. R., and Sutherland, E. W. (1963a). *J. Biol. Chem.* **238**, 3009.

Davoren, P. R., and Sutherland, E. W. (1963b). *J. Biol. Chem.* **238**, 3016.

DeRobertis, E., De Lores Arnaiz, G. R., Alberici, M., Butcher, R. W., and Sutherland, E. W. (1967). *J. Biol. Chem.* **242**, 3487.

DeWulf, H., and Hers, H. G. (1968). *European J. Biochem.* **6**, 558.

Drummond, G. I., and Perrott-Yee, S. (1961). *J. Biol. Chem.* **236**, 1126.

Entman, M. L., Levey, G. S., and Epstein, S. E. (1969). *Biochem. Biophys. Res. Commun.* **35**, 728.

Exton, J. H., Mallette, L. E., Jefferson, L. S., Wong, E. H. A., Friedmann, N., Miller, T. B., Jr., and Park, C. R. (1970). *Recent Prog. Hormone Res.* **26**, 411.

Gill, G. N., and Garren, L. D. (1970). *Biochem. Biophys. Res. Commun.* **39**, 335.

Gilman, A. G. (1970). *Proc. Natl. Acad. Sci. U. S.* **67**, 305.

Goldberg, N. D., Larner, J., Sasko, H., and O'Toole, A. G. (1969). *Anal. Biochem.* **28**, 523.

Grahame-Smith, D. G., Butcher, R. W., Ney, R. L., and Sutherland, E. W. (1967). *J. Biol. Chem.* **242,** 5535.

Green, H. N., and Stoner, H. B. (1950). *In* "Biological Actions of the Adenine Nucleotides," p. 65. Lewis, London.

Greengard, P., and Kuo, J. F. (1970). *Advan. Biochem. Psychopharmacol.* **3,** 287.

Greengard, P., Hayaishi, O., and Colowick, S. P. (1969). *Federation Proc.* **28,** 467.

Hardman, J. G., Davis, J. W., and Sutherland, E. W. (1966). *J. Biol. Chem.* **241,** 4812.

Hechter, O., Bär, H. P., Matsuba, M., and Soifer, D. (1969). *Life Sci.* **8,** 935.

Henion, W. F., Sutherland, E. W., and Posternak, Th. (1967). *Biochim. Biophys. Acta* **148,** 106.

Hirata, M., and Hayaishi, O. (1967). *Biochim. Biophys. Acta* **149,** 1.

Hittelman, K. J., and Butcher, R. W. (1971). Unpublished observations.

Humes, J. L., Rounbehler, M., and Kuehl, F. A., Jr. (1969). *Anal. Biochem.* **32,** 210.

Huttenen, J. K., Steinberg, D., and Mayer, S. E. (1970). *Biochem. Biophy. Res. Commun.* **41,** 1350.

Imura, H., Matsukura, S., Matsuyama, H., Setsuda, T., and Miyake, T. (1965). *Endocrinology* **76,** 933.

Jard, S., and Bernard, M. (1970). *Biochem. Biophys. Res. Commun.* **41,** 781.

Jefferson, L. S., Exton, J. H., Butcher, R. W., Sutherland, E. W., and Park, C. R. (1968). *J. Biol. Chem.* **243,** 1031.

Johnson, R. A., Hardman, J. G., Broadus, A. E., and Sutherland, E. W. (1970). *Anal. Biochem.* **35,** 91.

Jungas, R. L., and Ball, E. G. (1963). *Biochemistry* **2,** 383.

Krishna, G., Weiss, B., and Brodie, B. B. (1968). *J. Pharmacol. Exptl. Therap.* **163,** 379.

Kukovetz, W. R. (1968). *Arch. Pharmakol. Exptl. Pathol.* **260,** 163.

Kukovetz, W. R., and Poch, G. (1970). *Arch. Pharmakol. Exptl. Pathol.* **267,** 189.

Kuo, J. F., and DeRenzo, E. C. (1969). *J. Biol. Chem.* **244,** 2252.

Kuo, J. F., and Greengard, P. (1969). *Proc. Natl. Acad. Sci. U. S.* **64,** 1349.

Langan, T. A. (1969). *J. Biol. Chem.* **244,** 5763.

Lefkowitz, R. J., Roth, J., Pricer, W., and Pastan, I. (1970). *Proc. Natl. Acad. Sci. U. S.* **65,** 745.

Levey, G. S. (1970). *Biochem. Biophys. Res. Commun.* **38,** 86.

Loten, E. G., and Sneyd, J. G. T. (1970). *Biochem. J.* **120,** 187.

Mandel, L. R., and Kuehl, F. A., Jr. (1967). *Biochem. Biophys. Res. Commun.* **28,** 13.

Marsh, J. M. (1970a). *J. Biol. Chem.* **245,** 1596.

Marsh, J. M. (1970b). *Federation European Biochem. Soc.* **7,** 283.

Moore, P. F. (1968). *Ann. N. Y. Acad. Sci.* **150,** 256.

Moore, P. F., Iorio, L. C., and McManus, J. M. (1968). *J. Pharm. Pharmacol.* **20,** 368.

Murad, F., Chi, Y. M., Rall, T. W., and Sutherland, E. W. (1962). *J. Biol. Chem.* **237,** 1233.

Nair, K. G. (1966). *Biochemistry* **5,** 150.

Namm, D. H., and Mayer, S. E. (1968). *Mol. Pharmacol.* **4,** 61.

Neville, D. M. (1960). *J. Biophys. Biochem. Cytol.* **8,** 413.

Okabayashi, T., and Ide, M. (1970). *Biochim. Biophys. Acta* **220,** 116.

Øye, I., and Sutherland, E. W. (1966). *Biochim. Biophys. Acta* **127,** 347.

Pastan, I. (1966). *Biochem. Biophys. Res. Commun.* **25**, 14.

Pauk, G. L., and Reddy, W. J. (1967). *Anal. Biochem.* **21**, 298.

Pohl, S. L., Birnbaumer, L., and Rodbell, M. (1969). *Science* **164**, 566.

Posner, J. B., Hammermeister, K. E., Bratvold, G. E., and Krebs, E. G. (1964). *Biochemistry* **3**, 1040.

Posternak, Th., Sutherland, E. W., and Henion, W. F. (1962). *Biochim. Biophys. Acta* **65**, 558.

Rabinowitz, M., Desalles, L., Meisler, J., and Lorand, L. (1965). *Biochim. Biophys. Acta* **97**, 29.

Rall, T. W., and Sutherland, E. W. (1958). *J. Biol. Chem.* **232**, 1065.

Rall, T. W., and Sutherland, E. W. (1962). *J. Biol. Chem.* **237**, 1228.

Robison, G. A., Butcher, R. W., and Sutherland, E. W. (1967a). *Ann. N. Y. Acad. Sci.* **139**, 703.

Robison, G. A., Exton, J. H., Park, C. R., and Sutherland, E. W. (1967b). *Federation Proc.* **26**, 257.

Robison, G. A., Arnold, A., and Hartmann, R. C. (1969). *Pharmacol. Res. Commun.* **1**, 325.

Robison, G. A., Butcher, R. W., and Sutherland, E. W. (1971). "Cyclic AMP." Academic Press, New York.

Rodesch, F., Neve, P., Willems, C., and Dumont, J. E. (1969). *European J. Biochem.* **8**, 26.

Rosen, O. M. (1970). *Arch. Biochem. Biophys.* **137**, 435.

Rosen, O. M., and Rosen, S. M. (1969). *Arch. Biochem. Biophys.* **131**, 449.

Sattin, A., and Rall, T. W. (1970). *Mol. Pharmacol.* **6**, 13.

Senft, G. (1968). *Ann. N. Y. Acad. Sci.* **150**, 242.

Skelton, C. L., Levey, G. S., and Epstein, S. E. (1970). *Circulation Res.* **26**, 35.

Sneyd, J. G. T., Corbin, J. D., and Park, C. R. (1968). *In* "Pharmacology of Hormonal Polypeptides and Proteins" (N. Back, L. Martini, and R. Paoletti, eds.), pp. 367–376. Plenum Press, New York.

Steinberg, D., Vaughan, M., Nestel, P. J., Strand, O., and Bergström, S. (1964). *J. Clin. Invest.* **43**, 1553.

Steiner, A. L., Kipnis, D. M., Utiger, R., and Parker, C. (1969). *Proc. Natl. Acad. Sci. U. S.* **64**, 367.

Steiner, A. L., Parker, C. W., and Kipnis, D. M. (1970). *Advan. Biochem. Psychopharmacol.* **3**, 89.

Streeto, J. M., and Reddy, W. J. (1967). *Anal. Biochem.* **21**, 416.

Sutherland, E. W. (1951). *Ann. N. Y. Acad. Sci.* **54**, 693.

Sutherland, E. W. (1962). *Harvey Lectures* **57**, 17.

Sutherland, E. W., and Rall, T. W. (1958). *J. Biol. Chem.* **232**, 1077.

Sutherland, E. W., and Rall, T. W. (1960). *Pharmacol. Rev.* **12**, 265.

Sutherland, E. W., Rall, T. W., and Menon, T. (1962). *J. Biol. Chem.* **237**, 1220.

Sutherland, E. W., Øye, I., and Butcher, R. W. (1965). *Recent Progr. Hormone Res.* **21**, 623.

Tao, M., and Huberman, A. (1970). *Arch. Biochem. Biophys.* **141**, 236.

Thompson, W. J., and Appleman, M. M. (1971). *Biochemistry* **10**, 311.

Triner, L., Vulliemoz, Y., Schwartz, I., and Nahas, G. G. (1970). *Biochem. Biophys. Res. Commun.* **40**, 64.

Turtle, J. R., and Kipnis, D. M. (1967). *Biochem. Biophys. Res. Commun.* **28**, 797.

Vaes, G. (1968). *Nature* **219**, 939.

Vaughan, M., and Murad, F. (1969). *Biochemistry* **8**, 3092.

Walsh, D. A., Perkins, J. P., and Krebs, E. G. (1968). *J. Biol. Chem.* **243**, 3763.

Walsh, D. A., Krebs, E. G., Reimann, E. M., Brostrom, M. A., Corbin, J. D., Hickenbottom, J. P., Soderling, T. R., and Perkins, J. P. (1970). *Advan. Biochem. Psychopharmacol.* **3**, 265–285.

Walton, G. M., and Garren, L. D. (1970). *Biochemistry* **9**, 4223.

Weiss, B., and Costa, E. (1968). *Biochem. Pharmacol.* **17**, 2107.

Zor, U., Kaneko, T., Lowe, I. P., Bloom, G., and Field, J. B. (1969a). *J. Biol. Chem.* **244**, 5189.

Zor, U., Kaneko, T., Schneider, H. P. G., McCann, S. M., Lowe, I. P., Bloom, G., Borland, B., and Field, J. B. (1969b). *Proc. Natl. Acad. Sci. U. S.* **63**, 918.

CHAPTER 3

Multiple Hormonal Interactions. The Mammary Gland

Roger W. Turkington

I. INTRODUCTION

Experimental analysis of the molecular mechanisms influenced by hormones is usually carried out with regard to the action of a single hormone. Indeed, the important recent advances in our understanding of the hormonal regulation of protein synthesis have relied upon the demonstration that synthesis of a specific protein is to a large extent dependent upon a single hormonal inducer. However, it is clear that cellular metabolism in a large number of cell types is responsive to the regulatory influences of multiple hormones. Various aspects of protein synthesis in liver cells, for example, are affected by the actions of thyroid

hormone, growth hormone, epinephrine, insulin, glucagon, adrenocorticoid hormones, as well as others. It is thus a proper, although more
distant, goal of endocrine research to determine how multiple hormonal
signals may serve to integrate various molecular activities of a given
cell type.

The interactions of various hormones with a cell may occur at all
levels of regulation and organization. Different hormones may activate
the same enzyme, such as the activation of glycogen synthetase by
insulin or glucocorticoid hormones (Gold, 1970; DeWulf and Hers,
1968; Mersman and Segal, 1969). Different hormones may each act to
induce a single enzyme, such as in the induction of glutamine synthetase
in the embryonic chick retina by various adrenocorticoid hormones
(Moscona and Piddington, 1966, 1967; Moscona et al., 1968; Piddington
and Moscona 1965, 1967) or by thyroxine (Piddington, 1967). Hormones may share only certain steps in the induction process or give additive effects, as in the case of the stimulatory effects of glucagon and
insulin on the hydrocortisone-mediated induction of tyrosine aminotransferase in liver (Kenney et al., 1968; Kenney and Reel, 1971; Wicks
et al., 1969). A hormone may exert a "permissive" effect in that its presence
is required for induction in response to a second hormonal inducer,
although the first hormone may possess no inductive activity of its own
(Ingle, 1954).

While there are many instances of additive or synergistic actions of
multiple hormones at the cell organelle level, several antagonistic effects
are also observed. An important example of this is the opposing mechanisms by which the hydrolytic activity of lysosomes may be regulated.
The studies of de Duve et al. (1961) have designated a number of hormones which can potentially act upon lysosomes. Cortisol and other
glucocorticoids hormones have been shown to "stabilize" lysosomes
both in vitro (Weissman, 1965) and in vivo (Weissman and Thomas,
1964). Progesterone, testosterone, deoxycorticosterone, etiocholanolone,
and 5β-H steroids may serve to "labilize" lysosomes in vitro (de Duve
et al., 1961; Weissman, 1964; Weissman and Thomas, 1964; Bangham,
et al., 1965). It is possible that the activity of lysosomes may be modulated by the relative concentrations of hormones with opposing effects.
An important action of thyrotropin is to cause the activation of lysosomal
proteolysis of thyroglobulin to release the thyroid hormones (Wollman et al., 1964; Novikoff et al., 1964; Wetzel et al., 1965; Wollman,
1969). The relative activities of lysosomal enzymes in the seminiferous
tubules of the testis are modulated by gonadotropins, perhaps through
regulation of testosterone secretion by Leydig cells (Males and Turkington, 1971). Finally, the development of a specialized lysosomal

derivative, the spermatozoan acrosome containing hyaluronidase, is dependent upon the action of testosterone (Males and Turkington, 1970). Hormonal regulation of lysosomes would appear to be a fruitful field for future research on multiple hormonal interactions.

Various hormones may interact with proliferating cells to modify regulatory events in the cell cycle and thus determine the size of the cell population in a target organ (Turkington, 1968a, 1971a). As developing cells differentiate or mature in fetal development a different hormone may become the primary regulator of a hormone-dependent enzyme system (Greengard, 1969). Hormones may act in sequence in a series of adaptive changes occurring along the time axis of development to determine the final state of cell differentiation of a population of cells.

The hormonal regulation of molecular processes during the growth, differentiation, and secretory function of the mammary gland represents a prime model for the study of multiple hormonal interactions. The multiple regulatory processes which permit the mammary cells to develop and function in response to pregnancy occurring at discrete periods in the life of the animal are stimulated by a large number of systemic hormonal signals. Although the complexity of the hormonal signals has been defined by studies *in vivo* (Meites, 1956; Lyons, 1958; Lyons *et al.*, 1958; Folley, 1956), analysis of the molecular processes which may be involved has required a more defined system, the mouse mammary gland in organ culture. It is the purpose of this chapter to review a number of the hormone-dependent molecular mechanisms which appear to participate in the regulation of cell proliferation and differentiation in this model system, and to describe how multiple hormonal signals may serve to integrate a large number of complex regulatory mechanisms.

II. HORMONAL REGULATION OF MAMMARY CELL PROLIFERATION

A. INSULIN

The mammary glands of mice prior to the onset of lactation are comprised largely of fat tissue containing a branching ductal system of epithelial cells and connective tissue elements. In explants of this tissue cultured on chemically defined medium, the fat cells never proliferate;

4–6% of the mesenchymal cells are in the DNA synthetic phase at any point during the culture but their rate of proliferation is not significantly altered by hormones; and 70% or more of the epithelial cells can be induced by insulin to proliferate (Turkington, 1968a; Turkington and Topper, 1967; Stockdale and Topper, 1966). Although there is little evidence that insulin is a major stimulus to mammary epithelial cell proliferation *in vivo*, it is a potent stimulator in the organ culture model. Determinations of mitotic and thymidine-labeling indices and the harvesting of thymidine-labeled mitoses by treatment with colchicine (Turkington, 1968a) have established that 95% or more of the epithelial cells are in the G_1 phase of the cell cycle at the beginning of the organ culture period. As shown in Fig. 1, insulin induces major changes in RNA and protein synthesis during the first 8–12 hours of culture and subsequently a marked increase in the rate of DNA synthesis signals the entry of the cells into the S (DNA-synthetic) phase of the cell cycle. Increased rates of RNA synthesis have been observed in intact cells in terms of increased rates of ^{3}H-uridine incorporation into ribosomal and rapidly labeled nuclear RNA (Turkington and Riddle, 1970a; Turkington, 1970b) and in isolated nuclei by increased RNA polymerase activity.

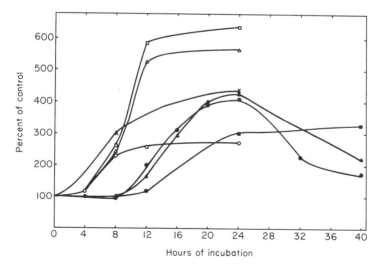

Fɪɢ. 1. Time course of the effect of insulin upon macromolecular synthesis in mouse mammary epithelial cells in organ culture. Rate of incorporation of $^{32}P_i$ into histones (□) or nonhistone nuclear proteins (Δ); rate of cytoplasmic nonmilk protein synthesis (○); rate of DNA synthesis (●); rate of histone synthesis (▲). Each point represents the incorporation of isotopic precursor during the preceding 4-hour labeling period. (✕) RNA polymerase activity; (■) DNA polymerase activity.

The activities at low ionic strength [nucleolar (Pogo *et al.*, 1967; Maul and Hamilton, 1967)] and at high $(NH_4)_2SO_4$ concentrations [chromosomal (Chambon *et al.*, 1968a,b)] are both stimulated approximately 300%. The increased amount of relatively stable RNA formed by intact cells is largely ribosomal RNA (Turkington, 1970b), although transfer RNA also increases proportionally (Turkington, 1969a). Associated with this increased transcriptional activity are increased rates of phosphorylation of histones and nonhistone nuclear proteins (Turkington and Riddle, 1969). The phosphorylation of these nuclear proteins represents esterification of phosphate to serine and threonine residues of the preformed polypeptide chains. Although phosphorylation would be expected to induce important changes in the charge densities of these molecules and thereby alter their interactions with the DNA and with each other, it is not yet clear whether the constant association of nuclear protein phosphorylation with increased gene transcription represents a mechanism by which transcription is regulated. Marked increases in the rate of cytoplasmic protein synthesis is also observed by 8 hours of the culture. The protein fraction represented in Fig. 1 is soluble cytoplasmic protein, but there is no change in the rate of milk protein formation at this time (see Section III,B).

The initiation of DNA replication appears to represent the major regulatory step in determining the rate at which most cells proliferate (epithelial cells of the epidermis, esophageal cardia cells, corneal cells and others may rest in G_2 and may have additional regulatory mechanisms) since the events of G_2 and mitosis occur subsequently (Epifanova, 1965). The action of insulin induces epithelial cells to initiate DNA replication (Turkington, 1968a) and subsequently to divide (Prop and Hendrix, 1965; Stockdale and Topper, 1966). The "wave" of incorporation of ^{3}H-thymidine into DNA represents only a partial synchrony of the cell population, since a number of cells fail to enter the DNA-synthetic period when insulin is removed after 12 hours of culture (Turkington, 1968a). As has been shown for a number of cell types (Robbins and Borun, 1967; Gurley and Hardin, 1968; Takai *et al.*, 1968) regulatory mechanisms exist in mammary epithelial cells for the synthesis of a new complement of histones. Although marked increases in protein synthesis occur during the G_1 period, histone synthesis occurs concomitantly with DNA synthesis (Marzluff *et al.*, 1969). Increases in the activity of DNA polymerase are observed during the S phase (Lockwood *et al.*, 1967b; Turkington, 1969b; Turkington and Ward, 1969a). Increases in the activity of this enzyme, which is assayed in extracts of the cytoplasm, are prevented by inhibitors of RNA or protein synthesis (Lockwood *et al.*, 1967b) suggesting that the increased activity may result from enzyme formation at this time. Ovine and bovine growth hormone can also stimulate DNA synthesis in these cells, although only a few percent of the cells are induced to initiate DNA synthesis by this hormone *in vitro* (Turkington, 1968a).

B. Epithelial Growth Factor

The epithelial growth factor is a biologically active protein discovered in the submaxillary glands of male mice in 1962 by Cohen. The highly purified polypeptide has a molecular weight determined by equilibrium sedimentation of approximately 6200 (Taylor *et al.*, 1970), a value in good agreement with its known amino acid composition (Cohen, 1965; Taylor *et al.*, 1970). The factor has subsequently been shown to be present in the submaxillary glands of both male and female animals, but only in rodent species (Turkington *et al.*, 1971). Mouse submaxillary explants in organ culture incorporate ^{14}C-amino acids into a protein which is identical to authentic epithelial growth factor by a number of criteria, indicating that this protein is a biosynthetic product of the submaxillary cells (Turkington *et al.*, 1971). In addition to its stimulation of protein synthesis in chick epidermis cells (Cohen, 1965; Cohen and Stastny, 1968), epithelial growth factor stimulates the synthesis of RNA and DNA and induces DNA polymerase in mammary epithelial cells in organ culture. These changes are of a similar magnitude and occur with a similar time course to those induced by insulin (Fig. 1). The observation that these effects are produced at very low concentrations of the factor ($8 \times 10^{-10} M$ or less) *in vitro* suggests that it may act as a hormonal regulator of mammary cell proliferation *in vivo* (Turkington, 1969b,c).

C. Estrogens

Estrogenic hormones represent the most potent hormonal agents associated with mammary gland growth *in vivo*. It is generally agreed that this effect requires the action of other hormones, since it is not observed in hypophysectomized animals. *In vitro* the single hormone 17β-estradiol does not affect the rate of DNA synthesis in mammary explants. However, insulin-mediated cell proliferation is markedly altered by the action of 17β-estradiol, and its effect may be inhibitory or permissive, depending upon its concentration. At low concentrations ($10^{-12} M$) 17β-estradiol inhibits insulin-mediated DNA synthesis by 70–80%. As the concentration of estradiol rises to $10^{-10} M$, maximal increases in DNA synthesis in response to insulin are permitted. Further increases in estradiol concentration into the "pharmacological" range result in moderately inhibitory effects. These effects represent largely a modification of the rate at which the cells enter the DNA-synthetic phase, and are shared qualitatively by estrone, estriol, and diethylstilbestrol. The fact that these effects occur at "physiological" concentrations (Baird, 1968; Korenman *et al.*, 1969) *in vitro* is consistent with the concept that estrogenic hormones may have a similar direct effect on mammary cells to regulate cell proliferation *in vivo* (Turkington and Hilf, 1968; Turkington, 1971b).

D. PROGESTERONE

Addition of progesterone (10^{-7} M) to the synthetic medium does not significantly alter the rate of incorporation of ^{3}H-thymidine into DNA by midpregnancy mouse mammary explants (Turkington *et al.*, 1967a). However, progesterone or one of its metabolites (Chatterton, 1971; Chatterton *et al.*, 1969) does appear to have a more selective effect on cell proliferation. Organ cultures of the whole mammary gland of the mouse have been used by Prop (1959, 1960, 1961, 1966) to study the effects of hormones on morphogenetic growth. Although alveolar cell differentiation *in vitro* requires only insulin, hydrocortisone, and prolactin (see Section III), the orderly arrangement of the differentiated cells in secretory lobules is promoted by progesterone. Progesterone induces "budding" at discreet sites in the mammary gland ductal system when applied locally *in vivo* (Chatterton, 1971) or when added to the organ culture medium. Increased rates of cell proliferation at the sites of ductal budding are demonstrable by ^{3}H-thymidine labeling of cells and autoradiography (Bresciani, 1968). This selective effect on cell proliferation permits lobular development and arborization of the ductal system in preparation for alveolar development. The rising plasma levels of progesterone during pregnancy may thus provide the signal for initiating a period of cell proliferation in the mammary gland. The molecular mechanisms involved in this action of progesterone are unknown.

III. HORMONE-DEPENDENT CELL DIFFERENTIATION

A. REGULATION OF MILK PROTEIN FORMATION

Alveolar cell differentiation in the mammary gland is also determined by the interaction of multiple hormones. The presence of insulin, hydrocortisone, and prolactin in the incubation medium causes the disordered nests of mammary epithelial cells to assume an ordered arrangement around enlarged alveolar lumina which become filled with secretory material (Rivera and Bern, 1961; Rivera, 1964; Stockdale *et al.*, 1966). Increases in the numbers of functionally differentiated cells is indicated biochemically by increased formation of the specific milk proteins casein and lactose synthetase. As shown in Table I, the single hormone insulin maintains the initial rate of casein synthesis and causes a slight increase in the activities of the two protein components of lactose synthetase. The combination of insulin and prolactin causes a moderate increase in the formation of these proteins. However, only the triple hormonal combination of insulin, hydrocortisone, and prolactin induces maximal increases. During development of the mammary gland *in vivo* the rate of formation of these milk proteins increases during pregnancy and lactation (Turkington *et al.*, 1968; Lockwood *et al.*, 1966). Thus these proteins serve as accurate biochemical markers of cell differentiation *in vitro* (Turkington, 1969d).

TABLE I

EFFECT OF VARIOUS HORMONES ON CASEIN SYNTHESIS AND LACTOSE SYNTHETASE
ACTIVITY IN MOUSE MAMMARY EXPLANTS[a]

Hormone system	Casein (cpm/ mg tissue-4 hr)	Lactose synthetase (pmoles/min-mg tissue)	
		Galactosyl transferase	α-Lactalbumin
Initial period	110	12	6
48-hour incubation			
Control	91	12	5
Insulin	112	18	8
Hydrocortisone	96	12	6
Prolactin	80	11	6
Insulin + hydrocortisone	106	17	7
Insulin + prolactin	160	21	11
Hydrocortisone + prolactin	88	12	5
Insulin + hydrocortisone + prolactin	465	62	24

[a] Midpregnancy mouse mammary explants were incubated for 48 hours on Medium 199 containing the indicated hormonal additions. Each hormone was present at a concentration of 5 μg/ml. Some explants were allowed to incorporate $^{32}P_i$ into casein during the initial period (0–4 hours) or during the 44–48-hour period of incubation. Each component of the lactose synthetase system was assayed separately after 48 hours of incubation.

The specialized function of lactose synthesis in the differentiated cells is completed by the enzyme lactose synthetase. This enzyme catalyzes the terminal and rate-limiting (Kuhn, 1968) step in the biosynthesis of lactose. It is composed of two components (Brew *et al.*, 1968; Brodbeck and Ebner, 1966b): a galactosyltransferase, which catalyzes reaction (1) in the absence of the second protein; and α-lactalbumin, which interacts with the galactosyltransferase to specify glucose as the substrate acceptor, as in reaction (2):

$$\text{UDP-galactose} + N\text{-acetylglucosamine} \rightleftharpoons N\text{-acetyllactosamine} + \text{UDP} \qquad (1)$$

$$\text{UDP-galactose} + \text{glucose} \rightleftharpoons \text{lactose} + \text{UDP} \qquad (2)$$

The formation of lactose thus depends upon hormonal induction (Turkington *et al.*, 1968) of two interacting proteins. During pregnancy the concentration of the galactosyltransferase rises to the nearly maximal enzyme concentrations observed in lactation. The α-lactalbumin "specifier" molecule (Brew *et al.*, 1968), however, remains low throughout pregnancy, but rises rapidly at the time of parturition to nearly maximal levels. Thus, lactose synthesis is largely inhibited until it is required for the nutrition of the offspring. That the lactose content of the gland is low until parturition occurs has been confirmed by direct measurement (Yokoyama, 1970). Several lines of evidence indicate that progesterone (or one of its intracellular metabolites) plays a regulatory role in the synthesis of lactose. It has been shown that prolactin and insulin induce both the galactosyltransferase and α-lactalbumin in epithelial cells pretreated with insulin and hydrocortisone (Turkington *et al.*, 1968). The kinetics of induction of the two proteins is synchronous (see Fig. 3), in contrast to the asynchrony of formation during pregnancy. The addition of progesterone ($4 \times 10^{-6} M$) to the medium, however, causes a selective inhibition of the induction of α-lactalbumin. Induction of the galactosyltransferase or of casein is not inhibited at this concentration of progesterone, *in vitro*. The injection of pregnant mice with depo-progesterone several days prior to parturition also prevents the rapid rise in α-lactalbumin activity normally observed at parturition (Turkington and Hill, 1969). The rise in α-lactalbumin at parturition occurs as plasma concentrations of progesterone are falling (Grota and Eik-Nes, 1967). Furthermore, the concentration of progesterone which is inhibitory to the induction of α-lactalbumin *in vitro* is nearly that present in plasma late in pregnancy in the rat (Grota and Eik-Nes, 1967; Van der Molen and Aakvaag, 1967), while progesterone concentrations similar to those found in lactating rats are not inhibitory. These observations support the concept that progesterone participates in the regulation of the onset of lactose synthesis at parturition by selectively inhibiting the synthesis of α-lactalbumin. In the case of this unique enzyme system in which the substrate is determined by the "specifier" protein, hormonal regulation of product formation involves primarily a regulation of the induction of the specifier component of the enzyme system (Turkington and Hill, 1969; Brew, 1969). The mechanism by which progesterone selectively inhibits the formation of a specific enzyme is not known. As will be discussed below, an early effect preceding the induction of α-lactalbumin by prolactin is an increase in RNA synthesis. Progesterone partially inhibits this increase, suggesting that its effect is manifested by reduced transcriptional activity.

B. Sequential Actions of the Hormones in Relation to the Cell Cycle

An advantage of the organ culture system is that hormonal stimuli may be defined in terms of which specific hormone(s) act upon the cells, their precise concentrations in the extracellular medium, and the time of onset and duration of hormonal action. It is true that some hormone effects exerted *in vitro* may depend upon changes previously effected *in vivo*. Additional, endogenous hormones may be present in the explanted tissue, but the experiments can be performed several days after explantation, a time point at which it is very likely that all endogenous hormones have been metabolized to inactive products. It is thus possible to analyze the sequence in which the requisite hormones are required to act. Figure 2 is a summary scheme of the sequence of actions of the various hormones in relation to the mammary epithelial

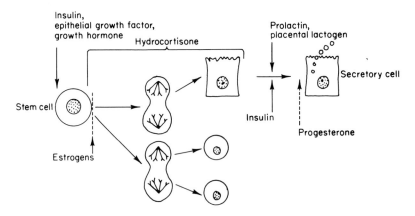

Fig. 2. Scheme of the sequence of actions of hormones on mammary epithelial cells during alveolar (secretory) cell differentiation in organ culture.

cell division cycle. A number of lines of evidence indicate that the undifferentiated epithelial cells present in the mammary gland must first divide in order to differentiate into secretory alveolar cells. The continuous presence of inhibitors of cell proliferation in the medium during the period of cell proliferation prevents any increase in the rate of casein synthesis and in the activity of lactose synthetase in response to the hormones insulin, hydrocortisone, and prolactin. The inhibitors which have been studied are colchicine, which arrests cells in mitosis (Stockdale and Topper, 1966; Turkington *et al.*, 1967b); and various androgenic hormones (Turkington and Topper, 1967), lithium ions (Turkington, 1968c), and hydroxyurea (Turkington, 1971b), all of which prevent mammary epithelial cells from entering the DNA-synthetic phase of the cell cycle. Addition of these agents at any point in the proliferative phase of the culture results in a decreased rate of milk protein formation by the postmitotic cell population. It has been shown that, although treatments with these different inhibitors can completely abolish cell proliferation, they do not completely prevent the action of prolactin in inducing the milk proteins themselves in control cultures of postmitotic cells (Turkington *et al.*, 1967b; Turkington, 1971a). Hydrocortisone or an equivalent adrenocorticoid (see Section IV) must act upon the cells prior to stimulation by prolactin. Cells formed in the absence of hydrocortisone require an approximately 48-hour period of exposure to this hormone before these newly formed daughter cells can synthesize the milk proteins in response to prolactin (Lockwood *et al.*, 1967a; Turkington *et al.*, 1967b, 1968; Turkington, 1968d, 1971b). Cell division mediated by either insulin or epithelial growth factor is sufficient to fulfill the requirements of the proliferative period for cell differentiation, but the action of prolactin in the postmitotic period requires the synergistic action specifically of insulin. When mammary gland explants cultured for 72 hours in the presence of insulin and hydrocortisone are rinsed free of insulin and placed in medium containing the single hormone prolactin, the effects observed with the hormonal combination of insulin and prolactin on RNA and protein synthesis are almost completely prevented (Lockwood *et al.*, 1967a; Turkington and Ward, 1969b; Turkington and Riddle, 1969, 1970a). Epithelial growth factor cannot synergize with prolactin to replace this hormonal effect of insulin (Turkington, 1969b). Placental lactogen has been found to be equivalent to prolactin for the induction of milk proteins (Turkington and Topper, 1966a; Turkington, 1968b; Turkington *et al.*, 1968) and morphological differentiation of mammary epithelial cells, and this hormone appears to function as a mammotropic hormone during pregnancy.

C. The Action of Prolactin

Figure 3 summarizes a characteristic sequence of changes in macro-molecular synthesis following the addition of prolactin to the culture medium of mammary explants treated for 96 hours with insulin and hydrocortisone. An early event in this sequence is a rapid increase in the rate of incorporation of ^{3}H-uridine into RNA by the epithelial cells (Turkington, 1968b; Turkington and Ward, 1969b). Increases in the activity of RNA polymerase [at both low salt concentrations and with $0.2 M$ (NH_4)$_2SO_4$] in isolated nuclei occur concomitantly, and reach a maximal value at approximately 24 hours after the addition of prolactin. Associated with this increase in transcriptive activity is a marked rise in the rate of phophorylation of histones and non-histone nuclear proteins (Turkington and Riddle, 1969). The action of insulin (Fig. 1) early in the culture period is to stimulate the phosphorylation of the F_2a_2, F_2b, F_1, and F_3 histones as well as several minor basic proteins of low electrophoretic mobilities (Turkington and Riddle, 1969), but this process does not lead to a change in the state of differentiation. The action of prolactin leads to a selective phosphorylation of histones,

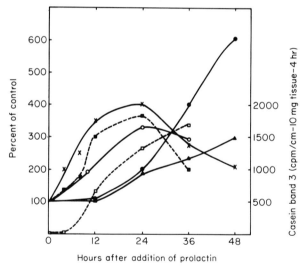

Fig. 3. Time course of the effect of prolactin and insulin on macromolecular synthesis in mammary epithelial cells pretreated with insulin and hydrocortisone for 96 hours. Rate of RNA synthesis ($\times$); rate of phosphorylation of nuclear proteins ($\bigcirc$); rate of synthesis of casein "band 3" ($\square$). Each point represents the incorporation of isotopic precursor during the preceding 4-hour labeling period. Enzymatic activities of the galactosyltransferase of lactose synthetase ($\bullet$) and of α-lactalbumin ($\blacktriangle$); ($\blacksquare$) RNA polymerase activity.

primarily the F_2a_2 and F_2b components, and is associated with the new expression of genes, i.e., the induction of milk proteins in the newly formed daughter cells. The initial rates of synthesis of the major casein proteins reflect the synthetic activity of the differentiated cells present in the tissue at the time of explantation and by 96 hours of culture this synthesis has fallen to zero. It is apparent that casein synthesis in the cells formed *in vitro* is undetectable until prolactin initiates the formation of these milk proteins as a new event in these cells (Turkington *et al.*, 1967b). Increases in the activities of the galactosyltransferase of lactose synthetase and of α-lactalbumin are subsequently observed. Increases in these milk proteins are inhibited by actinomycin D, mitomycin C, puromycin, and cycloheximide, a result consistent with the concept that increased activity represents the formation of additional enzymes, a process which depends upon concomitant RNA synthesis (Turkington *et al.*, 1968). The results shown in Fig. 3 suggest that an early effect of prolactin is on transcription, and that induction of milk proteins during this period is at least in part a result of this primary effect at the transcriptional level.

IV. THE ADRENOCORTICOID HORMONE REQUIREMENT

Multiple steroid hormones are formed by the adrenal cortical cells. Although the liver and kidney, respectively, have been regarded as the "target organs" for the glucocorticoid and mineralocorticoid classes of these hormones, it is clear that molecular processes in a wide range of cell types are regulated by them. Glycogen depositing, anti-inflammatory, and antitumor activities (Glenn, 1964) have been assayed *in vivo*. However, the many variables related to route of administration, nutritional factors, metabolism of the hormones by tissues other than the target tissue, etc., in endocrine-deprived animals posed limitations in terms of the analysis of structure–function relationships of steroid hormones. To determine more precisely the functional importance of various structural features of these hormones a number of *in vitro* systems have been studied. As shown in Table II, these systems involve interaction of a single hormone structure with a specific tissue or cell type to increase the rate of formation of a specific protein. Comparisons of relative hormonal activities can be made at hormone concentrations which are nearly "physiological," and with respect to a biochemical endpoint whose time course of development can be precisely defined. A compari-

TABLE II

MODEL SYSTEMS FOR THE ANALYSIS OF STRUCTURE–FUNCTION RELATIONSHIPS
OF ADRENOCORTICOID HORMONES *in Vitro*

System	Induced protein	Reference
1. Mammary gland organ culture	Casein	Turkington and Topper (1967)
2. Embryonic chick retina organ culture	Glutamine synthetase	Moscona and Piddington (1967)
3. HeLa cell culture	Alkaline phosphatase	Melnykovych (1962)
4. Hepatoma tissue culture cells	Tyrosine aminotransferase	Samuels and Tomkins (1971)
5. Lymph node organ culture	Secondary antibody response (steroid required only for cell viability)	Ambrose (1964)

son of various steroids for their relative activities in permitting induction of casein *in vitro* is shown in Table III. These structures fall into three activity groups within which good correlation exists between morphological indices of steroid effect and rates of casein synthesis: inactivity; moderate activity; and high activity. Reduction of the Δ^4 double bond of 11β-hydrocortisone to the 5β-dihydro form removes all activity, although a small amount of activity is retained in the 5α-dihydro form. For moderate activity the 4-pregnen nucleus must have a keto group at position 20 and either an 11β-ol or a 21-ol function. It may be noted that the introduction of an 11α-ol group into Reichstein's compound S obliterates the moderate activity of the parent compound. The structural requirements for high activity include a keto group at position 20, a 17α-OH or 18-al group, and either 11β-ol or 11-one functions.

Similar results in structure–function relationships have been observed in the embryonic chick retina system (Piddington and Moscona, 1967). In the lymph node system 11-deoxycorticosterone and 11β-hydroxyprogesterone are inactive (Ambrose, 1964), in contrast to the mammary system. Compounds which have moderate activity in the mammary system have been found to be nonstimulatory in the HeLa cells (Melnykovych, 1962). Responses to cortisone or prednisone appear to depend upon the conversion of these compounds to the 11β-ol form (Glenn, 1964). The failure of the hepatoma tissue culture cells (Samuels and Tomkins, 1970; Baxter and Tomkins, 1970) and HeLa cells to respond to these steroids suggests that these cells may be unable to perform this conversion. Thus the possibility exists that different cell types may respond differently to a given steroid structure. Greater similarity among

TABLE III

CASEIN SYNTHESIS AND HISTOLOGIC DIFFERENTIATION OF MAMMARY GLAND
EXPLANTS CULTURED IN THE PRESENCE OF INSULIN, PROLACTIN, AND
VARIOUS STEROIDS

Steroid ($3 \times 10^{-7} M$)	Modification of 4-pregnen structure	Histo-logic re-sponse	Casein synthesis[a]	
			cpm/ mg tissue	IP + steroid/ IP
None	—	—	150	—
Inactive				
5β-Dihydrocortisol	4,5β-dihydro; 11β,17α, 21-triol; 3,20-dione	0	127	0.8
Progesterone	3,20-dione	0	150	1.0
11α-Hydroxyprogesterone	11α-ol; 3,20-dione	0	149	1.0
17α-Hydroxyprogesterone	17α-ol; 3,20-dione	0	150	1.0
Reichstein's E	11β,17α,20,21-tetrol; 3-one	0	152	1.0
11α-Hydrocortisone	11α,17α,21-triol; 3,20-dione	0	146	1.0
Moderately active				
5α-Dihydrocortisol[b]	4,5α-dihydro; 11β,17α,21-triol; 3,20-dione	±	200	1.3
Deoxycorticosterone	21-ol; 3,20-dione	+	255	1.7
Reichstein's S	17α,21-diol; 3,20-dione	++	268	1.8
Corticosterone	11β,21-diol; 3,20-dione	++	285	1.9
11β-Hydroxyprogesterone	11β-ol; 3,20-dione	++	306	2.0
Highly active				
21-Deoxycortisol	11β,17α-diol; 3,20-dione	+++	370	2.5
Aldosterone	18-al; 11β,21-diol; 3,20-dione	+++	375	2.5
Cortisone	17α,21-diol; 3,11,20-trione	+++	387	2.6
11β-Hydrocortisone	11β,17α,21-triol; 3,20-dione	+++	389	2.6
Prednisolone	Δ^1; 11β,17α,21-triol; 3,20-dione	+++	390	2.6

[a] The rate of casein synthesis was measured by the incorporation of $^{32}P_i$ into casein during the final 4 hours of the 48-hour incubation period. (Reproduced by permission of the publishers of *Endocrinology*.) I, insulin; P, prolactin.

[b] The infrared spectrum indicated that this preparation contained no 11β-hydrocortisone.

cell types may be anticipated in terms of the initial binding of steroid hormones to specific receptor molecules. The relative binding activities of various steroid structures to rat thymus cells has been studied recently by Munck and Brinck-Johnsen (1968). These investigators demonstrated a rapid-binding activity in these cells which showed high affinity for cortisol. Competitive binding studies demonstrated that other physiologically active steroids could compete with cortisol-^{3}H for binding, although certain steroids which lack "glucocorticoid" activity also competed significantly for specific binding. The relative functional activities of adrenocorticoid hormones in intact cells cannot yet be interpreted in terms of their apparent relative abilities to bind to a receptor molecule. Structural changes which confer alterations in activity may also relate to differences in rates of entry into cells, competitive binding to non-receptors, and rates of metabolic conversion. For example, different relative activities may be observed by increasing the concentrations of the steroid hormones in the culture medium (Turkington *et al.*, 1967a). Whether the biological activities of combinations of steroids would be different from the activity of each component in any of the *in vitro* systems remains to be determined.

V. HORMONAL REGULATION OF RNA SYNTHESIS

At the time of this writing the Jacob-Monod (1961) operon concept involving the transcription of messenger RNA remains the simplest model to explain the known facts relating to the regulation of bacterial protein synthesis. However, the enormously greater degree of complexity of eucaryotic cells suggests that many additional levels of regulation may exist than are apparent in bacterial cells. The prominent and early changes in the rate of RNA synthesis by mammary epithelial cells after exposure to insulin and prolactin *in vitro* suggest that hormonal regulation of transcription may be of major importance in the induction of milk proteins. The RNA whose rate of formation is increased in response to these hormones has been found to be of multiple classes: rapidly labeled nuclear RNA; transfer RNA; and ribosomal RNA. In the experiment shown in Fig. 4 midpregnancy mouse mammary explants were allowed to incorporate ^{3}H-uridine into RNA during 20-minute labeling periods. Insulin caused a marked stimulation in the rate of synthesis of this rapidly-labeled RNA during the first hours of culture, and maximal increases were observed at approximately 24 hours of incubation. The addition of prolactin caused a second increase in rapidly labeled RNA in explants pretreated with insulin and hydrocortisone for 72 hours (postmitotic cells). This rapidly labeled RNA has been found to be pre-ribosomal RNA and nuclear RNA with heterogeneous sedimentation properties (Turkington, 1970b). The rapidly labeled nuclear RNA populations in mammary epithelial cells have been further charac-

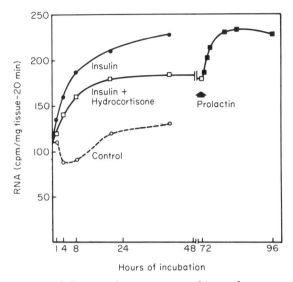

Fig. 4. Time course of the rate of incorporation of ^{3}H-uridine into rapidly labeled RNA (20 minutes labeling period) by mammary epithelial cells incubated with various hormones. (○) control; (●) insulin; (□) insulin and hydrocortisone; (■) insulin, hydrocortisone, and prolactin. Each hormone was present at a concentration of 5 μg/ml.

terized by RNA–DNA hybridization–competition experiments (Turkington, 1970d). Mammary epithelial cells were isolated from fat cells by treatment with crude collagenase and centrifugation. The cells were allowed to label RNA isotopically *in vitro* for 30 minutes. RNA prepared from isolated nuclei hybridized to the DNA's of various species in proportion to the known genetic relatedness of these species. Homologous binding of the RNA to DNA occurred with sufficient saturation to produce values in competition experiments which approached a predicted saturation-dependent curve. It was found that nuclear RNA derived from virginal mammary epithelial cells competed incompletely with ^{3}H-RNA derived from lactational cells. Reversal of the isotopic labeling and double-label experiments consistently provided evidence for a greater variety of hybridizable nuclear RNA species (or sequences) in the differentiated, lactational cells than could be detected in undifferentiated, virginal cells. This result suggests that new species of RNA are formed by transcription on newly activated genes during the process of hormone-dependent cell differentiation. The results must be interpreted with caution, however, since the kinetics of the hybridization reaction are not fully understood. The RNA species compared by competition may represent redundant or partially redundant sequences which can hybridize by mismatching, and thereby prevent the detection of unique sequences. The functions of the RNA's compared are also unknown, although they may function as activator RNA's (Britten and Davidson, 1969; Frenster, 1965) or messenger RNA's.

Evidence for increased messenger RNA utilization in the cytoplasm following increased transcriptive activity has been observed in studies on polysomes. Incubation of mammary explants on medium containing insulin results in a marked stimulation of ribosome formation and accumulation of polysomes (Turkington and Riddle, 1970a). Isotopic labeling experiments have demonstrated that these ribosomes are utilized by the daughter cell population for the formation of polysomes. As shown in Fig. 5, prolactin causes the formation of increased numbers of monosomes and polysomes. Casein synthesis commences at a time point when prolactin-induced polysomal aggregation is observed to occur (Fig. 6). The sequence of events suggests an activation of transcription which is then coupled to increased translational activity (Turkington and Riddle, 1970a).

The concentration of transfer RNA in the mammary epithelial cells is also under hormonal regulation. During pregnancy the proportion of epithelial cell RNA which is transfer RNA increases markedly (Turkington, 1969c). In the organ culture system insulin increases the rate of

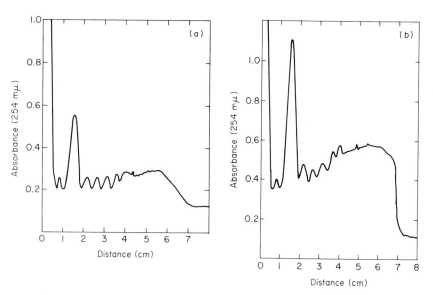

FIG. 5. Polysome profiles derived from mammary epithelial cells treated *in vitro* for 72 hours with insulin and hydrocortisone (a) and then during the 72–96 hour period with insulin, hydrocortisone, and prolactin (b).

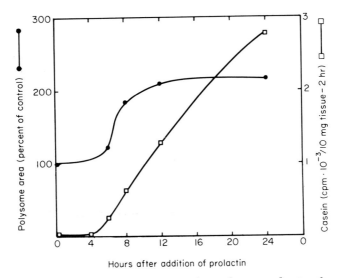

Fig. 6. Time course of the increases in polysomal area and rate of casein synthesis in response to prolactin. Mammary explants were incubated with insulin and hydrocortisone for 96 hours prior to addition of prolactin. Each value for the synthesis of casein "bands 1–3" represents the incorporation of $^{32}P_i$ during the preceding 2-hour labeling period.

total RNA synthesis. Transfer RNA is increased in proportion to total cell RNA, but the state of cell differentiation is not altered. Alveolar cell differentiation induced by insulin, hydrocortisone, and prolactin is characterized by further increases in total transfer RNA which are disproportionately greater than the increase in total cell RNA. In these experiments transfer RNA was measured by the mass of RNA which migrated in electrophoresis through polyacrylamide gels as 4 S RNA, and by functional activity in an amino acid acceptor assay in the presence of excess amino acyl synthetases, ATP, and ^{14}C-amino acids (Turkington, 1969c).

The assembly of transfer RNA molecules is completed by methylation of specific bases in the polynucleotide chain following its transcription on the DNA template (Fleissner and Borek, 1962, 1963). A number of transfer RNA methylating enzymes exhibiting specificity for particular bases and base sequences have been identified in a number of cell types (Hurwitz *et al.*, 1964a,b, 1965; Srinivasan and Borek, 1963). In the mammary gland the following specific enzymes for transfer RNA methylation have been identified: guanine N^1-methylase; guanine N^2, N^2-methylases; adenine 1-methylase; adenine N^6-methylase; uridine 5-methylase; and cytidine 5-methylase (Turkington, 1969a; Turkington and Riddle, 1970b). The activities of each of these enzymes have been measured by the rate of methylation of specific bases in *E. coli* K12 tRNA added to the assay mixture. Insulin induces a three- to fourfold increase in all these enzymes during the first 48 hours of mammary explant culture. Prolactin and insulin synergize to stimulate further increases in all enzyme activities in explants pretreated with insulin and hydrocortisone for 72 hours. These effects appear to relate to the formation of new enzyme molecules, since they are prevented by inhibitors of protein and RNA synthesis. The relative constancy of methylated base ratios formed by tissue extracts at various stages of development and after hormonal stimulation does not suggest that the methylation of transfer RNA governs the rate of formation of the milk proteins or regulates the expression of genes. However, the analysis of methylated base sequences in specific transfer RNA species may provide further insight into this problem. It appears, therefore, that mechanisms exist in the cell which coordinate the formation of transfer RNA polynucleotides with the induction of methylating enzymes for the final assembly of functional transfer RNA molecules.

It is apparent from these early studies that hormones which regulate the formation of specific milk proteins cause dramatic and rapid changes in the rate of formation of multiple classes of RNA's. The synthesis of rapidly labeled nuclear RNA, ribosomal RNA, and transfer RNA is increased. Subsequently ribosomes aggregate into polysomes at a time point when increased rates of formation of casein are observed. Although this temporal sequence of events appears clear, it does not provide a basis for establishing which of these steps in protein synthesis may be limiting for the synthesis of specific proteins. It is possible that these multiple reactions are integrated by gene activating circuits in the cell nucleus, and that the rate-limiting step is activation of a single gene. Such a mechanism would predict that the presence and concentration of the hormone itself would thus become an important rate-limiting factor. A model scheme representing the action of prolactin on RNA formation is shown in Fig. 7. It is to be emphasized that this is only a working model, and it is possible to construct other schemes of action from currently available data. The initial reaction of prolactin is apparently with some constituent of the cell surface, since prolactin covalently bonded to Sepharose beads can interact with the superficial plasma membrane structures of cultured mammary epithelial cells to stimulate nuclear RNA synthesis (Turkington, 1970c). Activation of those specific genes whose expression characterizes the mammary alveolar cell may be initially mediated by a signal (dashed arrow) received

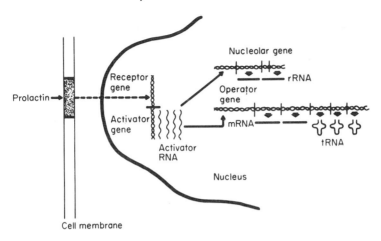

Fig. 7. Proposed scheme of action of prolactin on RNA synthesis.

at a specific receptor gene. This gene may influence a specific activator gene whose RNA product can stimulate in common the activities of structural genes which produce transfer RNA's; ribosomal RNA's; and messenger RNA's which code for the caseins, α-lactalbumin, the galactosyltransferase of lactose synthetase, the tRNA methylating enzymes, and perhaps other proteins. Such a class of activating RNA's may constitute part of the rapidly labeled nuclear RNA whose synthesis is stimulated by prolactin. Messenger RNA may constitute another segment of this RNA population. Operator genes which can bind by homologous base pairing to a single species of activator RNA could account for part of the redundancy in the base sequences found in the DNA (Britten and Kohn, 1966). Thus, activation of the synthesis of multiple types of RNA would be temporally integrated in response to a single hormonal signal. The phosphorylation of chromosomal proteins may play some role in the activation process. The synergistic action of insulin could be required at any step between the cell surface and the formation of the activator RNA, since rapidly labeled nuclear RNA synthesis and nuclear protein phosphorylation do not occur in the absence of insulin. A possible role for cytoplasmic repressor(s) cannot be excluded at this point. Activation of multiple classes of RNA by a single hormonal stimulus has been observed in a number of other systems (O'Malley, 1969). Although specific hormones might thus activate a specific master gene (receptor gene), it is possible that secondary activation circuits from these master genes might overlap, producing additive effects from some hormonal combinations. Multiple hormonal requirements, as in the case of the mammary gland, could exist for those cells in which a sufficient range of secondary activation circuits did not exist, or in which hormone-dependent regulatory steps existed at posttranscriptional levels as well. The further study of multiple hormone reactant systems may add new dimensions to our understanding of the complex interrelationships of such regulatory mechanisms.

VI. CONCLUDING COMMENTS

At the present time it can be said that there is no hormone whose mechanism of action is precisely understood. The study of multiple hormone reactant systems would thus seem to compound the complexity of the problem of hormonal regulation. Yet it is clear that regulation within many cell types is dependent upon multiple hormones. Indeed, the action of one hormone may not become evident apart from the permissive action of a second hormone. In the mammary gland the biological role of one hormone cannot be understood apart from knowledge relating to the actions of other hormones which regulate basic processes in these cells. Studies on the actions of insulin and prolactin indicate that the differentiation of mammary alveolar cells results in the formation of a cell type in which induction of specific proteins is regulated primarily at the transcriptional level. As described in some of the other chapters in this book, the differentiation of other cell types may limit hormonal regulation to only posttranscriptional or other types of mechanisms. Thus, the response of any cell to any hormone would appear to depend not only upon properties of the hormones but also upon the kinds of specialization and limitations which the process of differentiation has determined for that cell. The coming decade will certainly witness advances in our understanding of cell differentiation as well as the discovery of new, biologically active substances. Hopefully endocrine research will proceed to implicate all of the hormonal factors which interact at various levels of regulation, and to elucidate the interrelationships between hormonally responsive biochemical processes.

ACKNOWLEDGMENTS

This work was supported by the Veterans Administration, by Grant No. T-525 from the American Cancer Society, and by U. S. Public Health Service Grant No. CA-12904 from the National Cancer Institute.

REFERENCES

Ambrose, C. T. (1964). *Wistar Insti. Monograph* No. 1, p. 71.
Bangham, A. D., Standish, M. M., and Weissman, G. (1965). *J. Mol. Biol.* 13, 253.
Baird, T. (1968). *J. Clin. Endocrinol. Metab.* 28, 244–258.
Baxter, J. D., and Tomkins, G. M. (1970). *Proc. Natl. Acad. Sci. U. S.* 65, 709.
Bresciani, F. (1968). *Cell Tissue Kinetics* 1, 51–63.
Brew, K. (1969). *Nature* 222, 671–672.
Brew, K., Vanaman, T. C., and Hill, R. L. (1968). *Proc. Natl. Acad. Sci. U. S.* 50, 491–498.
Britten, R. J., and Davidson, E. H. (1969). *Science* 165, 349–357.
Britten, R. J., and Kohne, D. E. (1966). *Carnegie Inst. Wash., Yearbook* 65, 78.
Brodbeck, U., and Ebner, K. E. (1966a). *J. Biol. Chem.* 241, 762–764.
Brodbeck, U., and Ebner, K. E. (1966b). *J. Biol. Chem.* 241, 5526–5532.
Chambon, P., Ramuz, M., Mandel, P., and Doly, R. (1968a). *Biochim. Biophys. Acta* 157, 504.
Chambon, P., Karon, H., Ramuz, M., and Mandel, P. (1968b). *Biochim. Biophys. Acta* 157, 520.
Chatterton, R. T., Jr. (1971). *In* "Sex Steroids: Molecular Mechanisms" (K. W. McKerns, ed.), Appleton, New York (in press).
Chatterton, R. T., Jr., Chatterton, A. J., and Hellman, L. (1969). *Endocrinology* 85, 16.
Cohen, S. (1965). *J. Biol. Chem.* 237, 1555–1562.
Cohen, S., and Stastny, M. (1968). *Biochim. Biophys. Acta* 166, 427.
de Duve, C., Wattiaux, R., and Wibo, M. (1961). *Biochem. Pharmacol.* 9, 97.
DeWulf, H., and Hers, H. G. (1968). *European J. Biochem.* 6, 558.
Epifanova, O. I. (1965). "Hormones and the Reproduction of Cells." Moscow (Israel Program for Scientific Translations Ltd., and the National Science Foundation, Washington, D. C.).
Fleissner, E., and Borek, E. (1962). *Proc. Natl. Acad. Sci. U. S.* 48, 1199.
Fleissner, E., and Borek, E. (1963). *Biochemistry* 2, 1093.
Folley, S. J. (1956). "The Physiology and Biochemistry of Lactation." Springfield, Illinois.
Frenster, J. H. (1965). *Nature* 206, 680–683.
Glenn, E. M. (1964). *Hormonal Steroids; Biochem. Pharmacol., Therap. Proc. 1st Intern. Congr. Hormonal Steroids, 1962* Vol. 1, p. 319.
Gold, A. H. (1970). *J. Biol. Chem.* 245, 903–905.
Greengard, O. (1969). *Science* 163, 891.
Grota, L. J., and Eik-Nes, K. B. (1967). *J. Reprod. Fertility* 13, 83–91.
Gurley, L. R., and Hardin, J. M. (1968). *Arch Biochem. Biophys.* 128, 285.
Hurwitz, J., Gold, M., and Anders, M. (1964a). *J. Biol. Chem.* 239, 3462.
Hurwitz, J., Gold, M., and Anders, M. (1964b). *J. Biol. Chem.* 239, 3474.
Hurwitz, J., Anders, M., Gold, M., and Smith, I. (1965). *J. Biol. Chem.* 240, 1256.
Ingle, D. J. (1954). *Acta Endocrinol.* 17, 172.
Jacob, F., and Monod, J. (1961). *J. Mol. Biol.* 3, 318.
Kenney, F. T., and Reel, J. R. (1971). *In* "Hormonal Regulation" (M. Hamburgh and E. J. W. Barrington, eds.), pp. 161–168. Appleton, New York.
Kenney, F. T., Reel, J. R., Hager, C. B., and Wittliff, J. L. (1968). *In* "Regulatory

Mechanisms for Protein Synthesis in Mammalian Cells" (A. San Pietro, M. R. Lamborg, and F. T. Kenney, eds.), pp. 119–142. Academic Press, New York.

Korenman, S. G., Perrin, L. E., and McCallum, T. P. (1969). *J. Clin. Endocrinol. Metab.* **29,** 879–883.

Kuhn, N. J. (1968). *Biochem. J.* **106,** 743.

Lockwood, D. H., Turkington, R. W., and Topper, Y. J. (1966). *Biochim. Biophys. Acta* **130,** 493.

Lockwood, D. H., Stockdale, F. E., and Topper, Y. J. (1967a). *Science* **156,** 945–947.

Lockwood, D. H., Voytovich, A. E., Stockdale, F. E., and Topper, Y. J. (1967b). *Proc. Natl. Acad. Sci. U. S.* **58,** 658.

Lyons, W. R. (1958). *Proc. Roy. Soc.* **B149,** 303–325.

Lyons, W. R., Li, C. H., and Johnson, R. E. (1958). *Recent Progr. Hormone Res.* **14,** 219–254.

Males, J. L., and Turkington, R. W. (1970). *J. Biol. Chem.* **245,** 6080–6090.

Males, J. L., and Turkington, R. W. (1971). *Endocrinology* **88,** 579–588.

Marzluff, W. F., Jr., McCarty, K. S., and Turkington, R. W. (1969). *Biochim. Biophys. Acta* **190,** 517.

Maul, G. G., and Hamilton, T. H. (1967). *Proc. Natl. Acad. Sci. U. S.* **57,** 1371.

Meites, J. (1959). *In* "Reproduction in Domestic Animals" (H. H. Cole and P. T. Cupps, eds.), 1st ed., Vol. 1, pp. 539–593. Academic Press, New York.

Melnykovych, G. (1962). *Biochem. Biophys. Res. Commun.* **8,** 81.

Mersmann, H. J., and Segal, H. L. (1969). *J. Biol. Chem.* **244,** 1701.

Moscona, A. A., and Piddington, R. (1966). *Biochim. Biophys. Acta* **121,** 409–411.

Moscona, A. A., and Piddington, R. (1967). *Science* **158,** 496–497.

Moscona, A. A., Moscona, M. H., and Saenz, N. (1968). *Proc. Natl. Acad. Sci. U. S.* **61,** 160–167.

Munck, A., and Brinck-Johnsen, T. (1968). *J. Biol. Chem.* **243,** 5556–5565.

Novikoff, A. B., Essner, E., and Quintano, N. (1964). *Federation Proc.* **23,** 1010.

O'Malley, B. W. (1969). *Trans. N. Y. Acad. Sci.* [2] **31,** 478.

Piddington, R. (1967). *Develop. Biol.* **16,** 168–188.

Piddington, R., and Moscona, A. A. (1965). *J. Cell Biol.* **27,** 247–252.

Piddington, R., and Moscona, A. A. (1967). *Biochim. Biophys. Acta* **141,** 429–432.

Pogo, A. O., Littan, V. C., Allfrey, V. G., and Mirsky, A. E. (1967). *Proc. Natl. Acad. Sci. U. S.* **57,** 743.

Prop, F. J. A. (1959). *Nature* **184,** 379–380.

Prop, F. J. A. (1960). *Exp. Cell Res.* **20,** 256–258.

Prop, F. J. A. (1961). *Pathol. Biol., Semaine Hop.* **9,** 640–645.

Prop, F. J. A. (1966). *Exptl. Cell Res.* **42,** 386–388.

Prop, F. J. A., and Hendrix, S. E. A. M. (1965). *Exptl. Cell Res.* **40,** 277–281.

Rivera, E. M. (1964). *Proc. Soc. Exptl. Biol. Med.* **116,** 568.

Rivera, E. M., and Bern, R. A. (1961). *Endocrinology* **69,** 340–353.

Robbins, E., and Borun, T. W. (1967). *Proc. Natl. Acad. Sci. U. S.* **57,** 409.

Samuels, H. H., and Tomkins, G. M. (1970). *J. Mol. Biol.* **52,** 57.

Srinivasan, P., and Borek, E. (1963). *Proc. Natl. Acad. Sci. U. S.* **49,** 529.

Stockdale, F. E., and Topper, Y. J. (1966). *Proc. Natl. Acad. Sci. U. S.* **56,** 1283–1289.

Stockdale, F. E., Juergens, W. G., and Topper, Y. J. (1966). *Develop. Biol.* **13,** 266–281.

Takai, S., Borun, T. W., Muchmore, J., and Lieberman, J. (1968). *Nature* **219**, 860.
Taylor, J., Cohen, S., and Mitchell, W. (1970). *Federation Proc.* **29**, 670.
Turkington, R. W. (1968a). *Endocrinology* **82**, 540.
Turkington, R. W. (1968b). *Endocrinology* **82**, 575.
Turkington, R. W. (1968c). *Experientia* **24**, 226.
Turkington, R. W. (1968d). *Biochim. Biophys. Acta* **158**, 274.
Turkington, R. W. (1968e). *Current Topics Develop. Biol.* **3**, 199–218.
Turkington, R. W. (1969a). *J. Biol. Chem.* **244**, 5140.
Turkington, R. W. (1969b). *Exptl. Cell Res.* **57**, 79.
Turkington, R. W. (1969c). *Cancer Res.* **30**, 104.
Turkington, R. (1969d). *Exptl. Cell Res.* **58**, 296.
Turkington, R. W. (1970a). *In* "Hormone Regulation" (M. Hamburgh and E. J. W. Barrington, eds.), pp. 49–59. Appleton, New York.
Turkington, R. W. (1970b). *J. Biol. Chem.* **245**, 6690–6697.
Turkington, R. W. (1970c). *Biochem. Biophys. Res. Commun.* **41**, 1362–1367.
Turkington, R. W. (1970d). *Biochim. Biophys. Acta* **213**, 484–494.
Turkington, R. W. (1971a). *In* "The Sex Steroids: Molecular Mechanisms" (K. W. McKerns, ed.). Appleton, New York (in press).
Turkington, R. W. (1971b). *In* "Developmental Aspects of the Cell Cycle" (I. L. Cameron, G. M. Padilla, and A. M. Zimmerman, eds.), pp. 315–355. Academic Press, New York.
Turkington, R. W., and Hilf, R. (1968). *Science* **160**, 1457.
Turkington, R. W., and Hill, R. L. (1969). *Science* **163**, 1458–1460.
Turkington, R. W., and Riddle, M. (1969). *J. Biol. Chem.* **244**, 6040.
Turkington, R. W., and Riddle, M. (1970a). *J. Biol. Chem.* **245**, 5145–5152.
Turkington, R. W., and Riddle, M. (1970b). *Cancer Res.* **30**, 650–657.
Turkington, R. W., and Topper, Y. J. (1966a). *Endocrinology* **79**, 175–181.
Turkington, R. W., and Topper, Y. J. (1966b). *Biochim. Biophys. Acta* **127**, 366–372.
Turkington, R. W., and Topper, Y. J. (1967). *Endocrinology* **80**, 329–336.
Turkington, R. W., and Ward, O. T. (1969a). *Biochim. Biophys. Acta* **174**, 282–290.
Turkington, R. W., and Ward, O. T. (1969b). *Biochim. Biophys. Acta* **174**, 291–301.
Turkington, R. W., Juergens, W. G., and Topper, Y. J. (1965). *Biochim. Biophys. Acta* **111**, 573.
Turkington, R. W., Juergens, W. G., and Topper, Y. J. (1967a). *Endocrinology* **80**, 1139.
Turkington, R. W., Lockwood, D. H., and Topper, Y. J. (1967b). *Biochim. Biophys. Acta* **148**, 475.
Turkington, R. W., Brew, K., Vanaman, T. C., and Hill, R. L. (1968). *J. Biol. Chem.* **243**, 3382.
Turkington, R. W., Males, J. L., and Cohen, S. (1971). *Cancer Res.* **31**, 252.
Van der Molen, H. J., and Aakvaag, A. (1967). *In* "Hormones in Blood" (C. H. Gray and A. L. Bacharach, eds.), 2nd rev. ed., Vol. 2, pp. 221–303. Academic Press, New York.
Weissman, G. (1964). *Federation Proc.* **23**, 1038.
Weissman, G. (1965). *Biochem. Pharmacol.* **14**, 525.
Weissman, G., and Thomas, L. (1964). *Recent Progr. Hormone Res.* **20**, 215.
Wetzel, B. K., Spicer, S., and Wollman, S. H. (1965). *J. Cell Biol.* **25**, 593.
Wicks, W. D., Kenney, F. T., and Lee, K. L. (1969). *J. Biol. Chem.* **244**, 6008–6013.

Wollman, S. H. (1969). *In* "Lysosomes in Biology and Pathology" (J. T. Dingle and H. B. Fell, eds.), Vol. 2, p. 483. North-Holland Publ., Amsterdam.

Wollman, S. H., Spicer, S., and Burstone, M. S. (1964). *J. Cell Biol.* **21**, 191.

Yokoyama, I. (1970). *In* "Lactogenesis: The Initiation of Milk Formation" (M. Reynolds and S. J. Folley, eds.), p. 98. Univ. of Chicago Press, Chicago.

CHAPTER 4

The Catecholamines

G. A. Robison, R. W. Butcher, and E. W. Sutherland

I. INTRODUCTION

Our purpose in this chapter will be to summarize what is known about the actions and mechanism of action of epinephrine and nor-epinephrine (Fig. 1). The L-isomers of these compounds are widely distributed in nature, and have been found in all vertebrates studied. Although they may be absent in some invertebrates (von Euler, 1963), they have been detected in at least two species of protozoa (Janakidevi et al., 1966). In mammals, with which this chapter will be primarily

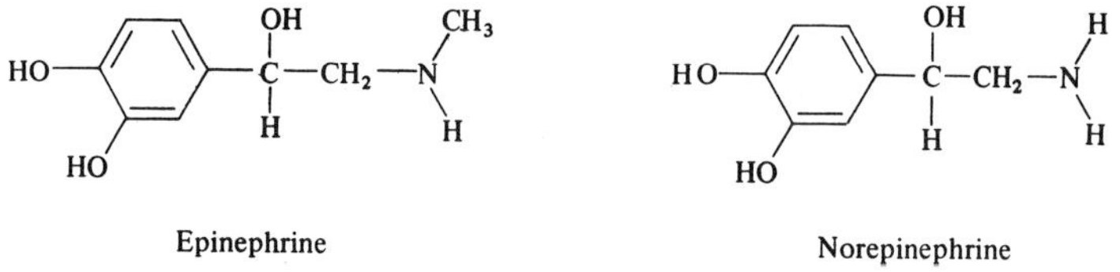

FIG. 1. Chemical structures of epinephrine and norepinephrine.

concerned, epinephrine is released from secretory cells of the adrenal medulla, and appears to function in these organisms primarily as a circulating hormone. Norepinephrine may also function in this capacity to some extent, but plays a more important role as the principal neuro-transmitter of the sympathetic nervous system (von Euler, 1966). A third catecholamine, dopamine, may also play an important physiological role, especially within the central nervous system (Hornykiewicz, 1966). It is not discussed in this chapter because its mechanism of action has not been carefully studied.

The catecholamines are sometimes referred to as nonessential hormones, but this characterization is valid in only a very limited sense. Adult mammals in which sympathoadrenal function is prevented (as by adrenal demedullation and either surgical or immunological sympathectomy or pharmacological denervation) can survive for long periods under carefully controlled laboratory conditions, but such animals cannot survive a variety of stresses associated with a normal environment (Cannon, 1939; Brodie *et al.*, 1966). Following Cannon, therefore, we can regard the catecholamines as primarily emergency hormones which help to maintain homeostasis in the face of changes in the external environment. Circumstances requiring "fight or flight" represent a special instance of this type of change, and are associated with an exaggerated sympathoadrenal response. In general, the functions which are stimulated by the catecholamines are those involving effort and the expenditure of energy. Hess (1948) referred to these effects as "ergotropic," as opposed to the "trophotropic" or assimilatory effects produced by stimulation of the parasympathetic nervous system and by certain anabolic hormones. The catecholamines can thus be regarded as an important part of what Hess referred to as the ergotropic system. Most of what we have learned about the catecholamines within recent years, as summarized in the following pages and elsewhere (e.g., Brodie *et al.*, 1966; Himms-Hagen, 1967; Sutherland and Robison, 1969), tends to support these earlier concepts. They can probably be applied to vertebrates in general, and possibly to many lower forms as well.

A discussion of the formation, metabolism, release, and reuptake of the catecholamines would be considerably beyond the scope of this chapter. These and other aspects of the subject were reviewed in some detail at the "Second Symposium on Catecholamines," the proceedings of which were published (Acheson, 1966). A more recent review by Himms-Hagen (1967) covered the role of the catecholamines as regulators of metabolism. We intend to refer to this review wherever possible, instead of referring individually to each of the 806 papers upon which it was based.

II. PROBLEMS OF CLASSIFICATION

The catecholamines produce a great variety of effects, and it is not surprising that many attempts have been made to classify them according to some sort of rational scheme. A method which has been widely used for at least the past decade is based on a concept originally developed by Ahlquist (1948). According to it, the effects of the catecholamines can be classified into three groups: (1) those which are mediated by adrenergic β-receptors; (2) those which are mediated by adrenergic α-receptors; and (3) those mediated neither by β-receptors nor by α-receptors, or for which this has not been established.

A more recent method is based on the results of biochemical studies. Here again, the effects of the catecholamines can be classified into three groups: (1) those which are mediated by an increase in the intracellular level of cyclic AMP (cAMP)[1]; (2) those which are mediated by a fall in the intracellular level of cAMP; and (3) those which are unrelated to cAMP or for which this has not been established.

In order to understand the possible relation between these two methods of classifying the effects of the catecholamines, it may be useful to briefly review the development of our concepts in this area. The idea that the catecholamines could interact with more than one type of receptor was based initially on some studies by Dale (1906). He found that an adrenal medullary extract ("adrenalin") caused an increase in blood pressure when injected into anesthetized cats. However, when these cats were pretreated with a mixture of ergot alkaloids ("ergotoxine"), then the injection of adrenalin caused a fall in blood pressure. Dale reasoned that there must be two types of adrenergic receptors, with the ones responsible for the increase in blood pressure normally predominating. When these were blocked by ergotoxine, then the effect

---

[1] See Chapter 2 in this volume.

of the other receptors was unmasked. The effects of epinephrine on the skin color of certain teleost fish were later explained in a similar fashion. Epinephrine ordinarily causes the skins of these fish to become lighter, but, after ergotoxine, it caused them to become darker.

The idea that there might be two types of adrenergic receptors in the same type of cell, mediating divergent effects depending on which type of receptor predominated, was decidedly unappealing to some investigators. That some cells contain two types of adrenergic receptors is today no longer questioned, but, even so, it should be noted that the functional significance of this type of arrangement is still quite obscure. It is understandable, in any event, that many attempts were made to explain the divergent effects of epinephrine in terms of a single type of receptor. Perhaps the most famous of these was that of Cannon and Rosenblueth (1937). They suggested that the interaction of epinephrine with its receptors led in some cells to the formation of a hypothetical substance which they called "sympathin I." This was postulated as the mediator of the "inhibitory" effects of epinephrine, such as the fall in blood pressure observed by Dale. In other cells the same type of interaction was thought to lead to the formation of "sympathin E," the mediator of the "excitatory" effects of sympathetic stimulation. At the time, Cannon and Rosenblueth regarded epinephrine as the only physiologically important catecholamine, and subsequent arguments about the sympathin theory were gradually obscured by the question of whether there might not be two catecholamines, as was later shown to be the case by Euler and his colleagues. Attempts were made by the writers of some textbooks to equate norepinephrine with sympathin E and epinephrine with sympathin I, but these were not successful.

The sympathin theory was finally laid to rest by Ahlquist (1948), who showed that at least some of the effects of the catecholamines could be separated into two groups, according to the order of potency of a series of catecholamines in producing them. One of the derivatives which Ahlquist used in this study, in addition to epinephrine and norepinephrine, was isoproterenol, in which the methyl group attached to the nitrogen in epinephrine is replaced by an isopropyl moiety. This drug is now widely used therapeutically as well as experimentally. Ahlquist found that the naturally occurring catecholamines were much more potent than isoproterenol in producing some of the effects of epinephrine, including most (but not all) of the effects which previous investigators had regarded as "excitatory." Isoproterenol was more potent than the naturally occurring catecholamines in producing the other effects of epinephrine, which included most of the "inhibitory" effects, such as the relaxation of smooth muscle, but also some of the "excitatory" effects, such as the increased rate and force of myocardial contraction. Since the order of potency of agonists did not correlate in any obvious way with the nature of the effects produced, Ahlquist resorted to the Greek alphabet. He suggested that until more was known about them, the receptors mediating these two classes of effects might be referred to, respectively, as α-receptors and β-receptors. This is the basis of the method of classification mentioned at the beginning of this section.

At the time of Ahlquist's original study, the only effects of epinephrine which could be blocked by drugs (such as ergotoxine) were those thought to be mediated by α-receptors. Consequently these drugs, including several other natural and synthetic ergot alkaloids as well as phentolamine and phenoxybenzamine, eventually came to be known as α-adrenergic blocking agents. The chemical structures of these various agents bear no obvious relation to each other or to the catecholamines, and their mechanism or mechanisms of action are correspondingly unclear (for a review, see Ghouri and Haley, 1969).

Drugs capable of selectively blocking the other effects of epinephrine were not available until Powell and Slater (1958) introduced dichloroisoproterenol (DCI), in which the phenolic hydroxyl groups of isoproterenol are replaced by chlorine. This became the first of a large series of compounds now known collectively as β-adrenergic blocking agents (Biel and Lum, 1966; Moran, 1967). Most of these drugs can be regarded as analogs of isoproterenol, such that they might be expected to act (as they do) as competitive antagonists of the catecholamines. It thus became possible to classify the effects of the catecholamines not only on the basis of the order of potency of agonists but also according to the type of blocking agent which prevented the response in question. Most of the known effects of the catecholamines have been so classified.

A problem which became increasingly apparent as more of the effects of the catecholamines were studied from this point of view was that while the rank order of potency of agonists was reasonably consistent for either of the two classes of receptors, the actual ratio of the potency of one agonist to another varied widely. Furthermore, as had been pointed out previously by Clark (1937), the relative potencies of adrenergic blocking agents may also vary from one response to the next. As discussed in more detail elsewhere (Robison *et al.*, 1969a), these findings gradually led to the recognition that α-receptors and β-receptors must each constitute a class or family of receptors, rather than a set of identical patterns of forces. It has been recognized for some time that a given type of receptor may differ considerably from one tissue to another within the same species and from one species to another within the same tissue. We are now beginning to realize that even within the same tissue in the same species, the properties of these receptors may change according to the age and hormonal state of the animal. Under these circumstances it is perhaps not surprising that some gray areas have begun to develop in which it is difficult to decide whether the adrenergic receptors mediating a particular response should be classified as α-receptors or as β-receptors, based only on a knowledge of the order of potency of agonists and adrenergic blocking agents. Our knowledge of the chemical nature of these receptors was never substantial, and what we think we know about them is presently in a state of considerable flux.

We can now turn to the second method of classifying the effects of the catecholamines, in hopes that it will bring clarity rather than more confusion. The importance of cAMP in at least one adrenergic response was recognized at an early date, for it was through the study of the hepatic glycogenolytic response that cAMP was discovered (Sutherland and Rall, 1958). After it was found that epinephrine acted in the liver by stimulating adenyl cyclase (see Sutherland and Rall, 1960, for a more detailed review), the order of potency of agonists was found to be the same as that used by Ahlquist to define the adrenergic β-receptor (Fig. 2). The discovery of cAMP coincided closely in time with the

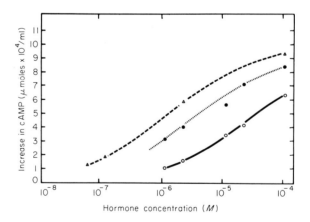

Fig. 2. Effect of increasing concentrations of three catecholamines on the formation of cAMP by dog liver adenyl cyclase. Washed particulate preparations were incubated with ATP and Mg^{2+} for 12 minutes at 30°C, in the presence of caffeine and the indicated concentration of a catecholamine. Formation of cAMP under these conditions in the absence of a catecholamine was 3.6×10^{-4} μmole/ml. ($\blacktriangle$) l-isopropylarterenol; ($\bullet$) l-epinephrine; ($\bigcirc$) l-norepinephrine. From Murad et al. (1962).

introduction of DCI, and it was shown that the stimulation of adenyl cyclase by the catecholamines could be competitively antagonized by DCI (Murad *et al.*, 1962). Subsequently, adenyl cyclase from a great variety of sources was found to be sensitive to stimulation by catecholamines, and in most cases the order of potency of agonists and the sensitivity to blockade by adrenergic blocking agents were such as to suggest the participation of adrenergic β-receptors. The concept thus arose (Robison *et al.*, 1969a) that these receptors and adenyl cyclase might be very closely related. Indeed, there is much evidence to suggest that these receptors constitute an integral component of the adenyl cyclase system in tissues where they occur, which is to say that all of the effects previously thought to be mediated by β-receptors may in fact be mediated by an increase in the intracellular level of cAMP. If so, we may be justified in redefining these receptors as those which mediate the stimulation of adenyl cyclase by catecholamines. Whether this will be preferable to simply abandoning the earlier method of classifying adrenergic receptors, as suggested by Ahlquist (1968), remains to be seen.

It is interesting to note, in view of the historical development of these concepts, that most of the effects which were thought to be mediated by sympathin I are now either known or thought to be mediated by cAMP. A difference between cAMP and sympathin I is that cAMP may also mediate some of the "excitatory" effects of the catecholamines, not to mention many of the effects of a great variety of other hormones.

Within recent years evidence has begun to accumulate to suggest that a number of effects associated with adrenergic α-receptors are mediated by a fall in the intracellular level of cAMP. We can note at this point that the catecholamines and the prostaglandins are presently unique in that they are the only hormones known which produce some of their effects by way of an increase in the level of cAMP and others by way of a decrease. The mechanism by which these hormones produce a fall in the level of cAMP is unknown. Whether all or only some of the effects mediated by adrenergic α-receptors are the result of a fall in the level of cAMP is likewise unknown.

Returning now to the two methods of classifying the effects of the catecholamines, as outlined at the beginning of this section, we can see that there is a considerable degree of overlap between them. Many of the effects classified as β-adrenergic effects are the same as those mediated by increases in the intracellular level of cAMP, secondary to the stimulation of adenyl cyclase, whereas those classified as α-adrenergic effects overlap with those mediated by a fall in the level of cAMP. Whether this overlap will eventually be seen as absolute or only partial seems unclear at the present time, and remains as a question for future research.

We can now go on to the known effects of the catecholamines, and see how (or if) they fit in with the concepts discussed to this point.

III. EFFECTS OF THE CATECHOLAMINES

A. HEPATIC EFFECTS

The stimulation of hepatic adenyl cyclase by catecholamines was mentioned previously (Fig. 2). It should be noted that glucagon also stimulates adenyl cyclase in the liver (Makman and Sutherland, 1964; Bitensky et al., 1968; Pohl et al., 1969) and has generally been found to be more potent in this regard than the catecholamines. Glucagon is also capable of causing a greater increase in the level of cAMP in the isolated perfused rat liver than any of the catecholamines (Robison et al., 1967; Exton and Park, 1968), although it is not clear in either case how the increase is apportioned between parenchymal and reticulo-endothelial cells. The result, in any event, is similar, and includes an increase in phosphorylase activity (Sutherland and Rall, 1960), a reduction in glycogen synthetase activity (DeWulf and Hers, 1968), and an increased rate of gluconeogenesis (Exton and Park, 1968). These effects lead to a net increase in the rate of hepatic glucose production, which contributes to the well-known hyperglycemic effect of the catecholamines (Himms-Hagen, 1967). Since the released glucose can be utilized by other tissues as a source of energy, it is easy to see how this fits in with the concept of the catecholamines as ergotropic hormones.

Circulating levels of catecholamines are generally in the range of 10^{-9} to 10^{-8} M, and are probably too low to produce a significant effect in the liver (Sokal et al., 1964). By contrast, norepinephrine released in response to splanchnic nerve stimulation may lead to a very profound effect (Shimazu and Amakawa, 1968), and this is probably the principal means by which the catecholamines affect the liver.

The adrenergic receptors mediating these effects in some species, such as dogs and cats, are characteristically β-receptors. In certain other species, such as rats and humans, they may have characteristics which cause them to resemble α-receptors (Ellis et al., 1967; Arnold and Mc-Auliff, 1968). For example, livers obtained from adult rats may not respond to isoproterenol at all and are relatively insensitive to the action of β-adrenergic blocking agents. The ability of certain ergot alkaloids to prevent the effects of epinephrine in these livers may be related in part to inhibition of adenyl cyclase (Murad et al., 1962) but perhaps more importantly to inhibition of the action of cAMP (Northrop, 1968). This is one of those gray areas mentioned previously, where the receptors are difficult to classify on the basis of the order of potency of agonists and adrenergic blocking agents. Since the livers of newborn rats do respond to isoproterenol (Wicks, 1969), the proper question for future research in this area may be to ask what happens to hepatic adrenergic receptors in some species in the course of development.

The glucocorticoids are necessary in order for cAMP to stimulate gluconeogenesis (Friedmann et al., 1967). These hormones do not affect the ability of glucagon to stimulate adenyl cyclase in the liver, but may exert an important influence on the sensitivity of hepatic adrenergic receptors. Here again, more research is needed.

An important role of cAMP in the developing liver is to stimulate the synthesis of certain gluconeogenic enzymes (Yeung and Oliver, 1968; Greengard, 1969; Wicks, 1969). However, whether the catecholamines play an important role in this regard, or whether the job is taken over primarily by glucagon, seems unclear at the time of this writing.

Other hepatic effects of the catecholamines which are mimicked by glucagon or exogenous cAMP include the stimulation of ketogenesis (Heimberg et al., 1969) and a transient increase in the rate of efflux of calcium and potassium (Friedmann and Park, 1968). An effect which could not be mimicked by glucagon or cAMP was the stimulation of phospholipid turnover (De Torrontegui and Berthet, 1966). The physiological significance of none of these effects is understood at the present time.

B. Pancreatic Effects

Glucose, by a mechanism which may require the participation of cAMP, acts directly on pancreatic islet tissue to stimulate the release of insulin (Mayhew et al., 1969; Lambert et al., 1969). Thus when blood glucose levels rise, as they do following a carbohydrate meal, for example, the level of circulating insulin also tends to rise. The released insulin then promotes the uptake and utilization of glucose by various peripheral tissues (Morgan et al., 1965; Park et al., 1968; see also Chapter 6 in this volume).

The catecholamines inhibit the release of insulin by glucose, and they appear to do this by interacting with adrenergic α-receptors (Porte, 1969), which in turn mediate a fall in the intracellular level of cAMP (Turtle and Kipnis, 1967). The net result of the increased level of cAMP in the liver combined with the reduced level in the pancreas is that the glucose released from the liver tends to be shunted to the central nervous system. This is important because the brain, unlike many peripheral tissues, is highly dependent upon glucose as an energy source. The utilization of glucose by the brain is thought to be less dependent on insulin than is the case in most peripheral tissues.

In the presence of α-adrenergic blocking agents, the catecholamines may actually stimulate the release of insulin (Malaisse *et al.*, 1967; Porte, 1969). This involves an interaction with adrenergic β-receptors and an increase in the islet level of cAMP (Turtle and Kipnis, 1967). Since α-receptors normally predominate insofar as the control of insulin release is concerned, and since α-adrenergic blocking agents are not thought to be produced naturally, the reason for β-receptors in these cells seems quite obscure.

The release of insulin from pancreatic β-cells is known to involve exocytosis (also known as "emiocytosis"), according to which the insulin-containing granules fuse with the plasma membrane and discharge their contents into the extracellular space (Lacy, 1967). This process, like many other cAMP-regulated processes, is known to require calcium (Lambert *et al.*, 1969). However, the mechanisms by which glucose and cAMP affect the process in pancreatic β-cells are unknown.

The catecholamines may also stimulate the release of enzymes from the exocrine pancreas. This occurs by way of adrenergic β-receptors and presumably involves an increase in the level of cAMP (Kulka and Sternlicht, 1968). Whether this is a physiologically important effect of the catecholamines seems uncertain at the present time. The same or a similar effect can be produced by parasympathomimetic agents and several trophotropic hormones.

C. ADIPOSE TISSUE

The catecholamines stimulate lipolysis (the conversion of triglycerides to glycerol and free fatty acids) in the adipose tissue of most species of animals which have been studied (Himms-Hagen, 1967). This effect involves an interaction with adrenergic β-receptors (Finger *et al.*, 1966; Aulich *et al.*, 1967) and a resulting increase in the intracellular level of cAMP (Butcher *et al.*, 1968). The latter effect is shown in Fig. 3,

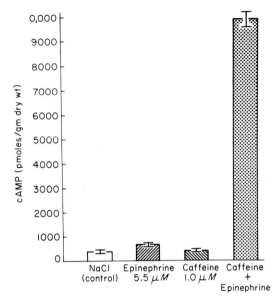

FIG. 3. Effect of epinephrine and caffeine on the level of cAMP in isolated rat fat cells. The cells were incubated under the indicated conditions for 10 minutes at 37°C. From Butcher *et al.* (1968).

which also illustrates the synergism between epinephrine (an adenyl cyclase stimulator) and caffeine (a phosphodiesterase inhibitor). Both circulating epinephrine and norepinephrine released from nerve endings (Weiss and Maickel, 1968) are probably important in regulating lipolysis in most species.

The mobilization of free fatty acids from triglycerides in adipose tissue is in many respects analogous to the mobilization of glucose from glycogen in the liver, and may even involve a similar mechanism. Lipase activation by cAMP was known to require ATP and Mg^{2+} (Rizack, 1964), and recently a cAMP-dependent protein kinase, similar to the one involved in phosphorylase activation in muscle, was obtained from adipose tissue (Corbin and Krebs, 1969). Since free fatty acids can be utilized as a source of energy by many peripheral tissues, their release from adipose tissue definitely serves an ergotropic function. The direct effect of the catecholamines on fat cells is enhanced by their tendency to inhibit the release of insulin, since insulin tends to reduce the level of cAMP in these cells (Park *et al.*, 1968). We should note also that free fatty acids inhibit the utilization of glucose by many peripheral tissues (Neely *et al.*, 1969). Thus the effect of the catecholamines to increase blood free fatty acid levels adds to their tendency to shunt glucose from the liver to the brain. The tendency for this to occur in response to sympathoadrenal discharge is very strong.

The action of the catecholamines in brown adipose tissue seems to be basically similar to their action in which adipose tissue (Butcher et al., 1968), although the overall effect may differ. For example, the increased respiratory rate which occurs in response to the catecholamines is much more profound in brown than in white adipose tissue (Himms-Hagen, 1967; Reed and Fain, 1968). This may be an important factor in the calorigenic response to the catecholamines.

Although adrenergic α-receptors are not prominent in the adipocytes of rats and perhaps many other species, they are prominent in human fat cells (Burns et al., 1970). In the presence of α-adrenergic blockade the stimulatory effects of the catecholamines on cAMP formation and lipolysis are enhanced, whereas in the presence of β-adrenergic blocking agents the catecholamines actually reduce the level of cAMP and inhibit lipolysis. The situation in the case of these cells is in a sense the opposite of that pertaining to pancreatic β-cells. Adrenergic β-receptors always seem to predominate in fat cells, and the reason for the presence of α-receptors seems quite obscure. Perhaps their presence in the fat cells of some species (like the presence of β-receptors in the pancreas) simply reflects one of Nature's interesting experiments. In retrospect, we can see that the ability of the catecholamines to increase the level of cAMP in fat cells and to reduce it in pancreatic β-cells would contribute to survival, whereas the opposite effects would not, at least not under the conditions which we know to be associated with the release of catecholamines. Objective as always, Nature seems to have been willing to give both types of receptors a chance.

The thyroid exerts a permissive effect insofar as the ability of the catecholamines to stimulate lipolysis is concerned. There is some evidence to suggest that this effect is related to the ability of thyroid hormones to stimulate the synthesis of adenyl cyclase in adipose tissue (Krishna et al., 1968).

D. Skeletal Muscle

The catecholamines interact with adrenergic β-receptors to increase the level of cAMP in skeletal muscle in all species studied. One effect of cAMP in this tissue is to increase the activity of a protein kinase, which catalyzes the phosphorylation and hence activation of phosphorylase b kinase, which in turn catalyzes the conversion of phosphorylase b to the more active phosphorylase a (Krebs *et al.*, 1966; Walsh *et al.*, 1968). The protein kinase which is affected by cAMP may be identical with glycogen synthetase kinase, which catalyzes the phosphorylation and hence *inactivation* of glycogen synthetase (Schlender *et al.*, 1969). The net result of these series of reactions is that the breakdown of muscle glycogen is accelerated. Besides providing energy for muscular contraction, the excess lactate which is released as a result of this process can be utilized by other tissues (Green and Goldberger, 1961) or be converted to glucose by the liver (Exton and Park, 1968). Lactate is released from muscle instead of glucose because, unlike the liver, muscle cells do not contain glucose-6-phosphatase (Cori, 1931). The conversion of muscle glycogen to blood lactate to blood glucose (which can of course be reconverted to muscle glycogen) is known as the Cori cycle. Because of its operation, we can see how the direct effect of the catecholamines on muscle may contribute further to the tendency of these hormones to shunt glucose from the liver and other peripheral tissues to the brain.

The ability of epinephrine to activate phosphorylase in muscle, and especially to potentiate phosphorylase activation in response to nerve stimulation (Helmreich and Cori, 1966), may contribute to the well-known defatiguing action of epinephrine (Bowman and Nott, 1969). Another component of this action may be the facilitation of neuromuscular transmission, which may involve an increase in the level of cAMP in nerve endings (Breckenridge *et al.*, 1967; A. L. Goldberg *et al.*, 1969). These effects may be especially important when we consider epinephrine as an emergency hormone. It is a common observation, for example, that frightened animals may be capable of performing physical feats which they could not ordinarily do.

On the other hand, it is also common for frightened animals to remain remarkably still. This could be the result of centrally mediated inhibition of peripheral nerve function, but could also be related to the fact that the direct functional effects of the catecholamines are different in different types of muscle (Bowman and Nott, 1969). In white skeletal muscle, also known as fast or phasic muscle, epinephrine prolongs the duration of the active state and thereby increases twitch tension. In red (also known as slow or tonic) skeletal muscle, epinephrine produces the opposite effects. In both cases these effects are mediated by β-receptors, but the sensitivity is such that only the effects in red muscle may be physiologically important (Bowman and Raper, 1967). The inhibition thus produced may account for the feeling of muscular weakness commonly experienced by patients following the injection of epinephrine. The possible role of cAMP as a mediator of these effects in skeletal muscle has not been carefully studied. It is interesting to note, however, that most of the adenyl cyclase in homogenates of white skeletal muscle is associated with fractions sedimenting with the sarcoplasmic reticulum (Rabinowitz et al., 1965), whereas the bulk of the adenyl cyclase in red skeletal muscle sediments with fragments of the plasma membrane, as in most other tissues which have been studied.

E. Cardiac Muscle

The catecholamines stimulate adenyl cyclase and increase the level of cAMP in the hearts of all mammals studied, and this occurs by way of an interaction with adrenergic β-receptors (Sutherland et al., 1968; Murad and Vaughan, 1969; Levey and Epstein, 1969). Glucagon also stimulates adenyl cyclase in these hearts, and does so by way of a different set of receptors. Since maximally effective concentrations of epinephrine and glucagon are not additive, these hormones presumably stimulate the same adenyl cyclase. Most of the adenyl cyclase activity in homogenates of cardiac muscle sediments with the plasma membrane fraction, but measurable activity also occurs in fractions containing fragments of the sarcoplasmic reticulum (Entman et al., 1969).

The ability of these hormones to stimulate cardiac adenyl cyclase almost certainly accounts for such effects as the activation of phosphorylase (Mayer et al., 1967) and lipolysis (Challoner and Steinberg, 1966), and may also account for their ability to increase the force of myocardial contraction. The positive inotropic response to these hormones is a complex response which requires the participation of an effect or factor produced during previous activity (Koch-Weser and Blinks, 1963). It is characterized by an increase in the rate of tension development, a decrease in the duration of the active state, and a more rapid rate of relaxation. At least some components of this response may be related to the ability of cAMP to accelerate the ATP-dependent uptake of calcium ions by fragments of the sarcoplasmic reticulum (Entman et al., 1969). This process in skeletal muscle preparations involves the phosphorylation of a membranal protein (Makinose, 1969). It is thus conceivable that a protein kinase similar to the one which catalyzes the phosphorylation of phosphorylase b kinase (Walsh et al., 1968) is involved in the effect of cAMP on calcium translocation.

The positive inotropic response to the catecholamines was previously thought to be mediated exclusively by β-receptors, but Govier (1968) has presented evidence to show that at least part of the response to the naturally occurring catecholamines involves interaction with α-receptors. Part of the response to these agents may therefore not be related to the stimulation of adenyl cyclase, and may even involve a fall in the level of cAMP in some cells. Much additional research is needed here.

The catecholamines also increase the rate of myocardial contractions, as well as the force of each individual beat. This is a β-adrenergic response, and might therefore be presumed to involve an increase in the level of cAMP in pacemaker cells. However, the biochemical basis of the positive chronotropic response has not been studied.

F. SMOOTH MUSCLE

The catecholamines produce divergent effects on the function of smooth muscle depending upon which type of receptor predominates. In general, α-receptors mediate contraction, while β-receptors lead to relaxation. The only well-established exception to this generalization occurs in intestinal smooth muscle, where the catecholamines produce relaxation by interacting with either α-receptors or β-receptors (Jenkinson and Morton, 1967). The situation in intestinal smooth muscle thus resembles that in the rat heart, where both types of receptors may stimulate contraction (Govier, 1968).

The catecholamines stimulate adenyl cyclase and increase the level of cAMP in smooth muscle structures containing adrenergic β-receptors (Bueding *et al.*, 1966; Dobbs and Robison, 1968). The effect of increasing concentrations of isoproterenol on the level of cAMP in the rat uterus is illustrated in Fig. 4, which also shows the classical shift of the dose–response curve to the right in the presence of propranolol, a potent β-adrenergic blocking agent. The effects produced by cAMP in smooth muscle include phosphorylase activation and an increase in the rate of production of lactic acid (Mohme-Lundholm, 1963; Lundholm *et al.*, 1966). There is also evidence that cAMP mediates relaxation (Bueding *et al.*, 1967; Dobbs and Robison, 1968; Moore *et al.*, 1968; Wilkenfeld and Levy, 1969), although the mechanism of this effect is poorly understood.

It should be noted that phosphorylase activation may occur during the contraction of smooth muscle whether induced by α-adrenergic agonists or by any other smooth muscle stimulant (Diamond and Brody, 1966; Brody and Diamond, 1967), and this effect is not mediated by an increase in the intracellular level of cAMP. Phosphorylase may also be activated in skeletal muscle by a mechanism not involving cAMP (Drummond *et al.*, 1969). The biochemical basis of α-adrenergic effects in smooth muscle is poorly understood, although in intestinal smooth muscle these effects are known to be associated with an increased permeability of the membrane to potassium ions (Jenkinson and Morton, 1967). Whether these effects are mediated by a fall in the level of

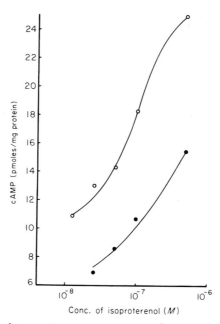

Fig. 4. Effect of increasing concentrations of isoproterenol on the level of cAMP in isolated rat uteri in the presence and absence of $5 \times 10^{-8} M$ propranolol. Theophylline (0.25 mM) was present in all incubations. Propanolol was added 10 minutes, theophylline 5 minutes, and isoproterenol 2 minutes before freezing. (○) isoproterenol and theophylline; (●) isoproterenol, theophylline, propranolol (5×10^{-8}). From Dobbs and Robison (1968).

cAMP in one or more cellular compartments has not been investigated.

The effects of the catecholamines in smooth muscle are responsible for a substantial proportion of the physiologically important effects of these hormones in the intact animal. The regulation of vascular smooth muscle (Bohr, 1967) may be especially important. Vasoconstriction mediated by α-receptors leads to an increase in total peripheral resistance, which is responsible in large measure for the rise in blood pressure characteristically associated with sympathetic stimulation. When combined with the vasodilation which occurs in vascular beds in which β-receptors predominate, this leads to a redistribution of blood flow which may be vital in many emergency situations.

G. The Calorigenic Effect

The ability of the catecholamines to increase the metabolic rate may at times be one of the most important functions of these hormones. For example, when normal rats are exposed to an environmental temperature of 4°C, they respond by increasing their metabolic rate from about 1350 cal/hour to about twice this value, and they survive under these conditions for relatively prolonged periods of time. Under the same conditions, by contrast, sympathoadrenalectomized rats lose heat at the rate of about 1350 cal/hour, and die within 3 hours at a body temperature of 15°C (Brodie *et al.*, 1966).

The overall response to cold exposure includes mechanisms of heat conservation (such as vasoconstriction and piloerection, mediated by adrenergic α-receptors) as well as heat production. Mechanisms for heat production can in turn be separated into two components, which are shivering and nonshivering calorigenesis (Himms-Hagen, 1967). The latter is the more important component, and depends upon the function of adrenergic β-receptors. Estler and Ammon (1969) found that doses of β-adrenergic blocking agents which were not lethal at normal temperatures reduced the survival rate of mice exposed to cold (0°C for 4 hours) from 82% to zero.

The calorigenic effect is probably the resultant of a great variety of other β-adrenergic effects, including the mobilization of glucose, lactic acid, and free fatty acids, even though no one of them may correlate well with the overall response. Furthermore, as reviewed in more detail by Himms-Hagen (1967), the relative importance of each of these effects may differ depending upon the age of the animal and other factors. An effect which may be especially important in younger animals is the stimulation of respiration in brown adipose tissue (Cockburn *et al.*, 1967; Reed and Fain, 1968). The thyroid plays an important permissive role in calorigenesis (Lutherer *et al.*, 1969).

Finally, in this section, we should note that the stimulation of adenyl cyclase tends itself to be a calorigenic process, quite apart from the various effects which the resulting increase in the level of cAMP might produce. The net result of the adenyl cyclase reaction in the presence of phosphodiesterase and myokinase is the production of 2 moles of ADP for every mole of ATP converted to cAMP. Under conditions of sympathoadrenal discharge the rate of turnover of cAMP is undoubtedly increased in a great variety of tissues, and the heat produced by this mechanism might be very substantial.

H. Glucose Oxidation

The catecholamines stimulate glucose oxidation in a variety of tissues, at least *in vitro*. Very little is known about either the physiological significance of this effect or the mechanism (or mechanisms) by which it is produced. In the rat heart (Satchell *et al.*, 1968), the effect was not prevented by doses of a β-adrenergic blocking agent which did block most of the other effects of epinephrine. In rat adipose tissue (Bray and Goodman, 1968), the effect was not prevented by a variety of procedures known to prevent the formation of cAMP in adipocytes. In thyroid tissue, Pastan *et al.* (1962) concluded that the effect was probably mediated by adrenochrome, an oxidation product of epinephrine. This might explain the effects observed in other tissues as well. Since the catecholamines are not thought to be converted to quinones to any substantial extent *in vivo*, their apparent ability to stimulate glucose oxidation may not be physiologically important. In the liver, the catecholamines and glucagon inhibit glucose oxidation (Williamson *et al.*, 1966).

I. Effects in Salivary Glands

The catecholamines interact with adrenergic β-receptors in the parotid gland (Yamamoto *et al.*, 1968) to stimulate adenyl cyclase and increase the intracellular level of cAMP (Robison *et al.*, 1969a; Malamud, 1969). This in turn leads to an increase in the rate of release of amylase (Babad *et al.*, 1967). Like many other cAMP-sensitive processes, the release of amylase is known to involve exocytosis (Amsterdam *et al.*, 1969). The presumably similar effect in the exocrine pancreas was mentioned previously in Section III,B. These effects of the catecholamines, involving the release of digestive enzymes, do not seem to fit the concept of the catecholamines as ergotropic agents, and indeed it is not obvious that they serve any useful function. Perhaps future research will teach us otherwise.

Another β-adrenergic effect in salivary glands is the stimulation of cell growth (Wells, 1967; Schneyer, 1969). This effect is not prominent following injection of either of the naturally occurring catecholamines, but is very striking in response to isoproterenol. It appears to involve an effect on protein synthesis which is followed, some hours later, by a marked stimulation of the rate of DNA synthesis (Sasaki *et al.*, 1969). This is, in turn, followed by mitotic activity and cell proliferation. Evidence that this response is mediated by cAMP includes the β-adrenergic nature of the effect, potentiation by theophylline, and the demonstration that exogenous cAMP can stimulate DNA synthesis in other cells (MacManus and Whitfield, 1969). It is conceivable that the cardiomegaly seen in response to high doses of isoproterenol (Stanton *et al.*, 1969) may be produced by the same unknown mechanism.

J. THE PINEAL GLAND

Stimulation by catecholamines of pineal gland adenyl cyclase has been extensively studied by Weiss and Costa (1968). The receptors involved in this effect could not be classified on the basis of the order of potency of agonists, since the naturally occurring catecholamines and isoproterenol were equally potent. Their classification as β-receptors was justified by the finding that the effects of the catecholamines could be antagonized by β-adrenergic blocking agents but not by α-adrenergic blocking agents. The finding that adenyl cyclase activity in these glands was increased by denervation (Weiss, 1969) may provide a useful starting point for studies of the biochemical basis of denervation supersensitivity (Cannon and Rosenblueth, 1937).

Sympathetic innervation of the pineal glands is important because without it the glands could not respond to changes in environmental lighting (Wurtman *et al.*, 1968; see also Chapter 4 in the first volume of this book). Among the effects which cAMP produces in these glands is an increase in the rate of conversion of tryptophan to melatonin (Shein and Wurtman, 1969). This may involve an increase in the rate of synthesis of both of the enzymes involved in this conversion. Hydroxyindole-O-methyltransferase, which catalyzes the conversion of serotonin to melatonin, is thought to be rate-limiting, but Shein and Wurtman found that the conversion of tryptophan to serotonin was also accelerated by epinephrine or cAMP. An effect of epinephrine which was not mimicked by exogenous cAMP was an apparent increase in the rate of tryptophan uptake.

The increased rate of formation of melatonin which is produced by cAMP in the pineal gland presumably leads to (or perhaps is caused by) an increase in the rate at which this hormone is released into the blood. Melatonin resembles insulin not only in this respect, but also in that it is capable of inhibiting the formation of cAMP in some cells. This was demonstrated in dorsal frog skin (Abe *et al.*, 1969), but may occur in some mammalian tissues as well.

K. MEMBRANE PERMEABILITY

The catecholamines reduce the permeability to water of the isolated toad bladder, and inhibit the opposite effect of vasopressin (Handler *et al.*, 1968). This effect of the catecholamines is mediated by adrenergic α-receptors and a fall in the intracellular level of cAMP (Turtle and Kipnis, 1967). A similar effect may occur in epithelial tissue in the distal nephron and collecting tubules of the mammalian kidney (Fisher, 1968). The catecholamines also inhibit chloride transport across intestinal mucosa (Field and McColl, 1968) and sodium transport across frog skin (Watlington, 1968). Both are α-receptor effects presumably mediated by a fall in the level of cAMP.

The catecholamines may also *increase* sodium and water permeability of ventral frog skin under some conditions. This is a β-receptor effect (Watlington, 1968) which can be potentiated by phosphodiesterase inhibitors and mimicked by exogenous cAMP (Bastide and Jard, 1968). Presumably, therefore, it is mediated by an increase in the level of cAMP in the epithelial cells involved. Little is presently known about the mechanisms by which cAMP alters the permeability of these cells (Orloff and Handler, 1967).

The increased permeability to potassium which the catecholamines produce in intestinal smooth muscle is known to be an α-receptor effect (Jenkinson and Morton, 1967), but whether it is mediated by a fall in the level of cAMP has not been studied.

L. Renin Production

The catecholamines may affect kidney function in a variety of ways (Williams, 1967). Besides altering the permeability to water and electrolytes, as mentioned in the preceding section, they may also alter the magnitude and direction of blood flow, by virtue of their effects on vascular smooth muscle. In addition, they are now known to stimulate the production of renin. That this is a direct effect on the renin-producing cells was demonstrated by Michelakis *et al.* (1969), who showed also that the effect could be mimicked by exogenous cAMP. We might assume, therefore, that this is a β-adrenergic effect, although this point was not tested. The mechanism by which cAMP stimulates the production of renin by these cells is unknown.

M. Effects in Blood

The shortening of the bleeding time which the catecholamines produce could be advantageous in many emergency situations. This effect is the resultant of at least three separate components, which are (1) peripheral vasoconstriction, mediated by adrenergic α-receptors, (2) platelet aggregation, also mediated by α-receptors, and (3) an increased rate of production of factor VIII, which is a β-receptor effect (Ingram and Vaughan Jones, 1966).

The effect on platelet aggregation has been studied biochemically. Agents such as the prostaglandins which inhibit aggregation stimulate platelet adenyl cyclase (Wolfe and Shulman, 1969; Marquis *et al.*, 1969) and increase the level of cAMP in intact platelets (Robison *et al.*, 1969b). The catecholamines reduce the level of cAMP in intact platelets, and this effect is prevented by α-adrenergic blocking agents but not by β-adrenergic blocking agents. It would thus appear that the stimulation of platelet aggregation is another α-receptor effect which is mediated by a fall in the intracellular level of cAMP. The mechanism by which cAMP tends to keep these cells apart is unknown. It is interesting to note that in certain species of cellular slime molds, cAMP plays an important role in *initiating* aggregation (Bonner *et al.*, 1969).

Another effect which the catecholamines have in blood is to inhibit the antigen-induced release of histamine from leukocytes. Since the catecholamines stimulate adenyl cyclase in these cells (Scott, 1970) and since the effect can be mimicked by exogenous cAMP (Lichtenstein and Margolis, 1968), it is presumably mediated by cAMP. The physiological significance of this effect is uncertain because of the uncertain significance of antigen-induced histamine release. It is at least clear that when β-receptor function is compromised, the ability to withstand anaphylactic shock is reduced (Szentivanyi, 1968). The protective effect of the catecholamines in this regard may be largely the result of their ability to oppose some of the *actions* of histamine and other agents, but inhibition of the release of histamine might contribute. This is an interesting effect because the release of histamine is thought to occur by exocytosis. As mentioned previously, all of the other exocytotic processes which have been studied from this point of view have been stimulated and not inhibited by cAMP. The mechanism of the effect is poorly understood in either case.

Although the mature red cells of at least some mammalian species do not contain adenyl cyclase, the nucleated erythrocytes of certain avian and amphibian species do contain adenyl cyclase which can be stimulated by catecholamines (Davoren and Sutherland, 1963; Rosen and Rosen, 1968). The receptors which mediate this effect have characteristics classically associated with adrenergic β-receptors. In the absence of catecholamines, the level of cAMP in these cells may be undetectable. In the presence of a catecholamine, however, the level may increase dramatically (Fig. 5), and the nucleotide is pumped out of the cells even against a concentration gradient. The physiological significance of this is completely unknown. It is at least conceivable that these cells represent an intermediate target organ for the catecholamines, and that the released cAMP goes on to influence other cells. An interesting discovery by Rosen and Rosen (1968) was that although the cells from both tadpoles and adult frogs contained adenyl cyclase, only the adult cells

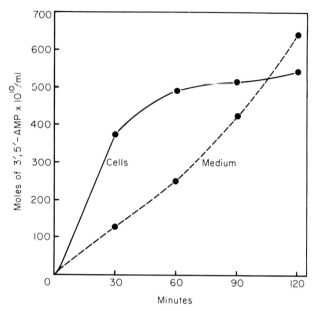

FIG. 5. The synthesis and release of cAMP by pigeon erythrocytes. Aliquots contained 1 ml of packed erythrocytes and 1 ml of medium (Krebs bicarbonate buffer). cAMP content of cell lysates and of media expressed per ml of packed cells and per ml of medium. Epinephrine ($5 \times 10^{-5} M$) added at time zero. From Davoren and Sutherland (1963).

contained β-receptors. Thus, whatever the function of this adrenergic effect may be, it would appear to be not necessary during all stages of development.

N. Effects on Skin Color

The control of skin color in fish, amphibians, and reptiles may depend on changes occurring in several types of cells, but perhaps most importantly upon the movement of melanin granules within skin melanophores. Dispersion of these granules leads to darkening, while contraction or "conspersion" leads to lightening. The catecholamines may produce either effect depending upon the type of receptor with which they interact (Novales and Davis, 1969; Goldman and Hadley, 1969). The melanophores of some species contain only α-receptors, in which case the catecholamines mimic the action of melatonin and produce melanin conspersion and skin lightening. Other species may contain only β-receptors, in which event the catecholamines mimic the action of melanocyte-stimulating hormone (MSH) and produce melanin dispersion and skin darkening. Still others may contain both types of receptors, in which event the effect of the catecholamines will depend upon whichever type predominates. In all cases studied, α-receptors mediate conspersion, whereas β-receptors mediate the opposite effect.

The role of cAMP has been studied in the dorsal skin of *Rana pipiens*, where MSH causes an increase in the level of cAMP and darkening, and where the catecholamines and melatonin reduce the level of cAMP and cause lightening (Abe *et al.*, 1969). The effects of the catecholamines but not of melatonin could be prevented by α-adrenergic blocking agents, whereas isoproterenol and β-adrenergic blocking agents had little or no effect. It would thus appear that the melanophores of *R. pipiens* (at least during the time of year at which these experiments were carried out) contain only α-receptors, and that the effect of the catecholamines in these cells represents another example of an α-receptor effect mediated by a fall in the level of cAMP. It is probably safe to assume that the β-receptor effects in other species are mediated by an increase in the level of cAMP (Novales and Davis, 1969; Goldman and Hadley, 1969).

The mechanism by which cAMP affects the movement of melanin granules is unknown. Like many other β-adrenergic effects, such as the release of insulin from the pancreas (Lambert *et al.*, 1969) and the activation of phosphorylase in several tissues (Namm *et al.*, 1968), the dispersion of melanin granules is known to require calcium ions (Novales and Davis, 1969). However, it is also true that many α-receptor effects (e.g., smooth muscle contraction and platelet aggregation) also require calcium. From the standpoint of mechanism, therefore, the significance of this requirement is not obvious.

We should add that while the physiological significance of the skin-darkening action of MSH seems reasonably clear (Novales and Davis, 1969), the significance of the ability of the catecholamines to either mimic or oppose this effect is still obscure.

O. Effects in the Central Nervous System

The catecholamines are thought to play an important role in regulating brain function (Acheson, 1966, pp. 713–803), but very little is known about this from the biochemical standpoint. It is known that β-adrenergic receptors are present in most brain areas and that they mediate the stimulation of adenyl cyclase leading to an increase in the intracellular level of cAMP (Klainer *et al.*, 1962; Kakiuchi and Rall, 1968). Dopamine had no effect on the level of cAMP in preliminary experiments with rat brain slices (Palmer *et al.*, 1969), but such experiments do not rule out the possibility that dopamine may affect adenyl cyclase in certain neurons.

One central adrenergic effect which seems clearly to be mediated by cAMP is the inhibition of cerebellar Purkinje fibers (Siggins *et al.*, 1969). However, the mechanism of this effect is quite obscure. A protein kinase which is sensitive to stimulation by cAMP has been isolated from brain (Miyamoto *et al.*, 1969). This enzyme may be identical to glycogen synthetase kinase (Schlender *et al.*, 1969), and indeed an effect of cAMP on brain glycogen synthetase has been observed (N. D. Goldberg and O'Toole, 1969). There is no evidence that brain phosphorylase kinase serves as a substrate for this enzyme, but the phosphorylation of other proteins may occur and this might, in turn, lead to some important functional changes.

Schmidt *et al.* (1970) have made the interesting observation that brain slices from newborn rats do not respond to norepinephrine with an increase in the level of cAMP for at least the first 3 days postpartum. The subsequent development of sensitivity to norepinephrine is illustrated in Fig. 6. Since adenyl cyclase activity can be detected in broken cell preparations of these brains even before birth, this may reflect the development of adrenergic receptors, possibly the same process which occurs in frog erythrocytes (Rosen and Rosen, 1968). These and other

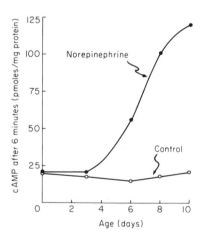

Fɪɢ. 6. Response of developing rat brain to norepinephrine. Brains were removed from rats of different ages and divided along the longitudinal fissure, with one half serving as the control for the other. Following a preincubation, chopped tissue slices were incubated for 6 minutes in the presence or absence of $10^{-5}\,M$ norepinephrine. Data plotted in terms of the level of cAMP present at the end of the 6-minute incubation. From Schmidt *et al.* (1970).

receptors may develop at different times in different cells (Greengard, 1969). Future studies along these lines may provide information which will be helpful in determining how the catecholamines and other hormones influence cell function.

We suggested previously (Robison *et al.,* 1969a) that the adenyl cyclase system in some cells may include both catalytic and regulatory subunits, and that the receptors for hormones which stimulate adenyl cyclase may be part of a regulatory subunit. If so, these recent observations would suggest that the system does not develop all at once, but rather that the individual components of the system may develop separately. Our ignorance in this area is still overwhelming, but the prospects for future progress seem reasonably bright.

IV. SUMMARY

The catecholamines produce a diverse array of effects in a great variety of animal tissues. Although seemingly very different, when viewed at the level of cell function, these effects may nevertheless have many features in common. Although the physiological significance of some of the effects of the catecholamines is obscure, many of them can be regarded as serving an ergotropic function, which is to say that they seem useful in situations requiring physical or mental effort. The catecholamines definitely promote the mobilization and utilization of stored sources of energy.

The catecholamines, like other hormones, influence cell function by interacting with specific patterns of forces which we call receptors. The ones with which catecholamines interact are called adrenergic receptors. There seem to be at least two different types of adrenergic receptors, which are known, for lack of a better terminology, as α-receptors and β-receptors. The exact configuration of these receptors seems to differ from one type of cell to another, but, in general, they can be distinguished according to the order of potency of agonists and/or according to the type of drug which blocks their function. α-Receptors are such that the naturally occurring catecholamines, epinephrine and norepinephrine, are generally more potent as agonists than is the synthetic derivative isoproterenol. The effects which are mediated by these receptors can be selectively prevented by one or more of a group of drugs known collectively as α-adrenergic blocking agents. (By "selectively," we mean that these drugs are effective in doses which do not prevent the effects mediated by β-receptors.) Some of these drugs do not resemble the catecholamines structurally, and their mechanism of action is poorly understood. β-Receptors are such that isoproterenol is generally as potent as or even more potent than either epinephrine or norepinephrine as an agonist. These receptors can be selectively blocked by one or more of a group of antagonists called β-adrenergic blocking agents, most of which can be regarded as analogs of isoproterenol.

Another way of classifying the effects of the catecholamines is according to whether they are mediated by an increase or a decrease in the intracellular level of cAMP. The overlap between those which are mediated by an increase in the level of cAMP and those which are mediated by adrenergic β-receptors is by now so extensive that it seems likely that these receptors constitute an integral part of an adenyl cyclase system. This hypothesis is supported by the fact that the stimulation of adenyl cyclase by catecholamines, even in washed particulate preparations, is mediated by β-receptors.

More recently, it has been possible to discern a considerable degree of overlap between adrenergic effects which are mediated by a fall in the level of cAMP and those which are mediated by α-receptors. The mechanism by which an interaction with these receptors leads to a fall in the intracellular level of cAMP is unknown, and the question of whether all or just some α-receptor effects are produced by this mechanism remains for future research. It is attractive to suppose that all of the physiologically important effects of the catecholamines result from either an increase or a decrease in the level of cAMP in one or more cellular compartments, but this has not been established.

The mechanism or mechanisms by which changes in the level of cAMP influence cell function are unknown in most cases. It is at least conceivable that all of the diverse effects which this nucleotide is known to be capable of producing can be related to its ability to increase the activity of one or more intracellular protein kinases. Its effects in any given cell would depend upon the type of protein phosphorylated.

The generalizations presented in this chapter leave many questions unanswered, and have even suggested a few which were not previously asked. Perhaps the best that can be said is that we know more about the actions of the catecholamines now than we knew at the turn of the century, even though our knowledge is still very incomplete.

ACKNOWLEDGMENTS

The authors were supported during the writing of this chapter by grants from the National Institutes of Health (HE-08332, AM-07462, and AM-16811) and the National Institute of Mental Health (MH-11468) of the U. S. Public Health Service. One of us (E. W. S.) is a Career Investigator of the American Heart Association.

REFERENCES

Abe, K., Robison, G. A., Liddle, G. W., Butcher, R. W., Nicholson, W. E., and Baird, C. E. (1969). *Endocrinology* **85,** 674.

Acheson, G. H. (1966). "Second Symposium on Catecholamines." Williams & Wilkins, Baltimore, Maryland.

Ahlquist, R. P. (1948). *Am. J. Physiol.* **153,** 586.

Ahlquist, R. P. (1968). *Ann. Rev. Pharmacol.* **8,** 259.

Amsterdam, A., Ohad, I., and Schramm, M. (1969). *J. Cell Biol.* **41,** 753.

Arnold, A., and McAuliff, J. P. (1968). *Experientia* **24,** 674.

Aulich, A., Stock, K., and Westermann, E. (1967). *Life Sci.* **6,** 929.

Babad, H., Ben-Zvi, R., Bdolah, A., and Schramm, M. (1967). *European J. Biochem.* **1,** 96.

Bastide, F., and Jard, S. (1968). *Biochim. Biophys. Acta* **150,** 113.

Biel, J. H., and Lum, B. K. B. (1966). *Progr. Drug Res.* **10,** 46.

Bitensky, M. W., Russell, V., and Robertson, W. (1968). *Biochem. Biophys. Res. Commun.* **31,** 706.

Bohr, D. F. (1967). *Ann. N. Y. Acad. Sci.* **199,** 799.

Bonner, J. T., Barkley, D. S., Hall, E. M., Konijn, T. M., Mason, J. W., O'Keefe, G., III, and Wolfe, P. B. (1969). *Develop. Biol.* **20,** 72.

Bowman, W. C., and Nott, M. W. (1969). *Pharmacol. Rev.* **21,** 27.

Bowman, W. C., and Raper, C. (1967). *Ann. N. Y. Acad. Sci.* **139,** 741.

Bray, G. A., and Goodman, H. M. (1968). *J. Lipid Res.* **9,** 714.

Breckenridge, B. McL., Burn, J. H., and Matschinsky, F. M. (1967). *Proc. Natl. Acad. Sci.* **57,** 1893.

Brodie, B. B., Davies, J. I., Hynie, S., Krishna, G., and Weiss, B. (1966). *Pharmacol. Rev.* **18,** 273.

Brody, T. M., and Diamond, J. (1967). *Ann. N. Y. Acad. Sci.* **139,** 772.

Bueding, E., Butcher, R. W., Hawkins, J., Timms, A. R., and Sutherland, E. W. (1966). *Biochim. Biophys. Acta* **115,** 173.

Bueding, E., Bulbring, E., Gercken, G., Hawkins, J. T., and Kuriyama, H. (1967). *J. Physiol. (London)* **193,** 187.

Burns, T. W., Langley, P. E., and Robison, G. A. (1970). *Clin. Res.* **18,** 86.

Butcher, R. W., Baird, C. E., and Sutherland, E. W. (1968). *J. Biol. Chem.* **243,** 1705.

Cannon, W. B. (1939). "The Wisdom of the Body." Norton, New York (Norton Library edition published 1963).

Cannon, W. B., and Rosenblueth, A. (1937). "Autonomic Neuro-effector Systems." Macmillan, New York.

Challoner, D. R., and Steinberg, D. (1966). *Am. J. Physiol.* **211,** 897.

Clark, A. J. (1937). *In* "Heffter's Handbuch der experimentellen Pharmakologie" (W. Heubner and J. Schuller, eds.), Vol. 4, Springer, Berlin. Reprinted 1970.

Cockburn, F., Hull, D., and Walton, I. (1967). *Brit. J. Pharmacol.* **21,** 568.

Corbin, J. D., and Krebs, E. G. (1969). *Biochim. Biophys. Res. Commun.* **36,** 328.

Cori, C. F. (1931). *Physiol. Rev.* **11,** 143.

Dale, H. H. (1906). *J. Physiol. (London)* **34,** 163.

Davoren, P. R., and Sutherland, E. W. (1963). *J. Biol. Chem.* **238,** 3009.

De Torrontegui, G., and Berthet, J. (1966). *Biochim. Biophys. Acta* **116,** 467.

De Wulf, H., and Hers, H. G. (1968). *European J. Biochem.* **6,** 558.

Diamond, J., and Brody, T. M. (1966). *J. Pharmacol. Exptl. Therap.* **152**, 212.

Dobbs, J. W., and Robison, G. A. (1968). *Federation Proc.* **27**, 352.

Drummond, G. I., Harwood, J. P., and Powell, C. A. (1969). *J. Biol. Chem.* **244**, 4235.

Ellis, S., Kennedy, B. L., Eusebi, A. J., and Vincent, N. H. (1967). *Ann. N. Y. Acad. Sci.* **139**, 826.

Entman, M. L., Levey, G. S., and Epstein, S. E. (1969). *Circulation Res.* **25**, 429.

Estler, C. J., and Ammon, H. P. T. (1969). *Can. J. Physiol. Pharmacol.* **47**, 427.

Exton, J. H., and Park, C. R. (1968). *Advan. Enzyme Regulation* **6**, 391.

Field, M., and McColl, I. (1968). *Federation Proc.* **27**, 603.

Finger, K. F., Page, J. G., and Feller, D. R. (1966). *Biochem. Pharmacol.* **15**, 1023.

Fisher, D. A. (1968). *J. Clin. Invest.* **47**, 540.

Friedmann, N., and Park, C. R. (1968). *Proc. Natl. Acad. Sci. U. S.* **61**, 504.

Friedmann, N., Exton, J. H., and Park, C. R. (1967). *Biochem. Biophys. Res. Commun.* **29**, 113.

Ghouri, M. S. K., and Haley, T. J. (1969). *J. Pharm. Sci.* **58**, 511.

Goldberg, A. L., Singer, J. J., and Henneman, E. (1969). *Federation Proc.* **28**, 457.

Goldberg, N. D., and O'Toole, A. G. (1969). *J. Biol. Chem.* **244**, 3053.

Goldman, J. M., and Hadley, M. E. (1969). *Gen. Comp. Endocrinol.* **13**, 151.

Govier, W. C. (1968). *J. Pharmacol. Exptl. Therap.* **159**, 82.

Green, D. E., and Goldberger, R. F. (1961). *Am. J. Med.* **30**, 666.

Greengard, O. (1969). *Science* **163**, 891.

Handler, J. S., Bensinger, R., and Orloff, J. (1968). *Am. J. Physiol.* **215**, 1024.

Heimberg, M., Weinstein, I., and Kohout, M. (1969). *J. Biol. Chem.* **244**, 5131.

Helmreich, E., and Cori, C. F. (1966). *Pharmacol. Rev.* **18**, 189.

Hess, W. R. (1948). "Die funktionelle Organisation des vegetativen Nervensystems." Benno Schwabe, Basel.

Himms-Hagen, J. (1967). *Pharmacol. Rev.* **19**, 367.

Hornykiewicz, O. (1966). *Pharmacol. Rev.* **18**, 925.

Ingram, G. I. C., and Vaughan Jones, R. (1966). *J. Physiol. (London)* **187**, 447.

Janakidevi, K., Dewey, V. C., and Kidder, G. W. (1966). *J. Biol. Chem.* **241**, 2576.

Jenkinson, D. H., and Morton, I. K. M. (1967). *J. Physiol. (London)* **188**, 387.

Kakiuchi, S., and Rall, T. W. (1968). *Mol. Pharmacol.* **4**, 367.

Klainer, L. M., Chi, Y. M., Friedberg, S. L., Rall, T. W., and Sutherland, E. W. (1962). *J. Biol. Chem.* **237**, 1239.

Koch-Weser, J., and Blinks, J. R. (1963). *Pharmacol. Rev.* **15**, 601.

Krebs, E. G., DeLange, R. J., Kemp, R. G., and Riley, W. D. (1966). *Pharmacol. Rev.* **18**, 163.

Krishna, G., Hynie, S., and Brodie, B. B. (1968). *Proc. Natl. Acad. Sci. U. S.* **59**, 884.

Kulka, R. G., and Sternlicht, E. (1968). *Proc. Natl. Acad. Sci. U. S.* **61**, 1123.

Lacy, P. E. (1967). *New Engl. J. Med.* **276**, 187.

Lambert, A. E., Junod, A., Stauffacher, W., Jeanrenaud, B., and Renold, A. E. (1969). *Biochim. Biophys. Acta* **184**, 529.

Levey, G. S., and Epstein, S. E. (1969). *Circulation Res.* **24**, 151.

Lichtenstein, L. M., and Margolis, S. (1968). *Science* **161**, 902.

Lundholm, L., Lundholm-Mohme, E., and Svedmyr, N. (1966). *Pharmacol. Rev.* **18**, 255.

Lutherer, L. O., Fegly, M. J., and Anton, A. H. (1969). *Federation Proc.* **28**, 1238.

MacManus, J. P., and Whitfield, J. F. (1969). *Proc. Soc. Exptl. Biol. Med.* **132**, 409.

Makinose, M. (1969). *European J. Biochem.* **10**, 74.

Makman, M. H., and Sutherland, E. W. (1964). *Endocrinology* **75**, 127.
Malaisse, W. J., Malaisse-Lagae, F., and Mayhew, D. (1967). *J. Clin. Invest.* **46**, 1724.
Malamud, D. (1969). *Biochem. Biophys. Res. Commun.* **35**, 754.
Marquis, N. R., Vigdahl, R. L., and Tavormina, P. A. (1969). *Biochem. Biophys. Res. Commun.* **36**, 965.
Mayer, S. E., Williams, B. J., and Smith, J. M. (1967). *Ann. N. Y. Acad. Sci.* **139**, 686.
Mayhew, D. A., Wright, P. H., and Ashmore, J. (1969). *Pharmacol. Rev.* **21**, 183.
Michelakis, A. M., Caudle, J., and Liddle, G. W. (1969). *Proc. Soc. Exptl. Biol. Med.* **130**, 748.
Miyamoto, E., Kuo, J. F., and Greengard, P. (1969). *Science* **165**, 63.
Mohme-Lundholm, E. (1963). *Acta Physiol. Scand.* **59**, 74.
Moore, P. F., Ioris, L. C., and McManus, J. M. (1968). *J. Pharm. Pharmacol.* **20**, 368.
Moran, N. C. (1967). *Ann. N. Y. Acad. Sci.* **139**, 649.
Morgan, H. E., Neely, J. R., Wood, R. E., Liebecq, C., Liebermeister, H., and Park, C. R. (1965). *Federation Proc.* **24**, 1040.
Murad, F., and Vaughan, M. (1969). *Biochem. Pharmacol.* **18**, 1053.
Murad, F., Chi, Y. M., Rall, T. W., and Sutherland, E. W. (1962). *J. Biol. Chem.* **237**, 1233.
Namm, D. H., Mayer, S. E., and Maltbie, M. (1968). *Mol. Pharmacol.* **4**, 522.
Neely, J. R., Bowman, R. H., and Morgan, H. E. (1969). *Am. J. Physiol.* **216**, 804.
Northrop, G. (1968). *J. Pharmacol. Exptl. Therap.* **149**, 22.
Novales, R. R., and Davis, W. J. (1969). *Am. Zoologist* **9**, 479.
Orloff, J., and Handler, J. (1967). *Am. J. Med.* **42**, 757.
Palmer, E. C., Sulser, F., and Robison, G. A. (1969). *Pharmacologist* **11**, 258.
Park, C. R., Crofford, O. B., and Kono, T. (1968). *J. Gen. Physiol.* **52**, 296s.
Pastan, I., Herring, B., Johnson, P., and Field, J. B. (1962). *J. Biol. Chem.* **237**, 287.
Pohl, S. L., Birnbaumer, L., and Rodbell, M. (1969). *Science* **164**, 566.
Porte, D. (1969). *Arch. Internal Med.* **123**, 252.
Powell, C. E., and Slater, I. H. (1958). *J. Pharmacol. Exptl. Therap.* **122**, 480.
Rabinowitz, M., DeSalles, L., Meisler, J., and Lorand, L. (1965). *Biochim. Biophys. Acta* **97**, 29.
Reed, N., and Fain, J. N. (1968). *J. Biol. Chem.* **243**, 2843.
Rizack, M. A. (1964). *J. Biol. Chem.* **239**, 392.
Robison, G. A., Exton, J. H., Park, C. R., and Sutherland, E. W. (1967). *Federation Proc.* **26**, 257.
Robison, G. A., Butcher, R. W., and Sutherland, E. W. (1969a). In "Fundamental Concepts in Drug-Receptor Interactions" (D. J. Triggle, ed.), pp. 59–91. Academic Press, New York.
Robison, G. A., Arnold, A., and Hartmann, R. C. (1969b). *Pharmacol. Res. Commun.* **1**, 325.
Rosen, O. M., and Rosen, S. M. (1968). *Biochem. Biophys. Res. Commun.* **31**, 82.
Sasaki, T., Litwack, G., and Baserga, R. (1969). *J. Biol. Chem.* **244**, 4831.
Satchell, D. G., Freeman, S. E., and Edwards, S. V. (1968). *Biochem. Pharmacol.* **17**, 45.
Schlender, K. K., Wei, S. H., and Villar-Palasi, C. (1969). *Biochim. Biophys. Acta* **191**, 272.

Schmidt, M. J., Palmer, E. C., Dettbarn, W. D., and Robison, G. A. (1970). *Develop. Psychobiol.* **3**, 53.

Schneyer, C. A. (1969). *Proc. Soc. Exptl. Biol. Med.* **131**, 71.

Scott, R. E. (1970). *Blood* **35**, 514.

Shein, H. M., and Wurtman, R. J. (1969). *Science* **166**, 519.

Shimazu, T., and Amakawa, A. (1968). *Biochim. Biophys. Acta* **165**, 335.

Siggins, G. R., Hoffer, B. J., and Bloom, F. E. (1969). *Science* **165**, 1018.

Sokal, J. E., Sarcione, E. J., and Henderson, A. M. (1964). *Endocrinology* **74**, 930.

Stanton, H. C., Brenner, G., and Mayfield, E. D., (1969). *Am. Heart J.* **77**, 72.

Sutherland, E. W., and Rall, T. W. (1958). *J. Biol. Chem.* **232**, 1077.

Sutherland, E. W., and Rall, T. W. (1960). *Pharmacol. Rev.* **12**, 265.

Sutherland, E. W., and Robison, G. A. (1969). *Diabetes* **18**, 797.

Sutherland, E. W., Robison, G. A., and Butcher, R. W. (1968). *Circulation* **37**, 279.

Szentivanyi, A. (1968). *J. Allergy* **42**, 203.

Turtle, J. R., and Kipnis, D. M. (1967). *Biochem. Biophys. Res. Commun.* **28**, 797.

von Euler, U. S. (1963). *In* "Comparative Endocrinology" (U. S. von Euler and H. Heller, eds.), Vol. 1, pp. 258–290. Academic Press, New York.

von Euler, U. S. (1966). *Pharmacol. Rev.* **18**, 29.

Walsh, D. A., Perkins, J. P., and Krebs, E. G. (1968). *J. Biol. Chem.* **243**, 3763.

Watlington, C. O. (1968). *Am. J. Physiol.* **214**, 1001.

Weiss, B. (1969). *J. Pharmacol. Exptl. Therap.* **168**, 146.

Weiss, B., and Costa, E. (1968). *J. Pharmacol. Exptl. Therap.* **161**, 310.

Weiss, B., and Maickel, R. P. (1968). *Intern. J. Neuropharmacol.* **7**, 393.

Wells, H. (1967). *Am. J. Physiol.* **212**, 1293.

Wicks, W. D. (1969). *J. Biol. Chem.* **244**, 3941.

Wilkenfeld, B. E., and Levy, B. (1969). *J. Pharmacol. Exptl. Therap.* **169**, 61.

Williams, R. L. (1967). *Perspectives Biol. Med.* **10**, 251.

Williamson, J. R., Garcia, A., Renold, A. E., and Cahill, G. F., Jr. (1966). *Diabetes* **15**, 183.

Wolfe, S. M., and Shulman, N. R. (1969). *Biochem. Biophys. Res. Commun.* **35**, 265.

Wurtman, R. J., Axelrod, J., and Kelly, D. E. (1968). "The Pineal." Academic Press, New York.

Yamamoto, I., Inoki, R., and Kohima, S. (1968). *European J. Pharmacol.* **3**, 123.

Yeung, D., and Oliver, I. T. (1968). *Biochemistry* **7**, 3231.

ADDENDUM

A number of papers concerned with the biochemical actions of the catecholamines were published since this chapter was written. A few which may be of special interest are listed below:

Bär, H.-P., and Hahn, P. (1971). Development of rat liver adenyl cyclase. *Can. J. Biochem.* **49**, 85.

Bitensky, M. W., Russell, V., and Blanco, M. (1970). Independent variation of glucagon and epinephrine responsive components of hepatic adenyl cyclase as a function of age, sex, and steroid hormones. *Endocrinology* **86**, 154.

Klein, D. C., Berg, G. R., and Weller, J. (1970). Melatonin synthesis: adenosine 3′,5′-monophosphate and norepinephrine stimulate N-acetyltransferase. *Science* **168**, 979.

MacManus, J. P., Whitfield, J. F., and Youdale, T. (1971). Stimulation by epinephrine of adenyl cyclase activity, cyclic AMP formation, DNA synthesis, and cell proliferation in populations of rat thymic lymphocytes. *J. Cell. Physiol.* **77**, 103.

McAfee, D. A., Schorderet, M., and Greengard, P. (1971). Adenosine 3′,5′-monophosphate in nervous tissue: increase associated with synaptic transmission. *Science* **171**, 1156.

Martorana, P. A. (1971). The role of cyclic AMP in isoprenaline-induced cardiac necroses in the rat. *J. Pharm. Pharmacol.* **23**, 200.

Reimann, E. M., Brostom, C. E., Corbin, J. D., King, C. A., and Krebs, E. G. (1971). Separation of regulatory and catalytic subunits of the cyclic AMP-dependent protein kinase(s) of rabbit skeletal muscle. *Biochem. Biophys. Res. Commun.* **42**, 187.

Rosen, O. M., Erlichman, J., and Rosen, S. M. (1970). The structure–activity relationships of adrenergic compounds that act on the adenyl cyclase of the frog erythrocyte. *Mol. Pharmacol.* **6**, 524.

Salzman, E. W., and Levine, L. (1970). Cyclic 3′,5′-adenosine monophosphate in human blood platelets. *J. Clin. Invest.* **50**, 131.

Schmidt, M. J., and Robison, G. A. (1971). The effect of norepinephrine on cyclic AMP levels in discrete regions of the developing rabbit brain. *Life Sci.* **10**(I), 459.

Schramm, M., and Naim, E. (1970). Adenyl cyclase of rat parotid gland: activation by fluoride and norepinephrine. *J. Biol. Chem.* **245**, 3225.

Soderling, T. R., Hickenbottom, J. P., Reimann, E. M., Hunkeler, F. L., Walsh, D. A., and Krebs, E. G. (1970). Inactivation of glycogen synthetase and activation of phosphorylase kinase by muscle cyclic AMP-dependent protein kinases. *J. Biol. Chem.* **245**, 6317.

CHAPTER 5

Subcellular Actions of Glucocorticoids

Gerald Litwack and Sanford Singer

I. INTRODUCTION

The liver and thymus are the main receptor organs for glucocorticoids. These assignments are arbitrary, however, and are based on the fact that glucocorticoids cause rapid and pronounced effects in these organs. The liver is the only organ found thus far that concentrates the hormone effectively *in vivo* in excess of the circulating level, although this property may be demonstrated in other tissues *in vitro* if the organ can be presented with enough of the hormone. Having a poor blood supply relative to the liver, the thymus does not concentrate the hormone *in vivo* but reacts rapidly to it and contains binding sites in the cytosol and in the nucleus which have structural requirements for binding that parallel hormonal potency *in vivo*.

The hormone affects protein synthesis rapidly in both liver and thymus, the latter being one of several tissues that involute after glucocorticoid treatment. The major emphasis of this chapter will concern the early events which may lead to eventual changes in protein synthesis as well as effects of the hormone on specific enzyme systems and upon glycogen synthesis and deposition. However, attempts to survey the entire voluminous recent literature will not be made, especially with regard to the effects of glucocorticoids on nucleic acids or on the rapidly turning-over enzymes, tyrosine aminotransferase and tryptophan pyrrolase, although there will appear references to this work where it is considered pertinent. These specific subjects are treated extensively in several chapters of both volumes of this work [see, for example, chapters by Greengard, Black and Axelrod, Tata, and Tomkins and Gelehrter, as well as in recent reviews elsewhere (Kenney, 1970; Kaplan and Pitot, 1970; Schimke and Doyle, 1970)].

The search for the first effect of the hormone within the cell at the molecular level is frustrated by the multiplicity of biochemical responses to glucocorticoids. Studies are available to indicate that corticosteroid action may not be mediated directly by cyclic AMP (Granner *et al.*, 1968; Kenney, 1970). Thus, the dilemma of a primary action or "first molecular event" concerning transcriptional or translational processes or both arises in the explanation of effects upon protein synthesis. Often, effects cannot be observed because of the limitations in methodology; for example, it is nearly impossible at the moment to measure the synthesis or accumulation of specific mRNA's for a few proteins whose syntheses are rapidly stimulated by glucocorticoids. One approach in deciphering the early effects of a hormone is to search for responses that temporally precede an established action; this will be useful if the cellular response is the consummation of a single chain of successive causally related events. Alternatively, there may be several discrete primary actions of glucocorticoids in target cells; some may set off chains of causally related events and some may not and each of these separate initial effects, followed, or not, by chains of events may contribute to the total response. The latter possibility is probably closer to the case for the hepatocyte, since there is evidence to separate effects on glycogen deposition or on glycolytic enzyme activity from the protein synthetic process of enzyme induction. In this framework, it is easy to justify a review of many of the actions of the hormone on specific biochemical processes.

II. SUBCELLULAR FATES AND BINDING OF GLUCOCORTICOIDS

Following the subcellular distribution and fates of steroid hormones and their metabolites in receptor organs is a useful approach for understanding their actions. Numerous reports of this general method have been made (DeVenuto *et al.*, 1962; Litwack *et al.*, 1963; Bellamy, 1963; Dingman and Sporn, 1965; Brunkhorst, 1966; Fanestil and Edelman, 1966; Litwack, 1967; Toft *et al.*, 1967; Maurer and Chalkley, 1967; Herman *et al.*, 1968; Jensen *et al.*, 1968; Munck and Brink-Johnsen, 1968; Mainwaring, 1969; Eurenius *et al.*, 1969). The liver is the main organ that concentrates corticosteroids significantly above the level in blood (Bradlow *et al.*, 1954; Sandberg *et al.*, 1957; Bellamy *et al.*, 1962). Although the thymus *in vivo* does not appear to concentrate corticosteroids, these substances have a profound involuting action on this organ as well as on other lymphocyte-containing tissues (Dougherty and White, 1944, 1945; Feigelson and Feigelson, 1964). The ability of the thymus to concentrate the hormone can be demonstrated *in vitro* when the gland is offered sufficient hormone in the medium. For these reasons, the liver and thymus may be accepted as representative target organs for corticosteroid action. Corticosteroids have an anabolic effect in liver (Trémolières *et al.*, 1954). Radioactive cortisol, injected intraperitoneally, accumulates rapidly in the liver, reaching a peak in concentration of the steroid and its metabolites in 30–45 minutes. By 45 minutes, most of the hormone (as much as 95%) is in the form of anionic metabolites, so that the concentration of unchanged cortisol must be maximal at a time considerably earlier than 45 minutes, probably at 5 or 10 minutes. The accumulation of radioactivity from cortisol at 45 minutes is similar in all affected compartments; that is, a peak in total cortisol activity (including metabolites) is reached by 30–45 minutes after injection except that the peak in cytosol precedes the peak in the nuclear fraction (Litwack et al., 1963). The peak, as expected, occurs much more rapidly if the hormone is injected directly into the blood stream (Morris and Barnes, 1967). The amount of radioactivity from the hormone is greatest in liver cytosol, considerable in the microsomal compartment and small in the nuclear fractions and mitochondria (Litwack et al., 1963; Litwack and Baserga, 1967; Mayewski and Litwack, 1969). The distribution between cytosol and microsomes is somewhat dependent on the mass of the hormone in the dose (Litwack et al., 1963). The subcellular compartmentation of corticosteroids in liver has been the subject of some careful and varied approaches. "Equilibrium fractionation" techniques have been used, for example (DeVenuto et al., 1962; DeVenuto and Muldoon, 1968). In this procedure the particulate fractions are carried through resuspension and centrifugation steps with cellular supernatant as the resuspending agent. This should insure that loose binding to subcellular particles is not disrupted by mass action effects which could occur if another solvent (buffer alone) were used. By this technique, greater amounts of cortisol or corticosterone are bound by the mitochondrial fraction of rat liver in vivo and in vitro than by the nuclei, microsomes, and supernatant, at variance with some of the findings mentioned above. The important difference between in vivo and in vitro experiments involves the rapid production of metabolites in vivo and the subsequent binding of these forms of the hormone by proteins of the cytoplasm (Litwack et al., 1965; Fiala and Litwack, 1966; Singer et al., 1970a). In this case, timing becomes very important, since the amount of exogenous unmetabolized corticosteroid within the cell decreases rapidly. Attempts have been made in our laboratory in in vitro experiments to diminish metabolism of the hormone; these studies will be mentioned below. The differences observed between subcellular fractionation involving sucrose–buffer and equilibrium may be understood if loose binding is washed away from particles in the absence of original cell supernatant. Extension of the subcellular approach involves two differing assumptions regarding hormonal action in liver. A consideration of hormonal function by direct action on the genome to derepress transcriptional sites has prompted studies of the action of the hormone in the nucleus and its actions in vitro on nuclear protein fractions, particularly histones. On the other hand, the idea of a primary molecular event of corticosteroids occurring in the cytoplasm setting off a chain of events leading to enzyme induction led to investigations of the events occurring in that compartment.

Functions of the hormone in both compartments appear to be important and possibly interrelated. Recent work detailing events occurring in the various subcellular compartments of liver and thymus is discussed below.

A. Liver Cytosol

After intraperitoneal injection of isotopic amount or hepatic enzyme inducing amounts (60 mg/kg) of cortisol (together with the radio-active hormone), there is a rapid intracellular accumulation in the liver of radioactivity amounting to about 15–20% of the dose, of which 30–45% is in cytosol by 45 minutes, when the maximal level of radioactivity has been achieved. Thereafter, there is a steady decline in radioactivity until about 4 hours when most of the isotope is gone from the organ (Litwack *et al.*, 1963). About 6–13% of the radioactivity in the cytosol at 45 minutes is bound to macromolecules. These consist of four separable proteins as shown in Fig. 1. They have been called binders I, II, III, and IV in the order of their elution from columns of DEAE Sephadex A-50. By 45 minutes after intraperitoneal injection, three anionic metabolites of cortisol are concentrated in the protein-bound and unbound

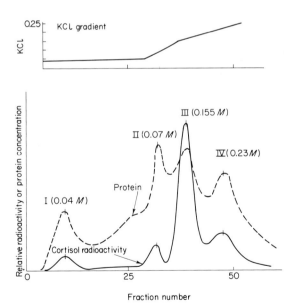

Fig. 1. A representative chromatogram of bound cortisol radioactivity from liver cytosol on a column of DEAE Sephadex A-50 showing the relative affinity of the four binding proteins for this ion-exchanger.

fractions. At least one of the two most negatively charged compounds contains sulfur-35 (when $H_2^{35}SO_4$ is administered) and may be a sulfate (Singer *et al.*, 1970a). The most polar metabolite is found exclusively in purified binder I, the next most polar is found exclusively in purified binder III, and unchanged cortisol and a weakly polar derivative with electrophoretic properties similar to the least anionic metabolite are found in binders II and IV. Binder IV has a relatively low affinity for cortisol metabolites but binds with a stronger affinity metabolites of testosterone and progesterone. These hormones have been shown by Samuels and Tomkins (1970) to prevent the action of glucocorticoids in tissue culture. Therefore, the possibility that binder IV functions as an anti-inducer needs to be investigated. Binder II, which associates with the least anionic metabolite and the unchanged corticosteroid, appears to bind a much higher percentage of the administered hormone 5–10 minutes after hormone administration. By 45 minutes, the binding of radioactivity to binder II has become relatively small, because binders I and III bind most of the radioactivity at this time.

A further discussion follows later on the possibility that binder II is the corticosteroid hormone "receptor" in liver. In studies with the hepatoma cell culture system, Gardner and Tomkins (1969) also have found an association of hormonal radioactivity with cytosol proteins. Of at least two binding proteins, the one chosen for study contained cortisol and one or two metabolites, depending on the mass of the hormone used in the experiment—the greater the mass, the more metabolite formation. In these cells, the metabolizing enzymes are low in concentration. In the liver system *in vivo* (Singer *et al.*, 1970b), radioactivity from corticosterone, testosterone, and progesterone eluted with all four of the cortisol metabolite binders. Cholesterol radioactivity did not bind to any of the cortisol metabolite binders. A quarter of the bound estradiol-17β radioactivity binds to binder I, and the rest fractionates in the chromatogram, distinct from cortisol metabolite-binding proteins. Aromatic carboxylic acids, like salicylate or *p*-aminobenzoate which mimic the action of corticosteroids in adrenalectomized rats by inducing tyrosine aminotransferase (Singer and Mason, 1965, 1967a), do not bind to the cortisol metabolite binding proteins. Deoxycorticosterone radioactivity binds to binder III. In the hepatoma cell culture system (Gardner and Tomkins, 1969), binding specificity was examined by gel filtration inspecting for coincidence in double label experiments in one peak of protein bound radioactivity. Cortisol, dexamethasone, corticosterone, aldosterone, deoxycorticosterone, progesterone, and 17α-hydroxyprogesterone coincided reasonably well with binding of marker cortisol-[14]C. Androst-4-ene-3,17-dione appeared to bind in this region as well, while testosterone showed little binding. Although estradiol-17β eluted with two macromolecular components, it did not bind to the protein fraction under inspection. If the protein binding system in the hepatoma cell is similar to the liver cell, the macromolecule studied in the hepatoma cell culture appears to bind with specificity similar to cortisol metabolite binder III and possibly binder I from liver. Recent work by Morris *et al.* (1970) confirms in many respects the results with binder III reported by Morey and Litwack (1969).

There are no direct data to implicate the cortisol metabolite binders in the process of hormone induction of hepatic enzymes. In 21 day rat fetuses, it is not possible to induce liver tyrosine aminotransferase by intraperitoneal glucocorticoid injection directly into the fetus (Greengard and Dewey, 1967), although the normal developmental rise is stimulated by cortisol immediately after birth (Litwack and Nemeth, 1965). In spite of several reports in the literature, our studies show that in the intact rat, there is no induction of liver tyrosine aminotransferase activity until about 2 weeks after birth, although the developmental rise of endogenous activity is present (Singer and Litwack, 1971). Examination of the fate of radioactive cortisol shows that macromolecular binding and metabolite formation was nearly absent in fetal liver, but both appeared in the newborn rat coinciding with or preceding the development of responsiveness to corticosteroids.

Binder I is a protein of unusual interest, although it is probably not the corticosteroid "receptor" protein. It is present in cytosol at a level of about 0.05% of the cytosol protein; it has been purified to homogeneity (Morey and Litwack, 1969) and has properties atypical of globular proteins (Table I). This protein is identical to the dimethylaminoazobenzene-binding protein (Litwack and Morey, 1970) isolated by Ketterer *et al.* (1967). Furthermore, it may be the same protein in cytosol which Bresnick *et al.* (1967) have partially fractionated and which binds 3-methylcholanthrene (Singer and Litwack, 1971). Since many of the carcinogens are metabolized through a sulfated intermediate (see E. C.

TABLE I

Some Physicochemical Properties of Cortisol Metabolite Binder I[a]

$s_{20,w}^0 \times 10^{13}$ seconds^{-1}	3.7
$D_{20,w}^0 \times 10^7$ cm^2 seconds^{-1}	11.8
Calculated molecular weight	31,000
Partial specific volume ($\bar{V}$)	0.75
Frictional ratio (f_{av}/f_{min})	2.07
Axial ratio (for prolate ellipsoid)	21

[a] From Litwack, 1971.

Miller and Miller, 1966, for example) and at least one of the anionic cortisol metabolites incorporates ^{35}S from labeled sulfuric acid, binder I might be a part of a sulfotransferase enzyme. While the protein itself is enzymatically inactive in this respect, it is curious that its amino acid composition is similar to bovine estrogen sulfotransferase B (Adams and Chulavatnatol, 1967) as shown in Table II. A marked difference

TABLE II

COMPARISON BETWEEN AMINO ACID COMPOSITION OF CORTISOL METABOLITE
BINDER I AND ESTROGEN SULFOTRANSFERASE B

| | Moles percent of total amino acids | |
Amino acid	Estrogen sulfotransferase[a]	Binder I[b]
Lysine	8.8	8.6
Histidine	2.4	1.2
Arginine	3.2	6.1
Asparagine	13.8	8.6
Threonine	5.0	3.7
Serine	6.7	3.7
Glutamic acid	9.7	11.0
Proline	5.7	4.9
Glycine	8.4	6.1
Alanine	9.1	7.4
Cysteine	Trace	Trace
Valine	6.0	6.1
Methionine	1.3	3.7
Isoleucine	1.3	3.7
Leucine	8.8	13.5
Tyrosine	2.4	3.7
Phenylalanine	5.8	4.9

[a] Data from Adams and Chulavatnatol (1967). These data are for the B form of the bovine sulfotransferase, molecular weight 191,000.

[b] Data from Morey and Litwack (1969). Rat liver binder I has a molecular weight of 37,000 by amino acid analysis and 31,000 by ultracentrifuge analysis (Table I). The rank concordance coefficient $r_s = (6Sd^2)/[n(n^{2-1})]$ (for explanation, see Litwack and Morey, 1970) is +0.85. This is judged to indicate a rather high rank concordance, since binder I and the dimethylaminoazobenzene-binding protein of liver cytosol have been shown unequivocally to be identical and the rank concordance value in this case for the amino acid analysis was +0.9 (Litwack and Morey, 1970). Also in favor of similarity between binder I and steroid sulfotransferase is that purified binder I contains an anionic metabolite, probably sulfated (Singer *et al.*, 1970a), and binder I can bind unmetabolized corticosteroids *in vitro* (Filler *et al.*, 1971). Against the identity of these proteins is the large difference in molecular weight; the failure, so far, of binder I to form aggregates of 190,000 daltons; and the apparent enzymatic inactivity of binder I. Also, the estrogen sulfotransferase appears to be a trimer with monomer subunit weight of 67,000 (Adams and Chulavatnatol, 1967).

between binder I and the sulfotransferase is that the 197,000 molecular weight enzyme is a trimer, each subunit having a molecular weight of 67,000 while the binder has a weight of 31,000, and to date, dimerization of the binding protein has not been observed which would be needed to approach the minimal molecular weight of the sulfotransferase subunit. In addition, binder I has two subunits each of approximately 20,000 daltons (Litwack *et al.,* 1971b; Ketterer *et al.,* 1971). That the amino acid compositions of these two proteins are similar is compelling, and further work must be done to rule out definitely any identity between the two macromolecules.

Recently, Baxter and Tomkins (1970) reported on the relationship between glucocorticoid binding and tyrosine aminotransferase induction in hepatoma tissue culture cells. Specific receptors in the cell approached saturation as the steroid concentrations required for maximal induction of enzymatic activity are reached. The association and dissociation phenomena of steroid from specific receptors are rapid enough to account for kinetics of induction and deinduction. The specific receptors are located in the nuclear fraction, although it was not made clear whether the nucleus itself was involved. A recent report (Beato *et al.,* 1970a), using the intact rat, provides evidence of a 4 S glycoprotein functioning to transport cortisol from the cytosol into the nucleus. More recent observations (Beato *et al.,* 1970b) infer that this protein has a molecular weight of 80,000 and an isoelectric pH of 4 (quite different properties from binder II studied in our laboratory; see below). Subsequent binding of the transport protein to nuclear macromolecules occurs and is somewhat analogous to estrogen binding and transport in the uterus (see Chapter 7 by Jensen). The binding reaction, carried out *in vitro* by Beato *et al.* (1970a) was faster at 37°C than at lower temperatures, a phenomenon similar to that observed by Baxter and Tomkins (1970) with binding in hepatoma cells. As opposed to the results of Beato *et al.* (1970a), all of the binding proteins (I–IV) we find, become labeled by radioactive corticosteroid in *in vitro* experiments under conditions where the two strongly anionic steroid metabolites are not formed (Filler *et al.,* 1971). These results suggest that although specific anionic cortisol metabolites are found on purified binders I and III at homogeneity, the structural requirements for binding may also include hydrophobic sites. Binder II, the protein present in the smallest concentration, appears to satisfy the requirements of a physiological hormone "receptor": it is saturated rapidly *in vivo* (within 5–10 minutes after intraperitoneal injection) at a level of steroid in the cytosol of about 0.1 nM; the forms bound are mainly unchanged cortisol; the binding is relatively loose and the concentration of this protein is low, in the range of 0.005% of the cytosol proteins; it is probable that the protein is either labile or that large conformational changes occur after the hormone is released from the complex, preventing rebinding (Filler *et al.*, 1971; Litwack *et al.*, 1971a). This fraction may resemble that described by Hackney *et al.* (1970) in mouse fibroblast culture.

B. Liver Microsomal Fraction

One of the consequences of administration of corticosteroids is an increase in aggregated ribosomes (Cammarano *et al.*, 1968). We have found that this effect is observable in rat liver 4 hours after intraperitoneal hormonal administration (Fig. 2)—to a lesser extent in 3 hours— and is undetectable by analytical ultracentrifugation prior to that time. Although direct interaction of the hormone with ribosomes to promote a greater percentage of functional polysomes would constitute an attractive mechanism of action (Tata, 1968), it is clear from time–course studies that this is a late response to the hormone and may not explain induction of enzymes with short half-lives. More likely, it is part of the overall response of the cell to an earlier sequence of direct hormonal actions. Work using the electron microscope (Rancourt and Litwack, 1968) indicates an early action on the endoplasmic reticulum of the hepatocyte. As soon as 15 minutes after intraperitoneal injection of cortisol in an immature, adrenalectomized male rat, abrupt changes occur involving conversion of much of the long parallel arrays of rough endoplasmic reticulum to vesiculated smooth membranes. There are no coincident electron-dense changes occurring in other cellular compartments until several hours or days later (Gustafsson and Afzelius, 1963; Orrenius and Ericsson, 1966; Weiner *et al.*, 1968; Kimberg *et al.*, 1968; Loeb and Kimberg, 1970). At the same time that the smooth vesiculated endoplasmic reticulum membranes begin to appear, the microsomal fraction starts to accumulate cortisol at a rate parallel to the rate for the whole liver. The hormone becomes bound to the smooth membranes in preference to the rough membranes (which bind some hormone but show no kinetic changes). Also, there is virtually no binding to the ribosomes (Mayewski and Litwack, 1969). This process continues from 15 to about 40 minutes after injection, at which time a steady state is reached. Bound radioactivity in the smooth membrane is not released by extensive water washing of either smooth or rough membranes but is extractable by butanol. Anionic metabolites, electrophoretically similar to those found in the cytosol are formed with time, suggesting hormone binding to metabolizing enzymes in the smooth

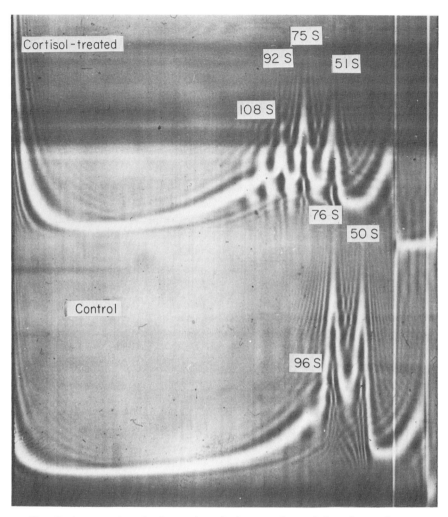

Fɪɢ. 2. A comparison in the analytical ultracentrifuge of the ribosomal patterns in the post-mitochondrial fractions of livers of 80 gm adrenalectomized male rats who received injections of saline (control) or cortisol (6 mg/100 gm body weight) for 4 hours. Values of S were determined by the ordinate maximum method using a Nikon microcomparator. (Litwack, 1971.)

membrane. Possibly there is binding to other structural sites which may be obscured by ribosomes in the rough membrane. If so, the hypothesis that corticosteroids act in the attachment of ribosomes to the endoplasmic reticulum would be useful for further experimentation (see also Rabin *et al.*, 1971).

C. Liver Mitochondria

A very small percentage of injected cortisol radioactivity was recovered in the mitochondrial fraction using standard procedures of subcellular fractionation (Litwack *et al.*, 1963; Morris and Barnes, 1967).
Shortly after intravenous administration of radioactive cortisol to animals
undergoing enzyme induction by a previous dose of the corticosteroid,
the levels in the mitochondrial fraction reached 1–2% of the total amount
in the cell (Morris and Barnes, 1967), whereas there was 5–10-fold that
amount in the microsomal fraction and 70–90-fold that percentage in
the cytosol (Morris and Barnes, 1967). In comparative experiments
where only a tracer, noninducing amount of cortisol was administered,
the amount in mitochondria was about the same, but microsomes were
higher (10–20% of hormonal radioactivity in the liver cell) at the expense
of the percentage in cytosol (Morris and Barnes, 1967), confirming
previous work (Litwack *et al.*, 1963). Cortisol increases the swelling
of mitochondria (DeVenuto and Westphal, 1965) and cortisone as well
as progesterone (Chance and Hollunger, 1963) specifically inhibit
mitochondrial dehydrogenases requiring pyridine nucleotides for electron
transfer (Gallagher, 1960). Binding of radioactive cortisol and corticosterone was studied *in vitro* in intact and sonicated mitochondria
prepared by equilibrium fractionation techniques described above. The
steroids were shown to be associated almost entirely with particulate
fractions of mitochondria consisting mainly of mitochondrial membrane
and high density particles. Little hormonal radioactivity was associated
with soluble proteins of mitochondria. It would be of interest to compare binding sites, other than metabolizing enzymes, in endoplasmic
reticulum to the mitochondrial membrane sites. The very small percentage of tracer amounts of the hormone far below physiological levels
(maximally about 8 ng) in the mitochondrial fraction suggest that the
mitochondria may represent a pathway for steroid hormone actions
separate from enzyme induction. Chronic administration of corticosteroid
causes electron dense changes in mitochondria (Loeb and Kimberg,
1970), but such changes are not observable in the time period before
enzyme induction.

D. Liver Nuclear Fraction

A very small portion of an injected dose of radioactive corticosteroid,
enters the nuclear fraction (Litwack *et al.*, 1963). Nuclear histones
have been considered to be possible regulators ("repressors") of trans-

criptional sites on the genome (Allfrey and Mirsky, 1962; Huang and Bonner, 1962). Karlson (1962) elaborated the hypothesis that hormones, through genomic interaction, control the synthesis of proteins in the receptor organ by regulating messenger RNA synthesis. Histones were considered to be the likely candidates for interaction with corticosteroids whose complex formation would necessitate removal of the histone(s) from the gene(s), thereby causing the transcription of the specific information. A great deal of work has been reported in support of this concept for other hormones as well as the corticosteroids.

Radioactivity from cortisol has been found complexed to rat liver nuclear histones after injection of the hormone *in vivo* or after incubation of surviving nuclei *in vitro* (Sluyser, 1966a, 1969) and also with histones from calf thymus *in vitro* (Sunaga and Koide, 1967a,b). Moreover, the template activity of liver chromatin is reported to increase when chromatin is prepared from adrenalectomized animals previously treated with cortisol for 4 hours (Dahmus and Bonner, 1965) or if the hormone is added *in vitro* (Stackhouse *et al.*, 1968). Hohmann and Cole (1969) have shown that cortisol alters the pattern of incorporation of precursors into lysine-rich histones during the period of cell proliferation in the rabbit mammary gland organ culture system (Stockdale and Topper, 1966) and claimed that these changes were related to the expression of casein in the functionally differentiated explants. This kind of effect would not be expected in the mature liver under conditions where cell growth and differentiation have been completed. The work reporting the interaction of cortisol *in vivo* and *in vitro* with histones in other systems implicates the arginine-rich histones as the fraction which binds the hormone significantly (Sluyser, 1966a,b, 1969; Sunaga and Koide, 1967a,b; Ohtsuka and Koide, 1969). In the earlier studies showing specific binding of cortisol radioactivity to arginine-rich histones *in vitro* (Sluyser, 1966a,b), the steroid bound to the histone fraction was about 1–3 μmoles steroid per mole histone (assuming a molecular weight of 12,000 for histone). This suggests a rather low affinity of the steroid for the arginine-rich fraction. However, a stoichiometric ratio of one to one could be achieved if, after the brief incubation in experiments described above (15 minutes at 37°C), the system was dialyzed overnight against 2 mM NaCl (Sluyser, 1966a). The extent of binding increased with increasing incubation times up to 48 hours. 21-Dehydrocortisol (C-21 aldehyde) had a much greater effect in stimulating the activity of RNA polymerase in fragmented nuclei, presumably by binding to the arginine-rich histones (Sunaga and Koide, 1968) and availing more transcribable information (Ohtsuka and Koide, 1969). There exists the possibility that a small amount of cortisol might be converted to the 21-dehydrocortisol and interacts with histones via Schiff base formation. For this interaction, it is improbable that the guanidino group of arginine would be preferred to the ε-amino group of lysine. Very recently, corticosteroid binding to arginine-rich histones has been reexamined thoroughly by Monder and Walker (1970). They showed that 21-dehydrocorticosteroids were present from 1 to 5% in tritiated preparations of parent compounds. Moreover, the specific binding of the 21-dehydrosteroids to arginine-rich histones could be explained by the selective interaction of the glyoxal side chain with the guanido residue (Takahashi, 1968). This model can be adopted to speculate upon the binding of 21-dehydrocortisol to arginine-rich histones (Fig. 3). The fact that the enzyme 21-dehydrosteroid reductase strongly favors the formation of the C-21 alcohol (Monder and White, 1963; Furfine and White, 1968) makes the enzymatic conversion to the 21-dehydro compound *in vivo* rather unlikely. But traces of copper in phosphate buffer as well as prolonged incubation times could give rise to the aldehyde derivative. Because of the relative lack of specificity in the structure of arginine-rich histones [for example, the amino acid sequences of arginine-rich histone from calf thymus and pea seedlings are practically identical (DeLange *et al.*, 1969], and the affinity of cortisol for this fraction seems low, claims of the significance of the binding of this hormone to the arginine-rich fraction ought to be made cautiously.

On the other hand, there are reports of experiments which support the Karlson hypothesis. Dahmus and Bonner (1965) reported that chromatin isolated 4 hours after *in vivo* treatment with cortisol exhibits approximately 30% higher template activity and this probably would be sufficient to account for enough mRNA production for enzyme induction. It would be interesting to know the time interval after cortisol

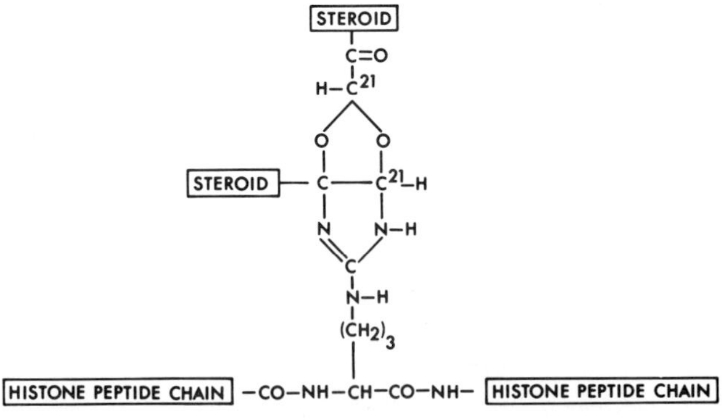

FIG. 3. A speculative model of the binding of 21-dehydrocorticosteroids to the arginine-rich histone fraction suggested by the results of Takahashi (1968).

treatment when the increase of transcriptional sites is first apparent. If this were a late effect—say, apparent at 2 hours and not before—then it might be considered to be a secondary manifestation perhaps reflecting a prior increase in the activity of RNA polymerase (see below). Since Dahmus and Bonner showed that treatment of isolated noninduced chromatin with the hormone *in vitro* failed to cause a stimulation in template activity, they postulated some intermediary, not preserved in isolated chromatin, between the hormone and its ultimate effect on transcribable sites. At the moment, arginine-rich histones, for the reasons offered above, seem unlikely candidates for the intermediary component. Although direct studies on the interaction of hormones and DNA have been made (Goldberg and Atchley, 1966; Cohen et al., 1969) which show some structural requirements for binding, it is difficult to imagine how a non-information containing small molecule could recognize a specific region of DNA and bind directly to that region to set off the changes required for enzyme induction. Very recently, Shelton and Allfrey (1970) have shown the specific response of a nuclear acidic protein, molecular weight 41,000, to a single injection of cortisol in the rat. The extent of stimulation varies with time after administration of the hormone and is evident within 2–3 hours, reaching a maximum of more than 200% by 7–8 hours. The function of this protein in the liver nucleus is unknown, but the authors advanced the suggestion that it may be specifically concerned in the regulation of chromosomal activity.

The experiments best supporting the Karlson idea are those which have been conducted by Sekeris and co-workers (Dukes et al., 1966; Schmid et al., 1967; Lukacs and Sekeris, 1967). In these studies, mainly with isolated surviving liver cell nuclei, the activity of DNA-dependent RNA polymerase was increased maximally within 10 minutes as a result of incubation with cortisol. A similar process requiring a much longer time period has been observed *in vivo* (Barnebei et al., 1965). The activity of nuclear RNA in translation (amino acid composition) appeared to be specific inasmuch as other hormones (testosterone, progesterone, androstenedione, pregnenolone, and 17α-hydroxyprogesterone) were ineffective. The enhancement of protein synthesis by addition of RNA from isolated nuclei previously incubated with cortisol ($3 \times 10^{-7} M$) was of the order of 50–70%. Nuclei isolated from adrenalectomized rats were more responsive to low concentrations of hormone than were nuclei isolated from normal animals. Fractionation of the nuclear RNA's into 55% and 70% fractions indicated that the stimulation of translation was not due to ribosomal RNA. The logical interpretation is that mRNA was synthesized in response to hormonal treatment which accounted for the increase of amino acid incorporation. With the current limitations in methodology, an unequivocal direct demonstration of mRNA production in response to specific hormones remains for the future. Nevertheless, the work of Finkel *et al.* (1966) and of Gelehrter and Tomkins (1967) is suggestive of an increase in the RNA of the 45 S ribosomal subunit particle as a result of glucocorticoid action in the whole animal and in the Morris hepatoma cell culture system. Recently, Beato *et al.* (1969) reported the rapid uptake of radioactive cortisol into isolated rat liver nuclei which reaches a steady state in 20 minutes of incubation at 37°C. There was no metabolic transformation of the hormone in the time period when the effects upon RNA template activity were reported. At later times, a small amount of cationic metabolite was found. Retention of the hormone by the nuclei apparently required sulfhydryl groups, since sulfhydryl blocking agents diminished uptake and accumulation of the hormone.

It would ultimately have to be shown that among the RNA species whose syntheses were stimulated upon incubation of isolated nuclei with cortisol, there were produced messenger RNA's for the synthesis of enzymes known to be induced by the hormone. Lang *et al.* (1968) have claimed the isolation of a mRNA fraction from the liver of cortisol-treated rats which when added to an *in vitro* protein synthesizing system gives rise to tyrosine aminotransferase activity. The appearance of the increment of enzyme activity was inhibited by puromycin and erythromycin. A more convincing analysis is needed, such as the demonstration of amino acid incorporation into the newly formed protein by use of the specific antibody technique, and the extent, if any, to which inactive enzyme is released from a bound state in the cell.

The distribution of corticosterone radioactivity in subcellular fractions of rat thymus at various times after intraperitoneal injection has been studied by Brunkhorst (1969b). The greatest concentration of radioactivity was present in the cytosol with smaller amounts in the particulate fractions. The subcellular distribution of radioactivity was similar to that described for liver by Litwack *et al.* (1963).

E. Whole Thymus Cells *in Vitro*

Incubation of thymus cells *in vitro* affords a useful tool for the study of hormone action because there are effects on the cells similar to those found *in vivo* and the problems of blood circulation, competition for hormone uptake, etc. are avoided. Much of the work with this system has been carried out by Munck and his collaborators (Bartlett *et al.*,

1962; Morita and Munck, 1964; Kattwinkel and Munck, 1966; Munck, 1968; Munck and Brinck-Johnsen, 1968). They demonstrated that glucocorticoids act directly on the thymus cell leading rapidly to decreased rates of glucose uptake owing to a block of glucose transport or phosphorylation appearing *in vitro* 15–20 minutes after exposure of cells to cortisol. The inhibition of glucose uptake clearly preceded effects on protein or nucleic acid metabolism. The activity of steroids (10^{-8} to $3 \times 10^{-6} M$) in reducing glucose uptake *in vitro* was in proportion to their glucocorticoid activity *in vivo* (Munck and Brinck-Johnsen, 1967). Other work is not in accord with the production of a defect in glucose uptake due to cortisol (Blecher, 1964). Cell cultures do not convert inactive cortisone to active cortisol, which does occur *in vivo*. At high concentrations *in vitro* ($10^{-5} M$ and higher) there emerges a pattern of "nonspecific" effects that are unrelated to glucocorticoid activity, but that may be due to the tendency of steroids to concentrate at interfaces (Knox *et al.*, 1964; Engel, 1961; Munck, 1957). These nonspecific actions are produced through mechanisms, and probably binding sites, that differ from those responsible for specific glucocorticoid effects (Munck, 1965). The specific glucocorticoid effects are abolished under anaerobic conditions. These studies have been extended by measuring binding of glucocorticoids to whole cells (Munck and Brinck-Johnsen, 1968). Nonspecific activity was accounted for by a fraction which at 37°C dissociates with a time constant under 15 seconds. A minor fraction, with a time constant of about 3 minutes, appears to consist of molecules responsible for specific glucocorticoid activity. The slowly dissociating (specific) fraction is bound rapidly, becomes saturated at physiological concentrations, depends upon cellular ATP levels, and is competed for by steroids in rough proportion to glucocorticoid activity. The specific fraction probably contains unaltered cortisol.

F. Thymus Cytosol Fraction

Radioactive cortisol or corticosterone binds rat thymus cytosol components (DeVenuto and Chader, 1966) as well as to the particulate fraction. Brunkhorst and Hess (1964) and Brunkhorst (1966) demonstrated binding in the cytosol of calf thymus in several components of the pH 5.1 fraction of the cytosol. The RNA content in the binding fraction was low, suggesting that the macromolecular binding site could be a protein. In our laboratory, the rat thymus cytosol binding system has been studied extensively (Litwack *et al.*, 1971a). The nature of the binding system aligns with the criteria of Munck and Brinck-

Johnsen for specific binding, with the exception that fluorinated glucocorticoids (dexamethasone, dexamethasone 21-phosphate, and tri-
amcinolone) are unable to compete with radioactive cortisol for the
binding site. Some evidence, although not unequivocal, obtained in our
laboratory now suggests that the fluorocorticosteroid-insensitive binder
may be an extracellular protein and consequently distinct from the specific "receptors" of the cytosol and nuclear fractions (Wira and Munck,
1970). Of interest is the conclusion of Brunkhorst and Hess (1964) that
there were multiple binding sites for cortisol in calf thymus. In contrast,
Schaumburg and Bojesen (1968), from thermodynamic studies on whole
thymocytes, suggested a single binding site for corticosteroids (about
2400 per cell). In their experiments, binding was measured as the retention of steroid radioactivity by centrifuged whole cells. This technique
does not render possible the localization of the subcellular fraction
involved in binding of the hormone or if the cell membrane binds part
of the hormone. Nevertheless, the order of corticosteroid potency (tri-
amcinolone was bound only 5% as well as cortisol) they observed was
similar to our findings with the supernatant binding site. However, a
surface protein separating with the supernatant fraction, may play a role
in preliminary binding prior to entrance into the cytosol (Litwack *et al.*,
1971b). Therefore, the cell membrane is probably not an important locus
for steroid binding and the cytosol protein could play an important role
in the sequence of events culminating in involution of the thymus. The
macromolecular cortisol binder in P1798 mouse lymphosarcoma cytosol
described by Hollander and Chiu (1966) seems to be very similar to the
thymus supernatant factor we observed *in vivo* and in a thymus explant
system. The ability of other steroids to compete for the radioactive cortisol binding site is similar in both cases, and Hollander and Chiu found
that the fluorinated glucocorticoid 9-α-fluoroprednisolone could not compete for binding in agreement with our data, but surprisingly, it enhanced the binding of radioactive cortisol in the lymphosarcoma cytosol.
In the case of the thymus supernatant fraction, the fluorinated glucocorticoids also did not compete with radioactive cortisol binding even at 1000
times the mass of cortisol; however, there was only slight stimulation of
cortisol binding by the fluorinated compound. The thymus explant
system demonstrated specificity for both cortisol and corticosterone as
well as other hormones within, or below physiological concentrations.
The supernatant macromolecule–steroid complex does not survive gel
filtration and has been measured by membrane filtration methods. As
much as 80% of supernatant radioactivity is in the bound form, and this
percentage decreases slowly over a 2 hour period. It follows first order
kinetics and provides a time constant substantially larger than that ob-

tained for specific binding of cortisol to intact thymus cells in culture (Munck and Brinck-Johnsen, 1968). The maximum binding is at 2–5 minutes in explant systems or following intraperitoneal injection *in vivo*. The half-life and hormone specificity studies indicate that the complex in *the supernatant* represents one of the hormone-specific binding sites. Preliminary data now suggest that specific binding to receptors in cytosol and nucleus may be preceded by loose binding to a surface or intercellular protein. The presence of a surface factor may be distinguished from receptors on the basis of its inability to bind fluorocorticosteroids.

G. THYMUS MICROSOMAL FRACTION

Several studies have confirmed the accumulation of cortisol or corticosterone in the microsomal fraction of rat thymus (Peña *et al.*, 1966; DeVenuto and Chader, 1966; Bottoms and Goetsch, 1967; Brunkhorst, 1969b). Thirty minutes after intravenous injection of tritiated corticosterone, the microsomal fraction of thymus contained 1–4% of the radioactivity in the subcellular fractions (Bottoms and Goetsch, 1967), but this is considerably less than the amount concentrated in liver microsomes (see preceding discussion). Recent work (Gabourel and Fox, 1965; Peña *et al.*, 1966; Brunkhorst, 1968) implicates a relatively early inhibition of incorporation of labeled amino acids into protein at the microsomal level and more specifically, it is believed by many workers, at the level of the ribosomes or their aggregation. Brunkhorst and Hess (1964) demonstrated an interaction *in vitro* between cortisol and the microsomal and the ribosomal fraction in addition to interaction with components of the cytosol. Peña *et al.* (1966) concluded that the involutionary effect of cortisol on rat thymus was at the ribosomal level and they provided data or deductions which tended to rule out the following mechanisms of hormone action: the extent of binding of messenger RNA to the ribosomes, the depression in RNA polymerase activity, an increase in acid or alkaline RNase activity, or augmented nuclear DNase activity. Other laboratories, however, report significant increases in acid RNase activity as early as 2½ hours after intraperitoneal injection of 9-α-fluoroprednisolone (Ambellan and Roth, 1967). Gabourel and Fox (1965) observed the disaggregation of thymic polysomes by 12 hours after cortisol administration and evident as early as 6 hours after administering the hormone to young rats. Whether the specific effect of the hormone is located in the ribosomal compartment remains to be discovered.

followed by a diminished degree of protein synthesis of ribosomal protein. Inhibition of protein synthesis, in turn, could lead to less RNA polymerase, less membrane transport protein, and less DNA polymerase enzyme, consequently less DNA template. The possibility was also provided by these workers that an early action of cortisol would be to activate or stimulate the synthesis of one or more inhibitors as mediators of the cortisol effects, and this would provide an explanation for some of the information they have obtained. In addition, there is a possibility that the primary action of cortisol in thymus is to inhibit ribosomal protein synthesis in a manner not mediated by mRNA synthesis. The work of Peña *et al.* (1966) indicates that the effects of cortisol in inhibiting ribosomal protein synthesis are not due to a decrease in messenger RNA. That both protein and RNA synthesis were inhibited simultaneously in thymus sites exposed to cortisol appears to be unexplained. These workers also indicate that the primary locus of cortisol inhibition of protein synthesis independent of effects on RNA formation might be at the translational control level. However, the considerable emphasis of relatively early effects of cortisol on nuclear DNA-dependent RNA polymerase in this organ suggests the possibility of one site of its action in the nucleus. Recently, Wira and Munck (1970) demonstrated that binding of corticosteroids to thymus nuclei could account for the specific type of binding they encountered using thymocyte cell suspensions, indicating the presence of glucocorticoid receptors in this fraction. However, they were unable to obtain direct binding between cortisol and isolated nuclei or a partially purified receptor from nuclei. This result suggests that the cytosol binder may play a direct role in binding and transport to the nuclear site. Glucocorticoids have a pronounced effect *in vivo* and *in vitro* on the RNA synthesis [particularly ribosomal RNA (Drews, 1969)], on RNA polymerase, and on incorporation of amino acids into nuclear fractions (Fox and Gabourel, 1967; Herranen and Brunkhorst, 1967; Brunkhorst, 1968). Multiple effects of the hormone probably involve more than one locus of action. The explanation for the site to which the fluorinated glucocorticoids bind preferentially probably is in the nucleus, which may be closer to the site of the ultimate specific corticosteroid effect in this organ.

III. INTERACTIONS OF CARCINOGENS IN THE CORTICO-STEROID BINDING SYSTEM OF LIVER CYTOSOL

For a long time, a permissive effect of the adrenal gland upon the production of liver tumors by chemical carcinogens has been known

(A. C. Griffin *et al.*, 1953; Robertson *et al.*, 1954; Perry, 1961; Reuber, 1963; Lotlikar *et al.*, 1964). For example, adrenalectomized rats fed 4-dimethylaminoazobenzene were relatively resistant to liver tumor induction (Symeonidis *et al.*, 1954; Symeonidis, 1963). Since corticosteroids appeared to promote chemical carcinogenesis in liver and absence of the steroids reduced the incidence of chemically induced tumors, it appeared that there must be at least one site in the hepatocyte at which both the steroid and chemical carcinogens interact. One such site appears to be the cortisol (metabolite) binder I (Litwack and Morey, 1970). Binder I for corticosteroids has been shown to be identical to the binder in cytosol of dimethylaminoazobenzene described by Ketterer *et al.* (1967). This conclusion was reached after demonstration of coincidence of double label from injected cortisol-³H and dimethylaminoazobenzene-¹⁴C after binder I had been purified to homogeneity. In addition, the physicochemical characteristics of binder I (Morey and Litwack, 1969) and of the dimethylaminoazobenzene binding protein (Ketterer *et al.*, 1967) agreed perfectly (Litwack and Morey, 1970). Also, binder I appears to be 3-methylcholanthrene-binding protein (Singer and Litwack, 1971), possibly the macromolecule indicated in studies of partial purification of such a factor by Bresnick *et al.* (1967; Hey-Ferguson and Bresnick, 1971) for liver cytosol. In contrast, only a very minor fraction of bound radioactivity derived from acetylaminofluorene is bound to binder I. This carcinogen is bound to five or six protein fractions (Barry *et al.*, 1969) which are clearly different from the corticosteroid binding series (Keats *et al.*, 1970). In the case of 3-methylcholanthrene, there appears

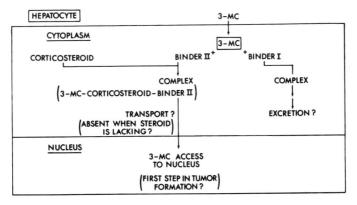

FIG. 4. Diagram of a speculation on the interaction of the carcinogen 3-methylcholanthrene with the corticosteroid (metabolite) protein binding system and how the interaction may be involved in the process of hepatic carcinogenesis. 3-MC = 3-methylcholanthrene.

to be significant labeling from the radioactive carcinogen of binder II as well as binder I. Since we believe binder II is the hormonal "receptor" in the cell (Filler *et al.*, 1971), it is possible that binder II carries the carcinogen to the nucleus only in the presence of corticosteroid, and in its absence, binding of the carcinogen would still occur, but transport to the nucleus might not occur. This speculation is diagrammed in Fig. 4. These ideas fit the observations on the relationship of the adrenal gland to the production of liver tumors by certain chemical carcinogens.

IV. EFFECTS OF GLUCOCORTICOIDS ON METABOLIC SYSTEMS AND CERTAIN ENZYMES

A. GLYCOGEN SYNTHESIS

The stimulation of hepatic glycogen deposition by adrenal corticosteroids is one of the more extensively studied phenomena in biochemical endocrinology. The term glucocorticoid is applied to cortisol and related adrenal steroid hormones which stimulate this process.

The classic study of Long *et al.* (1940) provided the basic information on glycogen deposition. These workers showed that the fasting of adrenalectomized rats results in abnormally rapid depletion of liver glycogen and that treatment of adrenalectomized rats with cortisol extracts or crystalline corticosteroids led to rapid and extensive glycogen deposition. Not all adrenal corticosteroids were equally effective, deoxycorticosterone having only a feeble effect as compared to corticosterone and dehydrocorticosterone. Also delineated was the relationship between the adrenal and the pituitary glands in glycogenesis. Hypophysectomy had the same effect as adrenalectomy in causing glycogen depletion, and glucocorticoid administration reversed this effect.

Although the ensuing years led to a great deal of research on the mechanics of glucocorticoid-mediated deposition of glycogen, little was known about the control of the process until the early 1960's. The discovery of hepatic glycogen synthetase (Leloir and Cardini, 1957; Leloir and Goldemberg, 1960) was an important step in leading to studies on regulation. This enzyme catalyzes the transfer of glucosyl units from UDPG to glycogen and is activated by glucose-6-phosphate (Leloir and Goldemberg, 1960). The enzyme has also been shown to be present in skeletal muscle (Villar-Palasi and Larner, 1958; Robbins *et al.*, 1959) and brain (Breckenridge and Crawford, 1960). Several investigators (Robbins *et al.*, 1959; Leloir *et al.*, 1959; Larner *et al.*, 1959; Leloir and

Goldemberg, 1960) showed that the synthetase pathway for glycogen deposition is favored *in vivo* by thermodynamic considerations and that it is independent of phosphorylase which can only act as a degradative enzyme under physiological conditions. The apparent dependence of the enzyme on glucose-6-phosphate *in vitro* led to the assumption by Leloir and Goldemberg (1960) that glycogen synthetase might serve as the control step for glycogen synthesis *in vivo*, and that this control might depend on the marked fluctuations of glucose-6-phosphate found under varying nutritional and endocrine states (Steiner and Williams, 1959). Steiner *et al.* (1961) treated diabetic rats with insulin or fasted rats with cortisol, which led to coincident rises in hepatic glycogen levels and hepatic glycogen synthetase activity. These results supported the thesis that glycogen synthetase activity controls glycogen deposition.

One of the most significant studies of the control of glucocorticoid-mediated glycogen synthesis was the work of Hornbrook *et al.* (1965, 1966), who examined the effects of lactate and cortisol on thirteen constituents of rat liver which could be precursors for glycogen synthesis. They assumed that glycogen synthesis could be accelerated either by increases in precursor levels which would elevate UDPG and push glyco-

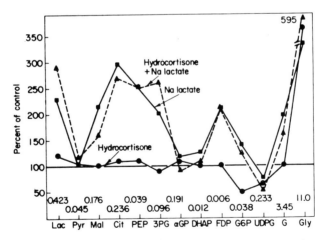

Fig. 5. Changes in thirteen constituents of rat liver following lactate and/or hydrocortisone administration. Rats were starved 24 hours and anesthetized with phenobarbital. Sodium lactate (0.75 gm/kg) was given intraperitoneally 60 minutes before sampling. Hydrocortisone (50 mg/kg) was injected subcutaneously 2 or 3 hours prior to excision of the liver (0.5 or 1.5 hours before phenobarbital). Control rats received isotonic saline. Control levels, recorded as mmoles per kilogram, are the averages for two rats. Levels in lactate-treated rats are the averages for two rats; the hydrocortisone and hydrocortisone plus lactate levels are the average ages for four rats. [See Fig. 6 for key to abbreviations. From Hornbrook *et al.* (1965).]

gen synthesis, or by the stimulation of the glycogen synthetase reaction which would pull precursors from various pools into glycogen and lower UDPG levels. Their preliminary data (Hornbrook et al., 1965) (Fig. 5) showed that while lactate and cortisol both stimulated glycogen synthesis, lactate administration resulted in rises in most of the precursors studied, including glucose-6-phosphate, while cortisol administration resulted only in a severe drop in UDPG and glucose-6-phosphate. These data suggested that lactate acted by a push mechanism and cortisol by a pull mechanism involving only the glycogen synthetase reaction. Furthermore, since the simultaneous administration of cortisol and lactate did not alter the other intermediate steps (Fig. 5), the effects of cortisol on other steps in the glycogenic pathway might not be involved in the stimulation of glycogen synthesis. Finally, their observation that glucose-6-phosphate levels fall after cortisol administration indicated that the increased glycogen levels cannot be explained by glucose-6-phosphate stimulation of the synthetase (Steiner et al., 1961). Hornbrook et al. (1966) also showed that adrenalectomy resulted in marked changes in glycogen precursor levels in liver—pyruvate, phosphoenolpyruvate, 3-phosphoglycerate, and UDPG were markedly increased as compared to normal controls; glycogen and most of the other precursors dropped dramatically. Cortisol administration markedly increased glycogen and glucose concentrations and reduced UDPG levels in half (Fig. 6). Most of the other precursor levels remained unchanged. The increase in hepatic glycogen due to cortisol is therefore associated with the acceleration of the glycogen synthetase step. It remained, at this point, to determine whether the increase in synthetase activity was due to *de novo* enzyme synthesis or to activation of the existing synthetase. That stimulation of the synthetase reaction is an activation phenomenon may be derived from the work of Lardy and his co-workers (Ray et al., 1964a,b). In adrenalectomized rats given glucose, cortisol administration increased hepatic glycogen levels even in the presence of actinomycin sufficient to block the rise of phosphoenolpyruvate carboxylase activity, which otherwise responds to cortisol (Kwam and Parks, 1960; Ray et al., 1964a,b). The effect of cortisol on glycogen synthesis is thus apparently independent of RNA and protein synthesis.

In their studies of this problem, the Lowry group (Hornbrook et al., 1966) examined the glucose synthetase activity from rats in various endocrine states as a function of UDPG concentration with and without glucose-6-phosphate. This was done to determine the total amount of glycogen synthetase and the relative amounts of the glucose-6-phosphate-dependent (D) and independent (I) forms of the enzymes (Hizukuri and Larner, 1964; Rosell-Perez et al., 1962). In adrenalectomized rats,

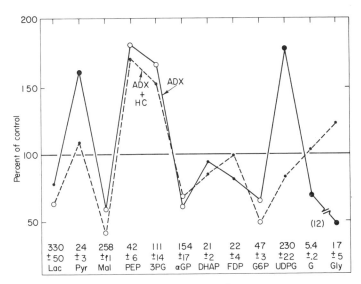

330	24	258	42	111	154	21	22	47	230	5.4	17
±50	±3	±11	±6	±14	±17	±2	±4	±3	±22	±.2	±5
Lac	Pyr	Mal	PEP	3PG	αGP	DHAP	FDP	G6P	UDPG	G	Gly

Fig. 6. The effects of adrenalectomy and hydrocortisone treatment on twelve metabolites in liver. The concentrations of the metabolites are expressed as percentages of the levels of starved normal control rats. These control values are recorded across the bottom of the figure and represent the means for four rats plus or minus the standard errors. Values are expressed as micromoles per kilogram wet weight of liver except for glucose and glycogen, which are expressed as millimoles per kilogram. The metabolites are arranged in order along the presumptive glycogenic pathway. (Substances believed not to be on the pathway—malate, glycero-P, and glucose—are placed next to close metabolic neighbors.) Points on the graph are connected for easier visualization. There were three or four rats in each group. All rats had been starved 24 hours. Hydrocortisone was given 3 hours before samples were taken. Abbreviations used are ADX, adrenalectomized rats; HC, hydrocortisone; Lac, lactate; Pyr, pyruvate; Mal, malate; PEP, P-pyruvate; 3PG, 3-P-glycerate; αGP, α-glycero-P; DHAP, dihydroxyacetone-P; FDP, fructose diphosphate; G6P, glucose 6-P; UDPG, UDP-glucose; G, glucose; and Gly, glycogen. Values marked with an open circle are significantly different from control levels at $P < 0.05$; those with a large closed circle are significantly different at $P < 0.01$. [From Hornbrook et al. (1966).]

the enzyme is almost entirely in the D form. In starved, intact rats given cortisol it is almost pure I[1] form. In intact or adrenalectomized rats given cortisol, the enzyme is a mixture of D and I forms. They also found that in fed, intact rats given cortisol, neither the I form nor total activity changes. This is consistent with the fact that there is no increase in glycogen deposition. After adrenalectomy, the I form drops, as does liver glycogen, with no change in total glycogen synthetase activity. But most

---

[1] The I form of glycogen synthetase is not completely glucose-6-phosphate-independent under physiological conditions.

significantly, while there is no change in total glycogen synthetase activity in fasted intact or adrenalectomized rats given cortisol, the I form of the enzyme increases in parallel with glycogen deposition (Table III). It would appear again that the glucocorticoid effect is the result of the activation of glycogen synthetase.

Further support for the role of glycogen synthetase in controlling glycogen deposition comes from the work of Segal and co-workers (Gold and Segal, 1966; Segal and Gonzales-Lopez, 1963). After the administration of prednisolone, the incorporation of labeled pyruvate, fructose, and glucose into glycogen was the same (Segal and Gonzales-Lopez, 1963), and there was little randomization of ^{14}C from injected glucose-1-^{14}C in isolated glycogen (Gold and Segal, 1966). Apparently, glucose is converted directly without prior degradation to trioses (Gold and Segal, 1966).

The mounting evidence that glycogen synthetase might be the control step in hormonally stimulated glycogen deposition has led to extensive *in vitro* studies geared to understanding the mechanism of the interconversion of the D and I forms of the enzyme and the properties of the enzyme under physiological conditions. In 1967, Gold and Segal showed that the incubation of hepatic glycogen synthetase preparations at 20°C led to marked increases in the activity of the D and I forms of the enzyme. [The apparent increase in the D forms is probably largely due to the fact that the I form is not totally glucose-6-phosphate-dependent under the conditions used (Hornbrook *et al.*, 1966)]. Mersman and Segal (1967) suggested that the reversible conversion of glucose-6-phosphate-dependent forms of the synthetase to the independent form, which they call b → a has the properties of an on–off switch for glycogen synthesis. They showed that at physiological concentrations of glucose-6-phosphate, UDPG, and P_i [the last stimulates the a form of the enzyme (DeWulf *et al.*, 1968; Mersman and Segal, 1967)], the b form (glucose-6-phosphate-dependent) is totally inactive. On the other hand, the a form is 50–100% active. Therefore, conditions where the b form predominates should stop glycogen synthesis. This has been found to be the case in starved adrenalectomized rats, where the synthetase is in this inactive form. Conversely, in starved hormone-treated adrenalectomized or normal rats (Hornbrook *et al.*, 1966; Mersman and Segal, 1969), where the a form is present or predominates after treatment, glycogen deposition occurs.

Mersman and Segal (1969) also made the striking observation that the *in vitro* activation of glycogen synthetase occurred to similar extents in tissue preparations from fed or starved intact rats or fed adrenalectomized rats. However, there was no activation and only trace amounts of synthetase activity in enzyme preparations from starved adrenal-ectomized rats. Prednisolone administration to starved adrenalectomized rats caused the a form to rise to normal levels and allowed the usual activation (Fig. 7). When synthetase-free fractions from normal rats were added to the inactive enzyme containing fraction from adrenal-ectomized rats, activation to normal levels was obtained (Mersman and Segal, 1969). The activating factor must be an enzyme by analogy with the synthetase activating system described in muscle by Larner and co-workers (Friedman and Larner, 1963; Hizukuri and Larner, 1964), which was shown to involve a specific kinase for the inactivation ($a \rightarrow b$) and a specific phosphatase for the activation ($b \rightarrow a$). Evidence for the exist-ence of the activating system in liver comes from the *in vitro* inhibitor studies of DeWulf and Hers (1968a). Therefore, glucocorticoid adminis-tration accelerates glycogen synthesis by effecting changes in either the synthetase kinase or phosphatase levels, and the amounts of glycogen synthetase protein remains constant. DeWulf and Hers (1968a) have studied the *in vivo* effects of varying endocrine state on glycogen syn-

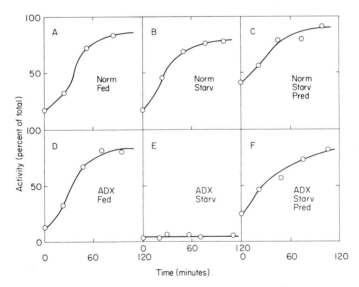

Fig. 7. Effects of adrenalectomy, fasting, and glucocorticoid treatment on activa-tion of glycogen synthetase *in vitro*. The abbreviations used are Norm, normal animals; ADX, adrenalectomized animals; Fed, fed *ad libitum*; Starv, fasted for 48 hours, Pred, 2 mg of prednisolone acetate per rat, administered 3 hours (C) or 4½ hours (F) before the animal was killed. Each point is an average of data from at least four animals. The *abscissa* is minutes of incubation of the crude extract at 20°. The absolute values of the total activity are available from Fig. 2 of the original reference. [From Mersman and Segal (1969).]

TABLE III

Effect of Hydrocortisone and Adrenalectomy on Glycogen and Glycogen Synthetase[a,b]

Treatment	Hours after hydrocortisone administration	Glycogen	Synthetase activity (V_{max}, moles/kg/hour)		K_s for UDP-glucose (mM)	
			− glucose-6-P	+ glucose-6-P	− glucose-6-P	+ glucose-6-P
Control						
Starved 24 hours	0	17 ± 5	52 ± 3	90 ± 8	5.6; 6.6	1.3; 1.3[c]
	1	11 ± 2	70 ± 6	89 ± 9	—	—
	2	33 ± 9	96 ± 7	103 ± 4	—	—
	3	60 ± 12	90 ± 6	89 ± 11	—	—
	6	79 ± 10	72 ± 6	85 ± 2	—	—
Fed ad lib.	0	252 ± 12	55 ± 10	146 ± 7	9.8	2.6[c]
	3	241 ± 21	45 ± 8	119 ± 11	9.8	1.8[c]
Adrenalectomized						
Fed ad lib.	0	—	22 ± 2	131 ± 9	14	8.3
Starved 24 hours	0	2 ± 1	15 ± 4	229 ± 9	10.0; 12.5	6.7; 9.9[c]
	3	21 ± 5	85 ± 11	187 ± 17	7.7; 8.0	2.4; 2.8
1 hour after lactate	0	3 ± 2	19 ± 6	218 ± 30	—	—
	3	64 ± 16	123 ± 13	147 ± 22	—	—

[a] This table is reproduced from Hornbrook *et al.* (1966).

[b] Values are averages ± standard error of the mean for three or four rats except for the K_s columns, which represent individual determinations. The maximal velocities in columns 4 and 5 were calculated from velocities observed with 9.5 mM UDP-glucose and the Michaelis–Menten equation. In each case, an average value of K_s, as recorded in the last two columns, was used for this calculation. The K_s values measured 3 hours after hydrocortisone administration were assumed to apply at 1, 2, and 6 hours as well (control animals starved 24 hours). The K_s values given first in each column are from Figs. 3 and 4; those given second were determined on different livers. Glycogen is expressed as millimoles per kilogram fresh liver, enzyme activities as millimoles per kilogram fresh liver per hour.

[c] In the case of these animals, an attempt was made to calculate the Michaelis constants of the pure I form in the presence of glucose-6-P. The V_{max} for the D form was taken as the difference between column 5 and column 4. The velocity of the D form activity at less than saturating levels of UDP-glucose was calculated from the Michaelis–Menten equation, assuming K_s = 8.3 mM. This value of K_s was the average obtained for all untreated adrenalectomized rats in which, as seen in the table, most of the activity is in the D form. The calculated contribution of the D form to the activity at each substrate concentration was then subtracted from the velocity determined in the presence of glucose-6-P. The differences were taken as the velocities for the I form when measured in the presence of glucose-6-P. From these net velocities, K_s values were estimated from Lineweaver–Burk plots. The values for K_s calculated in this way were 0.85, 1.7, 1.7, and 2.0 mM, respectively, for the starved control rats, fed control rats, fed control rats after hydrocortisone, and starved adrenalectomized rats after hydrocortisone.

thetase still further. The administration of glucagon, epinephrine, or cyclic AMP reversed the glucocorticoid-mediated activation of the hepatic enzyme and to a much lesser extent activated glycogen phosphorylase. The differences in sensitivity of the two enzymes to these agents could allow for a stoppage of glycogen synthesis without turning on glycogen degradation, demonstrating the sensitivity of the controlling step for glycogen synthesis. Hers *et al.* (1971) suggest that the *in vivo* activation of glycogen synthetase by glucocorticoids is due to increased activity of phosphorylase phosphatase which acts as a glycogen synthetase phosphatase. The difference between the phosphorylase and the synthetase is that the active forms of the enzymes are the phosphophorylase and the dephosphosynthetase. They show that the livers from mice (Stalmans *et al.*, 1970) pretreated with prednisolone several hours earlier have three to ten times as much phosphorylase phosphatase as do controls. Since the properties of phosphorylase phosphatase are not modified by glucocorticoid treatment, they suggest that glucocorticoid treatment causes more rapid synthesis of the enzyme. The increase in phosphorylase phosphatase accounts for the drop in phosphorylase activity *in vivo* after corticoids (DeWulf and Hers, 1968b).

The b $\rightarrow$ a conversion of the synthetase *in vitro* exhibits a 20 minute lag (Gold and Segal, 1967). Glucocorticoids given *in vivo* shorten the lag period and in all studies the lag period corresponds to the time needed to inactivate the phosphorylase present in the system (DeWulf *et al.*, 1970). Further, it was shown that phosphorylase a was a strong inhibitor of glycogen synthetase activation but phosphorylase b (the dephosphoenzyme) was not.

It is now obvious that the control of glucocorticoid-mediated glycogen deposition is at the level of the glycogen synthetase reaction. The probable control step involves the synthetase activating system.

B. Lipid Metabolism

The conversion of carbohydrate to lipid *in vivo* is a well documented phenomenon. Although the liver has been implicated as the most active site of lipid formation, adipose tissue, which functions to accumulate and store fat, has also been shown to be an active site of lipid synthesis (Feller, 1954; Feller and Feist, 1957; Hausberger *et al.*, 1954; Shapiro and Wertheimer, 1948).

Studies on hormonal regulation of lipid synthesis originally concerned the effects of insulin on the process, particularly the effects of diabetes on hepatic lipogenesis. Among the first implications of a role for glucocorticoids in the regulation of lipid metabolism was the work of Brady *et al.* (1951; Gurin and Brady, 1953), who observed that the impaired lipogenesis slices from depancreatized cats was correctable by adrenalectomy or hypophysectomy prior to preparation of the slices. Incorporation of acetate-^{14}C into liver slices from rats treated with cortisol (daily injection for 3 days prior to sacrifice) was inhibited up to 70%. Glucocorticoids cause inhibition of lipogenesis *in vivo* in other systems as well (Ashmore *et al.*, 1958; Munck, 1962; Munck and Koritz, 1962; Welt and Wilhelmi, 1950).

A large body of data on the action of glucocorticoids on lipogenesis has come from *in vitro* studies with adipose tissue. The adipose preparation is one of the few *in vitro* systems which shows hormonal effects. The earliest study in this system comes from Renold's laboratory (Jeanrenaud and Renold, 1960), where it was shown that the addition of glucocorticoids (3–30 μg/ml) to adipose tissue preparations resulted in increased fatty acid mobilization. On more prolonged incubation of the tissue preparations, natural glucocorticoids (Jeanrenaud and Renold, 1960; Munck, 1962; Phillips *et al.*, 1965) and dexamethasone (Fain *et al.*, 1963) markedly inhibited glucose oxidation and metabolism, lipogenesis, and protein synthesis.

The existence of simultaneous inhibition of glucose metabolism and stimulation of free fatty acid mobilization by glucocorticoids led the Renold group to suggest that decreased fatty acid reesterification might be responsible for the increased mobilization of fatty acids, since esterification requires glycerophosphate which is derived from glucose and adipose tissue does not phosphorylate free glycerol. Dexamethasone and cortisol both stimulated free fatty acid production without affecting lipolysis (Jeanrenaud and Renold, 1965; Jeanrenaud, 1967), justifying this hypothesis. Consequently, physiological levels of glucocorticoids may act by decreasing carbohydrate availability either by modifying glucose transport or changing some intracellular step in glucose metabolism. The work of Blecher (1965) supports the idea of modification of glucose transport. Blecher showed that when adipose cells were treated with phospholipase c, which presumably disrupts the lipoprotein in the cell membrane, cortisol-like inhibitions of glucose metabolism occur. Furthermore, treatment with excess phospholipase c abolished the effect of the glucocorticoid (Blecher, 1965), indicating the requirement for an intact cell membrane.

Despite the fact that the mechanism of action of glucocorticoids in the process is still unknown, several other properties of the system which may be of interest have been described. First, the need for prolonged incubation of adipose cell preparation in order to show glucocorticoid effects on lipogenesis suggested that *de novo* synthesis of protein might be required as in other glucocorticoid effects. In support of this possibility, Fain *et al.* (1965) showed that puromycin and actinomycin D suppressed the effect of cortisol on lipogenesis. Finally, free corticosteroids are involved in the process, since the addition of enough transcortin (corticosteroid binding globulin) to bind added cortisol, cortisone or corticosterone abolished their effect (Blecher, 1966). Furthermore, when dexamethasone or prednisolone were used, amounts of transcortin sufficient to bind the native glucocorticoids completely did not bind the synthetic ones completely and did not completely inhibit the effect of these hormones.

C. Steroid-Mediated Porphyria

Another *in vivo* steroid effect of great interest is the induction of porphyria in chick embryo liver cultures. Although none of the primary hormonal steroids elicit this response (Granick and Kappas, 1967b), a number of compounds which have up to now been considered their waste or detoxication products (Granick and Kappas, 1967b; Williams, 1959) do so. Therefore, a new, although indirect, role for hormonal steroids via their metabolites in control of a metabolic process may be visualized.

Potent inducing steroids are etiocholanolone and pregnanediol. Their activities far exceed those of the most potent nonsteroid porphyric drugs and chemicals reported previously (Granick, 1963, 1965). Cholesterol, the bile acids, and C-21 hydroxylated steroids (i.e., aldosterone and cortisol) (Granick and Kappas, 1967b) are without activity, as are the other parent steroid hormones. Glucuronides of even the most potent inducers are totally devoid of porphyria producing activity. Since steroid inducers are effective in chick blastoderm erythroid cells as well as in liver (Granick and Kappas, 1967a,b), these compounds may control heme biosynthesis in all cells.

The structural requirements for the induction of porphyria by a steroid appear to be a 5β-hydrogen in an androstane or pregnane nucleus and hydroxyl or keto groups at positions 3, 7, 11, or 20 (Granick and Kappas, 1967a,b). Activity is markedly decreased by substituting a 5α-hydrogen even with appropriate oxygenated group (i.e., for etiocholanolone 5βH/5αH = 6:1). Hydroxylation of the 21 position completely abolishes activity.

Steroid induction of porphyria seems similar to the induction process evoked by other drugs (Granick, 1963, 1965, 1966), so that it is likely that the steroids act at the same cellular sites. The initial and rate limiting enzyme in heme biosynthesis is δ-aminolevulinate synthetase. It has been shown that nonsteroid chemicals which induce porphyria act by causing *de novo* synthesis of this enzyme (Granick and Urata, 1963). Actinomycin D and puromycin, inhibitors of mRNA and protein synthesis, respectively, prevent this synthesis and block the formation of porphyrins (Granick, 1966). These agents block the steroid-mediated porphyria (Granick and Kappas, 1967b; Kappas and Granick, 1968). The steroid effect is also blocked by UDPGA (Granick and Kappas, 1967b; Kappas and Granick, 1968), but no other component of the UDPG pathway. Consequently, glucuronidation of the steroid by UDPG transferase is likely and is supported by the presence of the enzyme in liver (Dutton and Ko, 1966). Further support for the idea that steroid and nonsteroid inductions act at the same sites comes from the observation (Kappas and Granick, 1968) that suboptimal mixed doses give additive effects, while optimal mixed doses give no change in the amount and time course of induction.

Certain metalloporphyrins have been shown to inhibit the hepatic porphyria induced by nonsteroid chemicals such as allylisopropylacetamide (Granick, 1966). These compounds were found to have a similar effect on the steroid inductions (Kappas and Granick, 1968), supporting the conclusion that steroid and nonsteroid inductions of porphyria act by the same mechanism.

Granick *et al.* have proposed a mechanism for the steroid effect (Kappas and Granick, 1968) (Fig. 8). Control of porphyrin and heme synthesis in liver is thought to reside in a repressor–operator mechanism which regulates the activity of the structural gene (G_1), which codes for the rate-limiting ALA synthetase (E_1). All of the other enzymes ($E_2 \rightarrow E_7$) in the chain are present in excess. The repressor consists of an aporepressor to which a co-repressor (heme), the end product of the pathway, is bound. It is inactivated by inducers (i.e., steroids) which compete with heme for aporepressor protein. Inactivation leads to derepression of G_1 and *de novo* synthesis of the rate-limiting ALA synthetase and thus production of excess heme. As also shown, the conversion of steroids to inactive glucuronides turns off the steroid effect.

In conclusion, it must be noted that although steroids cause the same effect on intact chick embryo livers (Kappas *et al.*, 1968) as in tissue culture, no such effect has been as yet shown in rat or guinea pig liver. However, in both species the effect is readily induced by foreign chemicals of other classes (Granick and Urata, 1963; Marver *et al.*, 1966). The relative unresponsiveness of these animals to steroid induction appears, according to Granick (Kappas *et al.*, 1968), to denote the existence of additional mechanisms for control which may be particular to animal

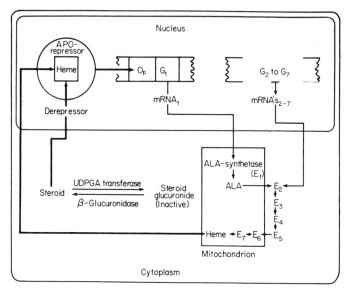

Fɪɢ. 8. Scheme of a proposed mechanism for steroid control of porphyrin and heme biosynthesis. None of the positions of the genes in the genome is known. This scheme is presented as a working hypothesis. UDPGA = uridine diphosphate glucuronic acid. [From Kappas and Granick (1968).]

cells (i.e., glucuronide formation). The opposite case has been found in chick blastoderm erthroid cells where steroids work but not other chemicals.

D. Alkaline Phosphatase

The alkaline phosphatase activity of a number of mammalian tissues has been shown to increase following the *in vivo* administration of glucocorticoids (Chieffi and Carfagna, 1960; Moog, 1952; Valentine *et al.*, 1954). The most extensively studied glucocorticoid-mediated increase in this enzyme is found in human tissue culture and was first described by Cox and MacLeod (1961) for HeLa cells. Prednisolone (0.5 μg/ml) added to tissue cultures caused a five- to twentyfold increase in alkaline phosphatase activity in some cell lines. Of all the hormones tested, only those with glucocorticoid activity were effective (Melnykouych, 1962; Nitowsky *et al.*, 1962). The stimulating effect appears to be specific for alkaline phosphatase, since the activities of a number of other enzymes including acid phosphatase (Cox and MacLeod, 1961, 1962, 1964) remain unchanged.

There is a slow doubling of alkaline phosphatase activity in a 24 hour period followed by a rapid linear increase of up to fifteenfold in the next 48 hours. The increase in enzyme activity could be explained by an increase in synthesis or by a decrease in degradation or a conformational change in the enzyme leading to increased activity of individual enzyme molecules. Several lines of evidence support the latter mechanism. M. J. Griffin and Cox (1966b) showed that the administration of a pulse of leucine-^{14}C had no effect on the total and specific radioactivity of partially purified alkaline phosphatase from control and prednisolone-treated HeLa S_3 cultures, although the hormone increased the enzyme activity sixfold. This observation is strengthened by immunochemical studies which show that the total and specific radioactivity of the antibody–enzyme complex is the same for control and induced cultures. Furthermore, the induced enzyme is much more labile at 64.5°C and has an initial velocity five times as great as the basal enzyme. Nitowsky and Herz (1963; Herz and Nitowsky, 1962) have shown, in liver cell culture, that the basal enzyme exists in heat stable and heat labile forms. The addition of prednisolone to liver tissue cultures causes an increase in the heat stable form of the enzyme.

Although these data suggest that enzyme activation may be involved in the hormone effect, it must be remembered that alkaline phosphatase is a heterogeneous enzyme consisting of several isozymes (M. J. Griffin and Cox, 1966b). If one of these isozymes had the properties of the induced enzyme and was produced at the expense of the other, *de novo* enzyme synthesis might pass unnoticed. This possibility is suggested by the observation that the prednisolone-mediated induction by alkaline phosphatase in HeLa cells (M. J. Griffin and Cox, 1966a) is blocked by the addition of puromycin at any time after prednisolone. There also appears to be an initial dependence of the effect on RNA synthesis, since the simultaneous addition of actinomycin D with prednisolone also blocks the effect. Although the effect may be due to a conformational change in the enzyme resulting in activation, the possibility that it is solely due to *de novo* protein synthesis has not been excluded.

E. RETINAL GLUTAMINE SYNTHETASE

Several laboratories have demonstrated that the glutamine synthetase activity of chick neural retina develops in a characteristic fashion that is coincident with a number of other aspects of retinal differentiation (Moscona and Hubby, 1963; Piddington and Moscona, 1965; Rudnick and Waelsch, 1955). The retinal enzyme is negligible at first and increases slowly until the sixteenth or seventeenth day *in ovo,* when it rises dramatically in close coincidence with the final maturation of the retina (Piddington and Moscona, 1965). The rise in glutamine synthetase activity can be obtained precociously if retinas are cultured *in vitro* in media containing adult, but not fetal serum (Kirk and Moscona, 1963; Moscona and Hubby, 1963; Moscona and Kirk, 1965; Reif and Amos, 1965).

Reif and Amos (1966) showed that an inducer was present in adult serum that was depleted during the *in vitro* induction process. When fresh adult serum was dialyzed and the dialyzate was added to fetal serum, this supplemented serum was capable of supporting the induction of glutamine synthetase. Moscona and Piddington (1966) and Reif-Lehrer and Amos (1968) showed that the injection of cortisol *in situ* or the addition of cortisol to fetal serum cultures allowed the induction to occur, suggesting that the hormone or some metabolite was the active inducing agent (cell proliferation was negligible in this experiment). A number of other related 11-hydroxy steroid hormones also induce *in vitro* or *in vivo* (Moscona and Piddington, 1967). In studies with embryos and with *in vitro* retinal cultures, Piddington and Moscona (1968) showed that the response of cortisol occurred when the hormone was added from day 7 on, but that the maximal response did not occur until day 10. These experiments show that the ability to respond to cortisol is present *in ovo* and *in vitro* long before the normal ontogenic response occurs, but that this inducibility increases with embryonic age. Furthermore, the *in vitro* response is maximized in much younger tissue than is the response *in vivo*.

The response of the retinal glutamine synthetase system to cortisol has been shown to be dependent on RNA and protein synthesis (Reif-Lehrer, 1968; Moscona *et al.,* 1968; Piddington and Moscona, 1968) in a fashion similar to other cortisol-mediated enzyme inductions and to the developmental rise of the enzyme during maturation (Kirk, 1965; Moscona and Hubby, 1963). Administration of cortisol and puromycin or cycloheximide (Moscona *et al.,* 1968; Reif-Lehrer and Amos, 1968), inhibitors of protein synthesis, prevented the appearance of the enzyme, and removal of these inhibitors allowed the induction to proceed. Work with cycloheximide allowed Moscona *et al.* (1968) to estimate a half-life of about 20 hours for the retinal glutamine synthetase.

Actinomycin D, like puromycin, completely prevented retinal glutamine synthetase induction when given together with cortisol (Moscona *et al.,* 1968; Reif-Lehrer and Amos, 1968). However, when it was given several hours after cortisol, it had no effect (Moscona *et al.,* 1968; Reif-Lehrer and Amos, 1968). A stable mRNA for glutamine synthetase made early in the sequence of events after cortisol administration could explain the lack of a requirement for RNA synthesis except early in the induction.

All the studies of the retinal glutamine synthetase system have not explained whether the increase in glutamine synthetase activity was due to *de novo* enzyme synthesis or to activation or assembly of precursors. Immunochemical studies (Alescio and Moscona, 1969) have shown that the effect is primarily due to *de novo* enzyme synthesis. Furthermore, it has been suggested that the rise in the enzyme due to cortisol is the result of an increase in synthesis relative to degradation (Alescio and Moscona, 1969).

A final facet of the retinal glutamine synthetase system that should not be ignored is the observation of Reif-Lehrer (1968). When retinas are cultured for extended periods (8–9 days) in fetal serum, they develop fairly high glutamine synthetase levels and are less sensitive to the addition of cortisol than would be expected. Reif-Lehrer observes that the loss of effectiveness of cortisol and the endogenous rise of enzyme activity in culture appear at the time the rise normally occurs *in ovo* (where total days equal the age of explant and days in culture). It is tempting to speculate as Reif-Lehrer did (1968) that the events leading to glutamine synthetase induction are preprogrammed, and that cortisol merely accelerates the process. However, a number of other possibilities for the endogenous rise should not be minimized. These are nonspecific loss of control mechanism due to prolonged culture time, *in vitro* conversion of inactive steroid molecules to inducers, and changes in degradation of the enzyme relative to its synthesis.

V. ON THE POSSIBLE ORIGIN OF THE HALF-LIVES OF CERTAIN COMPLEX ENZYMES AND ITS RELATIONSHIP TO STEROID INDUCTION

The specificity of the effects of glucocorticoids in the liver cell appears to involve cytosol enzymes with a short half-life, such as tyrosine aminotransferase and tryptophan pyrrolase. It would be useful to understand the properties of enzymes, which predispose a short half-life, as opposed to proteins that turn over at a much slower rate. In a review of this area of research it occurred to us that the short half-life may be an attribute of enzymes containing dissociable cofactors. This hypothesis is based on the assumption that the degradation of certain complex enzymes results from the discharge of the coenzyme producing a change in configuration to render the apoenzyme susceptible to proteolysis. In fact, it is tempting to suggest that enzyme degradation may occur via packaging of "susceptible enzyme conformers," perhaps a result of chain opening and aggregation and subsequent breakdown by and transfer to the lysosome. This viewpoint necessitates the assumption that protein degradation may occur at greater rates than the breakdown of the specific mRNA and therefore could represent the process limiting the rate of synthesis of a given protein. Presently, of course, it is not practical to suggest that this condition is really the true state of affairs. However, recent evidence of Levitan and Webb (1970) indicates, in the case of tyrosine aminotransferase induction in rat liver, that during the accumulation phase of enzymatic activity (up to 4 hours after corticosteroid treatment) enzyme degradation is turned off. This would fortify our assumption that degradation may control synthesis. Whether the control point of degradation, however, is change of protein conformation rendering it susceptible to breakdown, or the destruction of specific mRNA (Tomkins et al., 1969), or both processes, is unknown.

The work of several laboratories (Kenney, 1967; Grossman and Mavrides, 1967; Levitan and Webb, 1970) is consistent with the hypothesis that the degradation of tyrosine aminotransferase requires the continued synthesis of an enzyme of short half-life, presumably the degrading enzyme for tyrosine aminotransferase. Either the degrading enzyme is itself induced by steroid after the transaminase (its half-life or that of its mRNA would have to be longer than those of the transaminase) or the inducer of degrading enzyme could be a product of the steroid induction; the latter speculation is consistent with the possibility that aggregated transaminase apoenzyme (after dissociation of cofactor) could be the signal for synthesis of degrading enzyme or for transport to the site of degradation. In this connection, Hershko and Tomkins (1971) proposed that ATP participates in an early phase of enzyme degradation.

In Table IV, data are presented for a few enzymes which have been studied with regard to coenzyme dissociability, half-life, and steroid inducibility. From this limited list, there seems to be a correlation between properties of dissociability of coenzyme, short half-life, and inducibility by steroids. For example, steroid-inducible tyrosine aminotransferase, having a half-life of about 2 hours, contains a readily dissociable coenzyme (Diamondstone and Litwack, 1963; Litwack and Cleland, 1968). Tryptophan pyrrolase, with a short half-life of 2–2½ hours, is readily inducible and also has a rather freely dissociable coenzyme (Knox and Piras, 1967; Piras and Knox, 1967). On the other hand, complex enzymes, such as aspartate aminotransferase (Ogawa et

TABLE IV

Possible Relationships between Complex Enzyme Half-Life, Coenzyme Dissociability, and Glucocorticoid Induction

Enzyme	Rapidly inducible	Half-life (days)	Dissociability of coenzyme
Tyrosine aminotransferase	Yes	0.08[a]	Yes (PLP)[b]
Tryptophan pyrrolase	Yes	0.10[c]	Yes (hematin)[d]
Alanine aminotransferase	No	3–3.5[e]	No
Aspartate aminotransferase	No	11[f]	No

[a] See Kenney (1970).
[b] See Litwack and Cleland (1968); Rosenberg and Litwack (1970).
[c] See Schimke and Doyle (1970).
[d] See Knox and Piras (1967); Piras and Knox (1967).
[e] See Segal and Kim (1963); Kim (1969).
[f] See Ogawa *et al.* (1968).

al., 1968) and alanine aminotransferase (Segal and Kim, 1963; Kim, 1969), have much longer half-lives (Table IV) and are poorly inducible by glucocorticoids in early time periods; coincidentally, these less responsive enzymes have relatively tightly bound cofactors.

Admittedly, it is not yet clear whether the ease of dissociation of cofactor observed with the purified enzyme is a process which is operative to a significant extent in the cell. If this model is applicable to the cell, however, it could be predicted that any other substance capable of diminishing the dissociation of a coenzyme from the holoenzyme should mimic the action of the inducing steroid. In studies with tyrosine aminotransferase by Singer and Mason (1965, 1967a), various aromatic anions have been shown to act like steroids *in vivo* in adrenalectomized animals. From *in vitro* experiments, these authors (Singer and Mason, 1967b) deduced the actions of the anions to be the stabilization of the enzyme by preventing the coenzyme, pyridoxal-P, from dissociating. Interestingly, this type of induction was sensitive to inhibitors of protein synthesis suggestive of mass action effects (see below). The wide variation in the structures of compounds producing this effect suggest that stabilization of the cofactor can be accomplished in different ways. Among these is the possibility of producing conformers of the cytosol enzyme.

J. E. Miller and Litwack (1969a), using the ability of the basal or induced enzyme to metabolize tyrosine compared to monoiodotyrosine, gave support to the idea of physically different forms of tyrosine transaminase. Extension of such a hypothesis leads to the possibility that the conformeric pool of the enzyme would be in equilibrium with the

uninduced precursor enzyme. If the conformeric pool is newly established as a result of flooding the cytosol with a foreign compound of
the type mentioned above, the equilibrium would be displaced in favor
of converting the precursor to the conformeric form. The diversion of
the end product of protein synthesis to a new pool might then activate
the processes of translation and transcription from mass action changes
(end product removal), thus accounting for the sensitivity of induction
of tyrosine aminotransferase by aromatic anionic compounds to inhibitors
or protein synthesis (Singer and Mason, 1965).

In the context of mass action effects, it is worth mentioning the
hypothesis of Stent (1964; Richardson, 1969), who has suggested that
most, if not all, RNA synthesis may be controlled by a type of feedback
in which the rate of synthesis of an RNA species would depend upon
its rate of utilization. In this model, something would be necessary
to pull the RNA product away from the complex of RNA polymerase
and DNA for the RNA to be synthesized efficiently. In particular, a
feature of this speculation would be a close coupling of the rate of RNA
production to the rate of protein synthesis, thereby explaining the results
of all experiments in which the level of RNA from a particular gene
reflects the rate of synthesis of the protein encoded by the gene. Although these ideas relate mainly to bacterial systems, superimposition
on mammalian systems could lead to a consideration of the breakdown
of the protein itself as being the rate-controlling step in its synthesis.
This is especially attractive in view of information suggesting that
mRNAs of inducible enzymes of mammalian liver have much greater
turnover rates than was thought previously. In the case of tyrosine
aminotransferase, recent studies by Kenney (1970) suggest the half-life
of its mRNA is close to the value for the half-life of the enzyme.

With regard to different forms of cytosol tyrosine aminotransferase,
interesting studies have been reported by Oliver and his co-workers
(Holt and Oliver, 1969). They have shown that the enzyme responsive
to hormones mediated by cyclic AMP migrates differently in disk gel
electrophoresis than tyrosine aminotransferase activity stimulated by cortisol in newborn liver cytosol. One form was induced by the steroid and
migrated to a different position than the form induced by glucagon or
epinephrine. A third form appeared to be partially resolved from the
other two and responsive to the action of insulin in both fetal and newborn liver cytosols. In the case of fetal animals, the corticosteroid-
inducible form did not appear, nor was cortisol active in induction until
after birth (Litwack and Nemeth, 1965; Greengard and Dewey, 1967;
O. Greengard, Vol I of this treatise), although this hormone could induce
premature glycogen deposition in fetal liver (Greengard and Dewey,
1970). The interpretation of this work might be that different genes

exist for the same enzymes in cytosol. Each phenotypic product would differ significantly in charge to permit separation upon disk gel electrophoresis. Furthermore, each gene would be derepressed by a specific hormonal inducer; one gene being activated by glucagon, epinephrine, or cyclic AMP; another gene being activated by insulin; and a third by corticosteroids. In the fetal liver, a mitochondrial tyrosine aminotransferase accounts for the majority of the enzymatic activity during development (Fellman *et al.*, 1969; Koler *et al.*, 1969). In our unpublished studies, it is clear that in fetuses injected with glucagon according to the technique used by Greengard and Dewey (1967), cytosol enzyme was induced which was not derived by solubilization from the mitochondrial fraction. Since the mitochondrial enzyme,[2] in contrast to the cytosol enzyme, uses oxaloacetate (J. E. Miller and Litwack, 1969a), the activities of each form could be measured directly. It would be helpful to demonstrate multiple forms of the cytoplasmic enzyme by some technique in addition to polyacrylamide disk gel electrophoresis and to show differences in structure or kinetic properties. The question

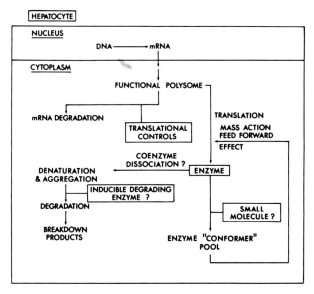

FIG. 9. Diagrammatic speculation involving translational controls of enzyme synthesis and degradation using tyrosine aminotransferase as a model.

[2] In published experiments by J. E. Miller and Litwack (1971), it has been shown unequivocally that mitochondrial tyrosine aminotransferase is identical to mitochondrial aspartate aminotransferase; the mitochondrial aspartate aminotransferase thus differs from the soluble enzyme by having a broader amino acid specificity, which includes aromatic amino acids (see also J. E. Miller and Litwack, 1969b).

of whether the multiple forms observed by Oliver's group represent different gene products or different conformational forms of a single gene product remains for further work.

Superimposed on this situation is the possibility of segregation of effects at the cellular level. Thus, it must be considered whether tyrosine aminotransferase exists in and is capable of being stimulated in cell types other than the hepatocyte. Recent work, for example, suggests that adenyl cyclase of reticuloendothelial cells and parenchymal cells of liver have different sensitivities to glucagon and epinephrine (Reik *et al.*, 1970). However, experiments in our laboratory involving isolation of hepatocytes from fetal liver treated *in vivo* with glucagon tend to rule out this last possibility (Nakajima and Litwack, 1971). Some of the ideas and speculations considered in this section are summarized in Fig. 9.

VI. CONCLUSIONS

It is clear that the mechanism of corticosteroid action in liver is more complicated than, for example, sex hormone action on the appropriate target cell. This is because the liver is an important site of steroid metabolism in addition to being a *target* cell. Moreover, it is apparent that as a result of the presence of corticosteroid there may be set off several chains of causally related events occurring simultaneously in the hepatocyte, and these separate chains of events may or may not be interrelated. Separate events appear as glycogen synthesis and/or deposition, stimulation of enzymes in gluconeogenesis not mediated by protein synthesis, and stimulation of enzymes requiring protein synthesis. In spite of this phlethora of activities, a picture of corticosteroid actions on the hepatocyte is beginning to emerge. The main rapid effects seem to be located in the cytosol, and the cell membrane seems, so far, not to be an important binding site. In the cytosol, there are at least four protein fractions which bind either corticosteroid metabolites, the unchanged hormone, or both. Two of these have been isolated and characterized. The possibility exists that one is either involved as a concentrating mechanism or it may be a part of an enzyme— perhaps a steroid sulfotransferase, although there is no solid evidence to support this suggestion. The other protein is of a low molecular weight and may, in the native state, be bound to another macromolecule. A third protein, which occurs in much lower concentrations than the other two, has the characteristics expected of a hormone receptor. There appear to be conformational changes involved in its binding to corticosteroids, and unfortunately, the corticosteroid is released from the bound state fairly easily and, so far as we know at present, it has not been possible to rebind this macromolecule with the corticosteroid. Almost nothing is known about the fourth protein except that it binds antiglucocorticoid agents and on this basis may function as an inhibitor.

Corticosteroid action in the thymus gland is somewhat less complicated than in the liver cell. Although much of the work on receptors is just beginning to emerge, it appears that there is a nuclear receptor(s) as well as a cytosol receptor. Undoubtedly the two are related; possibly the cytosol protein transfers the steroid to the nucleus, or as an alternative, each macromolecule functions independently in its own compartment. Many observations on RNA synthesis and protein synthesis indicate simultaneous changes in these processes and favor the latter alternative of separate functions. Fluorocorticosteroids are very active in producing the corticosteroid effects upon the thymocyte, yet these compounds do not bind to all supernatant fractions and this fraction may represent a surface factor distinct from cytosol and nuclear receptors.

The connection between receptor sites for corticosteroids and their effects on protein synthesis remains tenuous. It is hoped that extension of the work on cellular receptors will lead to the explanation of this relationship at the molecular level. One of the important new observations is that the mRNA's for certain rapidly turning over enzymes turn over themselves as rapidly as the proteins they translate. This throws a completely new light onto the question of the significance of susceptibility of a process to inhibitors of translation or transcription and favors the idea that our knowledge will proceed more directly through extending the work on the molecular fates of hormonal inducers than by the use of inhibitors of RNA or protein synthesis.

Corticosteroids promote glycogen deposition, a function that seems to be separate from the effects discussed above. Glycogen synthesis and deposition represent very complicated processes, and corticosteroids probably control a large part of the action of these processes upon glycogen formation by effects upon the glycogen synthetase system. Elaboration of this phenomenon may enlarge our understanding of the way in which corticosteroids can interact with catalytic proteins.

ACKNOWLEDGMENTS

Research carried out in the authors' laboratory is supported by research grants AM-08350 and AM-13531 from the National Institute of Arthritis and Metabolic Diseases, by CA-10439 from the National Cancer Institute, and by GB-8784 from the National Science Foundation.

REFERENCES

Adams, J. B., and Chulavatnatol, M. (1967). *Biochim. Biophys. Acta* **146**, 509.

Alescio, T., and Moscona, A. A. (1969). *Biochem. Biophys. Res. Commun.* **34**, 176.

Allfrey, V. G., and Mirsky, A. E. (1962). *Proc. Natl. Acad. Sci. U. S.* **48**, 1590.

Ambellan, E., and Roth, J. S. (1967). *Biochem. Biophys. Res. Commun.* **28**, 244.

Ashmore, J., Cahill, G. F., Jr., Hillman, R., and Renold, A. E. (1958). *Endocrinology* **62**, 621.

Barnebei, O., Romano, B., and DiBitonto, J. (1965). *Arch. Biochem. Biophys.* **109**, 266.

Barry, E. J., Malejka-Giganti, D., and Gutmann, H. R. (1969). *Chem.-Biol. Interact.* **1**, 139.

Bartlett, D., Morita, Y., and Munck, A. (1962). *Nature* **196**, 897.

Baxter, J. D., and Tomkins, G. M. (1970). *Proc. Natl. Acad. Sci. U. S.* **65**, 709.

Beato, M., Homoki, J., and Sekeris, C. E. (1969). *Exptl. Cell Res.* **55**, 107.

Beato, M., Braendle, W., Biesewig, D., and Sekeris, C. E. (1970a). *Biochim. Biophys. Acta* **208**, 125.

Beato, M., Schmid, W., Braendle, W., and Sekeris, C. E. (1970b). *Steroids* **16**, 207.

Bellamy, D. (1963). *Biochem. J.* **87**, 334.

Bellamy, D., Phillips, J. G., Jones, I. E., and Leonard, R. A. (1962). *Biochem. J.* **85**, 537.

Blecher, M. (1964). *J. Biol. Chem.* **239**, 1299.

Blecher, M. (1965). *Biochem. Biophys. Res. Commun.* **121**, 202.

Blecher, M. (1966). *Endocrinology* **79**, 541.

Blecher, M., and White, A. (1960a). *J. Biol. Chem.* **235**, 3404.

Blecher, M., and White, A. (1960b). *Biochem. Biophys. Res. Commun.* **3**, 471.

Bottoms, G., and Goetsch, D. D. (1967). *Proc. Soc. Exptl. Biol. Med.* **124**, 662.

Bradlow, H. L., Dobriner, K., and Gallagher, T. F. (1954). *Endocrinology* **54**, 343.

Breckenridge, B. M., and Crawford, E. J. (1960). *J. Biol. Chem.* **235**, 3054.

Bresnick, E., Liebelt, R. A., Stevenson, J. G., and Madix, J. C. (1967). *Cancer Res.* **27**, 462.

Brunkhorst, W. K. (1966). *Biochim. Biophys. Acta* **130**, 553.

Brunkhorst, W. K. (1968). *Endocrinology* **82**, 277.

Brunkhorst, W. K. (1969a). *Biochem. Biophys. Res. Commun.* **6**, 880.

Brunkhorst, W. K. (1969b). *Biochem. Biophys. Res. Commun.* **35**, 880.

Brunkhorst, W. K., and Hess, E. L. (1964). *Biochim. Biophys. Acta* **82**, 385.

Cammarano, P., Chinali, G., Gaetani, S., and Spadoni, M. A. (1968). *Biochim. Biophys. Acta* **155**, 302.

Chance, B., and Hollunger, G. (1963). *J. Biol. Chem.* **238**, 418.

Chieffi, G., and Carfagna, M. (1960). *Acta Embryol. Morphol. Exptl.* **3**, 213.

Cohen, P., Chin, R-C., and Kidson, C. (1969). *Biochemistry* **8**, 3603.

Cox, R. P., and MacLeod, C. M. (1961). *Nature* **190**, 85.

Cox, R. P., and MacLeod, C. M. (1962). *J. Gen. Physiol.* **45**, 439.

Cox, R. P., and MacLeod, C. M. (1964). *Cold Spring Harbor Symp. Quant. Biol.* **19**, 233.

Dahmus, M. E., and Bonner, J. (1965). *Proc. Natl. Acad. Sci. U. S.* **54**, 1370.

DeLange, R. J., Fambrough, D. H., Smith, E. L., and Bonner, J. (1969). *J. Biol. Chem.* **244**, 319.

DeVenuto, F., and Chader, G. (1966). *Biochim. Biophys. Acta* **121**, 151.

DeVenuto, F., and Muldoon, T. (1968). *Exptl. Cell Res.* **50**, 338.

DeVenuto, F., and Westphal, U. (1965). *Arch. Biochem. Biophys.* **112**, 187.

DeVenuto, F., Kelleher, P. C., and Westphal, U. (1962). *Biochim. Biophys. Acta* **63**, 434.

DeWulf, H., and Hers, H. G. (1968a). *European J. Biol. Chem.* **6**, 552.

DeWulf, H., and Hers, H. G. (1968b). *European J. Biochem.* **6**, 558.

DeWulf, H., Stalmans, W., and Hers, H. G. (1968). *European J. Biol. Chem.* **6**, 545.

DeWulf, H., Stalmans, W., and Hers, H. G. (1970). *European J. Biochem.* **15**, 1.

Diamondstone, T. I., and Litwack, G. (1963). *J. Biol. Chem.* **238**, 3459.

Dingman, C. W., and Sporn, M. B. (1965). *Science* **149**, 1251.

Dougherty, T. F., and White, A. (1944). *Endocrinology* **37**, 1.

Dougherty, T. F., and White, A. (1945). *Am. J. Anat.* **77**, 81.

Drews, J. (1969). *European J. Biochem.* **7**, 200.

Dukes, P. P., Sekeris, C. E., and Schmid, W. (1966). *Biochim. Biophys. Acta* **123**, 126.

Dutton, G. J., and Ko, V. (1966). *Biochem. J.* **99**, 550.

Engel, L. L. (1961). *In* "Mechanism of Action of Steroid Hormone" (C. A. Villee and L. L. Engel, eds.), pp. 85 and 107. Pergamon Press, Oxford.

Eurenius, K., Dalton, T. V., Lokey, H. J., and McIntyre, O. R. (1969). *Biochim. Biophys. Acta* **177**, 572.

Fain, J. N., Scow, R. O., and Chernick, S. S. (1963). *J. Biol. Chem.* **238**, 54.

Fain, J. N., Kovacev, V. P., and Scow, R. O. (1965). *J. Biol. Chem.* **240**, 3522.

Fanestil, D. D., and Edelman, I. S. (1966). *Proc. Natl. Acad. Sci. U. S.* **56**, 872.

Feigelson, P., and Feigelson, M. (1964). *In* "Actions of Hormones on Molecular Processes" (G. Litwack and D. Kritchevsky, eds.), p. 218. Wiley, New York.

Feller, D. D. (1954). *J. Biol. Chem.* **206**, 171.

Feller, D. D., and Feist, E. (1957). *J. Biol. Chem.* **228**, 275.

Fellman, J. H., Van Bellinghen, P. J., Jones, R. T., and Koler, R. D. (1969). *Biochemistry* **8**, 615.

Fiala, E. S., and Litwack, G. (1966). *Biochim. Biophys. Acta* **124**, 260.

Filler, R., Morey, K. S., and Litwack, G. (1971). Unpublished data.

Finkel, R. M., Henshaw, E. C., and Hiatt, H. H. (1966). *Mol. Pharmacol.* **2**, 221.

Fox, K. E., and Gabourel, J. D. (1967). *Mol. Pharmacol.* **3**, 479.

Friedman, D. L., and Larner, J. (1963). *Biochemistry* **2**, 669.

Furfine, C. S., and White, A. (1968). *J. Biol. Chem.* **243**, 1190.

Gabourel, J. D., and Fox, K. E. (1965). *Biochem. Biophys. Res. Commun.* **18**, 81.

Gallagher, C. H. (1960). *Biochem. J.* **74**, 38.

Gardner, R. S., and Tomkins, G. M. (1969). *J. Biol. Chem.* **244**, 4761.

Gelehrter, T. D., and Tomkins, G. M. (1967). *J. Mol. Biol.* **29**, 59.

Gold, A. H., and Segal, H. L. (1966). *Mol. Pharmacol.* **2**, 84.

Gold, A. H., and Segal, H. L. (1967). *Arch. Biochem. Biophys.* **120**, 359.

Goldberg, M. L., and Atchley, W. A. (1966). *Proc. Natl. Acad. Sci. U. S.* **55**, 989.

Granick, S. (1963). *J. Biol. Chem.* **238**, 2247.

Granick, S. (1965). *Ann. N. Y. Acad. Sci.* **123**, 188.

Granick, S. (1966). *J. Biol. Chem.* **241**, 1359.

Granick, S., and Kappas, A. (1967a). *J. Biol. Chem.* **242**, 4587.

Granick, S., and Kappas, A. (1967b). *Proc. Natl. Acad. Sci. U. S.* **57**, 1463.

Granick, S., and Urata, G. (1963). *J. Biol. Chem.* **238**, 821.

Granner, D., Chase, L. R., Aurbach, G. D., and Tomkins, G. M. (1968). *Science* **162**, 1018.

Greengard, O., and Dewey, H. K. (1967). *J. Biol. Chem.* **242**, 2986.

Greengard, O., and Dewey, H. K. (1970). *Develop. Biol.* **21**, 452.

Griffin, A. C., Rinfret, A. P., and Corsigilia, V. F. (1953). *Cancer Res.* **13**, 77.

Griffin, M. J., and Cox, R. P. (1966a). *J. Cell Biol.* **29**, 1.

Griffin, M. J., and Cox, R. P. (1966b). *Proc. Natl. Acad. Sci. U. S.* **56**, 946.

Grossman, A., and Mavrides, C. (1967). *J. Biol. Chem.* **242**, 1398.

Gurin, S., and Brady, R. O. (1953). *Recent Progr. Hormone Res.* **8**, 571.

Gustafsson, R. G., and Afzelius, B. A. (1963). *J. Natl. Cancer Inst.* **30**, 1045.

Hackney, J. F., Gross, S. R., Aronow, L., and Pratt, W. B. (1970). *Mol. Pharmacol.* **6**, 500.

Hausberger, F. X., Milstein, S. W., and Rutman, R. J. (1954). *J. Biol. Chem.* **208**, 431.

Herman, T. S., Finognari, G. M., and Edelman, I. S. (1968). *J. Biol. Chem.* **243**, 3849.

Herranen, A., and Brunkhorst, W. K. (1967). *Arch. Biochem. Biophys.* **119**, 353.

Hers, H. G., DeWulf, H., and Stalmans, W. (1971). *FEBS Letters* **12**, 73.

Hershko, A., and Tomkins, G. M. (1971). *J. Biol. Chem.* **246**, 710.

Herz, F., and Nitowsky, H. M. (1962). *Arch. Biochem. Biophys.* **96**, 506.

Hey-Ferguson, A., and Bresnick, E. (1971). *Mol. Pharmacol.* **7**, 183.

Hizukuri, S., and Larner, J. (1964). *Biochemistry* **3**, 1783.

Hohmann, P., and Cole, R. D. (1969). *Nature* **223**, 1064.

Hollander, N., and Chiu, Y. W. (1966). *Biochem. Biophys. Res. Commun.* **35**, 291.

Holt, P. G., and Oliver, I. T. (1969). *FEBS Letters* **5**, 89.

Hornbrook, K. R., Burch, H. B., and Lowry, O. H. (1965). *Biochem. Biophys. Res. Commun.* **18**, 206.

Hornbrook, K. R., Burch, H. B., and Lowry, O. H. (1966). *Mol. Pharmacol.* **2**, 106.

Huang, R. C., and Bonner, J. (1962). *Proc. Natl. Acad. Sci. U. S.* **48**, 1216.

Jeanrenaud, B. (1967). *Biochem. J.* **103**, 107.

Jeanrenaud, B., and Renold, A. E. (1960). *J. Biol. Chem.* **235**, 2217.

Jeanrenaud, B., and Renold, A. E. (1965). *Federation Proc.* **24**, Part 1, 343.

Jensen, E. V., Suzuki, T., Kawashima, T., Stumpf, W. E., Jungblut, P. W., and DeSombre, E. R. (1968). *Proc. Natl. Acad. Sci. U. S.* **59**, 632.

Kaplan, J. H., and Pitot, H. C. (1970). *Mammalian Protein Metab.* **4**, 338.

Kappas, A., and Granick, S. (1968). *J. Biol. Chem.* **243**, 346.

Kappas, A., Song, C. S., Levere, R. D., Sachson, R. A., and Granick, S. (1968). *Proc. Natl. Acad. Sci. U. S.* **61**, 509.

Karlson, P. (1962). *Perspectives Biol. Med.* **6**, 203.

Kattwinkel, J., and Munck, A. (1966). *Endocrinology* **79**, 387.

Keats, C. J., Singer, S., and Litwack, G. (1970). Unpublished experiments.

Kenney, F. T. (1967). *Science* **156**, 525.

Kenney, F. T. (1970). *Mammalian Protein Metab.* **4**, 131.

Ketterer, B., Ross-Mansell, P., and Whitehead, J. K. (1967). *Biochem. J.* **103**, 316.

Ketterer, B., Beale, D., Litwack, G., and Hackney, J. F. (1971). *Chem.-Biol. Interact.* **3**, 285.

Kim, Y. S. (1969). *Mol. Pharmacol.* **5**, 105.

Kimberg, D. V., Loud, A. V., and Weiner, J. (1968). *J. Cell Biol.* **37**, 63.

Kirk, D. L. (1965). *Proc. Natl. Acad. Sci. U. S.* **54**, 1345.

Kirk, D. L., and Moscona, A. A. (1963). *Develop. Biol.* **8**, 341.

Knox, W. E., and Piras, M. M. (1967). *J. Biol. Chem.* **242**, 2959.

Knox, W. E., Auerbach, V. H., and Lin, E. C. C. (1964). *Physiol. Rev.* **36**, 164.

Koler, R. D., Van Bellinghen, P. J., Fellman, J. H., Jones, R. T., and Behrman, R. E. (1969). *Science* **163**, 1348.

Kwam, D. C., and Parks, R. E. (1960). *Am. J. Physiol.* **198**, 21.

Lang, N., Herrlich, P., and Sekeris, C. E. (1968). *Acta Endocrinol.* **57**, 33.

Larner, J., Villar-Palasi, C., and Richman, D. J. (1959). *Ann. N. Y. Acad. Sci.* **82**, 345.

Leloir, I. F., and Cardini, C. E. (1957). *J. Am. Chem. Soc.* **79**, 6340.

Leloir, L. F., and Goldemberg, S. H. (1960). *J. Biol. Chem.* **235**, 919.

Leloir, L. F., Olauarria, S. N., Goldemberg, S. H., and Carvinatti, H. (1959). *Arch. Biochem. Biophys.* **81**, 508.

Levitan, I. B., and Webb, T. E. (1969). *J. Biol. Chem.* **244**, 341.

Levitan, I. B., and Webb, T. E. (1970). *J. Mol. Biol.* **48**, 339.

Litwack, G. (1967). *In* "Topics in Medicinal Chemistry" (J. R. Rabinowitz and R. M. Myerson, eds.), Vol. I, p. 3. Wiley (Interscience), New York.

Litwack, G. (1971). Unpublished experiments.

Litwack, G., and Baserga, R. (1967). *Endocrinology* **80**, 774.

Litwack, G., and Cleland, W. W. (1968). *Biochemistry* **7**, 2072.

Litwack, G., and Morey, K. S. (1970). *Biochem. Biophys. Res. Commun.* **38**, 1141.

Litwack, G., and Nemeth, A. M. (1965). *Arch. Biochem. Biophys.* **109**, 316.

Litwack, G., Sears, M. L., and Diamondstone, T. I. (1963). *J. Biol. Chem.* **238**, 302.

Litwack, G., Fiala, E. S., and Filosa, R. J. (1965). *Biochim. Biophys. Acta* **111**, 569.

Litwack, G., Neuklis, J. C., Koch, P. A., Kennedy, C. A., Holland, C. A., and Weaver, R. C. (1971a). Unpublished experiments.

Litwack, G., Morey, K. S., and Ketterer, B. (1971b). *In* "Drugs and Cellular Control Mechanisms" (B. R. Rabin, ed.). MacMillan, London, in press.

Loeb, J. N., and Kimberg, D. V. (1970). *J. Cell Biol.* **46**, 17.

Long, C. N. H., Katzin, B., and Fry, E. G. (1940). *Endocrinology* **26**, 309.

Lotlikar, P. D., Enomoto, M., Miller, E. C., and Miller, J. A. (1964). *Cancer Res.* **24**, 1835.

Lukacs, I., and Sekeris, C. E. (1967). *Biochim. Biophys. Acta* **134**, 85.

Mainwaring, W. I. P. (1969). *J. Endocrinol.* **44**, 323.

Makman, M. H., Nakagawa, S., and White, A. (1967). *Recent Progr. Hormone Res.* **23**, 195.

Marver, H. S., Tschudy, D. P., Percoth, M. G., and Collins, A. (1966). *J. Biol. Chem.* **241**, 2803.

Maurer, H. R., and Chalkley, G. R. (1967). *J. Mol. Biol.* **27**, 431.

Mayewski, R. J., and Litwack, G. (1969). *Biochem. Biophys. Res. Commun.* **37**, 729.

Melnykouych, G. (1962). *Biochem. Biophys. Res. Commun.* **8**, 81.

Mersmann, H. J., and Segal, H. L. (1967). *Proc. Natl. Acad. Sci. U. S.* **58**, 1688.

Mersmann, H. J., and Segal, H. L. (1969). *J. Biol. Chem.* **244**, 1701.

Miller, E. C., and Miller, J. E. (1966). *Pharmacol. Rev.* **18**, 805.

Miller, J. E., and Litwack, G. (1969a). *Biochem. Biophys. Res. Commun.* **36**, 35.

Miller, J. E., and Litwack, G. (1969b). *Arch. Biochem. Biophys.* **134**, 149.

Miller, J. E., and Litwack, G. (1971). *J. Biol. Chem.* **426**, 3234.

Monder, C., and Walker, M. C. (1970). *Biochemistry* **9**, 2489.

Monder, C., and White, A. (1963). *J. Biol. Chem.* **238**, 767.

Moog, F. (1952). *Ann. N. Y. Acad. Sci.* **55**, 57.

Morey, K. S., and Litwack, G. (1969). *Biochemistry* **8**, 4813.

Morita, Y., and Munck, A. (1964). *Biochim. Biophys. Acta* **43**, 150.

Morris, D. J., and Barnes, F. W. (1967). *Biochim. Biophys. Acta* **136**, 67.

Morris, D. J., Sarma, M. H., and Barnes, F. W. (1970). *Endocrinology* **87**, 486.

Moscona, A. A., and Hubby, J. L. (1963). *Develop. Biol.* **7**, 192.

Moscona, A. A., and Kirk, D. L. (1965). *Science* **148**, 519.

Moscona, A. A., and Piddington, R. (1966). *Biochim. Biophys. Acta* **121**, 409.

Moscona, A. A., and Piddington, R. (1967). *Science* **158**, 496.

Moscona, A. A., Moscona, M. H., and Saenz, N. (1968). *Proc. Natl. Acad. Sci. U. S.* **61**, 160.

Munck, A. (1957). *Biochim. Biophys. Acta* **24**, 507.

Munck, A. (1962). *Biochim. Biophys. Acta* **57**, 318.

Munck, A. (1965). *Endocrinology* **77**, 356.

Munck, A. (1968). *J. Biol. Chem.* **243**, 1039.

Munck, A., and Brinck-Johnsen, T. (1967). *Proc. 2nd Intern. Congr. Hormonal Steroids, Milan, 1966 Excerpta Med. Intern. Congr. Ser.* No. 132, p. 472. Excerpta Med. Found., Amsterdam.

Munck, A., and Brinck-Johnsen, T. (1968). *J. Biol. Chem.* **243**, 5556.

Munck, A., and Koritz, S. B. (1962). *Biochim. Biophys. Acta* **57**, 310.

Nakajima, O., and Litwack, G. (1971). Unpublished experiments.

Nitowsky, H. M., and Herz, F. (1963). *Biochem. Biophys. Res. Commun.* **11**, 261.

Nitowsky, H. M., Herz, F., and Luha, L. (1962). *Federation Proc.* **21**, Part. 2, 161.

Ogawa, Y., Kometani, Y., and Baba, Y. (1968). *Chem. & Pharm. Bull. (Tokyo)* **16**, 1948.

Ohtsuka, E., and Koide, S. S. (1969). *Biochem. Biophys. Res. Commun.* **35**, 648.

Orrenius, S., and Ericsson, J. L. E. (1966). *J. Cell Biol.* **28**, 181.

Peña, A., Dvorkin, B., and White, A. (1966). *J. Biol. Chem.* **241**, 2144.

Perry, D. J. (1961). *Brit. J. Cancer* **15**, 284.

Phillips, G. R., Herrera, M. G., and Renold, A. E. (1965). *Biochim. Biophys. Acta* **106**, 234.

Piddington, R., and Moscona, A. A. (1965). *J. Cell Biol.* **27**, 247.

Piddington, R., and Moscona, A. A. (1968). *Biochim. Biophys. Acta* **141**, 429.

Piras, M. M., and Knox, W. E. (1967). *J. Biol. Chem.* **242**, 2952.

Rabin, B. R., *et al.* (1971). *In* "Drugs and Cellular Control Mechanisms" (B. R. Rabin, ed.). MacMillan, London. In Press.

Rancourt, M. W., and Litwack, G. (1968). *Exptl. Cell Res.* **51**, 413.

Ray, P. D., Foster, D. O., and Lardy, H. A. (1964a). *J. Biol. Chem.* **239**, 3396.

Ray, P. D., Foster, D. O., and Lardy, H. A. (1964b). *Federation Proc.* **23**, 482.

Reif, L., and Amos, H. (1965). *Abstr. 16th Ann. Meeting Tissue Cult. Assoc. 1965* Paper No. 46.

Reif, L., and Amos, H. (1966). *Biochem. Biophys. Res. Commun.* **23**, 39.

Reif-Lehrer, L. (1968). *Biochem. Biophys. Res. Commun.* **33**, 984.

Reif-Lehrer, L., and Amos, H. (1968). *Biochem. J.* **106**, 425.

Reik, L., Petzold, G. L., Higgins, J. A., Greengard, P., and Barnett, R. J. (1970). *Science* **168**, 382.

Reuber, M. D. (1963). *Federation Proc.* **23**, 315.

Richardson, J. P. (1969). *Progr. Nucleic Acid Res. Mol. Biol.* **9**, 75.

Robbins, P. W., Traut, R. R., and Lipmann, F. (1959). *Proc. Natl. Acad. Sci. U. S.* **45**, 6.

Robertson, C. H., O'Neal, M. A., Richardson, H. L., and Griffin, A. C. (1954). *Cancer Res.* **14**, 549.

Rosell-Perez, M., Villar-Palasi, C., and Larner, J. (1962). *Biochemistry* **1**, 763.

Rosenberg, J. S., and Litwack, G. (1970). *J. Biol. Chem.* **245**, 5677.

Rudnick, D., and Waelsch, H. (1955). *J. Exptl. Zool.* **129**, 309.

Samuels, H. H., and Tomkins, G. M. (1970). *J. Mol. Biol.* **52**, 57.

Sandberg, A. A., Slaunwhite, W. R., and Antoniades, H. N. (1957). *Recent Progr. Hormone Res.* **13**, 209.

Schaumburg, B. P., and Bojesen, E. (1968). *Biochim. Biophys. Acta* **170**, 172.

Schimke, R. T., and Doyle, D. (1970). *Ann. Rev. Biochem.* **30**, 929.

Schmid, W., Gallwitz, D., and Sekeris, C. E. (1967). *Biochim. Biophys. Acta* **134**, 80.

Segal, H. L., and Gonzales-Lopez, C. (1963). *Nature* **200**, 143.

Segal, H. L., and Kim, Y. S. (1963). *Proc. Natl. Acad. Sci. U. S.* **50**, 912.

Shapiro, B., and Wertheimer, E. (1948). *J. Biol. Chem.* **173**, 725.

Shelton, K. R., and Allfrey, V. G. (1970). *Nature* **228**, 132.

Singer, S., and Litwack, G. (1971). *Cancer Res.* **31**, 1364.

Singer, S., and Mason, M. (1965). *Biochim. Biophys. Acta* **110**, 370.

Singer, S., and Mason, M. (1967a). *Biochim. Biophys. Acta* **146**, 443.

Singer, S., and Mason, M. (1967b). *Biochim. Biophys. Acta* **146**, 452.

Singer, S., Morey, K. S., and Litwack, G. (1970a). *Physiol. Chem. & Phys.* **2**, 117.

Singer, S., Morey, K. S., and Litwack, G. (1970b). Unpublished experiments.

Sluyser, M. (1966a). *J. Mol. Biol.* **19**, 591.

Sluyser, M. (1966b). *J. Mol. Biol.* **22**, 411.

Sluyser, M. (1969). *Biochim. Biophys. Acta.* **182**, 235.

Stackhouse, H. L., Chetsanga, C. J., and Tan, C. H. (1968). *Biochim. Biophys. Acta* **155**, 159.

Stalmans, W., DeWulf, H., Lederer, B., and Hers, H. G. (1970). *European J. Biochem.* **15**, 9.

Steiner, D. F., and Williams, R. H. (1959). *J. Biol. Chem.* **234**, 1342.

Steiner, D. F., Rauda, U., and Williams, R. H. (1961). *J. Biol. Chem.* **236**, 299.

Stent, G. S. (1964). *Science* **144**, 816.

Stockdale, F. E., and Topper, Y. J. (1966). *Proc. Natl. Acad. Sci. U. S.* **56**, 1283.

Sunaga, K., and Koide, S. S. (1967a). *Arch. Biochem. Biophys.* **122**, 670.

Sunaga, K., and Koide, S. S. (1967b). *Steroids* **9**, 451.

Sunaga, K., and Koide, S. S. (1968). *J. Pharm. Sci.* **57**, 2116.

Symeonidis, A. (1963). *Acta Unio Intern. Contra Cancrum* **19**, 771.

Symeonidis, A., Mulay, A. S., and Burgoyne, F. H. (1954). *J. Natl. Cancer Inst.* **14**, 805.

Takahashi, K. (1968). *J. Biol. Chem.* **243**, 6171.

Tata, J. R. (1968). *Nature* **219**, 313.

Toft, D., Shyamala, G., and Gorski, J. (1967). *Proc. Natl. Acad. Sci. U. S.* **57**, 1740.

Tomkins, G. M., Gelehrter, T. D., Granner, D., Martin, D., Samuels, H. H., and Thompson, E. B. (1969). *Science* **166**, 1474.

Trémolières, J., Derache, R., and Griffaton, G. (1954). *Ann. Endocrinol.* **15**, 694.

Valentine, W. N., Follette, J. H., Hardin, E. B., Beck, W. S., and Lawrence, J. S. (1954). *J. Lab. Clin. Med.* **44**, 219.

Villar-Palasi, C., and Larner, J. (1958). *Biochim. Biophys. Acta* **30**, 449.

Weiner, J., Loud, A. V., Kimberg, D. V., and Spiro, D. (1968). *J. Cell Biol.* **37**, 47.

Welt, I. D., and Wilhelmi, A. E. (1950). *Yale J. Biol. Med.* **23**, 99.

Williams, R. T. (1959). "Detoxication Mechanisms," Vol. II, Wiley, New York.

Wira, C., and Munck, A. (1970). *J. Biol. Chem.* **245**, 3436.

CHAPTER 6

Insulin Actions on Carbohydrate and Lipid Metabolism

Irving B. Fritz

I. INTRODUCTION

In today's mechanized world, it is, alas, all too easy to accumulate an exhaustive list of articles pertaining to almost anything. This is especially true for insulin. Since I have no desire to compete with computerized bibliographies in printing out compilations of references, an alternate approach has been sought, even if it should prove somewhat less comprehensive. Accordingly, an effort has been made to collate data from selected areas in an attempt to offer a unified interpretation of the role of insulin in intermediary metabolism and in biological processes generally. Unfortunately, the chances for successful completion of this task are negligible. I therefore approach the assignment with the proper amount of trepidation, but with the hope that schemes to be presented will be helpful in providing a useful perspective to the uninitiated while provoking the specialized researcher into refining or disproving the generalities to be ventured.

Two major problem areas will be considered. The first, the more biological, pertains to comparative aspects of the physiology and biochemistry of insulin. Arguments will be presented to support the thesis that the particular cellular effects of insulin in a given species are related to the metabolic adaptations which occurred during the evolution of that species. The different effects of insulin on adipose tissue from various species will be reviewed to illustrate this thesis. It appears likely that hormonal and enzymatic adaptations occurred during evolution which favored the survival of those organisms best able to solve problems associated with the regulation and coordination of metabolic pathways. For the optimal utilization of available substrates, food must be found, ingested, and adsorbed before it can be stored or used as an energy source. Within this framework, the gastrointestinal system may have evolved in conjunction with a hormonal system which would cooperatively influence the assimilation of absorbed foodstuffs. In this sense, the control of the secretion of various gastrointestinal hormones may be closely related to the control of glucagon and insulin secretion.

The second major problem area to be considered will be the molecular mode of action of insulin on metabolic processes. The theme will be developed that the primary action of insulin is to combine with specific receptors on the plasma membranes of insulin-responsive cells. The overt metabolic events which follow the "activation" of the receptor may be considered to be secondary phenomena reflecting the organization of the enzymatic machinery in relation to plasma membrane receptors, as determined by the cell's phenotype. If this reasoning is correct, the argument may be advanced that a detailed analysis of the effects of insulin on the rates of carbohydrate and lipid metabolic pathways may be expected to reveal much concerning the nature of the control of intermediary metabolism in specialized cells, a great deal about the biological role of insulin, but little if anything about the molecular mechanism of action of insulin. This viewpoint owes much to arguments previously developed by Hechter and Halkerston in their excellent review (1964).

When there is a relative excess or deficiency of insulin, the metabolic consequences manifested in a given tissue of a particular organism are envisaged to be several steps removed from the initial molecular sites of insulin action. The overall response to a change in insulin levels is a biological one, and appears to be a reflection of the types of adaptive patterns which were evolved to allow a coordinated metabolic control system to operate in the particular organism. The specific cellular metabolic responses to insulin vary from zero discernible effects (as in erythrocytes under physiological conditions) to profound influences on the rates of glucose entry, glycogen synthesis, lipogenesis, etc. (as in adipocytes from the rat's periepididymal fat pad). What salient differences exist among the various classes of cells which can account for their different abilities to respond to insulin?

The above formulation of the problems concerning the physiological and biochemical role of insulin determined the perspectives which guided the writing of this review.

II. COMPARATIVE PHYSIOLOGY AND BIOCHEMISTRY OF INSULIN ACTION

It is an interesting and possibly significant observation that carnivorous birds and mammals show a stronger tendency to hyperglycemia and glycosuria after pancreatectomy than do herbivorous species. (Gorbman and Bern, 1962, p. 220.)

A. The Effects of Insulin on Adipose Tissue from Different Species

In the volume on adipose tissue edited by Renold and Cahill (1965), the periepididymal fat pad of the rat received an enormous amount of attention. This particular preparation has been chosen by the majority of investigators working on adipose tissue because it is readily accessible, it is thin, it is bilaterally situated, and it can be easily manipulated for a vast variety of metabolic studies. In addition, the periepididymal fat pad has a high metabolic rate relative to that of most other white adipose tissue, and a great deal of information is available, allowing for comparison of data among different laboratories. Perhaps most important of all, although least spoken about, it is easiest to elicit reproducibly significant effects of hormones on this particular type of adipose tissue preparation. The periepididymal pad is *not* typical of all adipose tissue (Shafrir and Wertheimer, 1965). Adipose tissue preparations and adipocytes from several other species do not respond as dramatically, if at all, to hormonal stimulation. For examples, the reader should consult the reviews by Rudman (1963), Rudman *et al.* (1965), Rudman and Del Rio (1969), and that by Shafrir and Wertheimer (1965), which document the vagaries of responses by various types of adipose tissue from different species to hormones.

In the isolated periepididymal fat pad from rats, insulin addition *in vitro* has been shown to elicit a host of metabolic effects, which have been reviewed elsewhere (Vaughan and Steinberg, 1963; Ball and Jungas, 1964; Rodbell *et al.*, 1968; Jeanrenaud, 1968; Jeanrenaud and Renold, 1969). These include:

1. Enhancement of transport of sugars, such as glucose, galactose and 3-*O*-methyl glucose.

2. Increased utilization of glucose, with increased rates of conversion of glucose to CO_2, glyceride glycerol, total fatty acids, and glycogen.

3. Increased incorporation of ^{14}C-labeled precursors (glucose, pyruvate, and amino acids) into protein (see chapter by Manchester, this treatise).

4. Enhancement of transport of amino acids, such as α-amino isobutyric acid and methionine, independent of the presence of glucose in the medium (see chapter by Riggs, this treatise).

5. Inhibition of lipolysis induced by epinephrine or by several other agents which stimulate lipolysis, independent of the presence of glucose in the medium.

In addition, insulin administration *in vivo* but not *in vitro* has been shown to augment the conversion of stearate to oleate, and to increase the production of oleate from acetate (Gellhorn and Benjamin, 1966). This phenomenon, in contrast to the five listed above, requires a latent period of 6 to 12 hours between the time of hormone administration and the manifestation of the effect in adipose tissue. Although none of the first five events is inhibited by actinomycin D or by puromycin, the insulin effect on oleate formation is dependent on new RNA synthesis (Gellhorn and Benjamin, 1966).

Adipose tissue from other locations in the rat, and adipose tissue from other species, has not been investigated as carefully with respect to insulin responsiveness as has the periepididymal fat pad. Shafrir and Wertheimer (1965) have contrasted the considerable differences in metabolic behavior among depots of subcutaneous, omental, perirenal, and orbital fat, as opposed to adipose tissue associated with primarily supportive function. They reviewed work showing the lipolytic effects obtained with epinephrine were largest in the periepididymal fat pad, least in subcutaneous fat, and intermediate in perirenal adipose tissue preparations. Adipose tissue from rats, mice, hamsters, and dogs responded strongly to epinephrine or norepinephrine with a release of fatty acids and glycerol; there was a moderate response by adipose tissue from men and cats to catecholamines, and there was slight or no response to epinephrine reported in adipose tissue from rabbits, guinea pigs, pigs, and chickens (see Shafrir and Wertheimer, 1965, for review).

The effects of insulin on glucose metabolism by different types of adipose tissue have been examined in only a few species. Krahl (1951) was the first to demonstrate that insulin increased glucose uptake by rat adipose tissue from several sources (subcutaneous, mesenteric, and perirenal). Wertheimer observed that insulin increased the conversion of glucose and acetate to fatty acids in omental adipose tissue of cats and dogs, but not in paw fat (Wertheimer, unpublished observations, cited in Shafrir and Wertheimer, 1965). Insulin effects on glucose metabolism by adipose tissue from human beings (for review, see Gries and Steinke, 1967) were less pronounced than those obtained in rat periepididymal fat pad preparations. Human omental fat showed increased glucose uptake in response to insulin, with most of the incremental carbon appearing in glycogen and glyceride glycerol (Kahlenberg *et al.*, 1966). Under some conditions, insulin addition to human adipose tissue preparations increased glucose conversion to CO_2 and incorporation into fatty acids (Fessler *et al.*, 1965; Goldrick, 1967). Effects were moderate, and the stimulation was considerably less than that achieved with rat periepididymal fat preparations. Similarly, antilipolytic effects of insulin were obtained in isolated human adipocytes (Moskowitz and Fain, 1969).

In contrast, insulin had slight or no effects on glucose uptake and oxidation by adipose tissue from birds (Goodridge, 1964; Goodridge and Ball, 1965, 1967), and insulin exerted no antilipolytic activity in adipose tissue from chickens or pigeons (Goodridge and Ball, 1965; Goodridge, 1968). Di Girolamo and Rudman (1966) reported in a careful study that the effects of different kinds of insulin on glucose uptake by adipose tissue preparations from guinea pigs, rabbits, and hamsters were one-fifth to one-fiftieth as great as those elicited in rat periepididymal preparations. Steinke *et al.* (1965) also reported very slight effects of insulin isolated from several species on adipose tissue preparations from guinea pigs. O'Hea and Leveille (1968) found minimal effects of insulin on glucose metabolism by adipose tissue from pigs. Recent studies from my laboratory (Vavrik and Fritz, 1969) have also shown that insulin has negligible influence on glucose oxidation or on antilipolytic activity in adipocytes or in whole adipose tissue from guinea pigs, pigs, cows, and fetal calves.

I wish to postulate that the different behavior of adipose tissue from these various species may be related to different sorts of metabolic adaptations which have occurred in carnivorous and herbivorous animals; in those animals which are intermittent eaters as opposed to those which are constant nibblers; or in those animals which are forced to adapt to a particular mixture of substrates. The enzyme changes associated with fasting and refeeding have been investigated thoroughly (for review, see Tepperman and Tepperman, 1970). The great increases seen in lipogenesis during refeeding are most striking in tissues from rats and dogs, and are least pronounced in tissues from pigeons, chickens (Goodridge and Ball, 1967), guinea pigs, and rabbits (Shafrir and Wertheimer, 1965). The response in pigs is also rather moderate (O'Hea and Leveille, 1969). These observations suggest the generalization that carnivorous animals (i.e., predatory animals) are able to respond to an excess caloric load by rapidly increasing rates of lipogenesis and glycogenesis in both liver and adipose tissue. In contrast, herbivorous animals, especially ruminants, show a lesser response, particularly in adipose tissues (Hanson and Ballard, 1967; Ballard *et al.,* 1969). The diminished responses by adipose tissue from herbivores to insulin and epinephrine may be a reflection of this metabolic adaptation which has evolved in these species.

Since adipose tissue from ruminants is apparently less sensitive to insulin and to catecholamines than is adipose tissue from carnivorous animals, it would be anticipated that insulin deficiency might lead to relatively diminished rates of lipid mobilization and therefore to less severe diabetic manifestations in ruminants and in certain other herbivores. This appears to be the case. Young (1963) and Houssay (1959) described the differential effects of extirpation of the pancreas from various species. They reviewed literature showing that in many herbivorous mammals, insulin deficiency induces a relatively mild diabetic state, in which survival may be sustained without exogenous insulin administration. Thus, whereas hyperglycemia and glycosuria occur after ingestion of a high carbohydrate meal by alloxanized or depancreatized rabbits, calves, or goats, the blood sugar levels are almost normal in the fasted state, and there is relatively little ketonuria. Pancreatectomy of certain birds, such as domestic ducks, is followed by *hypo*glycemia, presumably because of the absence of glucagon (Mialhe, 1955).

It therefore appears that adipose tissue from mammals having carnivorous or omnivorous eating patterns is generally more sensitive to variations in insulin levels than is adipose tissue from mammals and birds possessing herbivorous eating habits. Information on the insulin responsiveness of adipose tissue from reptiles, amphibians, and fishes having different eating habits is apparently not yet available. It will be of interest to establish if the generalization formulated extends to these species. It may be that antilipolytic effects, and perhaps other actions of insulin on adipose tissue, are a relatively specialized evolutionary development restricted primarily to predatory animals which are adapted to sporadic eating habits. As Tepperman (1964) stated in an essay on "Adipose Tissue, Yang and Yin":

> The larger the fraction of the day the gastrointestinal tract is empty, the more prominent becomes the role of adipose tissue both in storing and releasing calories.

To this generalization, it is necessary only to add that in the special case of the cow, approximately 14 to 18% of its total weight is in its stomachs! The low level of prominence given to the hormonal control of adipose tissue in the cow and other ruminants which has been documented in this section, helps to substantiate "Tepperman's rule."

B. The Control of Secretion of Insulin in Different Species

This topic has been well reviewed previously by others (Randle *et al.*, 1968; Mayhew *et al.*, 1969; Behrens and Grinnan, 1969; Ungar *et al.*, 1967; Hales, 1967; Levine and Pfeiffer, 1968; W. Malaisse, 1969). It is listed here only to emphasize that the relative effects of glucose, amino acids, fatty acids, ketone bodies, gastrin, secretin, pancreozymin, glucagon, or vagal stimulation on increasing insulin secretion *in vivo* are likely to vary in different species, depending on the metabolic adaptations which have occurred in responses to dietary patterns.

In the introduction, it was suggested that it would be of survival value if digestion and assimilation of foodstuffs were coordinated. It would be advantageous to the organism to have mechanisms which enhance synthetic processes immediately after or even during the ingestion of foodstuffs. Stimuli and reflex arcs which triggered the secretion of hormones controlling the release of pancreatic digestive enzymes might thereby simultaneously trigger the secretion of insulin. This possibility has been discussed by Ungar *et al.* (1967) in their consideration of the "entero-insular axis."

In addition to the stimuli (secretin, pancreozymin, gastrin, and glucagon) which can potentially stimulate insulin secretion during the absorption of foodstuffs, perhaps in conjunction with vagal stimulation, other stimuli are required to sustain the increased rates of insulin secretion and to regulate the amounts secreted in response to the amount of substrate absorbed. These stimuli are the plasma concentrations of particular metabolites, especially glucose. Although propionate and butyrate are relatively potent secretogagues of insulin in ruminants (Manns and Boda, 1967), various sugars are more powerful in animals which absorb primarily hexoses or pentoses (Behrens and Grinnan, 1969; W. Malaisse, 1969). Under most circumstances, it is the plasma level of glucose which determines the rate of release of insulin. In man, insulin secretion apparently increases in response to elevations of glucose and leucine in an additive fashion (Fajans *et al.*, 1967; Behrens and Grinnan, 1969). Various reviews cited have considered the relative influences of ions, amino acids, fatty acids, neural regulation, and other hormones on insulin secretion. Proinsulin and the biosynthesis of insulin have been discussed by Steiner *et al.* (1969), and recent developments pertaining to this subject have been contributed by Yip and co-workers (Yip and Logothetopoulos, 1969; Tung and Yip, 1969). The mechanisms responsible for the conversion of proinsulin to insulin remain to be determined. Under some circumstances, proinsulin itself is secreted into plasma, but the physiological significance of proinsulin in plasma remains puzzling.

The mechanisms by which glucose and other agents stimulate insulin secretion are unknown. Glucose freely enters the β-cells of the pancreatic islets of the rabbit (Coore and Randle, 1964) and the rat (W. J. Malaisse *et al.*, 1968). Because mannoheptulose appears to inhibit insulin secretion by inhibiting glucose phosphorylation, Coore and Randle (1964) and W. J. Malaisse *et al.* (1968) have concluded that the stimulation of insulin secretion requires the formation of unidentified products of glucose metabolism rather than free glucose itself. This presumably differs from the mechanisms associated with the enhanced secretion elicited by leucine *in vivo* (Fajans *et al.*, 1967). In isolated rat pancreatic fragments, 10 mM leucine did not, whereas 25 mM leucine did, elicit insulin release in the absence of glucose (W. Malaisse, 1969, Table II-7). Mannoheptulose did not block the effects of leucine on insulin secretion in the presence of high concentrations of glucose (W. Malaisse, 1969).

Fragmentary pieces of information presented indicate that the control of the synthesis and secretion of insulin is very complex. The β-cell must have more than one type of receptor if the rate of insulin secretion by pancreatic cells in a given ionic environment can be modified by agents as diverse as sugars, amino acids, fatty acids, glucagon, sulfonylurea derivatives, and the various gastrointestinal hormones. The data are consonant with the conclusion that pancreatic acinar cells and β-cells of the islets each possess receptors which can detect certain chemical substances like pancreozymin and secretin. These data suggest the speculation that at least one portion of the hormonal controls which regulate insulin release may have evolved in conjunction with the systems which control pancreatic enzyme secretion. The quantitative significance of the control of insulin secretion by gastrointestinal hormones remains to be evaluated.

C. Comments on the Relationship between Islets and Acinar Cells in Different Species

The anatomical proximity of the islet cells and the acinar cells of the pancreas do not appear to have arisen accidentally. The two separate cell types are in the same organ in all vertebrates, with the exception of the early fishes. Does the physical juxtaposition imply a functional relationship among the various pancreatic cells? As indicated in the previous section, it is possible that some of the various agents which were evolved for the control of secretions of the acinar cells were also employed for the control of secretion of insulin by the β-cells of the islets.

True islets of Langerhans do not exist in the pancreases of certain selachian fishes (Ferner and Kern, 1964). Rather, there is a diffuse "islet organ" consisting of endocrine single cells surrounding the pancreatic ducts, a situation which appears to have its parallel during ontogenesis of the human fetus where solitary "insular duct organ" cells exist, distinct from the intertubular cell agglomerations, namely, the islets of Langerhans (Ferner and Kern, 1964). On the other hand, true islets do exist in the hagfish (the cyclostome, *Myxine glutinosa*). In this species, the islet cells are completely separated from the exocrine pancreatic cells, and are in close anatomical relation to the bile duct (Falkmer and Winbladh, 1964). Interestingly, the exocrine pancreatic parenchymal cells are found in the liver and in the intestinal epithelium of the hagfish. However, in spite of the close approximation of the islet cells to the bile duct, the products from the islets are secreted into the capillaries and not into the duct (Falkmer and Winbladh, 1964).

From the viewpoint of histogenesis, the islet cells of the hagfish are derived from the epithelium of the bile duct, and there is no evidence for transformation of the pancreatic acinar cells into insular-type cells in this species (Falkmer and Winbladh, 1964). However, there is evidence suggesting the possible common histogenesis of acinar and islet cells in the pancreas of the spiny mouse (Pictet *et al.*, 1967). Similarly, Wessels and Rutter (1969) and Rutter *et al.* (1968) have indicated that during embryogenesis of the rat pancreas, the acinar and islet cells have a common origin. In the teleost fish, such as the toadfish or the goosefish, discrete islets are embedded loosely in the infrahepatic connective tissue, surrounded by exocrine pancreatic parenchymal cells from which they can be readily separated (for example, see Sorenson *et al.*, 1969). In all species which are phylogenetically "higher" than teleosts, the discrete islets are directly adjacent to pancreatic acinar cells. It appears that in these various cell types which have a common histogenic origin from the primitive gut, the islet cells and the exocrine parenchymal cells remained together to form a common organ during the evolution of fishes. This anatomical relationship was sustained during the ensuing phylogenetic development of all vertebrates, perhaps in relation to the functional relationship suggested in the preceding section.

For a more detailed discussion of the histogenesis of the various types of pancreatic cells, the reader is referred to the articles by Rutter *et al.* (1968), Wessells and Rutter (1969), and the discussion by several authors (Renold, Creutzfeldt, Bander, Lacy, and Hellman) in the Second Capri Conference on the "Mechanism and Regulation of Insulin Secretion" (Levine and Pfeiffer, 1968). In addition, Sircus (1969) has reviewed the possibility of single vs multiple cell types in the origin of peptide-secreting pancreatic tumors in man.

D. Teleological Considerations Concerning Insulin Action in Different Species

From a teleological viewpoint, insulin may be regarded as a regulatory agent which evolved in vertebrates in response to the requirement for coordinated metabolic adaptation during various nutritional and functional states. Speculatively, the type of response needed by a vertebrate organism to cope efficiently with a sudden increase in food supply would be increased levels of a regulatory "anabolic hormone" which would favor synthetic pathways leading to the deposition of carbon from excess substrate into suitable stores. Insulin qualifies as a candidate for this "anabolic hormone," since it does, under appropriate conditions, stimulate glycogen synthesis, lipogenesis, and protein synthesis from glucose and amino acids. As previously indicated, these effects are most readily seen in tissues from carnivorous or predatory animals.

Consider the problem in logistics faced by wild adult carnivores. They eat irregularly from an uncertain food supply. They must be prepared on the one hand to exert tremendous effort for the hunt and the kill. When the prey is successfully ingested, the carnivore must be able to assimilate into endogenous fat, glycogen, and protein stores all the caloric intake in excess of that required to satisfy energy expenditure. This demands rapid increases in the rates of all anabolic pathways.

On the other hand, the wild carnivore must be prepared to survive while fasting for an indefinite interval. The endogenous stores of food-stuffs must be mobilized at rates just sufficient to meet energy requirements, and metabolic processes must be carefully modulated if there is to be minimal loss of carbon and nitrogen. In addition, the liver must be prepared to synthesize and release sufficient glucose to satisfy the needs of those cells which preferentially utilize glucose as substrate.

In the evolutionary search for agents which could be used to co-ordinate metabolic events in carnivorous animals, insulin was cast into a prominent role. Its appearance in vertebrate organisms would have been futile, however, unless more fundamental regulatory developments had preceded it. At a very early stage, primitive organisms had to evolve mechanisms which would immediately signal the presence of excess substrate or the absence of adequate substrate. Such signals are of obvious importance in the life cycles of all organisms. How, for example, does the slime mold *Dictyostelium discoideum* "know" that it "must" divide to form more myxamebae in the presence of suitable substrates, but that it "must" differentiate into a plasmodium and a fruiting body when substrate is lacking (Wright, 1966; Bonner *et al.*, 1969). More generally, in all cells, the regulation of the transcription of the genome requires specific "stimulus recognition sites" to respond appropriately to changes in the levels of inducers and repressors (Cohn, 1968). The concentration of particular nutrients in the plasma or in the surrounding medium is a powerful metabolic regulator or inducer in nearly all species.

The existence of systems in metazoan organisms which respond to changes in the metabolic environment implies the presence of receptors which can sense changes in the levels of substrates or specific "stimulating" molecules in appropriate compartments. Completion of the "metabolic reflex arc" also connotes the presence of an effector system which is altered by changes in the state of the receptor. Among various sensing devices which evolved in vertebrate organisms, the β-cells of the pancreatic islets of Langerhans evolved an exquisite sensitivity to altered concentrations of various metabolites in the surrounding fluid. As outlined in the previous sections, stored insulin is released and the rate of insulin synthesis is increased when glucose levels are above normal limits. In contrast, when glucose levels are depressed, insulin secretion is inhibited. Although changing glucose levels are perhaps among the most important regulators of the activity of the β-cells, there is a considerable list of other stimulating agents (glucagon; secretin; pancreozymin; gastrin; leucine and certain other amino acids; short chain fatty acids, etc.), and at least one humoral inhibitor (epinephrine). In addition, vagal influences on insulin secretory mechanisms in the intact animal suggest the existence of a tonic neural control which modulates the rate of insulin secretion. The role of these varying agents in allowing a coordinated control of the rate of insulin release during different nutritional circumstances in various species has been suggested in the previous sections.

Thus, under defined conditions, the level of insulin in plasma may serve as a reflection of the dietary status of the carnivorous animal. In turn, fluctuations in insulin concentrations have the capacity to trigger changes in metabolic activities in those cells which have receptors, specific for insulin, which are activated by the hormone in such a manner that the "activated" form of the receptors can alter the activities of other proteins, and thereby influence rates of specific metabolic pathways. Viewed in this manner, insulin may be regarded as a messenger which has the property of rapidly initiating changes in the metabolic behavior of responsive cells following appropriate changes in the environment. The mediation of the actions of insulin and dietary glucose in decreasing the rate of hepatic glucose production will be discussed in Section IV,A.

To permit prolonged survival during times of food deprivation, it is essential for certain cells to store in a convenient form the foodstuffs ingested during times of caloric excess. These "certain cells" of course include adipose tissue, which stores primarily triglyceride; and cardiac as well as skeletal muscles, which store primarily glycogen. In carnivorous animals, insulin acts directly on precisely these cells to stimulate greatly both lipogenesis and glycogen synthesis, respectively. These correlations hardly seem to be the result of an experimental accident, and the phenomena make it appear as though insulin were selected during evolution to serve as a mediator between varying caloric loads and the control of rates of metabolic pathways in particular tissues. This relation is most readily evident in animals with carnivorous or predatory eating habits. In the absence of insulin, glucose utilization is impaired *in vivo* in only those tissues which have been shown to be insulin-responsive *in vitro* with respect to rates of glucose uptake and utilization (Krahl, 1961).

To emphasize the importance of insulin as a regulator of coordinated metabolic events, it is perhaps useful to recall the striking fact that it is difficult if not impossible for a pancreatectomized rat or dog to grow or to become obese in the absence of administered insulin, even when dietary conditions are favorable and survival is relatively prolonged. On a high-protein diet, most of the ingested protein carbon is converted to glucose in the insulin-deficient organism (Krahl, 1961). As excess glucose becomes synthesized, the renal transport maximum for sugar is surpassed, and glucosuria results. This glucose loss is associated with a prohibitively high energy cost to the insulin-deficient animal, since a minimum of 6 moles of ATP is required to synthesize 1 mole of glucose from lactate or pyruvate, assuming zero recycling of glycolytic intermediates (Krebs, 1964). The energy expenditure would be even greater when gluconeogenesis from protein is involved. In the absence of insulin, net lipogenesis, glycogen synthesis, and protein synthesis rates remain very low.

The lowered levels of insulin during fasting can be shown to coordinate the implementation of many metabolic events which are of survival value to the intact organism. When the insulin concentration is decreased, fatty acid release from adipose tissue is enhanced. The elevated plasma levels of fatty acids permit an increased uptake and utilization by tissues which can use this substrate as an energy source (Fritz, 1961). The oxidation of fatty acids by muscle, adipose tissue, and liver in fact supplies nearly all the energy requirements of these organs when insulin is lacking and when the rate of cellular uptake of glucose is thereby decreased. It should be noted that glucose utilization is decreased not only because of the lowered insulin levels but also as a consequence of the inhibition by high levels of fatty acids of glucose utilization by cardiac and skeletal muscle (Randle *et al.*, 1963).

Lowered insulin levels and elevated rates of fatty acid oxidation are also associated with increased rates of hepatic gluconeogenesis (for reviews, see Lardy *et al.*, 1965; Williamson, 1967; Williamson *et al.*, 1968a; Fritz, 1967). The increased glucose production by the liver in the absence of insulin generates the substrate supply required by erythrocytes, by cells of the central nervous system, and by other cells which preferentially utilize glucose as fuel. These cells have transport systems for glucose which are independent of insulin (Krahl, 1961; Cahill and Owen, 1968). Thus, by complex, indirect but coordinated mechanisms, a lowered insulin level during starvation of carnivores in essense "funnels" available glucose to "insulin-nonresponsive cells" (i.e., brain and red blood cells) by excluding glucose synthesized by the liver from "insulin-responsive cells" (i.e., muscle and adipose tissue). Blood glucose levels are maintained, and glucose utilization by the brain is thus ensured. The integrated effects achieved by tissue reactions to low insulin levels during starvation afford a beautiful solution for protein conservation in the carnivorous animal, while allowing maintenance of energy metabolism at levels required to resume the hunt when conditions are favorable.

A similar set of arguments can be advanced to illustrate the importance of insulin adaptation to a large excess of carbohydrate and protein. Insulin in elevated concentrations increases glucose utilization by muscle and adipose tissue. Rates of glycogen synthesis, protein synthesis, and lipogenesis are greatly enhanced while the rate of gluconeogenesis is depressed.

It is for these reasons that from a physiological viewpoint, insulin may be regarded as a regulatory agent which permits animals with carnivorous eating habits to adapt metabolically in a *coordinated* manner during starvation and during times of caloric excess. Obviously, insulin could not exert its regulatory role unless more fundamental "primitive controls" existed to govern the interrelations of intermediary metabolism in organized multienzyme systems. Biochemical phenomena underlying the "primitive controls" associated with the mechanisms of fatty acid oxidation (Fritz, 1961), fatty acid synthesis (Masoro, 1962), glycolysis (Randle *et al.*, 1966; Newsholme and Gevers, 1967), gluconeogenesis (Krebs, 1964; Newsholme and Gevers, 1967), and protein synthesis (Lipmann, 1969; Lengyel and Söll, 1969) have been extensively reviewed elsewhere. The biochemical aspects of the control of intermediary metabolism are clearly of the most fundamental importance in contributing toward an understanding of the mechanisms by which any hormone might act to cause rapid changes in rates of complex pathways in organized systems. Most of the biochemical developments obviously preceded the evolution of vertebrates.

When searching for likely sites of interaction of the recently evolved hormones with the metabolic systems which developed at an earlier evolutionary stage, it is appealing to consider that hormones may exert their influence by modulating preexisting "pacemaker reactions" (Krebs, 1957). The organization of the multienzyme assemblies into discrete subcellular organelles is also of obvious importance. The most gross notion of compartmentation demands a separation of cell exterior from cell interior. In this connection, it is essential to note the general observation that almost all of the actions of insulin on metabolic processes are abolished in cell-free homogenate preparations (Krahl, 1961). This observation suggests that the biological actions of insulin require the presence of structurally organized systems. If insulin effects are obtained on isolated purified enzymes of carbohydrate or lipid metabolism, they will be difficult to interpret within a physiological context. The probable primary sites of action of insulin on receptors in the plasma membrane have been alluded to previously. These interactions will be discussed in detail in Section III.

The coordinate nature of the control of related multienzyme pathways in organized systems must be emphasized. Tepperman and Tepperman (1970) have demonstrated in a brilliant and provocative review that it is all but impossible to dissociate the interlocking sets of signals which control rates of lipogenesis, gluconeogenesis, or ketogenesis, respectively. In their words, "All of these processes share so much of the metabolic machinery one can only conceive of sets of control mechanisms, modulators and coupled pathways which, operationally, represent the metabolic counterpart of Sherrington's principle of reciprocal inhibition." The reader is referred to the article by Tepperman and Tepperman (1970) for documentation at several levels of biological organization.

From an evolutionary point of view, insulin may have assumed varying physiological roles in different species, depending upon the stage of development of intracellular, intercellular, and interorgan metabolic interrelations involved in special adaptations. Insulin from the pancreas has been obtained from animals representative of all classes of vertebrates, and the amino acid sequences of the different insulin molecules have been found to vary slightly in several species (Sanger, 1956, 1959). Overt chemical differences in primary structure may have their more obvious counterparts in different metabolic effects associated with insulin action in various species. As an example, contrast the metabolic differences between carnivores and ruminants.

In contrast to most carnivorous animals, herbivores often eat all day, grazing or nibbling on a relatively steady supply of vegetation. In the special case of ruminants, these dietary habits are associated with rather profound anatomical as well as biochemical and physiological adaptations. The ruminants evolved uniquely, presumably receiving advantage from their ability to use as their energy supply the huge amounts of vegetation covering much of the earth's terrain. The changes in the gastrointestinal system accommodated the presence of a bacterial flora in the ruminant's stomach which would degrade much of the ingested grains and grass to short-chain fatty acids for eventual transport to the liver via the portal circulation. In these species, the rate of hepatic glucose production is apparently governed primarily by the amount of propionate supplied to the liver, and the rate of gluconeogenesis is not increased during starvation (Ballard et al., 1969). Under circumstances in which bacterial fermentation is generating a nearly continuous supply of fatty acids, perhaps a lesser premium would be placed on developing multiple fine controls to regulate lipolysis and triglyceride formation in adipose tissue. As might be expected, lipogenesis from glucose by adipose tissue and liver from ruminants is slower than from acetate (Hanson and Ballard, 1967). The less severe diabetes of ruminants subjected to insulin deficiency has previously been commented upon. The inability of insulin to influence glucose metabolism by adipose tissue from these species has also been reviewed in the previous sections.

It appears reasonable to suggest that an analysis of the nature of different tissue and species specific responses to insulin may be expected to contribute information concerning hormonal and metabolic adaptations during evolution. If this is so, insulin may provide a tool with which to probe various metabolic control systems which have evolved in response to different nutritional stimuli.

III. EVIDENCE THAT MANY OF THE PHYSIOLOGICAL EFFECTS OF INSULIN ON INTERMEDIARY METABOLISM ARE SECONDARY TO THE ACTIONS OF INSULIN ON THE PLASMA MEMBRANE

A. GENERAL CONSIDERATIONS, AND STATEMENT OF A GENERAL HYPOTHESIS

The experimental and theoretical considerations which led Levine and Goldstein (1952, 1955) to the conclusion that insulin acts to facilitate glucose transport across certain cell membranes have been reviewed extensively (Krahl, 1961; Park *et al.*, 1961; Randle *et al.*, 1966; Hales, 1967). Eventually, various influences of insulin on metabolic processes were discovered which could not fit the "unitary hypothesis" proposed by Levine and Goldstein (1955) that all actions of insulin were indirect consequences of the facilitation of glucose entry into insulin-responsive tissues. Included among these phenomena are the antilipolytic action of insulin in the absence of glucose (Ball and Jungas, 1964); the effects of insulin on ion and amino acid transport (Riggs, this treatise); the enhancement of protein synthesis from amino acids or pyruvate in the absence of glucose (Wool and Krahl, 1959; Wool *et al.*, 1968; Manchester, this treatise); and the inhibition of gluconeogenesis in perfused livers (Mortimore, 1963; Jefferson *et al.*, 1968). In an attempt to save the "unitary hypothesis" concept, Krahl (1957, 1961) broadened the initial formulation of Levine and Goldstein (1955) by postulating that insulin interaction with cell membranes may alter metabolic rates of various pathways by changing the cytoskeleton within which multi-enzyme assemblies operated. In this attempt, Krahl (1957, 1961) anticipated the importance which must be ascribed to allosteric activators and inhibitors of enzymes (Monod *et al.*, 1963; Koshland, 1968).

In the light of present knowledge, it is possible to envisage the first effect of insulin to be an interaction with its unique receptor(s) on the plasma membrane. Following this reaction, one can speculate that the activated receptor is so organized that it can "trigger" a second metabolic event in an analogous manner, perhaps but not necessarily involving the activity of the adenyl cyclase system (Sutherland *et al.*, 1965; Butcher *et al.*, 1968b). In the general scheme, the activated receptor is postulated to have the property of influencing the activity of a second protein in its vicinity, whereas the nonactivated receptor does not have the same property. The change in activity of the second protein would then permit induction of subsequent changes in a cascading manner, until eventually there is sufficient amplification to register an overt change in the rate of a metabolic pathway. This change could be manifested by a change in the transport properties of the plasma membrane, or by an altered rate of product formation in a multienzyme sequence, i.e., increased rates of glucose entry, glycogen synthesis, fatty acid synthesis, etc. It is possible to envisage that the activated receptor activates many metabolic pathways independently of each other; or, alternatively, that the activated receptor influences only a single "transduction system"[1] (such as the adenyl cyclase system) and that the products of the "transduction system" (i.e., cAMP) trigger all subsequent changes in other metabolic pathways.

As indicated in the introductory comments, and in this scheme, the effects of insulin on carbohydrate and lipid metabolism are visualized as secondary and tertiary events, dependent on the phenotype of the cell and its functional state at the time of insulin stimulation. After insulin combines with its receptor, its primary action is completed. The ensuing metabolic events are determined by the detailed nature of the intervening metabolic machinery (in the vicinity of the specific insulin–receptor complex). Biologically, the specific responses are of enormous importance for the metabolic physiology of the cell and for the survival of the organism. These responses and control systems are obviously built into the phenotype of the cell and the genotype of the organism, as the result of the evolutionary process. A role for insulin in influencing these metabolic processes, however, is dependent upon a combination

[1] "Transduction system" is used to suggest the existence of a coupling system which can alter rates of particular intracellular metabolic pathways in response to changes in the states of receptors in the plasma membrane, and/or to changes in the plasma membrane configuration. The physical analog is a "transducer" which converts a change in mechanical pressure to an appropriate electrical signal which can then be amplified for recording or transmission. See Sections III,A and IV,B for elaboration.

of events. Of the cell types listed below, an overt insulin "effect" would be manifested only in cell type D.

Cell type A. No receptor to insulin exists.

Cell type B. A receptor exists, but no complete transduction system is present (or functional).

Cell type C. A receptor and a complete transduction system are present. However, part or all of the enzymic machinery required for overt manifestation of the metabolic pathway is missing because of phenotypic deletion. Alternatively, the enzyme system is present but nonfunctional.

Cell type D. Receptors, transduction systems, and one or more responsive and functional multienzyme systems are present.

The net effects of insulin on carbohydrate and fatty acid metabolism in three different types of cells are summarized in Table I. Because at least one positive effect of insulin can be elicited in each population, it follows that all cells described are of cell types C or D above; depending on the metabolic variable being measured.

B. Simulation or Imitation of Various Actions of Insulin on Metabolic Processes by Various Agents Which Interact with Plasma Membrane Components

1. Phospholipases

Although the presence of phospholipids in various cell membranes has been known for years, the specific functions of the phospholipids in conferring special properties on the plasma membrane remain speculative. One possible approach to the problem consists of altering the phospholipids of membranes enzymically, while attempting to correlate changes in structure with changes in function.

A successful exploitation of this approach was initiated by the studies of Rodbell and co-workers (1968; Rodbell, 1964, 1966; Rodbell and Jones, 1966). Phospholipase C at low concentrations increased glucose utilization, and the incorporation of labeled glucose into CO_2, fatty acids, and proteins by isolated adipocytes in a manner similar to that elicited by insulin. These data led to the formulation of the conclusion that insulin and phospholipase C action share one thing in common, namely the ability to alter the properties of the plasma membrane. Following this alteration, transport processes are changed (i.e., glucose entry is enhanced, and presumably the transport of other compounds such as certain amino acids, phosphate, or potassium ions is also increased). In association with the alteration of the configuration of the plasma membrane and the enhanced glucose entry, the rates of other intracellular metabolic events may be changed. This hypothesis was

TABLE I

NET EFFECTS OF INSULIN ON CARBOHYDRATE AND FATTY ACID METABOLISM IN DIFFERENT CELL TYPES

Metabolic process	Erythrocyte	Skeletal or cardiac muscle cell	Adipocyte (rat)
Glucose transport (or 3-O-methyl glucose transport)	0^a	+	+
Glucose to glycogen	0	+	+
Glucose to lactate or to CO_2	0	+	+
Inhibition of oxidation of long-chain fatty acids in the presence of glucose	0	+	+
Glucose to fatty acids	0	0 or slight	+
Glucose to glyceride glycerol	0	0 or slight	+
Inhibition of lipolysis in the absence of glucose	0	0	+
Evidence for change in permeability property of plasma membrane under special conditions	$+^a$	+	+

[a] See Section III,C,2 for elaboration.

strengthened by the observations that incubation of adipocytes with high concentrations of phospholipase C resulted in a disruption of the plasma membrane, and a simultaneous loss of insulin responsiveness (Rodbell, 1966). The hypothesis was also strengthened by the finding that the antilipolytic effects of insulin on adipocytes incubated in the absence of glucose could be simulated by the action of phospholipase C (Rodbell and Jones, 1966). The above observations have been amply confirmed and extended (Rodbell *et al.*, 1968; Blecher, 1965, 1966; 1968). Phospholipase A has effects similar to those of phospholipase C (Blecher, 1966, 1968). These experiments demonstrate that suitable alteration of phospholipids in the plasma membranes of adipocytes results in a set of structural changes which are associated with metabolic effects which are qualitatively identical to those evoked by insulin. In this sense, phospholipases have been shown to mimic the action of insulin.

2. Trypsin and Other Proteolytic Agents

Rieser and Rieser (1964a) were the first to indicate that trypsin and chymotrypsin could also mimic certain aspects of insulin action. They showed that treatment of intact rat diaphragms *in vitro* with proteases increased the rate of accumulation of sugars. The observations were followed soon thereafter by those of Kuo *et al.* (1966a,b), who demonstrated that not only low doses of trypsin and chymotrypsin but also papain, ficin, and two different bacterial proteases increased glucose oxidation by rat adipocytes. More recently, Weis and Narahara (1969) have shown that low concentrations of trypsin increased the rate of penetration of 3-O-methyl-D-glucose into frog sartorius muscle cells. Both trypsin and insulin increased the V_{max} without altering the K_m for sugar transport in this preparation (Weis and Narahara, 1969). Parenthetically, it should be noted that the effects of insulin on the kinetic parameters for the transport of sugars and amino acids vary in different preparations, in that sometimes the K_m value is lowered in the presence of insulin, while the V_{max} remains constant or is elevated (for details, see chapters by Riggs and by Manchester, this series).

In contrast to the effects of low doses of trypsin (about 2 $\mu g/ml$), high doses (1 mg/ml) did not alter the baseline rates of glucose utilization by adipocytes, or the rates of glucose incorporation into CO_2, fatty acids, or glyceride glycerol (Kono, 1969a; Fain and Loken, 1969). Instead, adipocytes incubated with high doses of trypsin lost their responsiveness to insulin. In one sense, this phenomenon is reminiscent of the failure of adipocytes to respond to insulin after having been treated with high concentrations of phospholipase (Rodbell, 1964). However, in that it suggests a specific impairment in the protein component of the plasma membrane, it will be discussed in more detail in Section III,C,2.

3. Polyene Antibiotics and Miscellaneous Reagents

Kuo (1968) recently demonstrated that low concentrations of polyene antibiotics increased glucose uptake by isolated adipocytes, and simultaneously decreased lipolysis. These antibiotics simulated some of the other effects of insulin, such as enhancement of incorporation of labeled palmitate into glycerides in the presence of glucose, and increased lipogenesis from glucose. Again, high concentrations of antibiotics (filipin, pimaricin, and nystatin) reversed these metabolic effects, presumably by causing disruption of the cell membrane, resulting from interactions of the antibiotics with phospholipid–cholesterol components in the plasma membranes of adipocytes. Relatively high concentrations of phospholipase C blocked the insulin-like effects of filipin and nystatin but not those of pimaricin, suggesting that this particular antibiotic may have a specific site of interaction with the adipocyte which may be rewarding to investigate further (Kuo, 1968).

Avenaciolide, which is an antifungal lactone, blocked the effects of insulin and proteolytic enzymes on the incorporation of ^{14}C-glucose into CO_2 or lipids by adipocytes (Kuo *et al.*, 1968). The antibiotic itself inhibited lipolysis induced by various agents, and therefore could not be used to examine possible effects on the antilipolytic action of insulin. It did not, however, alter the baseline rate of glucose utilization (Kuo *et al.*, 1968). Other agents which mimic at least some of the actions of insulin on adipocytes have been discussed by Ball and Jungas (1964). Various chemicals include arsenite (Kuo *et al.*, 1967), resulting perhaps from interactions of arsenite with sulfhydryl groups in plasma membrane proteins, ouabain (Ho and Jeanrenaud, 1967; Ho *et al.*, 1967), and an antifungal antibiotic deoxyfrenolicin (G. A. Ellestad, cited by Kuo, 1968). The complex effects of ouabain are discussed in detail by Riggs (this treatise). They do not always mimic the actions of insulin. Various thiol reagents have also recently been shown at various concentrations to act like insulin in inhibiting lipolysis in adipocytes and fat cell ghosts (Lavis and Williams, 1970).

The mechanisms of action of these agents on adipocytes is unknown, but they share with insulin at least one common property of interacting with some components in the plasma membrane. The components concerned, however, must be different ones in these various cases, since agents as diverse as phospholipase C, trypsin, mercaptoethanol, and arsenite can hardly be expected to react with the identical component. One is therefore forced to conclude that it is possible to mimic the metabolic effects elicited by insulin in rat periepididymal adipocytes by changing the physical properties of the plasma membrane in any of a number of acceptable ways. Various agents used react with proteins, phospholipids, the cholesterol–phospholipid components, and unknown components of the plasma membrane. The general formulation originally suggested by Rodbell (1964) remains a good working hypothesis to account for the ability of these diverse agents to simulate the actions of insulin. Configurations of the lipoproteins in the plasma membrane may be changed from laminated to a globular form by phospholipase C (Rodbell, 1964) and presumably by other agents listed above. How can the "correct" alteration in configuration of the plasma membrane evoke the metabolic effects which mimic those elicited by insulin? This question remains unsolved, but it may be speculated that a "transduction system" exists which relates the control of rates of transport and rates of certain multienzyme systems to the state of "activation" of the plasma membrane receptor. In this conjecture, the transducer is the "coupling system" which links the control of rates of discrete metabolic processes to changes in plasma membrane configuration. Phenomena described cannot be explained by postulating an increased rate of entry of glucose through "holes" in the plasma of membrane caused by treatment with these reagents, because the antilipolytic effect occurs in the absence of glucose.

C. Evidence for a Specific Insulin Receptor on the Plasma Membrane

1. Must Insulin Enter the Cell Interior to Exert its Metabolic Effects?

Since insulin action on several metabolic parameters seems to be intimately associated with its effects on the properties of plasma membranes, it is relevant to inquire whether insulin can exert all of its effects while remaining on the outside of the cell. This problem has recently been approached by examining the effects of insulin when it is covalently attached to large polymers. Cuatrecasas (1969) reported that insulin–Sepharose elicited the same effects in isolated rat adipocytes that free insulin did. This was the case when Sepharose was attached through either the α-amino group of the N-terminal residue of the β-chain (i.e., to phenylalanine), or through the ϵ-amino group of the lysyl residue of insulin. Insulin–Sepharose preparations increased glucose oxidation; and decreased lipolysis elicited by ACTH, theophylline, or dexamethasone plus growth hormone. Concentrations of insulin–Sepharose required to evoke these effects were only slightly greater than levels of free insulin needed to produce the same changes. Thus 1–3 μunits/ml of insulin–Sepharose increased glucose oxidation, while 10 μunits/ml inhibited lipolysis. Maximal effects were achieved with approximately 20–30 μunits/ml in both cases, and these doses compare favorably with concentrations of free insulin required to cause maximal effects on these two metabolic parameters (Cuatrecasas, 1969).

The results of these experiments strongly suggest that insulin need not penetrate the cell to increase rates of glucose transport and oxidation, or to inhibit rats of lipolysis. Sepharose particles were 60 to 300 μ in diameter, whereas the cell size varied from 50 to 100 μ. When labeled Sepharose was employed, Cuatrecasas (1969) reported that no uptake of ^{14}C by the cells could be detected. One caution, however, needs to be expressed. Before the above conclusion may be regarded as definitive, it will be necessary to prove that the Sepharose–insulin compound was not hydrolyzed during incubation with the adipocytes. Cuatrecasas (1969) felt that this was unlikely because the effects of the Sepharose–insulin on glucose oxidation were linear from 30 minutes to 4½ hours, with no evidence of any lag phase. The addition of antiinsulin serum immediately abolished the effects of Sepharose–insulin, and it could not do this unless both AIS and the Sepharose–insulin were in the same compartment, presumably the extracellular and not the intracellular space. Although Cuatrecasas (1969) minimizes the possibility of the formation of active free insulin through hydrolytic or proteolytic cleavage of the Sepharose–insulin compound, the possibility unfortunately remains open. It can be ruled out only by demonstrating that ultrafiltrates of the medium at the end of incubation contain no free insulin, and that no free insulin is bound to the adipocytes. This possibility proved to be all too real in similar experiments which were being simultaneously performed in my laboratory in the absence of knowledge concerning Cuatrecasas' work. Vavrik and I (1969) were investigating the effects of insulin covalently bound to Sephadex G-100 via an isothyocyanate linkage through the α-amino groups of the N-terminal residues. On the basis of an analysis of the amino acid content of the Sephadex–insulin provided by Dr. C. C. Yip, we observed that the Sephadex–insulin compound was approximately one-tenth as active as free insulin in increasing glucose oxidation and in inhibiting lipolysis in isolated rat periepididymal adipocytes. The effects obtained were linear, from 15 minutes to 3 hours of incubation, and there was no evidence of any lag phase. However, in some experiments, the ultrafiltrates of the media *did* contain free insulin, as judged by immunoassays and by bioassays with fresh adipocytes (Vavrik and Fritz, 1969). Finally, we were discouraged by finding that intact periepididymal fat pads as well as isolated adipocytes responded in a similar manner to the Sephadex–insulin preparations. Since whole pads retain a basement membrane which Rodbell (1964) has shown to be removed by the collagenase treatment required to prepare adipocytes, it is very unlikely that the Sephadex–insulin acted in the intact tissue without first being cleaved to free insulin. We were unable to inhibit this effect by adding inhibitors of proteolytic enzymes.

It is therefore apparent that before the conclusions of Cuatrecasas (1969) can be fully accepted, additional experiments must be performed to rule out the possibility of formation of free insulin from Sepharose–insulin incubated with adipocytes. Autoradiographs of cells incubated with ^{14}C- or ^{3}H-labeled insulin as opposed to insulin–Sepharose would be useful in permitting a more definitive conclusion. In favor of the assertion by Cuatrecasas (1969) that the Sepharose–insulin remained intact during the incubation procedures, he demonstrated that the doses of Sepharose–insulin required to elicit insulin-like effects were very low. The chemical characterization of the different Sepharose–insulin derivatives used was thorough (Cuatrecasas, 1969).

From the available data, it is plausible to believe that the interaction of insulin with the plasma membrane results in a series of intracellular metabolic events which are independent of the presence of insulin within the intracellular space. If Sepharose–insulin does not form free insulin during incubation, the use of this reagent may be expected to facilitate the studies on the isolation of receptor-like structures from plasma membranes.

2. Functional Evidence for the Existence of an Insulin Receptor

Kono (1969a) has shown that treatment of adipocytes with large doses of trypsin and other proteolytic enzymes abolished the responsiveness of the fat cells to insulin. In confirmation and extension of these observations, Fain and Loken (1969) demonstrated that adipocytes from white or brown adipose tissue treated with trypsin still responded to catecholamines with a normal enhancement of lipolysis, and to prostaglandin E_1 with a usual diminution of lipolysis. From these studies, it may be concluded that trypsin treatment of adipocytes destroys certain areas of the plasma membrane selectively (i.e., the structures which respond to insulin) while not damaging other areas (i.e., the structures which can be influenced by catecholamines, prostaglandin E_1, oxytocin, and ACTH; and the portions responsible for maintaining basal rates of transport of glucose).

In more recent studies, Kono (1969b) and Kono *et al.* (1969) have reported that the binding of insulin to adipocytes was abolished by treatment with high concentrations of trypsin. If these cells were then freed of trypsin by washing and incubating them with soybean trypsin inhibitor, Kono observed that the capacity to bind insulin was restored, and simultaneously the fat cells responded to insulin, as measured by an increased oxidation of glucose and an inhibition of lipolysis (Kono, 1969b; Kono *et al.*, 1969). The restoration process could be inhibited by the presence of cycloheximide or puromycin during incubation after the addition of trypsin inhibitor, suggesting that new protein synthesis was required to repair the receptor structure initially damaged by trypsin treatment (Kono, 1969b). Full details of these exciting observations have recently been published, and experiments reported suggest that this approach may lead to the identification and isolation of proteins involved in the insulin receptor structure (Kono, 1969c).

Related experiments have recently been reported by Maturo and Rieser (1969). These workers demonstrated that the addition of a reagent specific for tryptophan residues to rat diaphragm muscle preparations abolished the action of insulin on amino acid transport and protein synthesis. If insulin were added first, the inhibitory effects of the drug 2-hydroxy-5-nitrobenzyl bromide were largely prevented. The results suggest that insulin combination with its receptor on the plasma membrane of muscle cells is dependent on an interaction with specific tryptophan residues (Maturo and Rieser, 1969).

Hechter and Halkerston (1964) have discussed the role of insulin in relation to an SS–SH interchange reaction, and have critically reviewed the salient literature. There is no doubt that sulfhydryl reagents such as *N*-ethylmeleimide inhibit glycogen synthesis and protein synthesis in isolated rat diaphragms, presumably by inactivating sulfhydryl-containing enzymes associated with these processes. However, in the experiments of Carlin and Hechter (1962), these effects could not be prevented by preincubation of diaphragms with insulin prior to the addition of *N*-ethylmaleimide. Carlin and Hechter (1962) therefore concluded that the insulin augmentation of amino acid uptake, glycogen synthesis and protein synthesis were not mediated by a primary reaction between —SH groups of the receptor and the intrachain —S—S— bond of insulin. The inhibition of these processes by *N*-ethylmaleimide was assumed to involve phenomena which were secondary to insulin reaction with its receptor.

In adipocytes, the effects of sulfhydryl reagents on glucose metabolism are complex. At low doses and during short incubation times, *N*-ethylmaleimide and other sulfhydryl reagents elicit an insulin-like action, increasing glucose transport and oxidation (Carter and Martin, 1969; Kuo *et al.*, 1967; Minemura and Crofford, 1969). At higher concentrations or during longer periods of exposure, however, various sulfhydryl reagents inhibit insulin effects on these variables (Carter and Martin, 1969). Although plasma membrane sites are presumably involved, information concerning the nature of the interactions is not yet available. It remains impossible to make definitive conclusions concerning the role of the disulfide exchange reaction in insulin action, but no direct relationship has been demonstrated.

Other miscellaneous evidence indirectly points to the existence of insulin receptors on plasma membranes. For example, red cells are usually classified as nonresponsive to insulin because glucose utilization by erythrocytes is not accelerated by insulin under physiological conditions. Yet, under special conditions, insulin has been shown to influence permeability properties of red cell ghosts to hydrogen and hydroxide ions (Dormandy and Zarday, 1965; Dormandy, 1967). Chymotrypsin treatment of human red cells has also been reported to render erythrocytes responsive to insulin, as manifested by increased glucose uptake (Rieser and Rieser, 1964b).

In the absence of glucose, insulin increases the transmembrane potential of muscle cells, but increases potassium entry, a phenomenon

which can best be interpreted by assuming altered permeability properties of the plasma membrane (Zierler, 1957, 1958). In addition, the
general "leakiness" of muscle membranes is increased by insulin, as
manifested by an enhanced exit of proteins such as aldolase from
muscle preparations incubated in the presence of insulin (Zierler, 1958).
The resting electrical membrane potential of adipose tissue cells from
young rats is also increased by insulin in the absence of glucose (Biegelman and Hollander, 1962).

In view of the effects of insulin on erythrocytes under special conditions, it is appropriate to question the conventional classification of cell
types as "insulin-responsive" and "nonresponsive" (Dormandy, 1967).
This classification is actually an indication of the presence or absence
of a measurable anticipated metabolic effect which is assumed to be
associated with insulin action in an obligatory manner. In "nonresponsive" cells, the insulin receptor may be present and the molecular interaction with insulin may occur, but the transduction system or the
enzymic machinery required for manifestation of an overt metabolic
response may be absent. As discussed in Section II, the particular
cellular response to insulin is of enormous importance biologically in
coordinating metabolic activities in the whole organism during different
functional states. But the specific response to the molecular interaction
between receptor and insulin is not invariant, even in adipocytes from
different species. Another example of an insulin effect on a tissue usually
considered "non-responsive" is provided by the recent studies of Mahler
and Szabo (1967) on kidney. Glucose uptake by rat kidney slices was
stimulated by insulin only at low temperatures, or if alloxan was present.
The mechanisms by which the kidney preparations were rendered
insulin-responsive by these treatments are not known.

An analysis of the degree of insulin responsiveness by tissues of fetal
animals may eventually provide insight into the development of insulin
receptors. In young chick embryos, glucose uptake by cardiac tissue is
not influenced by insulin until the seventh day of incubation (Grillo
et al., 1964; Foa, 1965). By the ninth day of development, by which
time pancreatic insulin secretion has also commenced, maximal insulin
effects can be achieved. Until this time, the rate of glucose utilization
by heart is apparently independent of insulin action, and is not limited
by membrane permeability. It would be of great interest to determine
whether the plasma membranes of cardiac cells undergo chemical
changes during development which result in restriction of sugar transport, and whether or not insulin receptors exist at all stages of cardiac
development. If receptors are present in cardiac cells from the time
the heart appears, what changes occur after 7 days of incubation to

alter the transport properties of the cardiac cell membranes, and to allow manifestation of insulin responsiveness? Either the receptor becomes functional, the "transduction system" is developed, or the relationships among parts of the preexisting receptor–transducer–metabolic machinery system are altered so that the new configuration becomes a functional unit. Interestingly, insulin increased the incorporation of ^{14}C-acetate into fatty acids in embryonic hearts at a stage of development prior to the time at which the glucose transport system was stimulated (Foa *et al.*, 1965).

The responsiveness by fetal tissues of mammals to insulin has been investigated to only a slight extent. In fetal rats, insulin injection is followed by hypoglycemia (Picon and Montane, 1968), and at least under some conditions an increased incorporation of glucose into liver but not muscle glycogen (Manns and Brockman, 1969). However, when liver glycogen was analyzed 15 minutes after the injection of ^{14}C-glucose, no effect of insulin was obtained on glucose conversion to glycogen (Clark *et al.*, 1968). In fetal rhesus monkeys, muscle became insulin-responsive by the time of completion of 75% of term (125 days gestational age) (Bocek and Beatty, 1969). At early stages of development, glucose uptake and glycogen synthesis by fetal muscle cells were not stimulated by insulin. An analysis of what portion of the effector system is missing is likely to be rewarding in elucidating the train of events necessary for the usual cellular response in muscle from animals at a later stage of development.

3. Consideration of the Adenyl Cyclase System as the Potential "Transduction System" between the Activated Insulin Receptor and the Secondary Metabolic Effects of Insulin

Sutherland and co-workers have extensively reviewed the involvement of the adenyl cyclase system in mediating hormonal stimulation of various metabolic processes (Sutherland *et al.*, 1965; Sutherland and Robison, 1969; Butcher *et al.*, 1968b; review by Butcher *et al.* in this series). The relationship of the adenyl cyclase system to hormonal receptors has been provocatively discussed by Hechter and Halkerston (1964), who have broadly considered the general problems involved in determining the mechanisms of action of several hormones. They describe the "*N*th Effect Problem," and offer various logical approaches toward its solution. Insulin exerts multiple metabolic effects which are not necessarily dependent on each other, i.e., augmentation of transport of certain sugars, ions, and amino acids; enhancement of glucose oxidation, incorporation into fatty acids and glyceride glycerol; direct stimulation of glycogen synthesis; inhibition of lipolysis by rat adipose tissue; stimulation of protein synthesis by muscle and liver cells; inhibition of gluconeogenesis by liver cells; and others. Given this myriad of effects, is it conceivable that a single primary action of insulin could evoke them all? Or is it obligatory to postulate more than one "primary action"?

The addition of cyclic 3′,5′-AMP (cAMP) or its dibutyryl derivative to adipose tissue preparations (Butcher *et al.*, 1965; Butcher and Sutherland, 1967) or to perfused livers (Exton and Park, 1968a) duplicates the metabolic effects of epinephrine and glucagon. Thus, lipolysis is enhanced in rat adipocytes and gluconeogenesis is increased in perfused livers by epinephrine, glucagon, or by cAMP and its dibutyryl derivative. Insulin administration to these preparations exerts an antilipolytic action in the periepididymal fat pad (Butcher *et al.*, 1966) and an inhibition of gluconeogenesis in perfused rat livers (Exton and Park, 1968a). Simultaneously, the cAMP levels are decreased after insulin administration.

These observations have led to the conclusion that cellular cAMP concentrations are closely modulated by various hormonal agents, via augmentation or inhibition of the activities of adenyl cyclase and/or the phosphodiesterase which catalyzes the conversion of cAMP to 5′-AMP. Sutherland *et al.* (1965) have postulated that cAMP is a second messenger. It might influence metabolic processes by acting directly as an allosteric activator or inhibitor of enzymes; by enhancing phosphorylation of proteins and thereby altering their catalytic properties (e.g., Walsh *et al.*, 1968; Corbin and Krebs, 1969); or by influencing some stages of transcription or translation, by analogy with bacterial systems recently described (Perlman and Pastan, 1968a,b).

If insulin inhibited the activity of adenyl cyclase, and/or stimulated phosphodiesterase activity in the plasma membrane, the resulting fall in cAMP levels would inhibit rates of lipolysis and glycogenolysis, both of which processes have been shown in mammalian tissues to be stimulated by cAMP (for reviews, see Butcher and Sutherland, 1967; Butcher *et al.*, 1968b; Exton and Park, 1968b; Rodbell *et al.*, 1968). Although Hepp *et al.* (1969) initially reported observations indicating that insulin did not alter phosphodiesterase activity in adipose tissue, more recent findings by Loten and Sneyd (1970) indicate otherwise. Homogenates of isolated adipocytes from insulin-treated rats were shown to contain two separate phosphodiesterases, one having a low K'_m (approximately 0.9 μM) and the other a considerably higher K'_m (approximately 41 μM). The activity of the low K'_m but not of the high K'_m phosphodiesterase in adipocyte homogenates was increased in insulin-treated rats. Insulin addition *in vitro* had no apparent effect (Loten and Sneyd, 1970). This augmentation of the activity of the low K'_m phosphodiesterase by insulin may be of greater importance in lowering cAMP levels in adipose tissue than the inhibition of adenyl cyclase initially suggested by Jungas (1966).

The correlation among effects of insulin with decreased adenyl cyclase activity and lowered cAMP levels in adipocytes is good but not perfect. The increase in glucose transport and oxidation by adipocytes associated with insulin action is not inhibited by epinephrine and other lipolytic agents, even though cAMP levels are elevated (Rodbell *et al.*, 1968). Kuo and De Renzo (1969) have shown that proteolytic agents which mimic insulin action did *not* lower cAMP levels or decrease adenyl cyclase activity. From these observations, it appears that the inhibitory effects of insulin on adenyl cyclase activity may be independent of the stimulation of glucose transport and oxidation. If this is so, it may be deduced that if there is a primary or single site of action of insulin, it is not on the adenyl cyclase system. The cellular concentrations of cAMP cannot be the sole mediating factor which relate insulin action to metabolic effects. This area remains highly controversial because of difficulties of analysis of low levels of cAMP under physiological conditions; the possibility of intracellular compartmentation of cAMP; and the possible differences in pharmacological effects of cAMP and its less easily split dibutyryl derivative.

Protein synthesis by ribosomes from muscles of normal and diabetic animals was not influenced by adding cAMP or caffeine to the system (Wool *et al.*, 1968). However, Wool *et al.* (1968) reported briefly that these additions to isolated diaphragms did inhibit incorporation of labeled amino acids into proteins, an effect which is opposite to that associated with insulin action and one which is therefore consistent with the hypothesis that insulin effects on protein synthesis could have been mediated indirectly by a fall in cAMP levels. The possible role of cAMP in mediating insulin effects on protein synthesis is discussed more fully by Manchester (this treatise).

The influence of insulin on cAMP levels in diaphragm is not the same as that exerted in adipose tissue or liver. Craig *et al.* (1969) have shown that cAMP levels in rat diaphragm were not altered by insulin. Insulin increased the activity of transferase I (i.e., the glucose-6-phosphate independent form of glycogen transferase, called UDP-glucose: α-1,4-glucan-α-4-glucosyl transferase EC 2.4.1.11) without altering the level of cAMP in muscle (Larner *et al.*, 1968; Craig *et al.*, 1969). Moreover, although preincubation of diaphragm with insulin prior to addition of epinephrine did decrease the augmentation of cAMP levels induced by epinephrine, the glycogen phosphorylase activation was unaffected by insulin.

Many investigators have reported a fall in cAMP levels in intact adipose tissue or adipocytes after insulin addition (Butcher *et al.*, 1966, 1968a; Jungas, 1966; Kuo and De Renzo, 1969). In subcellular membranous particles isolated from fat cells, Vaughan and Murad (1969) showed that adenyl cyclase activity could be enhanced by epinephrine, ACTH, or glucagon. In these particles, however, insulin had no influence in the presence or absence of epinephrine on the adenyl cyclase system (Vaughan and Murad, 1969). Rodbell (1967) and Rodbell *et al.* (1968) had reported earlier that adenyl cyclase activity in adipocyte ghosts was not inhibited by insulin in the presence or absence of agents which increased adenyl cyclase activity in these preparations. Nevertheless, insulin still stimulated glucose utilization.

Several workers have succeeded in duplicating the lipolytic actions of catecholamines on adipocytes by adding cAMP or its dibutyryl derivative. Surprisingly, however, cAMP addition to rat diaphragm preparations was reported to increase glucose uptake and glycogen synthesis (Edelman *et al.*, 1966). In contrast, the dibutyryl derivative of cAMP when added to rat diaphragm inhibited these variables (Chambaut *et al.*, 1969). These same authors also reported that the dibutyryl derivative of cAMP inhibited the effects of insulin on uptake of galactose-1-^{14}C and α-amino-isobutyric acid by diaphragm, but did not inhibit the stimulation by insulin of glycogen synthesis or glucose uptake (Chambaut *et al.*, 1969). Yet Ensinck *et al.* (1969) reported that the dibutyryl derivative of cAMP inhibited several aspects of insulin action on rat hemidiaphragms, and they presented data suggesting that phosphodiesterase activity may have been stimulated by insulin. If so, this would have resulted in the observed fall in cAMP levels. However, Blecher *et al.* (1968) reported that insulin did *not* inhibit the lipolytic effects of the dibutyryl derivative of cAMP on adipose tissue. Explanations for these discrepancies are not evident.

In relation to the effects of insulin on the adenyl cyclase system in adipose tissue and muscle, it is apparent that no unifying statement is possible at this time. I believe that information summarized militates against the simplistic hypothesis that the primary mode of insulin action in muscle and adipose tissue is to inhibit a single adenyl cyclase system on the plasma membrane, and thereby to lower cAMP levels in "the" intracellular space. Birnbaumer and Rodbell (1969) and Birnbaumer *et al.* (1969) have presented rather convincing evidence for the existence of a single adenyl cyclase system in adipocyte ghosts, and multiple non-competitive sites or receptors for various hormones which can influence adipocyte metabolism (i.e., epinephrine, ACTH, glucagon, etc.). Insulin did not inhibit the cyclase system while continuing to influence glucose metabolism (Rodbell *et al.*, 1968). These data strengthen the conclusions of Butcher *et al.* (1968a) concerning the key role played by the adenyl cyclase system in the lipolytic actions of the various hormones which activate the "hormone sensitive lipase" in adipose tissue. While this may be regarded as established, a direct role of the adenyl cyclase system in mediating insulin action on adipose tissue and muscle must be considered unlikely at this time. The involvement of the adenyl cyclase system with insulin action on the liver provides an even more controversial topic which will be discussed in the next section (IV,A) when considering insulin effects on hepatic metabolism.

From combined observations, the tentative conclusion emerges that cAMP is probably not directly involved as a mediator in the action of insulin on muscle (Craig *et al.*, 1969); in the action of insulin on glucose transport and oxidation by adipose tissue (Rodbell *et al.*, 1968); nor in the action of various agents which mimic the antilipolytic actions of insulin (Kuo and De Renzo, 1969). The nature of the "transduction system" between plasma membrane receptor and intracellular metabolic process remains mysterious. As Wool *et al.* (1968) commented, "About insulin mechanism of action, it may truthfully be said that we know a great deal and understand nothing."

IV. SPECIFIC EFFECTS OF INSULIN ON CARBOHYDRATE AND FATTY ACID METABOLISM

A. DIFFERENT RESPONSES IN VARIOUS TISSUES

1. General

Since the phenomenology of insulin action has been so well reviewed elsewhere (Krahl, 1961), there is little justification in attempting more than a brief recapitulation here. The effects of insulin on protein synthesis are discussed in detail by Manchester (this series). The control of glycogen metabolism has been extensively discussed in a symposium devoted to this topic (Whelan and Cameron, 1964). Larner *et al.* (1964, 1968) have considered the role of insulin in stimulating glycogen synthesis and have summarized observations demonstrating an activation of the UDPG-α glucan transglucosylase. The effects of insulin on uptake of glucose and its metabolism by a skeletal and cardiac muscle have been reviewed by many, for example, Levine and Goldstein (1955), Morgan *et al.* (1965), and Park *et al.* (1961). The influences of insulin on transport of various substances are covered by Riggs (this series). Randle *et al.* (1966) have reviewed the interactions of insulin with muscle in relation to preferential substrate utilization and the inhibitory effects of fatty acids on glucose utilization (Randle *et al.*, 1963; Randle, 1966). More recently, however, conclusions concerning the inhibitory effects of fatty acids on glucose utilization by all skeletal muscles have been challenged (Cassens *et al.*, 1969; Schonfeld and Kipnis, 1968a,b). The effects of insulin on adipose tissue metabolism have been reviewed by Rodbell *et al.* (1968) and by Ball and Jungas (1964). The tissue specificity toward insulin action and the general metabolic effects of insulin have been well covered by Renold and Winegrad (1960), Krahl (1961), Ashmore and Carr (1964), Winegrad (1964), Hechter and Halkerston (1964), Levine (1965), and by Cahill and Owen (1968).

The combined effects of insulin on metabolic processes of various tissues contribute significantly toward allowing the coordination and control of metabolic rates of fatty acid and carbohydrate metabolism by the intact organism subjected to different nutritional environments. The relevant physiology of these metabolic processes has been discussed by Tepperman and Tepperman (1970) and in Sections I and II of this review. For convenience, the effects of insulin on these processes may be listed:

1. Increased glucose uptake by skeletal and cardiac muscle, adipocytes, leucocytes, mammary gland during lactation, fibroblasts, cartilage, and bone; but no discernible overt effect of insulin on glucose metabolism by red blood cells, kidney, intestinal cells, lymphoid tissue, testis, or brain under physiological conditions. Effects on erythrocytes and kidney slices under certain other conditions were discussed in Section III,C,2.

2. Increased rates of glycogen synthesis and glucose utilization by insulin-responsive cells. The increased glycogen synthesis obtained in resting muscle is not seen in contracting muscle, where the extra glucose uptake sponsored by insulin results primarily in increased glucose oxidation (Fritz, 1960).

3. Increased lipid uptake by adipose tissue, associated with an enhancement of lipoprotein lipase activity (Wing and Robinson, 1968).

4. Increased net formation of triglyceride in adipose tissue. This results in part from decreased rates of lipolysis; increased rates of α-glycerophosphate formation and fatty acid synthesis from glucose; and increased rates of glyceride formation in adipose tissue. Insulin does *not* increase fatty acid uptake by muscle in the absence of glucose. Insulin alone does not decrease the oxidation of long-chain fatty acids by muscle, but it enhances the glucose "sparing action" (Fritz and Kaplan, 1961).

5. Decreased rates of hepatic gluconeogenesis and ketogenesis. The role of insulin in liver metabolism merits a special discussion, which is covered in the succeeding section.

2. Liver

In a previous review, the argument was advanced that in the intact organism, the effects of insulin on liver might be mediated indirectly by the control of intermediates from extrahepatic tissues whose metabolism was more directly influenced by insulin (Levine and Fritz, 1956). For example, the plasma concentration of fatty acids which is elevated during insulin deficiency might indirectly increase rates of hepatic gluconeogenesis and ketogenesis as hepatic fatty acid oxidation rates were increased (Fritz, 1961, 1967). In this sense, insulin might indirectly decrease hepatic gluconeogenesis and ketogenesis in the intact animal by producing hypolipacidemia, thereby decreasing hepatic fatty acid uptake and oxidation. Under physiological circumstances in which the whole organism is being considered, this argument retains merit (Cahill *et al.*, 1966). However, in more recent years, an action of insulin directly on isolated liver preparations has been unequivocally demonstrated, confirming many of the original observations by Miller (1961). It remains relevant to evaluate the relative importance in liver metabolism of direct effects of insulin vs indirect consequences of extrahepatic actions of insulin, and to examine what is known concerning the mode of action of insulin on liver.

Mortimore (1963) showed that insulin addition decreased both urea and glucose production from endogenous substrates in the isolated perfused liver obtained from fasted rats. A larger inhibition of net glucose output was obtained in livers from fed rats during the period 30–150 minutes after beginning the perfusion. It seems that most of the inhibition associated with insulin was *not* a result of decreased oxidative deamination or enhanced incorporation of amino acids into proteins. The results indicated that insulin administration inhibited net glycogenolysis and glucose production *in vitro*, and that the effect was most pronounced when glucose levels in the perfusate were high Mortimore, 1963).

More recently, Jefferson *et al.* (1968) have demonstrated that after rats were rendered acutely diabetic by the injection of guinea pig anti-insulin serum, the isolated perfused livers had high rates of glucose production. These high rates were lowered to normal by the addition of insulin to the perfused liver preparations. In a related study, Exton and Park (1968a) demonstrated that administration of cAMP increased gluconeogenesis from labeled lactate in a manner which closely re-

sembled the effects elicited by epinephrine or glucagon. Jefferson *et al.*
(1968) indicated that the increased rates of gluconeogenesis in livers
from diabetic rats were associated with elevated levels of cAMP, and
they postulated that the high concentrations of this intermediate resulted
from the stimulation of the adenyl cyclase system by glucagon or by
catecholamines in the perfusate. The authors interpreted their results
by suggesting that insulin apparently inhibited adenyl cyclase activity,
thereby antagonizing the actions of glucagon. Although cAMP levels
rose following the administration of antiinsulin serum (AIS) *in vivo*,
this did not occur when the antibody was added to the isolated perfused
liver Jefferson *et al.*, 1968). Similarly, neither glucose nor urea production by the isolated preparation was increased by AIS addition *in vitro*.
In fact, none of the effects of AIS *in vivo* could be duplicated by its
addition to the isolated perfused livers.

Mackrell and Sokal (1969) have confirmed that the metabolic effects
of glucagon on perfused rat livers were generally antagonized by concomitant addition of insulin, but they showed that the degree of antag-
onism varied according to the metabolic pathway being investigated.
By varying the administered doses, these authors were able to demonstrate a dissociation of the antagonistic effects. For example, low doses
of insulin blocked urea production from endogenous substrates in the
presence or absence of glucagon, but even high doses of insulin failed
to inhibit the activation of phosphorylase which followed the administration of 0.3 μg glucagon (Mackrell and Sokal, 1969).

In the experiments reported by Jefferson *et al.* (1968), the addition
of physiological amounts of insulin to isolated liver preparations perfused
in the presence of glucose inhibited gluconeogenesis; increased glucose
incorporation into glycogen and fatty acids; and decreased potassium
loss into the medium. Jefferson *et al.* (1968) indicated that insulin action
in vivo was often more pronounced than that found in *in vitro* experiments, suggesting that variables of an unknown nature remain to be
defined. For example, all investigators appear to agree that glucose
and insulin do not appreciably inhibit ketogenesis by perfused livers
from diabetic rats (Wieland, 1968; Menahan and Wieland, 1969),
whereas insulin readily decreases hepatic ketogenesis *in vivo*. In view
of these observations, together with recent findings of Mackrell and
Sokal (1969), it is premature to conclude that insulin acts on liver
exclusively by lowering intracellular cAMP levels. Even though a role
for cAMP as possible mediator is evident (Exton and Park, 1968a; Jefferson *et al.*, 1968), it is apparent that glucagon activation of phosphorylase
in the presence of insulin, concomitant with an inhibition of urea formation in perfused livers in the presence of glucagon, cannot be mediated

by a change in concentration of a single component in a single compartment (Mackrell and Sokal, 1969). The existence of multiple adenyl cyclase systems controlling the concentrations in multiple intracellular cAMP pools remains a logical possibility. Although there is evidence for only a single hormone-sensitive adenyl cyclase in adipocytes (Birnbaumer and Rodbell, 1969), others have suggested separate adenyl cyclase systems in liver for epinephrine and glucagon (Bitensky *et al.*, 1968; Cohen and Bitensky, 1969). From the combined information, the unfortunate conclusion emerges that the mechanisms by which insulin exerts its effects on liver remain unknown.

Although the effects of insulin on hepatic metabolism appear to be enhanced in the presence of glucose (Mortimore, 1963; Krahl, 1961), the mechanisms are unclear, since insulin does not influence glucose entry or exit from liver cells (Cahill *et al.*, 1958; Hetenyi *et al.*, 1969). Hepatic glucose production and the role of insulin were reviewed in the previous "Actions of Hormones on Molecular Processes" by Ashmore and Carr (1964). In the intervening period, the chief developments have resulted from a reawakening interest in the use of perfused livers, and in a growing awareness of the role of the adenyl cyclase system in hormone action. Together with these developments has come a realization that metabolic control is very complex indeed, and that a detailed understanding of the molecular events associated with insulin action on these processes is not very imminent. As Winegrad (1964) stated in an accompanying chapter, ". . . the discussion of these effects of insulin on lipid metabolism in a volume entitled *Actions of Hormones on Molecular Processes* is not only premature but also outrageously presumptive." I readily admit that the same conclusion can unfortunately be drawn regarding the present state of knowledge.

In recent years, the control of glucose production and ketogenesis by the liver has been much discussed (Miller, 1961, 1965; Haft, 1967; Newsholme and Gevers, 1967; Fritz, 1967; Ashmore and Weber, 1968; McCraw *et al.*, 1968; Williamson *et al.*, 1968a,b, 1969; Krebs, 1964, 1966; Wieland, 1968; Exton and Park, 1968b; Menahan and Wieland, 1969). Since gluconeogenesis and ketogenesis are invariably greatly enhanced during insulin deficiency, even though high glucose levels are sustained *in vivo*, it would appear that hyperglycemia alone is insufficient to inhibit hepatic glucose production and ketogenesis in pancreatectomized animals. Yet, in isolated perfused livers from fed or fasted rats, recent experiments have demonstrated that some degree of intrinsic regulation by glucose levels exists in the absence of exogenous insulin, provided the preparations are well oxygenated (Ruderman and Herrera, 1968; Glinsman *et al.*, 1969). Others have reported that elevated glucose levels do *not* decrease glucose formation from lactate in perfused rat livers (Exton and Park, 1967; Jefferson *et al.*, 1968), whereas Sokal and Weintraub (1966) failed to obtain increased hepatic gluconeogenesis in response to hypoglycemia. The apparent discrepancy could be related to differences in the degree of oxygenation, since Glinsman *et al.* (1969) were able to elicit inhibition of glucose production by hyperglycemia only when a high concentration of red blood cells were present in the perfusate, allowing greater rates of oxygen consumption. Although the data of Glinsman *et al.* (1969) are probably more related to the control of glycogen synthesis and glycogenolysis than they are to gluconeogenesis, the studies of Ruderman and Herrera (1968) deal primarily with glucose production from alanine. Factors involved in the autoregulation of glucose production in the absence of insulin are poorly understood. It is hardly conceivable that simple mass action considerations prevail (Ashmore and Weber, 1968). When high lactate concentrations are present in the perfusate, and when the activities of enzymes associated with gluconeogenesis are high, the elevated glucose levels in the perfusing media are not likely to inhibit glucose production. Perhaps insulin facilitates the ability of the hepatocyte to respond to elevated glucose levels by inhibiting gluconeogenesis at a different site.

Insulin did not inhibit the increase in glucose production by perfused livers from fasted rats which was elicited by the dibutyryl derivative of cAMP (Menahan and Wieland, 1969), suggesting that the effects of insulin on liver are mediated at a stage prior to the formation of cAMP. However, in other experiments, Senft *et al.* (1968) reported that high doses of insulin increased phosphodiesterase activity in skeletal muscle, liver, and adipose tissue, whereas Glinsman and Mortimore (1968) indicated that insulin inhibited the effects of cAMP on glucose production from perfused livers of fed rats. Explanations for the different results are not apparent.

It is difficult to consider the effects of insulin on isolated perfused livers without simultaneously referring to conditions which prevail *in vivo* under physiological conditions. The overall net effects *in vivo* are unequivocal, i.e., insulin administration increases glycogen and fatty acid synthesis while decreasing hepatic glucose output and ketone formation. The time required *in vivo* for actions of insulin on metabolic processes in liver from diabetic animals to be manifested is greater than that needed to demonstrate enhanced glucose uptake by adipose and muscle tissue, and to observe lower fatty acid levels in plasma which follow decreased net rates of lipolysis (Renold *et al.*, 1955; Levine and Fritz, 1956; Fritz, 1961).

Insulin probably directly alters liver metabolism, perhaps by counteracting the effects of glucagon and catecholamines. In addition, insulin also influences metabolic pathways in extrahepatic tissues, thereby changing the amounts and mixtures of substrates which are presented to the liver (Tepperman and Tepperman, 1970). The molecular mechanisms by which these coordinated responses are mediated remain unknown. They result in a decreased release of fatty acids from adipose tissue and decreased rates of gluconeogenesis and ketogenesis by liver, together with increased rates of most anabolic processes. The factual details regarding the changes in the adenyl cyclase system in various cells during these processes remain to be described more precisely, and until there is agreement here, it is obvious that the functional role of the adenyl cyclase system in possibly mediating insulin action cannot be properly assessed. The interactions among the metabolic and hormonal controls which relate the rates of gluconeogenesis and ketogenesis to that of fatty acid oxidation (Fritz, 1967; Williamson *et al.*, 1968b, 1969) remain fertile fields for investigation.

Other aspects of lipid metabolism in relation to insulin action, previously discussed by Winegrad (1964), will not be considered further. The "lipid derangements of diabetes," including a discussion of cholesterol metabolism, have been covered by Siperstein (1960), and the feedback control of cholesterol synthesis has been reviewed by Siperstein and Fagan (1964).

B. A Consideration of Rapid Effects of Insulin vs Secondary Effects following Insulin Action

The argument has been developed that a consideration of the effects of insulin must clearly differentiate between the primary or molecular site of action and the secondary or cellular modes of action. Independent of the mechanisms by which the "transduction system" couples changes in the metabolic effector system in response to changes in the state of the receptor, it is clear that insulin provides a useful tool with which to probe the fundamental regulatory systems which modulate rates of carbohydrate or fatty acid metabolism in a multienzymatic pathway.

There are tertiary effects associated with insulin action. When the flux through a multienzymatic pathway is altered, the amounts of enzymes in that pathway are frequently changed. The signals for this change, and the mechanisms by which they are established are certain to provide a most exciting chapter in molecular biology. They are only incidental, however, to a study of the molecular site of insulin action.

Hechter and Halkerston (1964) have reviewed the problems associated with defining hormone action at various levels of organization, and have critically discussed the limitations of the *hormone–enzyme thesis* and the *hormone–gene thesis*. In terms which are more acceptable to the current mode, insulin might alter enzymatic activity in one of three general manners:

1. Induce a conformational change in some nonenzymatic cytostructural element, resulting in changes in permeability, and/or in activation of a "transduction system," which in turn would activate multienzyme pathways associated with the specific receptor–transducer assembly.

Examples of this would include the changes in transmembrane potential, the increased permeability shown by plasma membranes of muscle and adipose tissue to certain sugars, ions or amino acids which follow insulin addition; or an inhibition of activity of the adenyl cyclase system attached to the plasma membrane. This concept implies the existence of one or more sets of insulin-specific receptors on the plasma membrane whose state in some manner relates to the control of the activities of intracellular enzymes, and possibly to the control of the permeability properties of the plasma membrane.

2. Induce a conformational change directly in an enzyme system, thereby altering its activity.

Examples of this might include the adenyl cyclase system, although this appears most unlikely; or the glycogen synthetase system, but this also would appear unlikely if insulin in fact never penetrates to the cell interior.

3. Induce a change in gene expression, directly or indirectly, by altering transcription and/or translation in any of the many ways thus far conceived, and in any of the still larger number of ways which remain to be discovered. Examples follow:

(i) Altering the rate of transcription of parts of DNA associated with the synthesis of particular mRNA, either by affecting the operon or the promotor; or by influencing the activity of RNA polymerases.

(ii) Altering the rate of translation of the mRNA associated with the synthesis of particular proteins, either by affecting the rate of egress of mRNA from nucleus to cytoplasm to ribosomes; by affecting the stability of the mRNA; by altering the nature of the mRNA–ribosomal interactions; or by influencing any of the multiplicity of steps associated with the initiation, propagation, or termination of protein synthesis.

(iii) Altering the net amount of enzyme by influencing any other stage associated with its synthesis or degradation. These general possibilities for hormone action at a genic level are discussed more fully by Tata in Volume I of this treatise, who considers the sites of action of the growth promoting hormones.

Potential examples of insulin action at these levels include the effects of insulin on the synthesis of certain enzymes involved with fatty acid biosynthesis (Gellhorn and Benjamin, 1966); the synthesis of lipoprotein lipase in adipose tissue (Wing and Robinson, 1968); and the synthesis of specific hexokinases by various tissues (Hansen *et al.*, 1967; Katzen, 1967). All of these effects require hours or days to elicit the increase in enzyme synthesis. From data previously reviewed, it appears unlikely that the insulin molecule can gain access to the nucleus to obtain the possibility of interacting directly with the genic elements. If this set of mechanisms is not to be discarded as a potential site for insulin action, one therefore must invoke an indirect mediator resulting from insulin action, such as a lowered level of cAMP following an inhibition of the adenyl cyclase system, a change in ionic flux or some other effect which is a consequence of an allosteric interaction of insulin with its receptor on the plasma membrane. The same general arguments pertain to the stimulatory effects of insulin on protein synthesis by muscle, where insulin has no effects on isolated ribosomes (Wool *et al.*, 1968). The role of insulin in stimulating protein synthesis in muscle, and the possible mechanisms involved are discussed by Wool *et al.*, 1968; Manchester, and by Tata, this treatise.

Many of the actions of insulin on adipocytes have been mimicked by treatment of the cells with phospholipase C, low doses of trypsin and other proteolytic agents, or by exposure to polyene antibiotics (see Section III,B). None of these agents is likely to have a direct effect on the genome, and it appears unreasonable to anticipate that all three classes of compounds could influence transcription or translation in a short period of time, thereby inducing a "coordinated" response of increased permeability, increased glucose oxidation, increased fatty acid synthesis, and decreased lipolysis. In the presence of inhibitors of transcription and translation, insulin continues to evoke these responses (Carlin and Hechter, 1964; Gellhorn and Benjamin, 1966; Fain, 1964; Hechter and Halkerston, 1964; Manchester, this series). It therefore appears almost certain that the immediate cellular effects of insulin on increased glucose transport; increased glucose oxidation; increased conversion of glucose to glycogen and to fatty acids; and decreased triglyceride lipolysis are independent of *de novo* synthesis of enzymes. The effects of insulin on erythrocytes treated with chymotrypsin (Rieser and Rieser, 1964c) and on adipocyte ghosts (Rodbell *et al.*, 1968) also rule out the possibility that nuclear involvement is obligatory. The immediate cellular effects described, including the inhibition of adenyl cyclase activity, are examples of "fine controls" in the terminology of Krebs (1964) in that they occur quickly and are independent of new protein synthesis.

On the other hand, synthesis of various enzymes can be shown to be influenced indirectly by insulin. Following increased glucose uptake induced by insulin, levels of certain hexokinases in adipose tissue (Hansen *et al.*, 1967) and heart (Katzen, 1967), and the glucokinase content of liver (Sols *et al.*, 1964; Sharma *et al.*, 1964) increase. The augmented glucose uptake sponsored by insulin in adipose tissue and muscle is not dependent on the synthesis of extra hexokinase, however, since puromycin does not block the metabolic effects of insulin on adipose tissue, except for the influence on protein synthesis (Fain, 1964).

During chronic insulin deficiency, hepatic levels of pyruvate carboxylase, phosphoenolpyruvate carboxykinase, fructose-1,6-diphosphatase and glucose-6-phosphatase are elevated, and these increased activities apparently reflect new protein synthesis, as judged by studies with the usual inhibitors (Weber *et al.*, 1967). Yet, gluconeogenesis rates are increased immediately after the administration of antiinsulin serum to normal rats, long before new enzyme synthesis occurs (Jefferson *et al.*, 1968). As would be anticipated from these observations, insulin administration eventually lowers the level of the above enzymes over a course of days (Weber *et al.*, 1965). But insulin administration *in vivo* or to perfused livers decreases gluconeogenesis in a matter of minutes to hours (see Section IV,A). It may therefore be concluded that the activities of the "regulatory" enzymes associated with gluconeogenesis quickly change in response to insulin, and long-range adjustments occur which alter the absolute levels of these enzymes in an adaptation to the altered flux in the multienzyme pathway.

These enzyme adaptations to changes in rates of metabolic pathways doubtless reflect changes in levels of available insulin, and implementation of the adaptation requires operation of all machinery associated with enzyme-forming systems. Because the adaptations occur relatively slowly and require changes in enzyme levels which are secondary to changes in flux, these types of regulations have been labeled "coarse controls." This terminology is obviously relevant only to a discussion of animal cells which already contain a full complement of enzymes dictated by the cell's phenotype. The long-range effects of insulin on these "coarse controls" is to change the relative distribution of enzymes within the cell. The effect is an indirect one, and it is therefore erroneous to conclude that insulin itself is an inducing agent for glucokinase in liver or a suppressing agent for the controlling enzymes of gluconeogenesis in liver. At a descriptive level, of course, it is a factual statement that insulin treatment over a period of days *does* result in decreased hepatic levels of the key gluconeogenic enzymes (i.e., pyruvate carboxylase, phosphoenolpyruvate carboxykinase, fructose-1,6-diphosphatase and glucose-6-phosphatase), and in increased levels of the key glycolytic enzymes (i.e., glucokinase, phosphofructokinase, and pyruvate kinase) (Weber *et al.*, 1965, 1966). At the present time, however, it is not permissible to do more than speculate on the possible mechanisms by which this is accomplished, and there is no justification to conclude that ". . . insulin integrates hepatic metabolic function at the genic action level by influencing enzyme biosynthesis" (Weber *et al.*, 1966). The increases in glycogen synthetase, the regulatory hepatic glycolytic enzymes and the enzymes of fatty acid synthesis, as well as the suppression of the enzymes associated with the control of gluconeogenesis (Weber *et al.*, 1966), are phenomena secondary to the alterations in rates of metabolic pathways less deviously influenced by insulin. There is no evidence that insulin directly acts as a repressor or inducer of enzyme synthesis by interaction with any part of the transcription or translation apparatus. The possibility that altered concentrations of other agents—the ubiquitous cAMP, for example—may influence transcription or translation in mammalian cells remains to be determined. In any case, the changes in enzyme levels associated with chronic insulin excess or deficiency are not required for manifestation of the *in vitro* effects of insulin on increased rates of glucose transport, glycogen synthesis, fatty acid synthesis, and antilipolysis; or inhibition of gluconeogenesis and ketogenesis. In short, the long-range changes in enzyme concentrations in tissues of insulin-deficient organisms are a consequence of the altered metabolic pathway rates, and not vice versa.

From these considerations, it seems reasonable (to me) to propose that insulin does *not* exert its metabolic effects by directly interacting with an enzyme involved in carbohydrate or lipid metabolism, nor by directly altering the rate of genic transcription or translation. It appears that insulin action indirectly results in rapid changes of activities of certain existing enzymes, with subsequent changes in the flux through particular multienzyme pathways. Following the altered flux, the rates of formation of appropriate enzymes are eventually changed.

It is considerably easier to state how insulin does not act than how it does. The hypothesis has been developed that the effects on carbohydrate and lipid metabolism are most probably mediated by activating specific receptors on the plasma membrane, inducing conformational changes which initiate a cascade effect culminating in rapid and reversible changes of activities of specific enzymes in organized structures. But this is little more than a guess, and will remain so until the precise nature of the receptors is known, and the chemical and physical nature of the postulated "transduction system" is determined. Only then will it be possible to determine if insulin has single or multiple sites of action.

V. SUMMARY AND CONCLUSIONS

Two problem areas were considered: (1) the biological aspects of insulin action, associated with the coordination of metabolic pathways in the intact organism; and (2) the molecular aspects of insulin action which lead to changes in metabolic rates.

A. Biological

From an analysis of the comparative physiology and biochemistry of insulin action, it was suggested that the particular cellular effects of insulin in a given species were related to metabolic adaptations which occurred during the evolution of that species.

Effects of insulin on adipose tissue obtained from animals with carnivorous and predatory eating habits were compared with those on adipose tissue obtained from ruminants and herbivores. The antilipolytic action of insulin were shown to be evident primarily in adipose tissues from carnivorous animals. Adipose tissue from ruminants and herbivorous birds were reported to have relatively low rates of fatty acid synthesis from glucose, and insulin had but little, if any, effect on glucose metabolism by adipose tissue from these species. The physiological implications of these differences in metabolic behavior among species were discussed in relation to a consideration of the biological effects of insulin, and in relation to the significance of "insulin-responsive tissues" vs "insulin-nonresponsive tissues." The tendency for diabetes to be most severe in carnivorous animals after pancreatectomy was discussed.

After considering evolutionary aspects of insulin physiology, a thesis was suggested concerning the nature of the functional relation between the pancreatic acinar cells and the islet cells. Although insulin secretion may be controlled primarily by levels of metabolites such as glucose in the perfusing medium, other factors were also shown to play a significant role. The facts were reviewed that pancreatic acinar and β-cells each possess receptors able to detect chemical substances such as secretin and pancreozymin. These data suggested the generalization that one portion of the hormonal and nutritional controls which regulate insulin release may have evolved in conjunction with the systems which control pancreatic enzyme secretion. The survival value of coordinating digestion and absorption with the assimilation of foodstuffs was discussed.

B. MOLECULAR

Evidence was presented that many of the physiological effects of insulin on intermediary metabolism could be secondary to actions of insulin on the plasma membrane. Although there is no proof for the existence of a molecular interaction between a specific receptor of the plasma membrane and insulin, considerable indirect evidence points toward an action of insulin at this locus. Many of the metabolic effects elicited by insulin on muscle cells and adipocytes can be imitated by several agents which interact with lipid, protein, or lipoprotein components of the cell membrane. Many of the actions of insulin or carbohydrate and fatty acid metabolism were shown to involve changes in transport across the plasma membrane or changes in the properties of membrane-bound enzymes.

Preliminary evidence was presented in support of the notion that insulin need not enter the cell interior to elicit its metabolic effects. Experiments were summarized which favored the concept that the primary action of insulin is to combine with specific receptors on the plasma membrane, thereby inducing changes in the physical nature of the cell membrane.

Evidence was reviewed favoring the existence of a hypothetical "transduction system" which could be activated by the insulin-altered receptor, and which could couple rates of metabolic processes in a multienzyme pathway to changes in the state of the receptor. The adenyl cyclase system was evaluated as the potential "transduction system" for insulin action, but it was concluded that the primary site of action of insulin is most probably not at the level of the adenyl cyclase system. Further, evidence was reviewed which indicated that the intracellular concentrations of cAMP cannot be the sole mediating factor which relates insulin action to metabolic effects elicited in adipocytes, muscle or liver cells. The involvement of changes in the adenyl cyclase system was reviewed in relation to insulin action on antilipolysis in adipose tissue, glycogen synthesis in muscle, and gluconeogenesis in liver.

Finally, the primary influence of insulin on "fine controls" was emphasized in interpreting the metabolic effects which follow insulin action. The changes in enzyme concentrations elicited by long-term administration of insulin or by long-term insulin deficiency were interpreted as a consequence of the altered metabolic pathway rates, and not vice versa.

Efforts were made to correlate what little is known about the molecular mode of insulin action with the vast amount of information available on the cellular and physiological aspects of insulin action. The coordinate nature of insulin action, in integrating pathways of carbohydrate and lipid metabolism in the intact organism, was emphasized.

C. Epilogue

The two problem areas—molecular and biological—offer two different levels of organization with which to approach the effects of insulin on metabolic processes. On the one hand, insulin may be regarded as a powerful chemical tool with which to probe the control of the synthesis of particular enzymes, to probe the fundamental regulatory systems which modulate rates of enzyme activities in organized assemblies, or to probe the nature of the postulated receptors on plasma membranes and the mechanisms by which the hypothetical transduction processes relate the changes in configurational state of the plasma membrane to changes in enzymic activities. On the other hand, the physiological role of insulin in the intact organism can be investigated to ascertain how metabolic events are coordinated, not only within cells but also among cells of different organs. Equally interesting questions may then be asked concerning the unique metabolic adaptations which have occurred during evolution.

ACKNOWLEDGMENTS

It is a pleasure to acknowledge the important role which enjoyable discussions with colleagues and friends have played in shaping the nature of this review. I am particularly grateful to Helen Fritz, Marty Rodbell, and Jay Tepperman for continuing dialogues. I also wish to thank several members of the Banting and Best Department of Medical Research, who patiently read the first draft and offered many constructive criticisms. Among these colleagues, I am especially indebted to Alan Goodridge, John Logothetopoulos, and Francis Rolleston for valuable suggestions. In addition, it is a pleasure to thank Rachmiel Levine for providing additional references and for asking provocative questions. I also am happy to express warm gratitude to Miss Jackie Taillon for efficiently and uncomplainingly transcribing my faulty scrawl into impeccable print.

ADDENDUM

To the reader interested in learning what has transpired in this field recently, I recommend the "IV Capri Conference on the Pathogenesis of Diabetes Mellitus," edited by R. Luft and P. Randle, which appeared in 1970 as Supplement 1 of Volume VII of *Acta Diabetologia Latina*. This article by Rodbell *et al.* [Rodbell, M., Birnbaumer, L., Pohl, S. L., Michael, H., and Krans, J. (1970). *Acta Diabetologia Latina*, VII, Suppl. 1, pp. 9–57] on "Properties of the adenyl cyclase systems in liver and adipose cells: The mode of action of hormones" makes for especially interesting reading, and other articles in the supplement are equally provocative and informative. The book edited by E. Cerasi and R. Luft, Nobel Symposium 13, entitled "Pathogenesis of Diabetes Mellitus" (Almqvist and Wiksell, Stockholm, Sweden, 1970), is also "must-reading" for insulin aficionados. Recent advances pertaining to insulin actions on white adipose tissue are covered in "Adipose Tissue, Regulation and Metabolic Function," edited by B. Jeanrenaud and D. Hepp (Academic Press, New York, 1970). Insulin effects on brown fat cells have been reviewed by Nora Reed and John N. Fain [*In* "Brown Adipose Tissue," (1970). (O. Lindberg, ed.), pp. 207–224. American Elsevier]. The next volume in the "Handbook of Physiology" series, edited by D. Steiner and N. Freinkel, deals with the "Endocrine Pancreas" and is now in press. Finally, with the 50th anniversary of the discovery of insulin being celebrated in many symposia to be held all over the world during 1971, it is likely that a plethora of books will appear in 1972 describing the latest on insulin action. To the making of revisions, there is no end.

REFERENCES

Ashmore, J., and Carr, L. (1964). *In* "Actions of Hormones on Molecular Processes" (G. Litwack and D. Kritchevsky, eds.), p. 360. Wiley, New York.

Ashmore, J., and Weber, G. (1968). *In* "Carbohydrate Metabolism and its Disorders" (F. Dickens, P. J. Randle, and W. J. Whelan, eds.), Vol. 1, p. 335. Academic Press, New York.

Ball, E. G., and Jungas, R. L. (1964). *Recent Progr. Hormone Res.* **20**, 183.

Ballard, F. J., Hanson, R. W., and Kronfeld, D. S. (1969). *Federation Proc.* **28**, 218.

Behrens, O. K., and Grinnan, E. L. (1969). *Ann. Rev. Biochem.* **38**, 83.

Biegelman, P. M., and Hollander, P. B. (1962). *Proc. Soc. Exptl. Biol. Med.* **110**, 590.

Birnbaumer, L., and Rodbell, M. (1969). *J. Biol. Chem.* **244**, 3477.

Birnbaumer, L., Pohl, S. L., and Rodbell, M. (1969). *J. Biol. Chem.* **244**, 3468.

Bitensky, M. W., Russel, V., and Robertson, W. (1968). *Biochem. Biophys. Res. Commun.* **31**, 706.

Blecher, M. (1965). *Biochem. Biophys. Res. Commun.* **21**, 202.

Blecher, M. (1966). *Biochem. Biophys. Res. Commun.* **23**, 68.

Blecher, M. (1968). *Gunma Symp. Endocrinol.* **5**, 145.

Blecher, M., Merlino, N. S., and Ro'Ane, J. T. (1968). *J. Biol. Chem.* **243**, 3973.

Bocek, R. M., and Beatty, C. H. (1969). *Endocrinology* **85**, 615.

Bonner, J. T., Barkley, D. S., Hall, E. M., Konijin, T. M., Mason, J. W., O'Keefe, G., III, and Wolfe, P. B. (1969). *Develop. Biol.* **20**, 72.

Butcher, R. W., and Sutherland, E. W. (1967). *Ann. N. Y. Acad. Sci.* **139**, 849.

Butcher, R. W., Ho, R. J., Meng, H. C., and Sutherland, E. W. (1965). *J. Biol. Chem.* **240**, 4515.

Butcher, R. W., Sneyd, J. G. T., Park, C. R., and Sutherland, E. W., Jr. (1966). *J. Biol. Chem.* **241**, 1651.

Butcher, R. W., Baird, C. E., and Sutherland, E. W. (1968a). *J. Biol. Chem.* **243**, 1705.

Butcher, R. W., Robison, G. A., Hardman, J. G., and Sutherland, E. W. (1968b). *Advan. Enzyme Regulation* **6**, 357.

Cahill, G. F., Jr., and Owen, O. E. (1968). *In* "Carbohydrate Metabolism and its Disorders" (F. Dickens, P. J. Randle, and W. J. Whelan, eds.), Vol. 1, p. 497. Academic Press, New York.

Cahill, G. F., Jr., Ashmore, J., Earle, A. S., and Zottu, S. (1958). *Am. J. Physiol.* **192**, 491.

Cahill, G. F., Jr., Herrera, M. G., Morgan, A. P., Soeldner, J. S., Steinke, J., Levy, P. L., Reichard, G. A., Jr., and Kipnis, D. M. (1966). *J. Clin. Invest.* **45**, 1751.

Carlin, H., and Hechter, O. (1962). *J. Biol. Chem.* **237**, PC1371.

Carlin, H., and Hechter, O. (1964). *Proc. Soc. Exptl. Biol. Med.* **115**, 127.

Carter, J. R., and Martin, D. B. (1969). *Biochim. Biophys. Acta* **177**, 521.

Cassens, R. G., Bocek, R. M., and Beatty, C. H. (1969). *Am. J. Physiol.* **217**, 715.

Chambaut, A. M., Eboué-Bonis, D., Hanoune, J., and Clauser, H. (1969). *Biochem. Biophys. Res. Commun.* **34**, 283.

Clark, C. M., Jr., Cahill, G. F., Jr., and Soeldner, J. S. (1968). *Diabetes* **17**, 362.

Cohen, K. L., and Bitensky, M. W. (1969). *J. Pharmacol. Exptl. Therap.* **169**, 80.

Cohn, M. (1968). *Symp. Intern. Soc. Cell Biol.* **7**, 1.

Coore, H. G., and Randle, P. J. (1964). *Biochem. J.* **93**, 66.

Corbin, J. D., and Krebs, E. G. (1969). *Biochem. Biophys. Res. Commun.* **36**, 328.

Craig, J. W., Rall, T. W., and Larner, J. (1969). *Biochim. Biophys. Acta* **177**, 213.

Cuatrecasas, P. (1969). *Proc. Natl. Acad. Sci. U. S.* **63**, 450.

Di Girolamo, M., and Rudman, D. (1966). *Am. J. Physiol.* **210**, 721.

Dormandy, T. L. (1967). *Symp. Intern. Soc. Cell Biol.* **6**, 275.

Dormandy, T. L., and Zarday, Z. (1965). *J. Physiol. (London)* **180**, 684.

Edelman, P. M., Edelman, J. C., and Schwartz, I. L. (1966). *Nature* **210**, 1017.

Ensinck, J. W., Touber, J. L., and Stoll, R. W. (1969). *Diabetes* **18**, Suppl. 1, 337.

Exton, J. H., and Park, C. R. (1967). *J. Biol. Chem.* **242**, 2622.

Exton, J. H., and Park, C. R. (1968a). *J. Biol. Chem.* **243**, 4189.

Exton, J. H., and Park, C. R. (1968b). *Advan. Enzyme Regulation* **6**, 391.

Fain, J. N. (1964). *Biochim. Biophys. Acta* **84**, 636.

Fain, J. N., and Loken, S. C. (1969). *J. Biol. Chem.* **244**, 3500.

Fajans, S. S., Floyd, J. C., Jr., Knopf, R. F., and Conn, J. W. (1967). *Recent Progr. Hormone Res.* **23**, 617.

Falkmer, S., and Winbladh, L. (1964). *In* "The Structure and Metabolism of the Pancreatic Islets" (S. E. Brolin, B. Hellman, and H. Knutson, eds.), p. 17. Pergamon Press, Oxford.

Ferner, H., and Kern, H. (1964). *In* "The Structure and Metabolism of the Pancreatic Islets" (S. E. Brolin, B. Hellman, and H. Knutson, eds.), p. 3. Pergamon Press, Oxford.

Fessler, A., and Beck, J. C. (1965). *Biochim. Biophys. Acta* **106**, 199.

Foà, P. P., Melli, M., Berger, C. K., Billinger, D., and Guidotti, G. G. (1965). *Federation Proc.* **24**, 1046.

Fritz, I. B. (1960). *Am. J. Physiol.* **198**, 807.

Fritz, I. B. (1961). *Physiol. Rev.* **41**, 52.

Fritz, I. B. (1967). *Perspectives Biol. Med.* **10**, 643.

Fritz, I. B., and Kaplan, E. (1961). *Am. J. Physiol.* **200**, 1047.

Gellhorn, A., and Benjamin, W. (1966). *Advan. Enzyme Regulation* **4**, 19.
Glinsmann, W. H., and Mortimore, G. E. (1968). *Am. J. Physiol.* **215**, 553.
Glinsmann, W. H., Hern, E. P., and Lynch, A. (1969). *Am. J. Physiol.* **216**, 698.
Goldrick, R. B. (1967). *J. Lipid Res.* **8**, 581.
Goodridge, A. G. (1964). *Comp. Biochem. Physiol.* **13**, 1.
Goodridge, A. G. (1968). *Am. J. Physiol.* **214**, 902.
Goodridge, A. G., and Ball, E. G. (1965). *Comp. Biochem. Physiol.* **16**, 367.
Goodridge, A. G., and Ball, E. G. (1967). *Am. J. Physiol.* **213**, 245.
Gorbman, A., and Bern, H. A. (1962). "A Textbook of Comparative Endocrinology." Wiley, New York.
Gries, F. A., and Steinke, J. (1967). *Metab., Clin. Exptl.* **16**, 693.
Grillo, T. A. I., Okuno, G., Guidotti, G., Price, S., and Foà, P. P. (1964). *In* "The Structure and Metabolism of the Pancreatic Islets" (S. E. Brolin, B. Hellman, and H. Knutson, eds.), p. 157. Pergamon Press, Oxford.
Haft, D. E. (1967). *Am. J. Physiol.* **213**, 219.
Hales, C. N. (1967). *Essays Biochem.* **3**, 73.
Hansen, R., Pilkis, S. J., and Krahl, M. E. (1967). *Endocrinology* **81**, 1397.
Hanson, R. W., and Ballard, F. J. (1967). *Biochem. J.* **105**, 529.
Hechter, O., and Halkerston, I. D. K. (1964). *In* "The Hormones" (G. Pincus, K. V. Thimann, and E. B. Astwood, eds.), Vol. 5, p. 697. Academic Press, New York.
Hepp, K. D., Menahan, L. A., Wieland, O., and Williams, R. H. (1969). *Biochim. Biophys. Acta* **184**, 554.
Hetenyi, G., Jr., Norwich, K. H., Studney, D. R., and Hall, J. D. (1969). *Can. J. Physiol. Pharmacol.* **47**, 361.
Ho, R. J., and Jeanrenaud, B. (1967). *Biochim. Biophys. Acta* **144**, 61.
Ho, R. J., Jeanrenaud, B., Posternak, T., and Renold, A. E. (1967). *Biochim. Biophys. Acta* **144**, 74.
Houssay, B. A. (1959). *In* "Symposium on Comparative Endocrinology" (A. Gorbman, ed.), p. 639. Wiley, New York.
Jeanrenaud, B. (1968). *Ergeb. Physiol., Biol. Chem. Exptl. Pharmakol.* **60**, 57.
Jeanrenaud, B., and Renold, A. E. (1969). *In* "Physiopathology of Adipose Tissue" (J. Vague, ed.), p. 20. Excerpta Med. Found., Amsterdam.
Jefferson, L. S., Exton, J. H., Butcher, R. W., Sutherland, E. W., and Park, C. R. (1968). *J. Biol. Chem.* **243**, 1031.
Jungas, R. L. (1966). *Proc. Natl. Acad. Sci. U. S.* **56**, 757.
Kahlenberg, A., Rubinger, J., and Kalant, N. (1966). *Can. J. Biochem.* **44**, 645.
Katzen, H. M. (1967). *Advan. Enzyme Regulation* **5**, 335.
Kono, T. (1969a). *J. Biol. Chem.* **244**, 1772.
Kono, T. (1969b). *Federation Proc.* **28**, 508.
Kono, T. (1969c). *J. Biol. Chem.* **244**, 5777.
Kono, T., Crofford, O. B., and Park, C. R. (1969). *Diabetes* **18**, Suppl. 1, 335.
Koshland, D. E., Jr. (1968). *Advan. Enzyme Regulation* **6**, 291.
Krahl, M. E. (1951). *Ann. N. Y. Acad. Sci.* **54**, 649.
Krahl, M. E. (1957). *Perspectives Biol. Med.* **1**, 69.
Krahl, M. E. (1961). "The Action of Insulin on Cells." Academic Press, New York.
Krebs, H. A. (1957). *Endeavour* **16**, 125.
Krebs, H. A. (1964). *Proc. Roy. Soc.* **B159**, 545.
Krebs, H. A. (1966). *Advan. Enzyme Regulation* **4**, 339.
Kuo, J. F. (1968). *Arch. Biochem. Biophys.* **127**, 406.
Kuo, J. F., and De Renzo, E. C. (1969). *J. Biol. Chem.* **244**, 2252.

Kuo, J. F., Holmlund, C. E., and Dill, I. K. (1966a). *Life Sci.* **5**, 2257.

Kuo, J. F., Holmlund, C. E., Dill, I. K., and Bohonos, N. (1966b). *Arch. Biochem. Biophys.* **117**, 269.

Kuo, J. F., Dill, I. K., and Holmlund, C. E. (1967). *Biochim. Biophys. Acta* **148**, 683.

Kuo, J. F., Dill, I. K., Holmlund, C. E., and Bohonos, N. (1968). *Biochem. Pharmacol.* **17**, 345.

Lardy, H. A., Foster, D. O., Young, J. W., Shrago, E., and Ray, P. D. (1965). *J. Cellular Comp. Physiol.* **66**, Suppl. 1, 39.

Larner, J., Rosell-Perez, M., Friedman, D. L., and Craig, J. W. (1964). *Ciba Found. Symp., Control Glycogen Metab.* p. 273.

Larner, J., Villar-Palasi, C., Goldberg, N. O., Bishop, J. S., Huijing, F., Wenger, J. I., Sasko, H., and Brown N. B. (1968). *Advan. Enzyme Regulation* **6**, 409.

Lavis, V. P., and Williams, R. H. (1970). *J. Biol. Chem.* **245**, 23.

Lengyel, P., and Söll, D. (1969). *Bacteriol. Rev.* **33**, 264.

Levine, R. (1965). *Federation Proc.* **24**, 1071.

Levine, R., and Fritz, I. B. (1956). *Diabetes* **5**, 209.

Levine, R., and Goldstein, M. S. (1952). *Brookhaven Symp. Biol.* **5**, 73.

Levine, R., and Goldstein, M. S. (1955). *Recent Progr. Hormone Res.* **11**, 343.

Levine, R., and Pfeiffer, E. F., eds. (1968). *In* "Acta Diabetologica Latina," Vol. 5, Suppl. 1, pp. 11, 389, 417, 436, and 446. Il Ponte, Milan.

Lipmann, F. (1969). *Science* **164**, 1024.

Loten, E. G., and Sneyd, J. G. T. (1970). *Biochem. J.* **120**, 187.

McCraw, E. F., Peterson, M. J., Yarnell, G., and Ashmore, J. (1968). *Advan. Enzyme Regulation* **6**, 57.

Mackrell, D. J., and Sokal, J. E. (1969). *Diabetes* **18**, 724.

Mahler, R., Stafford, W. S., Tarrant, M. E., and Ashmore, J. (1964). *Diabetes* **13**, 297.

Mahler, R. J., and Szabo, O. (1967). *Proc. Soc. Exptl. Biol. Med.* **125**, 879.

Malaisse, W. J. (1969). "Etude de la sécrétion insulinique in vitro." Editions Arscia, Presse Acad. Eur., Brussels.

Malaisse, W. J., Lea, M. A., and Malaisse-Lagae, F. (1968). *Metab., Clin. Exptl.* **17**, 126.

Manns, J. G., and Boda, J. M. (1967). *Am. J. Physiol.* **212**, 747.

Manns, J. G., and Brockman, R. P. (1969). *Can. J. Physiol. Pharmacol.* **47**, 917.

Masoro, E. J. (1962). *J. Lipid Res.* **3**, 149.

Maturo, J. M., and Rieser, P. (1969). *Federation Proc.* **28**, 508.

Mayhew, D. A., Wright, P. H., and Ashmore, J. (1969). *Pharmacol. Rev.* **21**, 183.

Menahan, L. A., and Wieland, O. (1969). *European J. Biochem.* **9**, 55.

Mialhe, P. (1955). *Compt. Rend.* **241**, 1500.

Miller, L. L. (1961). *Recent Progr. Hormone Res.* **17**, 539.

Miller, L. L. (1965). *Federation Proc.* **24**, 737.

Minemura, T., and Crofford, O. B. (1969). *J. Biol. Chem.* **244**, 5181.

Monod, J., Changeux, J. P., and Jacob, F. (1963). *J. Mol. Biol.* **6**, 306.

Morgan, H. E., Neely, J. R., Wood, R. E., Liebecq, C., Liebermeister, H., and Park, C. R. (1965). *Federation Proc.* **24**, 1040.

Mortimore, G. E. (1963). *Am. J. Physiol.* **204**, 699.

Moskowitz, J., and Fain, J. N. (1969). *J. Clin. Invest.* **48**, 1802.

Newsholme, E. A., and Gevers, W. (1967). *Vitamins Hormones* **25**, 1.

O'Hea, E. K., and Leveille, G. A. (1968). *Comp. Biochem. Physiol.* **26**, 1081.

O'Hea, E. K., and Leveille, G. A. (1969). *J. Nutr.* **99**, 345.

Park, C. R., Morgan, H. E., Henderson, M. J., Regen, D. M., Cadenas, E., and Post, R. L. (1961). *Recent Progr. Hormone Res.* **17**, 493.

Perlman, R. L., and Pastan, I. (1968a). *Biochem. Biophys. Res. Commun.* **30**, 656.

Perlman, R. L., and Pastan, I. (1968b). *J. Biol. Chem.* **243**, 5420.

Picon, L., and Montane, M. (1968). *Compt. Rend.* **267**, 860.

Pictet, R., Orci, L., Gonet, A. E., Rouiller, C., and Renold, A. E. (1967). *Diabetologia* **3**, 188.

Randle, P. J. (1966). *Diabetologia* **2**, 237.

Randle, P. J., Garland, P. B., Hales, C. N., and Newsholme, E. A. (1963). *Lancet* i, 785.

Randle, P. J., Garland, P. B., Hales, C. N., Newsholme, E. A., Denton, R. M., and Pogson, C. I. (1966). *Recent Progr. Hormone Res.* **22**, 1.

Randle, P. J., Ashcroft, S. J. H., and Gill, J. R. (1968). *In* "Carbohydrate Metabolism and its Disorders" (F. Dickens, P. J. Randle, and W. J. Whelan, eds.), Vol. 1, p. 427. Academic Press, New York.

Renold, A. E., and Cahill, G. F., Jr. (1965). *In* "Handbook of Physiology" (Am. Physiol. Soc., J. Field, ed.), Sect. 5, p. 483. Williams & Wilkins, Baltimore, Maryland.

Renold, A. E., and Winegrad, A. I. (1960). *In* "Diabetes" (R. H. Williams, ed.), p. 129. Harper (Hoeber), New York.

Renold, A. E., Hastings, A. B., Nesbett, F. B., and Ashmore, J. (1955). *J. Biol. Chem.* **213**, 135.

Rieser, P., and Rieser, C. H. (1964a). *Proc. Soc. Exptl. Biol. Med.* **116**, 669.

Rieser, P., and Rieser, C. H. (1964b). *Arch. Biochem. Biophys.* **105**, 20.

Rodbell, M. (1964). *J. Biol. Chem.* **239**, 375.

Rodbell, M. (1966). *J. Biol. Chem.* **241**, 130.

Rodbell, M. (1967). *Biochem. J.* **105**, 2P.

Rodbell, M., and Jones, A. B. (1966). *J. Biol. Chem.* **241**, 140.

Rodbell, M., Jones, A. B., Chiappe de Cingolani, G. E., and Birnbaumer, L. (1968). *Recent Progr. Hormone Res.* **24**, 215.

Ruderman, N. B., and Herrera, M. G. (1968). *Am. J. Physiol.* **214**, 1346.

Rudman, D. (1963). *J. Lipid Res.* **4**, 119.

Rudman, D., and Del Rio, A. E. (1969). *Endocrinology* **85**, 209.

Rudman, D., Di Girolamo, M., Malkin, M. F., and Garcia, L. A. (1965). *In* "Handbook of Physiology" (Am. Physiol. Soc., J. Field, ed.), Sect. 5, p. 533. Williams & Wilkins, Baltimore, Maryland.

Rutter, W. J., Kemp, J. D., Bradshaw, W. S., Clark, W. R., Ronzio, R. A., and Saunders, T. G. (1968). *J. Cell. Physiol.* **72**, Part II, 1

Sanger, F. (1956). *Ciba Found. Colloq. Endocrinol.* **9**, 110.

Sanger, F. (1959). *Science* **129**, 1340.

Schonfeld, G., and Kipnis, D. M. (1968a). *Am. J. Physiol.* **215**, 513.

Schonfeld, G., and Kipnis, D. M. (1968b). *Diabetes* **17**, 422.

Senft, G., Schultz, G., Munske, K., and Hoffmann, M. (1968). *Diabetologia* **4**, 322.

Shafrir, E., and Wertheimer, E. (1965). *In* "Handbook of Physiology" (Am. Physiol. Soc., J. Field, ed.), Sect. 5, p. 417. Williams & Wilkins, Baltimore, Maryland.

Sharma, C., Manjeshwar, R., and Weinhouse, S. (1964). *Advan. Enzyme Regulation* **2**, 189.

Siperstein, M. D. (1960). *In* "Diabetes" (R. H. Williams, ed.), p. 102. Harper (Hoeber), New York.

Siperstein, M D., and Fagan, V. M. (1964). *Advan. Enzyme Regulation* **2**, 249.

Sircus, W. (1969). *Gut* **10**, 506.

Sokal, J. E., and Weintraub, B. (1966). *Am. J. Physiol.* **210**, 63.

Sols, A., Salas, M., and Vinuela, E. (1964). *Advan. Enzyme Regulation* **2**, 177.

Sorenson, R. L., Lindall, A. W., and Lazarow, A. (1969). *Diabetes* **18**, 129.

Steiner, D. F., Clark, J. L., Nolan, C., Rubenstein, A. H., Margoliash, E., Aten, B., and Oyer, P. E. (1969). *Recent Progr. Hormone Res.* **25**, 207.

Steinke, J., Miki, E., and Cahill, G. F., Jr. (1965). *New Engl. J. Med.* **273**, 1464.

Sutherland, E. W., and Robison, A. (1969). *Diabetes* **18**, 797.

Sutherland, E. W., Øye, I., and Butcher, R. W. (1965). *Recent Progr. Hormone Res.* **21**, 623.

Tepperman, J. (1964). *In* "Fat as a Tissue" (K. Rodahl and B. Issekitz, eds.), p. 394. McGraw-Hill, New York.

Tepperman, J., and Tepperman, H. M. (1970). *Federation Proc.* **29**, 1284.

Tung, A. K., and Yip, C. C. (1969). *Proc. Natl. Acad. Sci. U. S.* **63**, 442.

Ungar, R. H., Ketterer, H., Dupre, J., and Eisentraut, A. M. (1967). *J. Clin. Invest.* **46**, 630.

Vaughan, M., and Murad, F. (1969). *Biochemistry* **8**, 3092.

Vaughan, M., and Steinberg, D. (1963). *J. Lipid Res.* **4**, 193.

Vavrik, G., and Fritz, I. B. (1969). Unpublished observations.

Walsh, D. A., Perkins, J. P., and Krebs, E. G. (1968). *J. Biol. Chem.* **243**, 3763.

Weber, G., Singhal, R. L., and Srivastava, S. K. (1965). *Advan. Enzyme Regulation* **3**, 43.

Weber, G., Singhal, R. L., Stamm, N. B., Lea, M. A., and Fisher, E. A. (1966). *Advan. Enzyme Regulation* **4**, 59.

Weber, G., Lea, M. A., Convery, H. J. H., and Stamm, N. B. (1967). *Advan. Enzyme Regulation* **5**, 257.

Weis, L. S., and Narahara, H. T. (1969). *J. Biol. Chem.* **244**, 3084.

Wessels, N. K., and Rutter, W. J. (1969). *Sci. Am.* **220**, No. 3, 36.

Whelan, W. J., and Cameron, M. P., eds. (1964). *Ciba Found. Symp., Control Glycogen Metab.* pp. 1–415.

Wieland, O. (1968). *Advan. Metab. Disorders* **3**, 1.

Williamson, J. R. (1967). *Advan. Enzyme Regulation* **5**, 229.

Williamson, J. R., Browning, E. T., and Olson, M. S. (1968a). *Advan. Enzyme Regulation* **6**, 67.

Williamson, J. R., Browning, E. T., Scholz, R., Kreisberg, R. A., and Fritz, I. B. (1968b). *Diabetes* **17**, 194.

Williamson, J. R., Browning, E. T., Thurman, R. G., and Scholz, R. (1969). *J. Biol. Chem.* **244**, 5055.

Winegrad, A. I. (1964). *In* "Action of Hormones on Molecular Processes" (G. Litwack and D. Kritchevsky, eds.), p. 382. Wiley, New York.

Wing, D. R., and Robinson, D. S. (1968). *Biochem. J.* **109**, 841.

Wool, I. G., and Krahl, M. E. (1959). *Am. J. Physiol.* **196**, 961.

Wool, I. G., Stirewalt, W. S., Kurihara, K., Low, R. B., Bailey, P., and Oyer, D. (1968). *Recent Progr. Hormone Res.* **24**, 139.

Wright, B. E. (1966). *Science* **153**, 830.

Yip, C. C., and Logothetopoulos, J. (1969). *Proc. Natl. Acad. Sci. U. S.* **62**, 415.

Young, F. G. (1963). *In* "Comparative Endocrinology" (U. S. von Euler and H. Heller, eds.), Vol. 1, p. 371. Academic Press, New York.

Zierler, K. L. (1957). *Science* **126**, 1067.

Zierler, K. L. (1958). *Am. J. Physiol.* **192**, 283.

CHAPTER 7

Estrogens and Progestins

Elwood V. Jensen and Eugene R. DeSombre

I. INTRODUCTION

Although the steroid sex hormones exert some influence on a great many tissues of vertebrate organisms, a principal action usually taken as a measure of biologic activity is their remarkable trophic effect in tissues of the reproductive tract, which require continued exposure to the hormone for optimal growth and function. Whether such "hormone dependency" is a phenomenon of deletion or acquisition has not been established. During the process of differentiation, the hormone-dependent tissues may lose some important factor which must be restored to them for efficient biosynthetic performance. On the other hand, they may acquire some mechanism of biochemical restraint which must be removed or neutralized by the hormone's action. Because of current concepts in microbial molecular biology, it is attractive to consider that cells of hormone-dependent tissues may contain inhibitors of specific genetic function and that the hormone acts in some way to switch on these repressed genes. Experimental evidence, however, has not established that gene derepression is the initial event leading to the multiplicity of biochemical alterations associated with overall hormonal response. For the present, considerations of the mechanism of sex hormone action must recognize that the primary event may be of either a positive (restorative) or a negative (derepressive) nature.

The action of humoral agents at the subcellular level may be studied from two standpoints: (1) what the hormone does to the tissue and (2) what the tissue does with the hormone. During the past decade, considerable information relevant to endocrine mechanisms has been acquired from both types of experimental approach. The influence of administered sex hormones on the rates of incorporation of labeled precursors into cellular constituents, both *in vivo* and *in vitro*, has demonstrated many rapid biochemical effects in dependent tissues of hormone-deprived animals. The sensitivity of these responses to what presumably are selective inhibitors of protein or ribonucleic acid biosynthesis has provided some insight as to their chronologic interrelation. Determination of the uptake and chemical fate of physiological amounts of radioactive hormones in various tissues of experimental animals has led to the recognition that target tissues contain unique amounts of characteristic extranuclear proteins, now generally called hormone receptors, which associate with the steroid and accompany it to its ultimate site of fixation in the nucleus. It is presumed that the hormone–receptor interaction and the acceleration of biosynthetic processes are closely interrelated.

In the following presentation, an attempt is made to summarize the early biochemical effects of the estrogenic and progestational hormones in target tissues, to describe the nature of the hormone–receptor interaction, and finally, to consider the possible role of the receptor proteins in the elicitation of hormonal response.

II. EARLY BIOCHEMICAL EFFECTS IN TARGET CELLS

A. Estrogens

As has been reviewed in more detail elsewhere (Mueller, 1960, 1965; Hechter and Halkerston, 1964; Segal and Scher, 1967; Hamilton, 1968; Williams-Ashman and Reddi, 1971), the estrogenic hormones exert a marked influence on the levels and metabolism of a great many cellular components in target tissues. Although it is generally considered that most of these effects are secondary phenomena resulting from the initial stimulation of some key biochemical process, it is entirely possible that estrogens exert more than one primary effect on the target cell. In particular, the estrogen-induced release of uterine histamine (Spaziani and Szego, 1958; Szego, 1965), which appears to be involved in the rapid onset of hyperemia and water imbibition, is difficult to correlate with the findings regarding estrogen–receptor interaction and genome activation and may well represent a separate hormonal action which augments the overall biological effect.

In an effort to elucidate the initial step or steps in the estrogenic stimulation of uterine growth, investigators have attempted to establish the chronologic sequence of biochemical events *in vivo*, both by determining the earliest detectable response and by studying the effect of presumably selective inhibitors of RNA and protein synthesis on the various estrogen-induced alterations in the immature or ovariectomized rat uterus. Although an increase in the uterine content of phospholipid (Mueller, 1960), and glycogen (Bitman *et al.*, 1965) can be detected 1–2 hours after estrogen administration, the total RNA and protein levels do not rise until 6 and 12 hours, respectively, with an increase in DNA coming much later (Mueller, 1960; Billing *et al.*, 1969c). By determining the incorporation of labeled precursors, it can be demonstrated that the rate of overall protein synthesis is accelerated between 2 and 4 hours after hormone administration (Mueller *et al.*, 1961; Noteboom and Gorski, 1963), whereas an increase in the rate of RNA synthesis, particularly in the nucleus, can be detected at 1 hour (Gorski and Nicolette, 1963; Hamilton, 1964; Gorski and Nelson, 1965). Uteri excised 2 hours after estrogen injection show an enhanced ability to incorporate labeled precursors into phospholipid and RNA *in vitro*, but this stimulatory effect is lost as the uterine segments are maintained under *in vitro* conditions (Aizawa and Mueller, 1961; Gorski and Nicolette, 1963).

Examination of only the rapidly labeled nuclear RNA reveals a striking enhancement of tritiated uridine incorporation, which is detectable 2 minutes after estrogen injection, reaches a maximum of five to six times the control level at 20 minutes, and then declines as increased incorporation of the labeled precursor into microsomal RNA becomes evident (Hamilton *et al.*, 1965, 1968; Means and Hamilton, 1966). This rapidly stimulated RNA appears to be a ribosomal or preribosomal type which then passes from the nucleus to the cytoplasm. Certain other investigators, however, have failed to confirm this early effect of estrogen on the synthesis of RNA in the nucleus (Joel and Hagerman, 1969; Billing *et al.*, 1969b; Greenman, 1970). Because the estrogen treatment also causes an increased influx of tritiated uridine, presumably by an effect on cell permeability related to the water imbibition phenomenon, there is some uncertainty, also recognized by the original investigators (Hamilton *et al.*, 1968), as to whether the extremely rapid estrogen-induced labeling of nuclear RNA *in vivo* may be an artifact due to a change in the specific activity of the intracellular uridine pool rather than an actual stimulation of RNA synthesis.

Apart from the question of the significance of the 20 minute labeling phenomenon, there is general agreement that an enhanced capacity for RNA synthesis evident 1–2 hours after hormone administration is certainly an important response of the uterus to estrogen and is probably conducive to the increased rate of total protein synthesis which follows. This is substantiated by the increased RNA polymerase activity observed in uterine nuclei isolated from estrogen-treated animals 1–4 hours after hormone administration (Noteboom and Gorski, 1963; Gorski, 1964; Hamilton *et al.*, 1965, 1968; Nicolette and Mueller, 1966; Gorski and Morgan, 1967; Nicolette *et al.*, 1968; Barry and Gorski, 1971). After estrogen stimulation, the RNA produced, either *in vivo* or in isolated uterine nuclei, appears to be of a ribosomal type and is different in composition from that produced in the absence of estrogen as indicated by nearest neighbor frequency analysis and hybridization experiments (Barton and Liao, 1967; Teng and Hamilton, 1968; Hamilton *et al.*, 1968; Trachewsky and Segal, 1968; Billing *et al.*, 1969a). The appearance of new species of RNA after estrogen stimulation has also been demonstrated in the rabbit uterus and hen oviduct, as well as in the liver of the rabbit, the hen, and the lizard (Church and McCarthy, 1970; Hahn *et al.*, 1969a,b). Possibly relevant to the synthesis of new species of RNA are observations of the stimulation by estrogen of tRNA methylase activity in the uterus but not the liver of the ovariectomized pig (Sharma and Borek, 1970) and in the chick oviduct (Hacker, 1969).

Once the new population of uterine RNA's has been produced under the influence of estrogen, they appear to possess the ability to initiate uterine growth without need for the hormone. When instilled into the uterine lumen of ovariectomized rats, RNA isolated from rat uteri excised 4–12 hours after estrogen administration was found to induce hypertrophy of the uterine endometrium similar to that evoked by estrogen itself (Segal *et al.*, 1965; Unhjem *et al.*, 1968). Similarly, protein synthesis in the uteri of immature rats is stimulated following intrauterine application of RNA from the uteri of estrogen-treated but not of non-treated rats (Fencl and Villee, 1971). The foregoing effects on the uterus are not seen with RNA obtained from liver or vagina, and they are abolished by treatment of the uterine RNA with ribonuclease.

The mechanism by which estrogen effects an increase in the rate of RNA synthesis in the uterine nucleus has been the subject of extensive interest and investigation. It is not clear whether this stimulation results from an effect of the hormone on chromatin template activity, RNA polymerase activity, RNA transport from nucleus to cytoplasm, or a combination of factors; evidence supporting all these possibilities has been reported. Uterine chromatin, isolated from estrogen-treated rats, shows increased DNA template activity when assayed in a RNA polymerase system using a bacterial enzyme (Barker and Warren, 1966; Teng and Hamilton, 1968) and that from rabbit endometrium an even greater enhancement, demonstrable 10 minutes after hormone injection, when assayed with the enzyme obtained from endometrial nuclei (Church and McCarthy, 1970). It has been suggested (Teng and Hamilton, 1969) that the activation of chromatin may involve synthesis of new acidic proteins which overcome an inhibitory effect on transcription by the uterine histones. On the other hand, careful analysis of the incorporation of nucleotides into RNA by nuclei isolated from estrogen-stimulated rats indicates that the increased rate of precursor incorporation does not involve the synthesis of more RNA chains, as would be the case if new template sites were being made available, but rather it appears to result from the production of longer chains, suggesting an effect on the activity of the enzyme (Barry and Gorski, 1971). Changes in selective transport of nuclear RNA to the cytoplasm have been observed in the rabbit uterus after estrogen stimulation (Church and McCarthy, 1970).

That the overall uterotropic effect, accompanied by an increase in various biosynthetic activities, is not a simple phenomenon resulting directly from stimulation of general RNA synthesis was recognized very early by the finding that the estrogen-induced enhancement of RNA synthesis, determined either *in vivo* or in isolated uterine nuclei, is abolished not only by injection of actinomycin D (Ui and Mueller, 1963), but also by inhibitors of protein synthesis, such as puromycin or cycloheximide (Mueller *et al.*, 1961; Noteboom and Gorski, 1963; Gorski and Axman, 1964; Gorski and Morgan, 1967). The effect of cycloheximide on the 20 minute incorporation of uridine into rapidly labeled nuclear RNA is difficult to evaluate because under the conditions of these experiments cycloheximide causes a marked increase of labeling in uteri of animals receiving no estrogen (Hamilton *et al.*, 1968). All these inhibitors also block the early stimulation of phospholipid synthesis (Mueller *et al.*, 1961; Gorski *et al.*, 1965) and glucose metabolism (Nicolette and Gorski, 1964; Gorski and Morgan, 1967; D. E. Smith and Gorski, 1968). These observations suggest that all these biochemical responses observed 1–2 hours after estrogen administration are secondary phenomena resulting from the activation of some earlier process which is sensitive to inhibitors of both RNA and protein synthesis.

The need for some type of continued protein synthesis in the estrogenic stimulation of nuclear RNA polymerase activity is indicated by two interesting observations concerning the influence of various treatments of the whole uterine tissue during the period between excision from the hormone-treated animal and preparation of the nuclei for polymerase assay (Nicolette and Mueller, 1966; Nicolette *et al.*, 1968). Incubation of the uterine tissue at either 37°C or 4°C maintains the estrogen-induced activation, but incubation at 23°C leads to a decrease in stimulated nuclear RNA polymerase activity which can be gradually restored by subsequent incubation at 37°C. The resulting conclusion that polymerase activation requires the continued availability of a protein which is stable at 4°C, consumed at 23°C, and continuously resynthesized at 37°C is supported by the further observation that incubation of the tissue at 37°C with cycloheximide likewise results in a decrease in RNA polymerase activity in the nuclei from estrogen-treated but not from control uteri, and that this activity, along with protein synthesizing ability, can be restored by incubation of the tissue in fresh medium to wash out the cycloheximide.

On the basis of the foregoing observations, it is evident that during the first hour after estrogen administration there are changes in the metabolism of uterine RNA, lipid, and glucose that precede the overall stimulation of protein synthesis. Because of their sensitivity both to actinomycin D and to puromycin and cycloheximide, these early changes appear to require the synthesis of RNA and protein in amounts too small to contribute to the overall labeling pattern. Examples of such specific uterine proteins synthesized rapidly in response to estrogen have been reported. On starch gel electrophoresis of cytosol from immature rat uteri, which have been either excised from animals injected with radioactive leucine or incubated with the labeled amino acid *in vitro*, a single new radioactive protein band is evident (Notides and Gorski, 1966). By using different isotopes to label the proteins of the control and the hormone-treated animals, respectively, the sensitivity of the detection procedure has been substantially increased (Fig. 1); these later experiments indicate that the ability to synthesize the specific protein is inhibited by actinomycin D and that the effect is detectable 30–40 minutes after estrogen administration, reaching a maximum in 1–2 hours, after which it declines (Mayol and Thayer, 1970; Barnea and Gorski, 1970; DeAngelo and Gorski, 1970). The specific protein synthesis appears to result from the production of a new messenger RNA, which is not sensitive to puromycin or cycloheximide and which shows indirect evidence of being present 15 minutes after estrogen administration (DeAngelo and Gorski, 1970). Acrylamide gel electrophoresis indicates that the new protein consists of at least two components with isoelectric points, as determined by

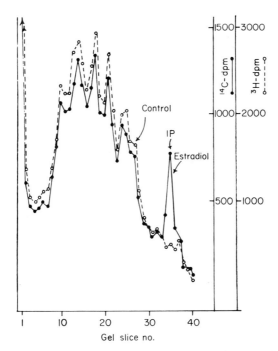

FIG. 1. Radioactivity distribution on starch gel electrophoresis of soluble proteins of uteri excised from immature rats 30 minutes after injection of 0.5 ml saline, with and without 5 μg estradiol. Estrogen-treated uteri incubated 2 hours at 37°C with 2 μCi leucine-^{14}C (175 mCi/mmole); control uteri with 5 μCi leucine-^{3}H (2.0 Ci/mmole). IP indicates peak of induced protein. (From Barnea and Gorski, 1970.)

electrofocusing, of between 3.5 and 4 (Mayol and Thayer, 1970). The capacity for synthesizing the new protein also can be induced by incubating the uteri with hyperphysiological (Mayol and Thayer, 1970) or nearly physiological (Katzenellenbogen and Gorski, 1971) levels of estradiol *in vitro,* so that this phenomenon, along with the action of transformed estrogen–receptor complex on isolated uterine nuclei described in Section IV, represent the only confirmed examples of an early biochemical effect elicited by estrogen *in vitro.*

Very recently it has been reported that the administration of estrogen to ovariectomized rats which have received an intraluminal application of a labeled amino acid mixture, results in the rapid incorporation of isotope into an acidic protein (pI 4–5) found in the arginine-rich histone fraction (F3) of the uterus (Barker, 1971). Increased synthesis of the specific protein, accompanied by a reduction in the total amount of these histones, is detectable 15 minutes after estrogen administration and does not appear to be sensitive to actinomycin D.

The relation of the two examples of estrogen-induced protein to each other, to the protein synthesis that appears to be required for RNA polymerase activation in uterine nuclei (Nicolette *et al.*, 1968), and to the estrogen–receptor interaction described in Sections III and IV remains to be established. It seems probable, however, that this rapid induction phenomenon, which in one case at least is demonstrable in an *in vitro* system, will provide important insight into the molecular mechanism of estrogen action.

B. Progestins

Although a wealth of information is available regarding the gross biological and morphological responses to progestins in tissues of the reproductive tract, systematic investigations of the early hormonal effects on biochemical processes have been relatively few. Much of the detailed information concerning the early effects of progestins in target tissue cells has been obtained from experiments with the estrogen-prestimulated chick oviduct, since in this organ progestins induce the synthesis of a specific protein, avidin (O'Malley *et al.*, 1967, 1969). This hormone-specific induction has been observed after the administration of progesterone or other progestational hormones (O'Malley *et al.*, 1967) to diethylstilbestrol-treated chicks *in vivo* (Korenman and O'Malley, 1968) and to minced oviduct tissue *in vitro* (O'Malley, 1967), as well as to oviduct cells maintained in tissue culture (O'Malley and Kohler, 1967a,b). The stimulation of avidin synthesis, detectable 10 hours after hormone treatment *in vivo* or 6 hours *in vitro,* takes place under conditions where there is no increase in other major oviduct proteins, such as ovalbumin and lysozyme (O'Malley, 1967).

During the induction of avidin synthesis, progesterone does not increase the incorporation of tritiated thymidine into DNA. The fact that partial blockage of DNA synthesis by hydroxyurea does not inhibit or delay avidin synthesis provides further indication that progesterone action does not require new synthesis of DNA (O'Malley and McGuire, 1968). New DNA-dependent RNA synthesis is required for the hormonal effect, as shown by the fact that actinomycin D administered at the same time as progesterone causes a 90% reduction in the stimulation of avidin production without inhibiting general protein synthesis (O'Malley *et al.*, 1969). When actinomycin D is administered 6 hours after the progesterone, an increased rather than a decreased rate of avidin synthesis is observed (O'Malley and McGuire, 1968). This phenomenon of "superinduction" is similar to that described for glucocorticoid action in hepatoma cells *in vitro* (Tomkins *et al.*, 1969).

Although no change in the total RNA content results from *in vitro* exposure of oviduct tissue to progesterone, there is a significant initial decrease in the specific activity of rapidly labeled nuclear RNA which is followed by a marked rise in its specific activity prior to the appearance of avidin (O'Malley *et al.*, 1969). A similar fall and subsequent rise is seen in the RNA polymerase activity of isolated oviduct nuclei, measured either in the presence or absence of ammonium sulfate, after administration of progesterone to chicks *in vivo*, whether or not they have been pre-stimulated with estrogen (W. L. McGuire and O'Malley, 1968).

The action of progesterone appears to increase chromatin template activity and to induce the synthesis of new species of RNA, as determined by DNA–RNA hybridization and nearest neighbor frequency analysis (O'Malley and McGuire, 1969; O'Malley *et al.*, 1968, 1969). These effects on RNA synthesis occur before any influence on avidin production is evident.

On the basis of the foregoing experimental observations, it appears that by an as yet unknown mechanism, the progestational hormones bring about the expression of new regions of DNA template, giving rise to new species of RNA which are involved in the synthesis of avidin. The relation of these effects to the progesterone–receptor interactions, described in Section III, remains to be established.

III. HORMONE–RECEPTOR INTERACTIONS

A. Estrogens

1. Binding of Estrogens by Target Tissues in Vivo and in Vitro

The presence in estrogen-responsive tissues of characteristic hormone-binding components, now called estrogen receptors or estrophiles, was first indicated by the striking affinity of these tissues for the hormone *in vivo*. Following the administration of physiological amounts of tritiated estradiol to immature rats (Jensen, 1960; Jensen and Jacobson, 1960; Gupta, 1960) or tritiated hexestrol to young goats and sheep (Glascock and Hoekstra, 1959), the uterus, vagina, and anterior pituitary were found to take up and retain the radioactive hormone against a marked concentration gradient with the blood (Fig. 2). Although extensive metabolic transformation of administered estradiol occurs in such tissues

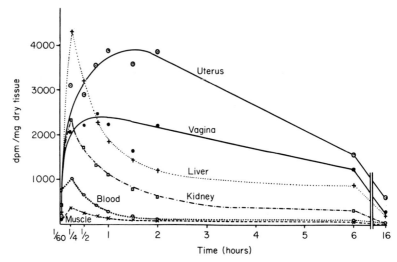

Fig. 2. Tissue tritium levels after single subcutaneous injection of 98 ng (11.5 μCi) estradiol-6,7-³H in 0.5 ml saline to immature rats. Each point based on six animals. (From Jensen and Jacobson, 1960.)

as the liver, and the blood contains a great mixture of both free and conjugated metabolites, only unchanged estradiol is taken up and bound by the uterus of the immature rat (Jensen and Jacobson, 1962) or mouse (Stone, 1964). The resulting conclusion that estradiol initiates uterine growth without itself undergoing metabolic transformation has proved consistent with much subsequent evidence. Although the immature rat uterus appears unable to oxidize the estradiol to estrone, the uterus of the adult rat (Pack and Brooks, 1970; Wenzel *et al.*, 1970) and the rabbit (Jütting *et al.*, 1967; Jungblut *et al.*, 1967b), as well as human endometrium (Sweat *et al.*, 1967; Gurpide and Welch, 1969), can convert estradiol to estrone, either *in vivo* or *in vitro*.

Studies by a number of investigators have provided further information about the biological fate of estrogenic hormones in the reproductive tract of the mouse (Stone, 1963; Stone *et al.*, 1963; Stone and Martin, 1964; Stone and Baggett, 1965a; Terenius, 1965; Folman and Pope, 1969), the rat (Roy *et al.*, 1964; Talwar *et al.*, 1964; Noteboom and Gorski, 1965; King and Gordon, 1966; Jensen *et al.*, 1966; Brecher and Wotiz, 1967; Kato and Villee, 1967b; Callantine *et al.*, 1968; DeHertogh *et al.*, 1971a,b), the monkey (Eisenfeld *et al.*, 1971), and the human (Davis *et al.*, 1963; Brush *et al.*, 1967). Estradiol is specifically bound in all regions of the uterus, but its concentration is higher in the endometrium than in the myometrium (Alberga and Baulieu, 1965, 1968; Flesher,

1965; Jensen, 1965b, King and Gordon, 1966). The binding sites appear to possess stereospecificity, inasmuch as the uptake of tritiated estradiol by the rat uterus is inhibited by an excess of nonradioactive estradiol but not by its 17-epimer, estradiol-17α (Noteboom and Gorski, 1965). Studies of estradiol incorporation as a function of dose indicate that the interaction of estrogens with target tissues in the immature rat consists of two distinct phenomena—an uptake process, which is not saturable with considerably hyperphysiological amounts of administered hormone, and a retention process, which becomes saturated as the dose exceeds the physiological level (Jensen *et al.*, 1967a).

Binding of estradiol by the uterus appears to be influenced by the hormonal state of the animal. Although the binding capacity and receptor content of the adult rat uterus are less than that of the immature animal (Eisenfeld and Axelrod, 1966; Hughes *et al.*, 1969; Feherty *et al.*, 1970) and gradually decrease with age (Lee and Jacobson, 1971), removal of the ovaries is followed by a significant decrease in receptor concentration (J. L. McGuire and Lisk, 1968; Hughes *et al.*, 1969). Variation in uterine receptor content with ovarian cycle (Feherty *et al.*, 1970; DeHertogh *et al.*, 1971b; Lee and Jacobson, 1971) provides further indication of hormonal control of receptor capacity.

Although the uptake by hypothalamus is quite low in comparison to that by pituitary, uterus, or vagina, careful investigation by both biochemical methods (Eisenfeld and Axelrod 1965, 1967, Kato and Villee, 1967a; J. L. McGuire and Lisk, 1969; Kahwanago *et al.*, 1970; Eisenfeld, 1970; Attramadal and Aakvaag, 1970) and by autoradiography (Michael, 1965; Stumpf, 1968b; Pfaff, 1968; Attramadal, 1970) has demonstrated the presence of receptor sites for estradiol in hypothalamic tissue. Specific estrogen binding is observed in mammary glands of the rat (Sander, 1968; Sander and Attramadal, 1968a), the mouse (Puca and Bresciani, 1968b, 1969a), and the human (Deshpande *et al.*, 1967), and in certain hormone-dependent mammary tumors in the rat (King *et al.*, 1965b, 1966; Jensen, 1965b; Mobbs, 1966, 1968, 1969; Jungblut *et al.*, 1967a; Jensen *et al.*, 1967c; Sander and Attramadal, 1968b; Kyser, 1970) and in the human (Demetriou *et al.*, 1964; Braunsberg *et al.*, 1967; Deshpande *et al.*, 1967; Johansson *et al.*, 1970). The presence of estrogen receptors in human breast cancer tissue appears to be a requirement for response of the patient to such ablative endocrine therapy as adrenalectomy or hypophysectomy (Folca *et al.*, 1961; Jensen *et al.*, 1971b).

The uptake of estradiol by target tissues is markedly decreased by simultaneous administration of one of several chemically similar compounds known from previous work to block the uterine growth response to estrogens. This phenomenon of binding inhibition was first observed with MER-25 (or ethamoxytriphetol) (Jensen, 1962) and subsequently with the more potent antagonists, clomiphene (Roy *et al.*, 1964; Wyss *et al.*, 1968b; Kahwanago *et al.*, 1970), Upjohn 11,100A (or nafoxidine) (Jensen, 1965a,b), and Parke-Davis CI-628, originally called CN-55,945-27 (Callantine, 1967). Inasmuch as these reagents have no effect on the low levels of estrogen which appear in the nontarget tissues (Jensen *et al.*, 1966), they appear to be selective inhibitors of the interaction of estrogen with receptor sites and have proved of considerable value in distinguishing specific from nonspecific binding. The quantitative correlation between the reduction in estrogen uptake and the inhibition of uterine growth following the administration of varying doses of nafoxidine (Jensen, 1965b) provides evidence that estrogen–receptor interaction plays an important role in the uterotrophic process.

Although the binding of estradiol to uterine receptor sites is sensitive to antiestrogens of the MER-25 type, it is not inhibited by puromycin or actinomycin D (Jensen, 1965a,b), substances also known to block the overall growth response to estrogens as well as the early acceleration of many biochemical processes in the uterus (Mueller *et al.*, 1961; Ui and Mueller, 1963). This observation suggests that the interaction of the steroid with the receptor is an early step in the uterotrophic process, preceding the acceleration of those biosynthetic reactions which are sensitive to actinomycin D or puromycin.

In contrast to their striking incorporation of estradiol, rat uterus, vagina, and anterior pituitary exhibit little affinity for estrone. When estrone is administered to the immature rat, a part of it is reduced to estradiol which accumulates in the uterus in approximately one-tenth the amount that would result from a similar dose of estradiol itself (Jensen and Jacobson, 1962). Hexestrol, 17α-methylestradiol, 17α-ethynylestradiol and, to a lesser extent, estriol all show marked uptake and retention by target tissues, and each is incorporated without chemical transformation (Jensen, 1965b; Jensen *et al.*, 1966); mestranol, on the other hand, does not bind to receptors but undergoes gradual demethylation, probably in the liver, to furnish 17α-ethynylestradiol which accumulates in the uterine tissue. Thus, the physiological interaction with target tissues appears to require the presence of free hydroxyl or phenolic groups at both extremeties of the estrogen molecule.

When excised uterine tissue is exposed to dilute solutions of tritiated estradiol at physiological temperatures *in vitro*, an association of hormone with receptor takes place which shows all the principal characteristics of the *in vivo* phenomenon (Jungblut *et al.*, 1965; Stone and Baggett, 1965b; Terenius, 1966; Jensen *et al.*, 1966, 1967b; Maurer and Chalkley, 1967; Wyss *et al.*, 1968b). This interaction *in vitro* does not

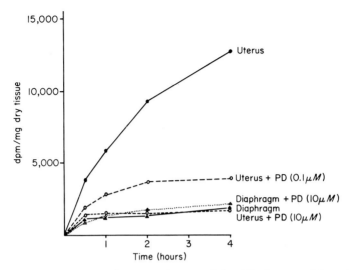

FIG. 3. Tritium levels in slit uterine horns and hemidiaphragms of immature rats after stirring in 0.12 nM estradiol-^{3}H (57 Ci/mmole) at 37°C in Krebs-Ringer-Henseleit glucose buffer, pH 7.3, in the presence and absence of an estrogen antagonist, Parke-Davis CI-628. Each point is the median value of five specimens.

require the presence either of oxygen or of added nutrients. If an inhibitor of specific estradiol binding, such as nafoxidine, CI-628, or clomiphene, is present in the incubation medium, the uptake of estradiol by uterine tissue is reduced to the low level observed with diaphragm or other nontarget tissues, which represents nonspecific binding not sensitive to the inhibitor (Fig. 3). Using an *in vitro* system, a dependence of estrogen binding on sulfhydryl groups can be demonstrated (Terenius, 1967; Jensen *et al.*, 1967b,d; Shyamala and Gorski, 1969; Steggles and King, 1970). Treatment of uterine tissue with sulfhydryl-blocking reagents before exposure to estradiol prevents specific hormone uptake, whereas such treatment of uteri previously exposed to estradiol, either *in vivo* or *in vitro*, causes rapid release of the bound hormone.

The foregoing studies of the biochemical fate of estrogenic hormones *in vivo* and *in vitro* establish the principal characteristics of the specific interaction of estrogens with the estrophilic components of intact target tissues and provide a basis for evaluating the significance of estrogen-binding phenomena in broken cell systems. The sensitivity to sulfhydryl reagents and to selective inhibitors such as nafoxidine and Parke-Davis CI-628 affords valuable criteria for distinguishing the physiological estrogen–receptor interaction from artifacts of nonspecific binding to macromolecules or organelle surfaces.

2. Estrogen–Receptor Complexes and Their Intracellular Localization

Cell fractionation experiments, confirmed by autoradiographic investigations, indicate two sites of estrogen binding in target tissues. When uterine homogenates from estradiol-treated rats are subjected to differential centrifugation, either in sucrose or in hypotonic medium, the incorporated hormone appears principally in two fractions, the high-speed supernate, or cytosol, and the heavy, or nuclear myofibrillar, sediment (Talwar *et al.*, 1964; Noteboom and Gorski, 1965; Jensen, 1965a; King and Gordon, 1966; Baulieu *et al.*, 1967; Jensen *et al.*, 1967a). Although some investigators originally reported that the cytosol radioactivity is predominant, our own studies and those of Gorski indicate that up to 6 hours after estradiol administration, most of the labeled steroid appears in the nuclear fraction with a smaller amount (20–30%) present in the cytosol. Similar results are obtained with anterior pituitary (King *et al.*, 1965a); in rat mammary tumor, a somewhat greater proportion of hormone (85–90%) is bound in the nucleus (Kyser, 1970). If the binding inhibitor nafoxidine is administered in amounts sufficient to partially inhibit the uptake of estradiol, the ratio of nuclear to cytosol radioactivity in the uterus remains essentially unchanged, suggesting a relation between the two sites of binding (Jensen *et al.*, 1967a).

Autoradiographic localization of tritiated estradiol in rat uterus, using a dry mount technique which minimizes steroid translocation during tissue processing (Stumpf and Roth, 1966), demonstrates a distribution pattern similar to that obtained by cell fractionation (Stumpf, 1968a, 1969; Jensen *et al.*, 1967a,b, 1969a). In all regions of the uterus, most of the radioactive hormone is seen in the nucleus; the extranuclear radioactivity varies from 15–20% of the total in the epithelial glands and myometrium to 35–40% in the lamina propria, strengthening the conclusion that the radioactivity of the cytosol represents extranuclear estradiol. This correlation of the results of autoradiography with those of cell fractionation provides reassurance that the high estradiol content of the nucleus is not an artifact of redistribution taking place during cell disruption. The autoradiographic studies indicate further that the nuclear localization of estradiol is not in the nucleolus (Stumpf, 1969).

The radioactive estradiol taken up by the immature rat uterus is associated with a different form of the receptor substance in the cytosol than in the nucleus. The fact that the hormone in the cytosol is bound to a macromolecule was first indicated by its failure to be included on gel filtration through Sephadex (Talwar *et al.*, 1964). A valuable procedure for characterizing the receptor substances became available with the observation (Toft and Gorski, 1966) that, on ultracentrifugation in

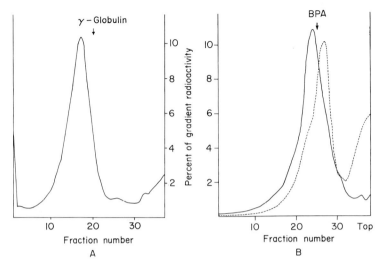

Fɪɢ. 4. Sedimentation pattern of radioactive estradiol–receptor complexes obtained from immature rat uteri. (A) Uterine cytosol, from untreated animals, made 5 n*M* in estradiol-³H and centrifuged in a 10–30% sucrose gradient at 308,000 g for 12 hours at 1°C. (B) Cytosol plus 5 n*M* added estradiol-³H (broken line) and nuclear extract (solid line) from uteri excised from immature rats 1 hour after subcutaneous injection of 100 ng (20.8 *μ*Ci) estradiol-³H centrifuged in a 5–20% sucrose gradient containing 400 m*M* potassium chloride at 284,500 g for 12 hours at 2°C. Total cpm on gradient: (A) 30,240; (B) cytosol 35,380, nuclear extract 6035. Arrows indicate positions of γ-globulin and bovine plasma albumin markers. (Part B from Jensen *et al.*, 1969b.)

a sucrose gradient, the cytosol complex sediments as a discrete band (Fig. 4A) with a coefficient[1] originally believed to be 9.5 S but later found to be about 8 S (Erdos, 1968; Rochefort and Baulieu, 1968). In the presence of sodium or potassium chloride at concentrations of 0.2 *M* or higher, the 8 S complex is reversibly transformed into a more slowly

[1] The sedimentation coefficient figures of 8, 5, and 4 are convenient approximations based on the sedimentation peaks of crude mixtures in sucrose gradients in relation to those of standard proteins, such as yeast alcohol dehydrogenase (7.4), γ-globulin (7.0), and bovine plasma albumin (4.6). The sedimentation rate of the cytosol complex in low salt varies with the degree of dilution. With cytosol from a 20% homogenate, the complex sediments significantly faster than γ-globulin (Fig. 4A) and slightly faster than ADH; after tenfold dilution, the complex sediments about the same as γ-globulin. The actual sedimentation coefficient of the nuclear complex in salt-containing gradients is probably close to 5.8 S. In salt-containing sucrose gradients, the cytosol complex from calf uterus sediments somewhat faster than that from rat uterus. Precise values for the sedimentation coefficients of these complexes must await determination in the analytical ultracentrifuge after the receptor proteins have been isolated in purified form.

sedimenting entity (Erdos, 1968; Korenman and Rao, 1968; Rochefort and Baulieu, 1968), which in salt-containing sucrose gradients migrates just behind bovine plasma albumin (Fig. 4B) or about 4 S (Jensen *et al.,* 1969b). Although this 4 S moiety has been generally considered to be a subunit of the 8 S complex, one cannot exclude the possibility that it is the intact 8 S complex which, in the presence of salt, undergoes extensive conformational change.

The major part of the uterine estradiol, which is found in the nuclear fraction, appears to be associated with chromatin (King *et al.,* 1966; Maurer and Chalkley, 1967; Teng and Hamilton, 1968). The bound hormone can be solubilized, unaccompanied by detectable DNA, by extraction with 0.3 M potassium chloride at pH 7.4 (Jungblut *et al.,* 1967b; Jensen *et al.,* 1967b), or more effectively, with 0.4 M potassium chloride at pH 8.5 (Puca and Bresciani, 1968a), to yield an estradiol–receptor complex which is clearly distinguishable from the 4 S unit of the cytosol complex in that it sediments at about 5 S, somewhat faster than bovine plasma albumin (Fig. 4B). In our early experiments (Jensen *et al.,* 1967b), as well as certain studies of others (Puca and Bresciani, 1968a; Steggles and King, 1970), the nuclear extract was found to sediment at about 5 S whether or not salt is present in the sucrose gradient. More recently, we, as well as others (Korenman and Rao, 1968), find consistently that the complex in the nuclear extract aggregates to a 8–9 S form unless salt is present. The reason for this variable behavior of the nuclear complex under low salt conditions is not clear.

The uterus of the adult rat differs from that of the immature rat in that a portion of its cytosol receptor sediments in the 4 S form in the absence of salt (Steggles and King, 1969, 1970). A similar phenomenon is observed with cytosol from adult human and monkey uteri (Wyss *et al.,* 1968a) and sheep endometrium (Zimmering *et al.,* 1970), as well as from some, but not all, receptor-containing human breast cancers (Jensen *et al.,* 1971b). After ovariectomy or hypophysectomy, the cytosol receptor pattern is similar to that of the immature rat (Steggles and King, 1970), suggesting a hormonal influence on the properties of the cytosol receptor protein as well as on the total binding capacity discussed earlier.

When immature rat or calf uteri are incubated with dilute solutions of tritiated estradiol at 37° C *in vitro,* the intracellular distribution of uterine radioactivity, as well as the formation of 8 S and 5 S complexes, is quite similar to that observed after hormone administration *in vivo* (Jungblut *et al.,* 1967b; Jensen *et al.,* 1967b, 1969a). But if the tissue is exposed to hormone at 2° C, the major portion (70–75%) of the radioactive steroid appears as 8 S complex in the cytosol fraction and is seen in the extranuclear region on autoradiography (Jensen *et al.,* 1968,

1969a,b; Gorski *et al.*, 1968; Shyamala and Gorski, 1969; Rochefort and Baulieu, 1969). When such uteri, rich in extranuclear 8 S complex, are warmed briefly to 37°C, redistribution of the steroid takes place within the tissue to yield predominantly nuclear bound steroid, extractable as 5 S complex, as determined both by fractionation and by autoradiographic techniques. These observations indicate that radioactive estradiol, which associates with the extranuclear receptor in the cold, can be transferred to its nuclear binding site by a process which is temperature-dependent.

The 8 S estradiol–receptor complex, or its 4 S modification, is formed directly, even in the cold, simply by adding tritiated estradiol to the cytosol fraction of uteri not previously exposed to hormone (Toft *et al.*, 1967; Jungblut *et al.*, 1967b; Jensen *et al.*, 1967b). As in the whole tissue, this interaction in the isolated cytosol is prevented by the presence of nafoxidine or CI-628 (Jensen *et al.*, 1969c, 1971b). The total cytosol receptor content of a tissue can be readily estimated by adding an excess of tritiated estradiol to the cytosol and determining the amount of bound hormone. This can be done by measuring the radioactivity present in the 8 S sedimentation peak (Toft *et al.*, 1967; Jensen *et al.*, 1968), adsorbed by hydroxyapatite (Erdos *et al.*, 1970) or by powdered glass in the presence of magnesium ions (Clark and Gorski, 1969; Notides, 1970), precipitated by protamine (Steggles and King, 1970), or remaining in solution after removal of unbound steroid by Sephadex gel filtration (Talwar *et al.*, 1968; Puca and Bresciani, 1969b, Lee and Jacobson, 1971) or adsorption on charcoal (Korenman, 1968, 1969; Méšter *et al.*, 1970). The sedimentation method, although somewhat more laborious, is by far the most accurate and should be used to calibrate other assay procedures.

Using the sucrose gradient technique, it can be demonstrated that immature rat uterus contains a minimum of 100 femtomoles of 8 S binding capacity per milligram of wet tissue, corresponding to an average of about 100,000 cytosol receptor sites per uterine cell (Jensen *et al.*, 1968). Lower values reported in the literature probably reflect losses of the labile receptor protein during homogenization and assay procedures. All rat tissues examined appear to contain some of the 8 S binding protein, but target tissues show a much higher content than nontarget tissues (Jensen *et al.*, 1969c). Thus, the difference between target and nontarget tissues with respect to receptor protein appears to be quantitative rather than qualitative.

3. Cytosol Dependence of Nuclear Binding

In contrast to the 8 S receptor protein, which is a preexisting component in the uterine cytosol of hormone-deprived animals, there is no evidence for the presence of the 5 S binding protein in the uterine nucleus before estradiol administration. No 5 S complex is formed either by addition of estradiol to an extract of uterine nuclei or by direct treatment of the nuclei themselves, although it is readily produced when estradiol is incubated either with whole uterine homogenate (Fig. 5) or with purified nuclei or washed nuclear sediment in the presence of the cytosol fraction (Jensen *et al.,* 1967b, 1968, 1969c; Musliner *et al.,* 1970). As is nuclear binding in whole uterine tissue, this production of the 5 S complex in isolated nuclei is temperature-dependent. Exposure of uterine nuclei to cytosol and estradiol at 2°C results in a small uptake of radioactivity which, on salt extraction, sediments as 4 S complex, whereas incubation at temperatures of 25°–37°C gives a much higher incorporation of radioactivity, which is extracted predominantly or exclusively as 5 S complex, depending on the length of the incubation period. If, before mixing with nuclei, the cytosol is heated to 45°C, which destroys the ability of the receptor protein to bind estradiol, no 5 S complex is obtained in the nuclei, demonstrating clearly an important

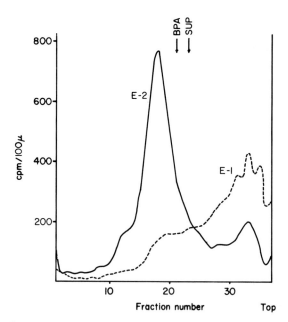

Fɪɢ. 5. Sedimentation pattern of potassium chloride extracts of nuclear sediment after incubation of a 10% uterine homogenate in 10 mM tris, pH 8.2, for 30 minutes at 25°C in the presence of 5 nM estradiol-³H (E-2) or estrone-³H (E-1). Centrifuga-tion in a 5–20% sucrose gradient containing 400 mM potassium chloride at 250,000 g for 16 hours at 4°C. SUP indicates position of 4 S cytosol (supernatant) complex.

role of the intact cytosol complex in the origin of the 5 S nuclear complex.

More recently it has been found that a 5 S complex, similar in most respects[2] to that observed in the nuclear extract, is produced by warming a cytosol–estradiol mixture in the absence of nuclei (Brecher *et al.*, 1970; Jensen *et al.*, 1971a). This observation suggests that the 4 S binding unit of the cytosol complex is first converted to a 5 S form which then associates with an "acceptor" site in the uterine nucleus.[3] The temperature dependence of 5 S complex formation in cytosol alone is similar to that observed on incubation with nuclei, and in both cases the rate of 5 S complex production is accelerated with increasing pH over the range 6.5–8.5 and retarded by the presence of EDTA. Both processes require the presence of estradiol and will not take place with estrone. Although estrone forms a typical 8 S complex and 4 S binding unit when added to uterine cytosol in the cold, after warming with estrone the 4 S unit remains essentially unchanged (Jensen *et al.*, 1971a). If nuclei are present during this incubation, they incorporate a significant amount of radioactive estrone, but this is not extractable as 5 S complex (Fig. 5). The failure of estrone to promote the 4 S to 5 S conversion of the cytosol binding unit explains our previous finding (unpublished) that, after incubation of immature rat uteri with estrone *in vitro*, 8 S complex is present in the cytosol fraction, but no 5 S complex can be extracted from the nuclei. We have observed that diethylstilbestrol, hexestrol, estriol, and 17α-ethynylestradiol all promote 4 S to 5 S transformation, whereas quinestrol (17α-ethynylestradiol 3–cyclopentyl ether) does not, confirming the previous demonstration (p. 226) of the need for hydroxyl or phenolic groups at both extremities of the hormone molecule.

The participation of the extranuclear receptor protein in the formation of the nuclear estrogen–receptor complex is further indicated by the decrease in cytosol receptor content that takes place as estradiol reacts with uterine tissue *in vivo* to become localized in the nucleus. Not only is the total 8 S receptor content of the cytosol less after a large dose of estradiol than after a smaller one (Jensen *et al.*, 1968), but following

---

[2] The estradiol–receptor complex obtained by warming a mixture of estradiol and uterine cytosol sediments slightly faster in salt-containing sucrose gradients than does the complex extracted from the nucleus (Jensen *et al.*, 1971a). Whether this small but consistent discrepancy in sedimentation rate represents a difference in composition of the two "5 S" complexes or whether it results from a difference in protein milieu between cytosol and nuclear extract is not certain.

[3] The ability of preformed 5 S cytosol complex both to bind to isolated uterine nuclei and to stimulate their RNA polymerase activity on exposure in the cold (p. 247) strongly suggests that the temperature-dependent step is the 4 S to 5 S conversion of the cytosol binding unit.

the injection of a physiological dose of hormone there is a progressive fall in cytosol receptor level for a period of 4 hours, after which the receptor content is gradually restored, apparently by resynthesis (Jensen *et al.*, 1969b). Depletion of cytosol receptor accompanying nuclear binding is also observed *in vitro* (Shyamala and Gorski, 1969; Musliner *et al.*, 1970); exposure to high levels of estradiol causes almost complete disappearance of cytosol receptor, both *in vivo* (Jensen *et al.*, 1969c) and *in vitro* (Giannopoulos and Gorski, 1971).

Uterine nuclei appear to contain a specific acceptor site which binds the 5 S estradiol–receptor complex. On incubation with estradiol in uterine cytosol, uterine nuclei show a greater uptake of radioactive hormone than do nuclei from nontarget tissues (Brecher and Wotiz, 1967; Jensen *et al.*, 1969c; Musliner *et al.*, 1970), and with uterine nuclei more of the hormone is extracted as distinct 5 S complex. In the case of diaphragm nuclei, some unexplained transformation takes place to yield an extracted complex sedimenting more slowly than the 4 S binding unit; this is sometimes accompanied by a second entity which sediments at about 4.5 S (Jensen *et al.*, 1969c; Musliner *et al.*, 1970).

4. Properties and Purification of Estrogen Receptor Proteins

The estrogen receptor substances of uterine tissue appear to be mainly protein in composition, inasmuch as both the 8 S cytosol complex (Toft and Gorski, 1966) and the 5 S nuclear complex (Puca and Bresciani, 1968a; Jensen *et al.*, 1971a) are destroyed by the action of proteases but not by nucleases. The 8 S complex binds to ribonuclease to form a more rapidly sedimenting species (Jensen *et al.*, 1969c); this phenomenon probably reflects a general ability of the cytosol complex to associate with basic proteins and peptides as indicated by its precipitation with protamine or polylysine (King *et al.*, 1969; Steggles and King, 1970). The presence of a lipid moiety in the cytosol receptor is indicated by the transformation of the 8 S complex to a 4 S form under the action of lipase (Erdos, 1968), while the possibility that it contains phosphorus is suggested by an apparently successful attempt in our laboratory to label the 8 S receptor protein with ^{32}P by the intraluminal instillation of radioactive orthophosphate *in vivo*.

Despite a report to the contrary (Puca and Bresciani, 1970), bound estradiol is clearly liberated from the 8 S cytosol complex by organic mercurials (Jensen *et al.*, 1967d), provided that the uteri have been previously washed to remove contaminants, probably of serum origin, which have a tendency to aggregate with the cytosol complex under the action of these reagents. In contrast, the nuclear complex is not as readily cleaved by sulfhydryl reagents. Although in some instances we have observed partial or total release of bound estradiol, in other experiments, both in our laboratory and elsewhere (Puca and Bresciani, 1970), treatment of the nuclear extract with organic mercurials or N-ethylmaleimide was found to produce a more rapidly sedimenting complex (10–12 S), accompanied by highly aggregated material. This difference between the cytosol and nuclear complexes in reactivity toward sulfhydryl reagents suggests that sulfhydryl groups in the receptor protein may become inaccessible during the 4 S to 5 S transformation.

The association of estradiol with uterine receptor proteins is an extremely strong interaction. Studies of estradiol binding as a function of hormone concentration—using Sephadex gel filtration (Puca and Bresciani, 1969b; Erdos *et al.*, 1969; Lee and Jacobson, 1971); adsorption on charcoal (Korenman, 1970; Méster *et al.*, 1970), powdered glass (Clark and Gorski, 1969; Notides, 1970), or hydroxyapatite (Erdos *et al.*, 1970; Best-Belpomme *et al.*, 1970); protamine precipitation (Steggles and King, 1970); sucrose gradient centrifugation (Toft *et al.*, 1967); or equilibrium dialysis (Erdos *et al.*, 1968; Baulieu and Raynaud, 1970) to distinguish bound from unbound steroid—have indicated the association constant for the 8 S cytosol complex from uteri of various species to be in the range of 10^9 to 10^{10} M^{-1}. By the gel filtration technique, the K_A of the nuclear complex from calf uteri was likewise found to be 10^9 M^{-1} (Puca and Bresciani, 1969b), although the cytosol receptor of human uterus, after warming with estradiol at 37°C, which presumably transforms the binding unit to a 5 S form, shows a value of 10^{12} (Hähnel, 1971). In our own laboratory, such nonequilibrium procedures as gel filtration or charcoal adsorption give values of 10^{10} or lower for the rat or calf cytosol complex, but a kinetic dialysis technique indicates a K_A of about 2×10^{11} M^{-1}. Similarly, calculations based on association–dissociation kinetics indicate the association constant of the calf cytosol complex to be about 10^{12} M^{-1} (Best-Belpomme *et al.*, 1970). These higher values are in agreement with estimates calculated from the uptake and retention of estradiol by rat uteri *in vivo* (Bush, 1965; DeHertogh *et al.*, 1971a) and *in vitro* (Alberga and Baulieu, 1968).

The remarkably tight binding of estradiol to receptor appears to result from an extremely low rate of dissociation (Ellis and Ringold, 1971; Truong and Baulieu, 1971). This may explain the fact that, once the complex is formed, the tritiated estradiol does not readily exchange *in vitro*, even in the presence of a large excess of unlabeled hormone, and that the complex can be studied and purified without need for the continued presence of unbound hormone. The nuclear complex, in which the binding appears as strong or stronger than in the cytosol one, is readily dissociated at 45°C; the liberated estradiol can be removed by filtration through Sephadex to yield the uncomplexed 5 S receptor protein which then can react again with estradiol (Puca and Bresciani, 1968a, 1969b).

Whether the 8 S form of the cytosol receptor observed in low salt represents a more compact or otherwise less buoyant modification of an asymmetric 4 S protein, an aggregate of 4 S estrogen-binding units or a 4 S unit associated with a nonbinding moiety is not certain. Both in our laboratory and elsewhere (Vonderhaar *et al.*, 1970b), it has been found that the radioactive complex obtained from the 4 S sedimentation peak of a salt-containing sucrose gradient runs more slowly (about 7 S) than the original complex when it is recentrifuged in a salt-free gradient. This phenomenon has been interpreted as evidence for a partial separation of binding and nonbinding components by sedimentation difference (Vonderhaar *et al.*, 1970b). However, the same degree of dilution of the original cytosol without centrifugation causes a similar decrease in the sedimentation rate of the cytosol complex, invalidating any conclusions regarding centrifugal separation of receptor components, except that a nonreaggregable 4 S subunit cannot be prepared by differential sedimentation of the salt-dissociated 8 S complex.

In crude uterine cytosol, the 8 S complex is a rather unstable substance, tending both to decompose and to form large aggregates with other cytosol components. In combination with estradiol, the receptor becomes somewhat more stable toward decomposition, but its tendency to aggregate is enhanced, especially in the presence of magnesium or manganese ions (Brecher *et al.*, 1969). The binding of the 8 S complex to powdered glass in the presence of Mg^{2+} forms the basis of an ingenious assay for the cytosol receptor (Clark and Gorski, 1969).

Because of its instability and tendency toward aggregation, isolation of the purified cytosol receptor protein has proved difficult. Attempted purification by affinity chromatography, using estradiol linked to benzyl-cellulose, polystyrene or Agarose (Jungblut *et al.*, 1967b; Jensen *et al.*, 1967b; Vonderhaar and Mueller, 1969; Cuatrecasas, 1970), has not been successful. Although such columns remove the estrogen-binding capacity of uterine cytosol, the receptor cannot be recovered again in an active form.

Purification of the binding unit of the cytosol receptor by conventional techniques was facilitated by the observation (DeSombre *et al.*, 1969; Jensen *et al.*, 1969c) that addition of calcium ions and salt to uterine cytosol, prepared in the presence of EDTA, yields a "stabilized"

4 S binding unit which does not revert to the 8 S form when the salt is removed and which is highly resistant to aggregation. The effect of calcium appears to result from its activation of an enzyme present in uterine cytosol prepared in EDTA that removes a portion of the receptor molecule which is responsible for aggregation (Puca, 1971). With mature rat uteri, loss in the ability to reform the 8 S complex in low salt also takes place on aging of the salt-dissociated cytosol complex in the cold or after incubation of the cytosol at 37°C (Vonderhaar *et al.*, 1970a,b).

Although the calcium-stabilized 4 S complex no longer will undergo transformation to the 5 S form, either in the presence or absence of uterine nuclei, it does contain the estrogen-binding unit of the cytosol complex, so that information concerning its composition and structure should provide insight into the nature of at least part of the receptor molecule. By ammonium sulfate precipitation, Sephadex G-200 filtration, and DEAE cellulose chromatography, the calcium-stabilized 4 S complex of calf uterine cytosol obtained by high speed centrifugation has been purified about 5000-fold (DeSombre *et al.*, 1969), and that from low-speed cytosol about 1000-fold (DeSombre *et al.*, 1971a), corresponding to purities of about 5% and 1%, respectively, if there is one estradiol bound per 4 S unit. This partially purified 4 S complex shows an apparent molecular weight (G-200 elution) of about 75,000 and an isoelectric point of 6.4, in contrast to respective values of 200,000 and 5.8 observed with the 8 S cytosol complex. Subsequent studies involving determination of Stokes radii indicate more accurate molecular weights of 236,000 for the 8 S complex and 61,000 for the stabilized 4 S complex, and isoelectric points of 6.6–7.0 and 6.2, respectively (Puca *et al.*, 1971). The product from low-speed cytosol has been further purified by acrylamide gel electrophoresis to yield a material showing a single radioactive protein band by amido black staining (DeSombre *et al.*, 1971a), probably the first time the receptor protein has been detected by any criterion except the radioactivity of the steroid bound to it.

Under most conditions, the 5 S complex extracted by potassium chloride from the nucleus undergoes aggregation to a 8–9 S form when the salt is removed. Unlike the binding unit of the cytosol complex, the nuclear complex is not stabilized toward this aggregation by treatment with calcium ions. However, after ammonium sulfate precipitation followed by gel filtration in the presence of potassium chloride, the nuclear complex loses its tendency to aggregate in low salt and can be further purified by ion-exchange chromatography and/or acrylamide gel electrophoresis at pH 8.8, where it moves considerably faster than the calcium-stabilized 4 S complex of the cytosol. In this way, the nuclear complex prepared by incubating estradiol and calf uterine cytosol with pre-extracted calf uterine nuclei has been obtained in substantially purified form. This partially purified nuclear complex shows clear differences from the stabilized 4 S complex, both in sedimentation and electrophoretic properties (DeSombre *et al.*, 1971b).

B. PROGESTINS

1. Binding of Progestins by Target Tissues in Vivo and in Vitro

The first attempts to demonstrate specific progesterone binding gave no evidence for the presence of characteristic progestin receptors in uterus or other target tissues. The observation that the ability of the ovariectomized mouse vagina to retain locally administered progesterone is markedly increased after treatment with estrogen (Podratz and Katz-man, 1968) suggested that the level of progesterone-binding substances in target tissues may be enhanced by estrogen prestimulation. Subsequent experiments have firmly established the estrogen dependence of pro-gesterone binding, and during the past two years, rapid progress has been made in the study of progesterone–receptor interactions, both *in vivo* and *in vitro*.

In comparison to estrogens, considerably fewer studies with pro-gesterone have been carried out in the whole animal, inasmuch as investigators have tended to proceed directly to *in vitro* incubations of tissue segments and to binding studies with cell fractions. A few careful *in vivo* investigations have been carried out, which provide a basis of reference for evaluating binding phenomena in cell-free systems.

The ovariectomized guinea pig uterus shows a small uptake and re-tention of progesterone *in vivo;* this incorporation is increased seven-fold (Fig. 6) by pretreatment of the animal with estrogen (Falk and Bardin, 1970). In the same tissue, estrogen priming significantly increases the concentration of uterine receptor molecules (Milgrom *et al.*, 1970). Although concentration of progesterone above the blood level is not observed in the chick oviduct, specific progesterone binding to macro-molecules can be demonstrated both *in vivo* and *in vitro*, with a binding capacity after diethylstilbestrol pretreatment which is twenty times greater than that observed in oviducts from chicks not treated with estrogen (O'Malley *et al.*, 1969, 1970). In the ovariectomized rabbit, the incorporation of progesterone by uterus *in vivo* is greater than that by thigh muscle; the uptake in uterus but not in muscle is increased two-to fourfold by preliminary administration of estradiol (Wiest and Rao,

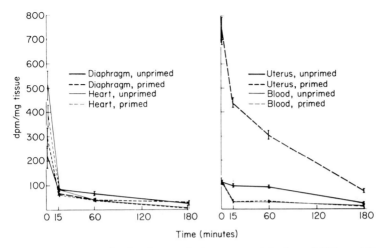

Fig. 6. Tissue tritium levels after single intravenous injection of 286 ng (50 μCi) progesterone-1,2-³H to castrated guinea pigs. Estrogen-primed animals received 1 μg estrone twice daily for 2 days. Each point is the mean of 10 animals. (From Falk and Bardin, 1970.)

1971). The binding of progesterone by the uterus and vagina is increased by estrogen pretreatment in the ovariectomized hamster and varies with ovarian cycle in the intact hamster (Reuter *et al.*, 1970). Progesterone uptake *in vitro* has been observed in uterine segments from immature rats, in which case estrogen prestimulation apparently is not required for substantial progesterone binding to occur (J. L. McGuire and DeDella, 1971). The effect of estrogen priming on the properties of the receptor molecules is described in the next section.

The specificity of progesterone binding, as defined by a limited capacity of binding sites, is demonstrated both *in vivo* (Falk and Bardin, 1970) and *in vitro* (J. L. McGuire and DeDella, 1971) by the diminution of radioactive progesterone uptake by the presence of unlabeled progesterone but not of estradiol, testosterone, or cortisol. Similarly, tritiated cortisol does not show selective uptake by the uterine tissue of the estrogen-primed guinea pig (Falk and Bardin, 1970).

Although the progesterone administered undergoes extensive metabolic transformation in the whole animal (Falk and Bardin, 1970) and is readily reduced to 5α-pregnane-3,20-dione by isolated uterine nuclei of estrogen-treated castrated rats (Armstrong and King, 1970), the steroid taken up and specifically bound by target tissues appears to be chiefly progesterone itself. One and three hours after tritiated progesterone injection, unchanged progesterone comprises 88 and 72%, respectively, of the radioactivity present in the estrogen-primed guinea pig uterus (Falk and Bardin, 1970); the remainder of the uterine radioactivity may reflect the level of other radioactive substances present in the blood plasma (Fig. 6). Up to 2 hours after progesterone administration to the estrogen-primed ovariectomized rabbit, most of the nuclear and nearly all of the extranuclear steroid bound in the uterus can be identified as progesterone (Wiest and Rao, 1971). However, 4 hours after injection of progesterone into the ovariectomized rat, most of the uterine radio-activity is found to be a polar unconjugated progesterone metabolite present in seven times the plasma level (Reel *et al.*, 1969; J. L. McGuire and DeDella, 1971). The uterine concentration of this substance is not sensitive to estrogen pretreatment, and its relation to specific proges-terone–receptor interaction is not clear.

On incubation with rat uterine tissue *in vitro*, progesterone appears to be incorporated without chemical change (J. L. McGuire and DeDella, 1971). The same is true for brief *in vitro* treatment of chick oviduct (O'Malley *et al.*, 1970), although on incubations of 1 hour or longer extensive conversion of progesterone to polar metabolites takes place (O'Malley *et al.*, 1969). It appears that target tissues can actively metabolize progesterone but that the initial interaction of progesterone with receptor substances takes place without metabolic transformation of the steroid. This conclusion is substantiated by studies in cell-free systems to be described later.

2. Progestin–Receptor Complexes and Their Intracellular Localization

Cell fractionation experiments indicate that, in target tissues of the estrogen-prestimulated animal, progesterone is specifically bound both in the cytosol and in the nucleus. Predominantly nuclear localization, similar to that described for estrogens, is observed with progesterone in guinea pig uterus (Milgrom, 1971), although cytosol and nuclear binding of progesterone were found to be about equal in the ovariectomized rabbit uterus (Wiest and Rao, 1971) and in chick oviduct more radio-active steroid appears in the cytosol than in the nucleus (O'Malley *et al.*, 1970, 1971a). Only a few preliminary attempts at autoradiographic localization of progestins in target tissues have been reported; these indi-cate cytoplasmic rather than nuclear localization in the rat uterus for both progesterone (Rogers *et al.*, 1966) and norethynodrel (Stumpf, 1968a).

As in the case of estrogens, progesterone binding in the nucleus but not the cytosol is markedly temperature-dependent. After exposure of chick oviduct segments to tritiated progesterone at 0°C *in vitro*, the incorpo-rated radioactivity appears almost exclusively in the cytosol; when these tissues containing extranuclear progesterone are then incubated at 37°C, the nuclear radioactivity steadily increases until at 30 minutes 75% of the radioactivity has shifted to the nucleus (O'Malley *et al.*, 1970, 1971a).

The progesterone present in both the cytosol and nuclear fractions of target tissue cells is bound to macromolecules which can be characterized by the technique of sucrose gradient ultracentrifugation. As in the case of estrogen, the progesterone–receptor complex present in the nucleus is solubilized by extraction with 0.3 or 0.4 M potassium chloride. That the complex actually is intranuclear is indicated by its failure to be released when the outer nuclear membrane is removed by Triton X-100 (O'Malley *et al.*, 1971a). After administration of the hormone *in vivo* (Fig. 7A) or exposure of tissue segments to progesterone at 37°C *in vitro*, the complexes of both the cytosol and the nuclear extract from chick oviducts sediment at about 4 S in sucrose gradients containing potassium chloride (O'Malley *et al.*, 1970, 1971a). The cytosol complex can be prepared in higher yield by direct addition of tritiated progesterone to the supernatant fraction (Fig. 7B); this product sediments at 3.8 S in salt-containing gradients, but as a mixture of 5 S and 8 S components in salt-free gradients (O'Malley *et al.*, 1970, 1971b; Sherman *et al.*, 1970). The cytosol complex of chick oviduct also can be recognized by its elution from Agarose columns; using this technique, no receptor can be detected in the cytosol of chick lung or spleen (Sherman *et al.*, 1970).

Not only is the total amount of cytosol receptor increased by estrogen

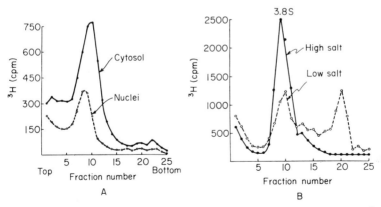

FIG. 7. Sedimentation patterns of radioactive progesterone–receptor complexes obtained from chick oviduct. (A) Cytosol and nuclear extract from tissue, excised 8 minutes after intravenous injection of 845 ng (90 μCi) progesterone-^{3}H, centrifuged in a 5–20% sucrose gradient containing 300 mM potassium chloride at 204,000 g for 16 hours at 1°C. (B) Oviduct cytosol from untreated chicks made 10 nM in progesterone-^{3}H and centrifuged under similar conditions in a 5–20% sucrose gradient in the presence and absence of 300 mM potassium chloride. (From O'Malley *et al.*, 1970.)

pretreatment (O'Malley *et al.*, 1970; Milgrom *et al.*, 1970; Rao and Wiest, 1971), but its sedimentation behavior in low-salt sucrose gradients is influenced by this prestimulation. With the ovariectomized rabbit uterus that has not been primed with estrogen, the progesterone–receptor complex sediments at about 4 S in low salt, either after administration of progesterone *in vivo* (Wiest and Rao, 1971) or on direct addition of the hormone to the cytosol (J. L. McGuire and DeDella, 1971) After estrogen pretreatment, sedimentation peaks are observed at both 8 S and 4 S in salt-free gradients but only at 4 S in gradients containing potassium chloride (Wiest and Rao, 1971). The nuclear extract from these uteri shows a 4 S sedimentation peak, even in low salt. With the ovariectomized guinea pig not primed with estrogen, the complex formed by adding tritiated progesterone to the uterine cytosol sediments at 4–5 S in low salt; after estrogen priming, the cytosol complex, obtained either after progesterone injection *in vivo* or addition of the hormone to the cytosol, sediments at 6.7 S in the absence of salt, shifting to 4.3 in salt-containing sucrose gradients (Milgrom *et al.*, 1970).

Thus, it appears that in rabbit and guinea pig uterus, estrogen prestimulation causes the 4 S binding unit of the cytosol progesterone receptor to convert partly or entirely to a form which sediments more rapidly in low salt gradients. This is the opposite of its effect on the estrogen receptor of rat uterus, where the cytosol complex of the immature or ovariectomized rat sediments exclusively at 8 S in low salt but that of the animal with functioning ovaries exists partially in a 4 S form (Steggles and King, 1970). The influence of estrogen on the progesterone complex is not a direct effect on the receptor protein, inasmuch the addition of estradiol to rabbit cytosol does not alter the sedimentation pattern (Wiest and Rao, 1971).

The presence of specific progesterone receptors in rat uterus has not been established with certainty. After incubation of tritiated progesterone with segments of traumatized pseudopregnant rat uterus at 37°C (Reel *et al.*, 1970) or addition of the hormone to uterine cytosol from estrogen-primed castrated rats (Milgrom and Baulieu, 1970), the cytosol contains progesterone as a 4 S complex. But in contrast to the interactions of progesterone with chick oviduct or rabbit and guinea pig uterus, which are neither shared nor inhibited by cortisol, rat uterine cytosol does form a 4 S complex with cortisol as well as with progesterone, suggesting that the interaction in rat uterus might involve corticoid-binding proteins from the blood. Although the progesterone and cortisol complexes are reported to possess different thermal stabilities (Reel *et al.*, 1970), the marked similarities in their properties observed by others (Milgrom and Baulieu, 1970), including precipitation by antibodies to rat serum, renders the significance of these complexes open to question until more experimental work has been done.

Binding to the receptor substances of chick oviduct and guinea pig or rabbit uterus is specific for progesterone and other progestational compounds, such as norethindrone, norethynodrel, medroxyprogesterone acetate, and chlormadinone, and in general is not seen with cortisol, aldosterone, estrogens, or androgens (O'Malley *et al.*, 1970; Milgrom *et al.*, 1970; J. L. McGuire and DeDella, 1971; Wiest and Rao, 1971). From its ability to compete with progesterone binding, 5α-pregnane-3,20-dione shows significant affinity for progesterone receptors in chick oviduct (O'Malley *et al.*, 1970) and guinea pig uterus (Milgrom *et al.*, 1970) but is less tightly bound in rabbit uterus (Wiest and Rao, 1971). Only with the cytosol receptor of chick oviduct does testosterone appear to compete for progesterone binding sites (Sherman *et al.*, 1970).

3. Cytosol Dependence of Nuclear Binding

In similarity with estrogen–receptor interaction, the cytosol progesterone–receptor complex is formed directly on mixing the hormone with the cytosol fraction of target tissues, and there is no evidence for the presence of any receptor substance in the nucleus before the tissue has been exposed to progesterone. Incubation of chick oviduct nuclei with tritiated progesterone in buffer gives no extractable progesterone complex unless oviduct cytosol is also present, in which case the 4 S nuclear complex is readily formed (O'Malley *et al.*, 1971a). In contrast to the marked temperature-dependence of nuclear binding observed with whole oviduct tissue *in vitro* (O'Malley *et al.*, 1970, 1971a), the interaction of isolated oviduct nuclei with progesterone and cytosol gives a better yield of 4 S nuclear complex at 0°C than at 23°C or 37°C (O'Malley *et al.*, 1971a). This result may reflect thermal instability of the receptor protein in a cell-free system.

The participation of the progesterone–receptor complex of oviduct cytosol in the formation of the nuclear complex is further indicated by the depletion of cytosol receptor content which takes place when whole oviduct tissue interacts with progesterone *in vitro*, as well as by the cytosol specificity of nuclear binding (O'Malley *et al.*, 1971a). If oviduct nuclei are incubated with progesterone in lung or liver cytosol, no 4 S complex can be extracted from them.

When lung or liver nuclei are incubated with tritiated progesterone and oviduct cytosol, radioactive hormone is taken up, but none of this is extracted as 4 S complex (O'Malley *et al.*, 1971a). Thus, oviduct nuclei appear to possess characteristic acceptor sites for the cytosol complex which are not present in lung and liver nuclei. This nuclear acceptor site appears to be associated with the chromatin; experiments in which the separated constituents of the chromatin from different tissues are reassembled in various combinations indicate that the specificity of the nuclear acceptor site for the cytosol progesterone–receptor complex lies in the acidic nuclear proteins rather than in the histones or the DNA (Spelsberg *et al.*, 1971, O'Malley *et al.*, 1971b).

4. Properties and Purification of Progesterone Receptor Proteins

Like the estrogen receptors, the progesterone-binding substances of target tissues appear to be thermolabile, sulfhydryl-containing proteins. The cytosol complexes of chick oviduct (Sherman *et al.*, 1970) and rabbit uterus (Wiest and Rao, 1971) are cleaved by treatment with pronase but not by RNase or DNase; the oviduct complex, as well as that of guinea pig uterus (Milgrom *et al.*, 1970), is destroyed by warming to 60°C or by exposure to *p*-hydroxymercuribenzoate in the cold.

From the ratio of bound to free steroid after sedimentation in sucrose gradients, the dissociation constant of the cytosol complex of chick oviduct has been estimated as $8 \times 10^{-10}\ M$ (Sherman *et al.*, 1970) and that of the guinea pig uterus as $5 \times 10^{-10}\ M$ (Milgrom *et al.*, 1970). Using charcoal to separate free from bound steroid, a K_D of about $2 \times 10^{-10}\ M$ is obtained for rabbit uterus (Rao and Wiest, 1971). The concentration of cytosol binding sites reported for chick oviduct and guinea pig uterus can be expressed as approximately 75 and 20 femtomoles per milligram of fresh tissue, respectively. These values are in the same range as those reported for estradiol receptor sites in rat uterus. The cytosol progesterone complex also can be assayed by the binding to glass powder in the presence of magnesium ions (O'Malley *et al.*, 1971b) in a manner similar to the estrogen receptor (Clark and Gorski, 1969).

Like the cytosol complex, the nuclear complex of chick oviduct is destroyed by warming to 60°C or by treatment with pronase or *N*-ethylmaleimide (O'Malley *et al.*, 1971a). Unlike the estrogen complexes, the nuclear and cytosol progesterone–receptor complexes of chick oviduct cannot be differentiated in the presence of potassium chloride, either by sedimentation or by elution behavior on Agarose columns. By the latter criterion, the apparent molecular weights of both complexes are approximately 100,000 (O'Malley *et al.*, 1971a).

On gel filtration, ion-exchange chromatography, acrylamide gel electrophoresis, and isoelectric focusing, the progesterone–receptor complex of chick oviduct cytosol is resolved into two components; these differ with respect to molecular size and charge, with isoelectric points of 4.0 and 4.5, respectively (O'Malley *et al.*, 1971b). By the sequence of ammonium sulfate precipitation, gel filtration with Agarose, ion-exchange chromatography on DEAE cellulose, and sucrose gradient centrifugation, this cytosol complex, stabilized by the presence of thioglycerol, has been purified approximately 2500-fold.

IV. HORMONE–RECEPTOR INTERACTION PATTERN AND ITS BIOCHEMICAL SIGNIFICANCE

On the basis of a variety of self-consistent experimental evidence described in the foregoing sections, it appears that estrogens and progestins interact with their respective target tissues by similar two-step mechanisms in which the hormone first binds to an extranuclear receptor protein, which is a characteristic component of hormone-dependent tissues. By a temperature-dependent process, the steroid–receptor complex is translocated to the nucleus, where it associates with a specific acceptor site—again characteristic of the target tissue—and in some way causes the acceleration of certain nuclear biosynthetic processes. In the case of estrogens, nuclear transfer is either accompanied (Fig. 8, pathway I) or preceded (Fig. 8, pathway II) by conversion of the receptor binding unit from a 4 S to a 5 S form; with progesterone, no characteristic alteration of the receptor during nuclear transfer has yet been demonstrated.

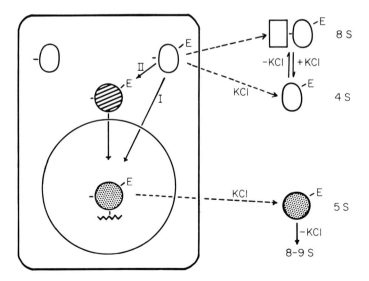

FIG. 8. Two-step interaction pattern of estrogen (E) with receptors in uterine cells.

A relation between the cytosol and nuclear estrogen–receptor complexes in rat uterine tissue was first suggested by observations that nafoxidine inhibits cytosol and nuclear binding to the same degree (Jensen *et al.*, 1967a), by considerations that the cytosol protein (which is present in excess amount and can associate directly with estradiol) might serve as the nonsaturable "uptake receptor" for subsequent nuclear retention (Jensen *et al.*, 1967b), and by the finding that more radioactivity is bound to uterine nuclei on incubation with tritiated estradiol in the presence of uterine cytosol than in its absence (Brecher *et al.*, 1967; Brecher and Wotiz, 1968). The proposal of a two-step interaction mechanism (Gorski *et al.*, 1968; Jensen *et al.*, 1968), now modified in certain details (Fig. 8) on the basis of subsequent information concerning the 4 S binding unit and its transformation to a 5 S form (Jensen *et al.*, 1971a), rests principally on three pieces of experimental evidence—the cytosol requirement for 5 S complex production in isolated uterine nuclei, the temperature-induced shift of extranuclear 8 S estradiol to nuclear 5 S estradiol in uterine tissue *in vitro*, and the striking temporary depletion of cytosol receptor protein which takes place *in vivo* as estradiol becomes bound in rat uterine nuclei. An analogous mechanism for the interaction of progesterone with chick oviduct is likewise indicated by the requirement for oviduct cytosol in nuclear complex formation, the temperature-dependence of nuclear binding and the depletion of cytosol receptor content when oviduct tissue reacts with progesterone *in vitro* (O'Malley *et al.*, 1970, 1971a). In the case of progesterone, there is evidence that the specificity of the nuclear acceptor site involves the acidic protein components of oviduct chromatin (Spelsberg *et al.*, 1971).

How the steroid induces the receptor protein to move to the nucleus and how the hormone leaves the nucleus and the cell once its function is completed are important questions about which little is known. It has been suggested (Jungblut *et al.*, 1970) that the cytosol receptor is not free in the cytoplasm but is a part of the cell membrane or endoplasmic reticulum from which it is extracted during homogenization, and that elements of this structure accompany the hormone–receptor complex in its transfer to the nucleus. Recent photomicroscopic evidence indicates that lysosomes of uterine cells are induced to migrate to the nucleus after stimulation with estrogen *in vivo*, suggesting that these structures may function as carriers of the extranuclear estradiol–receptor complex (R. E. Smith and Szego, 1971). Nuclear turnover of estradiol appears to be considerably more rapid than is implied by the overall radioactivity retention pattern, as indicated by the fact that after the injection of a physiological dose of estradiol to the immature rat, the depletion of uterine cytosol receptor content is four to five times greater than can be accounted for by the estradiol present in the nucleus (Jensen *et al.*, 1971a). It is possible that on leaving the nucleus estradiol encounters more extranuclear receptor and repeats the interaction cycle so that each estradiol molecule may effect the transfer of several receptor molecules to the nucleus before it finally escapes from the cell.

In considering how the foregoing sequence of steroid–receptor interactions might be related to the hormone-induced acceleration of biosynthetic reactions in the target cell nucleus, one must recognize two alternative possibilities—the protein may be needed to carry the hormone to the nucleus or the steroid may serve to promote nuclear transfer of the protein (Jensen *et al.*, 1969b,c, 1971a). Although the receptor system may be simply a transport device to deliver the hormone to the proper nuclear location, where it leaves the receptor and exerts its action by some undefined mechanism, it is attractive to consider that the receptor protein itself may play a role in some key nuclear process and that the function of the steroid is to enable the protein to reach its action site. The presence of increased amounts of extranuclear receptor in the hormone-responsive tissues may reflect the inability of this protein to penetrate the nucleus in such tissues until association with the steroid promotes its conversion to an active form (pathway II, Fig. 8).

That the transformed receptor protein may be the active species in estrogen action is suggested by the effect of the 5 S but not the 4 S complex in enhancing RNA synthesis in isolated uterine nuclei. Recently it was observed (Raynaud-Jammet and Baulieu, 1969) that nuclei isolated in sucrose from heifer endometrium show a significant increase in their ability to incorporate radioactive nucleotide into RNA *in vitro* after they have been incubated with uterine cytosol containing estradiol but not with cytosol or estradiol alone. It was then shown (Mohla *et al.*, 1971a,b) that this enhancement of RNA synthetic capacity takes place only under conditions which permit transformation of the receptor from the 4 S to the 5 S form. Calf endometrium nuclei are activated by incubation for 30 minutes at 25°C with cytosol containing estradiol, but not with cytosol and estrone, which, as discussed earlier, can not effect 4 S to 5 S conversion. No effect of cytosol plus estradiol is seen after incubation with nuclei at 0°C; however, if the hormone–cytosol mixture is first warmed to effect transformation, activation of the nuclei can then be effected in the cold. The 5 S estradiol receptor complex extracted by potassium chloride from previously treated uterine nuclei is fully active in stimulating fresh nuclei. The tissue specificity of the phenomenon is indicated by the fact that, after incubation with estradiol in rat uterine cytosol, nuclei from immature rat uterus show markedly increased synthetic capacity, whereas the already high levels of RNA synthesis in rat liver and kidney nuclei are not changed by incubation with estradiol, either in their own cytosols or in uterine cytosol.

The foregoing enhancement of RNA synthetic capacity in isolated uterine nuclei involves significant increase in "soluble" as well as "aggregate" RNA polymerase activity, indicating that at least part of the phenomenon is independent of any effect on chromatin template function (Mohla *et al.*, 1971b). This conclusion is also indicated by experiments in which the hormone–receptor mixture is added directly to the RNA polymerase assay system (Beziat *et al.*, 1970; Hough *et al.*, 1970; Arnaud *et al.*, 1971a). Although experimental controls are not described, addition of the salt-dissociated cytosol complex (presumably transformed from the 4 S to the 5 S form, inasmuch as complexing with estradiol is effected at 37°C), as well as the 5 S complex extracted from the nucleus, appears to cause a significant increase in the activity of the aggregate enzyme prepared from heifer endometrium nuclei, in contrast to the soluble enzyme which is not stimulated. In subsequent studies it was shown that it is the RNA polymerase of the uterine nucleolus which is affected by the addition of cytosol complex (Arnaud *et al.*, 1971b).

The degree of enhancement (50–200%) of RNA synthetic capacity of uterine nuclei when they are treated with the estradiol–receptor complex *in vitro* is comparable to that observed when the hormone is administered *in vivo* (Gorski, 1964; Nicolette *et al.*, 1968; Hamilton *et al.*, 1968) and considerably greater than that which would correspond to new messenger for a single protein species. Thus, the relation of this effect to the formation of the induced proteins discussed in Section II,A is not clear. Still, the tissue and steroid specificity associated with this nuclear stimulation suggests that the phenomenon may be of physiological significance and that it may provide a valuable system for evaluating the biological activity of purified receptor proteins when they become available, leading to a more detailed understanding of the mechanism of estrogen action.

The two-step sequence, involving nuclear transfer of an extranuclear receptor protein, represents a general pattern of interaction, not only for estrogenic and progestational hormones, but for other classes of steroid hormones as well. As summarized in more detail elsewhere (Jensen *et al.*, 1971a), recent studies of Liao, Mainwaring, Baulieu, Sekeris, Tomkins, Munck, and Edelman have demonstrated that target tissues for androgens, glucocorticoids, and mineralocorticoids likewise possess extranuclear receptor proteins specific for the particular steroid hormone which show remarkable similarities in their general properties. In all cases, the hormone forms an initial complex with the receptor protein, which, by a temperature-dependent process, is then transferred to the nucleus, where hormonal action appears to be initiated.

It is tempting to speculate that the two-step steroid–receptor interaction mechanism represents one of two general patterns for hormonal control in mammalian cells. In the case of certain catecholamine and peptide hormones, it appears likely that a primary action of the hormone is to activate an adenyl cyclase system at the cell membrane to generate a cyclic nucleotide, which then serves as a second messenger, carrying out a specific action somewhere in the cell (Sutherland and Robison, 1966). In the case of the steroid hormones, it is possible that it is the hormone-activated receptor protein, present in unique amounts in the particular target tissue, which delivers the regulatory message. When receptor proteins are isolated in pure form and the details of the hormone-dependent thermal transformation and nuclear fixation are elucidated, we should have a much clearer understanding of the fundamental mechanism of steroid hormone action.

REFERENCES

Aizawa, Y., and Mueller, G. C. (1961). *J. Biol. Chem.* **236**, 381.

Alberga, A., and Baulieu, E. E. (1965). *Compt. Rend.* **D261**, 5226.

Alberga, A., and Baulieu, E. E. (1968). *Mol. Pharmacol.* **4**, 311.

Armstrong, D. T., and King, E. R. (1970). *Federation Proc.* **29**, 250.

Arnaud, M., Beziat, Y., Guilleux, J. C., Hough, A., Hough, D., and Mousseron-Canet, M. (1971a). *Biochim. Biophys. Acta* **232**, 117.

Arnaud, M., Beziat, Y., Guilleux, J. C., and Mousseron-Canet, M. (1971b). *Compt. Rend.* **D272**, 635.

Attramadal, A. (1970). *Z. Zellforsch. Mikrosk. Anat.* **104**, 572.

Attramadal, A., and Aakvaag, A. (1970). *Z. Zellforsch. Mikrosk. Anat.* **104**, 582.

Barker, K. L. (1971). *Biochemistry* **10**, 284.

Barker, K. L., and Warren, J. C. (1966). *Proc. Natl. Acad. Sci. U. S.* **56**, 1298.

Barnea, A., and Gorski, J. (1970). *Biochemistry* **9**, 1899.

Barry, J., and Gorski, J. (1971). *Biochemistry* **10**, 2384.

Barton, R. W., and Liao, S. (1967). *Endocrinology* **81**, 409.

Baulieu, E. E., and Raynaud, J. P. (1970). *European J. Biochem.* **13**, 293.

Baulieu, E. E., Alberga, A., and Jung, I. (1967). *Compt. Rend.* **D265**, 454.

Best-Belpomme, M., Fries, J., and Erdos, T. (1970). *European J. Biochem.* **17**, 425.

Beziat, Y., Guilleux, J. C., and Mousseron-Canet, M. (1970). *Compt. Rend.* **D270**, 1620.

Billing, R. J., Barbiroli, B., and Smellie, R. M. S. (1969a). *Biochem J.* **112**, 563.

Billing, R. J., Barbiroli, B., and Smellie, R. M. S. (1969b). *Biochim. Biophys. Acta* **190**, 52.

Billing, R. J., Barbiroli, B., and Smellie, R. M. S. (1969c). *Biochim. Biophys. Acta* **190**, 60.

Bitman, J., Cecil, H. C., Mench, M. L., and Wren, T. R. (1965). *Endocrinology* **76**, 63.

Braunsberg, H., Irvine, W. T., and James, V. H. T. (1967). *Brit. J. Cancer* **21**, 714.

Brecher, P. I., and Wotiz, H. H. (1967). *Steroids* **9**, 431.

Brecher, P. I., and Wotiz, H. H. (1968). *Proc. Soc. Exptl. Biol. Med.* **128**, 470.

Brecher, P. I., Vigersky, R., Wotiz, H. S., and Wotiz, H. H. (1967). *Steroids* **10**, 635

Brecher, P. I., Pasquina, A., and Wotiz, H. H. (1969). *Endocrinology* **85**, 612.

Brecher, P. I., Numata, M., DeSombre, E. R., and Jensen, E. V. (1970). *Federation Proc.* **29**, 249.

Brush, M. G., Taylor, R. W., and King, R. J. B. (1967). *J. Endocrinol.* **39**, 599.

Bush, I. E. (1965). *Proc. 2nd Intern. Congr. Endocrinol., London, 1964* p. 1324. Excerpta Med. Found., Amsterdam.

Callantine, M. R. (1967). *Clin. Obstet. Gynecol.* **10**, 74.

Callantine, M. R., Clemens, C. E., and Shih, Y. (1968). *Proc. Soc. Exptl. Biol. Med.* **128**, 382.

Church, R. B., and McCarthy, B. J. (1970). *Biochim. Biophys. Acta* **199**, 103.

Clark, J. H., and Gorski, J. (1969). *Biochim. Biophys. Acta* **192**, 508.

Cuatrecasas, P. (1970). *J. Biol. Chem.* **245**, 3059.

Davis, M. E., Wiener, M., Jacobson, H. I., and Jensen, E. V. (1963). *Am. J. Obstet. Gynecol.* **87**, 979.

DeAngelo, A. B., and Gorski, J. (1970). *Proc. Natl. Acad. Sci. U. S.* **66**, 693.

DeHertogh, R., Ekka, E., Vanderheyden, I., and Hoet, J. J. (1971a). *Endocrinology* **88**, 165.

DeHertogh, R., Ekka, E., Vanderheyden, I., and Hoet, J. J. (1971b). *Endocrinology* **88**, 175.

Demetriou, J. A., Crowley, L. G., Kushinsky, S., Donovan, A. J., Kotin, P., and MacDonald, I. (1964). *Cancer Res.* **24**, 926.

Deshpande, N., Jensen, V., Bulbrook, R. D., Berne, T., and Ellis, F. (1967). *Steroids* **10**, 219.

DeSombre, E. R., Puca, G. A., and Jensen, E. V. (1969). *Proc. Natl. Acad. Sci. U. S.* **64**, 148.

DeSombre, E. R., Chabaud, J. P., Puca, G. A., and Jensen, E. V. (1971a). *J. Steroid Biochem.* **2**, 95.

DeSombre, E. R., Ikeda, M., Tanaka, S., Smith, S., and Jensen, E. V. (1971b). *Abstr. 53rd Meeting, Endocrine Soc. San Francisco,* p. 149.

Eisenfeld, A. J. (1970). *Endocrinology* **86**, 1313.

Eisenfeld, A. J., and Axelrod, J. (1965). *J. Pharmacol. Exptl. Therap.* **150**, 469.

Eisenfeld, A. J., and Axelrod, J. (1966). *Endocrinology* **79**, 38.

Eisenfeld, A. J., and Axelrod, J. (1967). *Biochem. Pharmacol.* **16**, 1781.

Eisenfeld, A. J., Gardner, W. U., and van Wagenen, W. L. (1971). *Am. J. Obstet. Gynecol.* **109**, 124.

Ellis, D. J., and Ringold, H. J. (1971). *In* "Biochemical Endocrinology: III. The Sex Steroids: Molecular Mechanisms" (K. W. McKerns, ed.). Appleton, New York. In press.

Erdos, T. (1968). *Biochim. Biophys. Res. Commun.* **32**, 338.

Erdos, T., Gospodarowicz, D., Bessada, R., and Fries, J. (1968). *Compt. Rend.* **D266**, 2164.

Erdos, T., Bessada, R., and Fries, J. (1969). *FEBS Letters* **5**, 161.

Erdos, T., Best-Belpomme, M., and Bessada, R. (1970). *Anal. Biochem.* **37**, 244.

Falk, R. J., and Bardin, C. W. (1970). *Endocrinology* **86**, 1059.

Feherty, P., Robertson, D. M., Waynforth, H. B., and Kellie, A. E. (1970). *Biochem. J.* **120**, 837.

Fencl, M. M., and Villee, C. A. (1971). *Endocrinology* **88**, 279.

Flesher, J. W. (1965). *Steroids* **5**, 737.

Folca, P. J., Glascock, R. F., and Irvine, W. T. (1961). *Lancet* **II**, 796.

Folman, Y., and Pope, G. S. (1969). *J. Endocrinol.* **44**, 203.

Giannopoulos, G., and Gorski, J. (1971). *J. Biol. Chem.* **246**, 2524.

Glascock, R. F., and Hoekstra, W. G. (1959). *Biochem. J.* **72**, 673.

Gorski, J. (1964). *J. Biol. Chem.* **239**, 899.

Gorski, J., and Axman, M. C. (1964). *Arch. Biochem. Biophys.* **105**, 517.

Gorski, J., and Morgan, M. S. (1967). *Biochim. Biophys. Acta* **149**, 282.

Gorski, J., and Nelson, N. J. (1965). *Arch. Biochem. Biophys.* **110**, 284.

Gorski, J., and Nicolette, J. A. (1963). *Arch. Biochem. Biophys.* **103**, 418.

Gorski, J., Noteboom, W. D., and Nicolette, J. A. (1965). *J. Cellular Comp. Physiol.* **66**, Suppl., 91.

Gorski, J., Toft, D., Shyamala, G., Smith, D., and Notides, A. (1968). *Recent Progr. Hormone Res.* **24**, 45.

Greenman, D. L. (1970). *Endocrinology* **87**, 716.

Gupta, G. N. (1960). Ph.D. Dissertation, Dept. Biochem., University of Chicago.

Gurpide, E., and Welch, M. (1969). *J. Biol. Chem.* **244**, 5159.

Hacker, B. (1969). *Biochim. Biophys. Acta* **186**, 214.

Hahn, W. E., Schjeide, O. A., and Gorbman, A. (1969a). *Proc. Natl. Acad. Sci. U. S.* **62**, 112.

Hahn, W. E., Church, R. B., and Gorbman, A. (1969b). *Endocrinology* **84**, 738.

Hähnel, R. (1971). *Steroids* **17**, 105.

Hamilton, T. H. (1964). *Proc. Natl. Acad. Sci. U. S.* **51**, 83.

Hamilton, T. H. (1968). *Science* **161**, 649.

Hamilton, T. H., Widnell, C. C., and Tata, J. R. (1965). *Biochim. Biophys. Acta* **108**, 168.

Hamilton, T. H., Widnell, C. C., and Tata, J. R. (1968). *J. Biol. Chem.* **243**, 408.

Hechter, O., and Halkerston, I. D. K. (1964). *In* "The Hormones" (G. Pincus, K. V. Thimann, and E. B. Astwood, eds.), Vol. 5, pp. 697–825. Academic Press, New York.

Hough, D., Arnaud, M., and Mousseron-Canet, M. (1970). *Compt. Rend.* **D271**, 603.

Hughes, A., Smith, S., DeSombre, E. R., and Jensen, E. V. (1969). *Federation Proc.* **28**, 703.

Jensen, E. V. (1960). *Proc. 4th Intern. Congr. Biochem., Vienna, 1958* Vol. 15, p. 444. Pergamon, Oxford.

Jensen, E. V. (1962). *Recent Progr. Hormone Res.* **18**, 461.

Jensen, E. V. (1965a). *Proc. 2nd Intern. Congr. Endocrinol., London, 1964* p. 420. Excerpta Med. Found., Amsterdam.

Jensen, E. V. (1965b). *Can. Cancer Conf.* **6**, 143.

Jensen, E. V., and Jacobson, H. I. (1960). *In* "Biological Activities of Steroids in Relation to Cancer" (G. Pincus and E. P. Vollmer, eds.), pp. 161–178. Academic Press, New York.

Jensen, E. V., and Jacobson, H. I. (1962). *Recent Progr. Hormone Res.* **18**, 387.

Jensen, E. V., Jacobson, H. I., Flesher, J. W., Saha, N. N., Gupta, G. N., Smith, S., Colucci, V., Shiplacoff, D., Neumann, H. G., DeSombre, E. R., and Jungblut,

P. W. (1966). *In* "Steroid Dynamics" (G. Pincus, T. Nakao, and J. F. Tait, eds.), pp. 133–157. Academic Press, New York.

Jensen, E. V., DeSombre, E. R., and Jungblut, P. W. (1967a). *In* "Hormonal Steroids" (L. Martini, F. Fraschini, and M. Motta, eds.), pp. 492–500. Excerpta Med. Found., Amsterdam.

Jensen, E. V., DeSombre, E. R., Hurst, D. J., Kawashima, T., and Jungblut, P. W. (1967b). *Arch. Anat. Microscop. Morphol. Exptl.* **56**, Suppl., 547.

Jensen, E. V., DeSombre, E. R., and Jungblut, P. W. (1967c). *In* "Endogenous Factors Influencing Host-Tumor Balance" (R. W. Wissler, T. L. Dao, and S. Wood, Jr., eds.), pp. 15–30. Univ. of Chicago Press, Chicago.

Jensen, E. V., Hurst, D. J., DeSombre, E. R., and Jungblut, P. W. (1967d). *Science* **158**, 385.

Jensen, E. V., Suzuki, T., Kawashima, T., Stumpf, W. E., Jungblut, P. W., and DeSombre, E. R. (1968). *Proc. Natl. Acad. Sci. U. S.* **59**, 632.

Jensen, E. V., DeSombre, E. R., Jungblut, P. W., Stumpf, W. E., and Roth, L. J. (1969a). *In* "Autoradiography of Diffusible Substances" (L. J. Roth and W. E. Stumpf, eds.), pp. 81–97. Academic Press, New York.

Jensen, E. V., Suzuki, T., Numata, M., Smith, S., and DeSombre, E. R. (1969b). *Steroids* **13**, 417.

Jensen, E. V., Numata, M., Smith, S., Suzuki, T., Brecher, P. I., and DeSombre, E. R. (1969c). *Develop. Biol.* Suppl. 3, 151.

Jensen, E. V., Numata, M., Brecher, P. I., and DeSombre, E. R. (1971a). *In* "The Biochemistry of Steroid Hormone Action" (R. M. S. Smellie, ed.), *Biochem. Soc. Symp.* 32, pp. 133–159. Academic Press, New York.

Jensen, E. V., Block, G. E., Smith, S., Kyser, K., and DeSombre, E. R. (1971b). *In* "Prediction of Responses to Cancer Therapies" (T. C. Hall, ed.), *Natl. Cancer Inst. Monograph 34*, pp. 55–70. U. S. Gov't. Printing Office, Washington, D. C.

Joel, P. B., and Hagerman, D. D. (1969). *Biochim. Biophys. Acta* **195**, 328.

Johansson, H., Terenius, L., and Thorén, L. (1970). *Cancer Res.* **30**, 692.

Jungblut, P. W., Morrow, R. I., Reeder, G. L., and Jensen, E. V. (1965). *Abstr. 47th Meeting, Endocrine Soc., New York*, p. 56.

Jungblut, P. W., DeSombre, E. R., and Jensen, E. V. (1967a). *Abhandl. Deut. Akade. Wiss. Berlin, Kl. Med.* pp. 109–123.

Jungblut, P. W., Hätzel, I., DeSombre, E. R., and Jensen, E. V. (1967b). *Colloq. Ges. Physiol. Chem.* **18**, 58.

Jungblut, P. W., McCann, S., Görlich, L., Rosenfeld, G. C., and Wagner, R. (1970). *In* "Research on Steroids" (C. Conti, ed.), Vol. 4, pp. 213–232. Vieweg-Pergamon, Braunschweig.

Jütting, G., Thun, K. J., and Kuss, E. (1967). *European J. Biochem.* **2**, 146.

Kahwanago, I., Heinrichs, W. L., and Herrmann, W. L. (1970). *Endocrinology* **86**, 1319.

Kato, J., and Villee, C. A. (1967a). *Endocrinology* **80**, 567.

Kato, J., and Villee, C. A. (1967b). *Endocrinology* **80**, 1133.

Katzenellenbogen, B. S., and Gorski, J. (1971). *Federation Proc.* **30**, 1214.

King, R. J. B., and Gordon, J. (1966). *J. Endocrinol.* **34**, 431.

King, R. J. B., Gordon, J., and Inman, D. R. (1965a). *J. Endocrinol.* **32**, 9.

King, R. J. B., Cowan, D. M., and Inman, D. R. (1965b). *J. Endocrinol.* **32**, 83.

King, R. J. B., Gordon, J., Cowan, D. M., and Inman, D. R. (1966). *J. Endocrinol.* **36**, 139.

King, R. J. B., Gordon, J., and Steggles, A. W. (1969). *Biochem. J.* **114**, 649.

Korenman, S. G. (1968). *J. Clin. Endocrinol. Metab.* **28**, 127.
Korenman, S. G. (1969). *Steroids* **13**, 163.
Korenman, S. G. (1970). *Endocrinology* **87**, 1119.
Korenman, S. G., and O'Malley, B. W. (1968). *Endocrinology* **83**, 11.
Korenman, S. G., and Rao, B. R. (1968). *Proc. Natl. Acad. Sci. U. S.* **61**, 1028.
Kyser, K. A. (1970). Ph.D. Dissertation, Dept. Physiol., University of Chicago.
Lee, C., and Jacobson, H. I. (1971). *Endocrinology* **88**, 596.
McGuire, J. L., and DeDella, C. (1971). *Endocrinology* **88**, 1099.
McGuire, J. L., and Lisk, R. D. (1968). *Proc. Natl. Acad. Sci. U. S.* **61**, 497.
McGuire, J. L., and Lisk, R. D. (1969). *Neuroendocrinology* **4**, 289.
McGuire, W. L., and O'Malley, B. W. (1968). *Biochim. Biophys. Acta* **157**, 187.
Maurer, H. R., and Chalkley, G. R. (1967). *J. Mol. Biol.* **27**, 431.
Mayol, R. F., and Thayer, S. A. (1970). *Biochemistry* **9**, 2484.
Means, A. R., and Hamilton, T. H. (1966). *Proc. Natl. Acad. Sci. U. S.* **56**, 1594.
Méšter, J., Robertson, D. M., Feherty, P., and Kellie, A. E. (1970). *Biochem. J.* **120**, 831.
Michael, R. P. (1965). *Brit. Med. Bull.* **21**, 87.
Milgrom, E. (1971). Personal communication.
Milgrom, E., and Baulieu, E. E. (1970). *Endocrinology* **87**, 276.
Milgrom, E., Atger, M., and Baulieu, E. E. (1970). *Steroids* **16**, 741.
Mobbs, B. (1966). *J. Endocrinol.* **36**, 409.
Mobbs, B. (1968). *J. Endocrinol.* **41**, 339.
Mobbs, B. (1969). *J. Endocrinol.* **44**, 463.
Mohla, S., DeSombre, E. R., and Jensen, E. V. (1971a). *Federation Proc.* **30**, 1214.
Mohla, S., DeSombre, E. R., and Jensen, E. V. (1971b). *Biochem. Biophys. Res. Commun.* (submitted for publication).
Mueller, G. C. (1960). *In* "Biological Activities of Steroids in Relation to Cancer" (G. Pincus and E. P. Vollmer, eds.), pp. 129–145. Academic Press, New York.
Mueller, G. C. (1965). *In* "Mechanisms of Hormone Action" (P. Karlson, ed.), pp. 228–239. Academic Press, New York.
Mueller, G. C., Gorski, J., and Aizawa, Y. (1961). *Proc. Natl. Acad. Sci. U. S.* **47**, 164.
Musliner, T. A., Chader, G. J., and Villee, C. A. (1970). *Biochemistry* **9**, 4448.
Nicolette, J. A., and Gorski, J. (1964). *Arch. Biochem. Biophys.* **107**, 279.
Nicolette, J. A., and Mueller, G. C. (1966). *Biochem. Biophys. Res. Commun.* **24**, 851.
Nicolette, J. A., Lemahieu, M. A., and Mueller, G. C. (1968). *Biochim. Biophys. Acta* **166**, 403.
Noteboom, W. D., and Gorski, J. (1963). *Proc. Natl. Acad. Sci. U. S.* **50**, 250.
Noteboom, W. D., and Gorski, J. (1965). *Arch. Biochem. Biophys.* **111**, 559.
Notides, A. C. (1970). *Endocrinology* **87**, 987.
Notides, A., and Gorski, J. (1966). *Proc. Natl. Acad. Sci. U. S.* **56**, 230.
O'Malley, B. W. (1967). *Biochemistry* **6**, 2546.
O'Malley, B. W., and Kohler, P. O. (1967a). *Biochem. Biophys. Res. Commun.* **28**, 1.
O'Malley, B. W., and Kohler, P. O. (1967b). *Proc. Natl. Acad. Sci. U. S.* **58**, 2359.
O'Malley, B. W., and McGuire, W. L. (1968). *J. Clin. Invest.* **47**, 654.
O'Malley, B. W., and McGuire, W. L. (1969). *Endocrinology* **84**, 63.
O'Malley, B. W., McGuire, W. L., and Middleton, P. A. (1967). *Endocrinology* **81**, 677.

O'Malley, B. W., McGuire, W. L., and Middleton, P. A. (1968). *Nature* **218**, 1249.
O'Malley, B. W., McGuire, W. L., Kohler, P. O., and Korenman, S. G. (1969). *Recent Progr. Hormone Res.* **25**, 105.
O'Malley, B. W., Sherman, M. R., and Toft, D. O. (1970). *Proc. Natl. Acad. Sci. U. S.* **67**, 501.
O'Malley, B. W., Toft, D. O., and Sherman, M. R. (1971a). *J. Biol. Chem.* **246**, 1117.
O'Malley, B. W., Sherman, M. R., Toft, D. O., Spelsberg, T. C., Schrader, W. T., and Steggles, A. W. (1971b). *In* "Advances in the Biosciences" (G. Raspé, ed.), Vol. 7, pp. 213–231. Pergamon, Oxford.
Pack, B. A., and Brooks, S. C. (1970). *Endocrinology* **87**, 924.
Pfaff, D. W. (1968). *Endocrinology* **82**, 1149.
Podratz, K. C., and Katzman, P. A. (1968). *Federation Proc.* **27**, 497.
Puca, G. A. (1971). Personal communication.
Puca, G. A., and Bresciani, F. (1968a). *Nature* **218**, 967.
Puca, G. A., and Bresciani, F. (1968b). *European J. Cancer* **3**, 475.
Puca, G. A., and Bresciani, F. (1969a). *Endocrinology* **85**, 1.
Puca, G. A., and Bresciani, F. (1969b). *Nature* **223**, 745.
Puca, G. A., and Bresciani, F. (1970). *Nature* **225**, 1251.
Puca, G. A., Nola, E., Sica, V., and Bresciani, F. (1971). *In* "Advances in the Biosciences" (G. Raspé, ed.), Vol. 7, pp. 97–113. Pergamon, Oxford.
Rao, B. R., and Wiest, W. G. (1971). *Federation Proc.* **30**, 1213.
Raynaud-Jammet, C., and Baulieu, E. E. (1969). *Compt. Rend.* **D268**, 3211.
Reel, J. R., Lee, S., and Callantine, M. R. (1969). *Abstr. 51st Meeting, Endocrine Soc., New York*, p. 113.
Reel, J. R., VanDewark, S. D., Shih, Y., and Callantine, M. R. (1970). *Abstr. 52nd Meeting, Endocrine Soc., St. Louis*, p. 83.
Reuter, L. A., Ciaccio, L. A., and Lisk, R. D. (1970). *Federation Proc.* **29**, 250.
Rochefort, H., and Baulieu, E. E. (1968). *Compt. Rend.* **D267**, 662.
Rochefort, H., and Baulieu, E. E. (1969). *Endocrinology* **84**, 108.
Rogers, A. W., Thomas, G. H., and Yates, K. M. (1966). *Exptl. Cell Res.* **40**, 668.
Roy, S., Mahesh, V. B., and Greenblatt, R. B. (1964). *Acta Endocrinol.* **47**, 669.
Sander, S. (1968). *Acta Endocrinol.* **58**, 49.
Sander, S., and Attramadal, A. (1968a). *Acta Endocrinol.* **58**, 235.
Sander, S., and Attramadal, A. (1968b). *Acta Pathol. Microbiol. Scand.* **74**, 169.
Segal, S. J., and Scher, W. (1967). *In* "Cellular Biology of the Uterus" (R. M. Wynn, ed.), pp. 114–150. Appleton, New York.
Segal, S. J., Davidson, O. W., and Wada, K. (1965). *Proc. Natl. Acad. Sci. U. S.* **54**, 782.
Sharma, O. K., and Borek, E. (1970). *Biochemistry* **9**, 2507.
Sherman, M. R., Corvol, P. L., and O'Malley, B. W. (1970). *J. Biol. Chem.* **245**, 6085.
Shyamala, G., and Gorski, J. (1969). *J. Biol. Chem.* **244**, 1097.
Smith, D. E., and Gorski, J. (1968). *J. Biol. Chem.* **243**, 4169.
Smith, R. E., and Szego, C. M. (1971). *Abstr. 53rd Meeting, Endocrine Soc., San Francisco*, p. 151.
Spaziani, E., and Szego, C. M. (1958). *Endocrinology* **63**, 669.
Spelsberg, T. C., Steggles, A. W., and O'Malley, B. W. (1971). *J. Biol. Chem.* **246**, 4188.
Steggles, A. W., and King, R. J. B. (1969). *Acta Endocrinol. Suppl.* **138**, 36.
Steggles, A. W., and King, R. J. B. (1970). *Biochem. J.* **118**, 695.

Stone, G. M. (1963). *J. Endocrinol.* **27**, 281.

Stone, G. M. (1964). *Acta Endocrinol.* **47**, 433.

Stone, G. M., and Baggett, B. (1965a). *Steroids* **6**, 277.

Stone, G. M., and Baggett, B. (1965b). *Steroids* **5**, 809.

Stone, G. M., and Martin, L. (1964). *Steroids* **3**, 699.

Stone, G. M., Baggett, B., and Donnelly, R. B. (1963). *J. Endocrinol.* **27**, 271.

Stumpf, W. E. (1968a). *Endocrinology* **83**, 777.

Stumpf, W. E. (1968b). *Science* **162**, 1001.

Stumpf, W. E. (1969). *Endocrinology* **85**, 31.

Stumpf, W. E., and Roth, L. J. (1966). *J. Histochem. Cytochem.* **14**, 274.

Sutherland, E. W., and Robison, G. A. (1966). *Pharmacol. Rev.* **18**, 145.

Sweat, M. L., Bryson, M. J., and Young, R. B. (1967). *Endocrinology* **81**, 167.

Szego, C. M. (1965). *Federation Proc.* **24**, 1343.

Talwar, G. P., Segal, S. J., Evans, A., and Davidson, O. W. (1964). *Proc. Natl. Acad. Sci. U. S.* **52**, 1059.

Talwar, G. P., Sapori, M. L., Biswas, D. K., and Segal, S. J. (1968). *Biochem. J.* **107**, 765.

Teng, C. S., and Hamilton, T. H. (1968). *Proc. Natl. Acad. Sci. U. S.* **60**, 1410.

Teng, C. S., and Hamilton, T. H. (1969). *Proc. Natl. Acad. Sci. U. S.* **63**, 465.

Terenius, L. (1965). *Acta Endocrinol.* **50**, 584.

Terenius, L. (1966). *Acta Endocrinol.* **53**, 611.

Terenius, L. (1967). *Mol. Pharmacol.* **3**, 423.

Toft, D., and Gorski, J. (1966). *Proc. Natl. Acad. Sci. U. S.* **55**, 1574.

Toft, D., Shyamala, G., and Gorski, J. (1967). *Proc. Natl. Acad. Sci. U. S.* **57**, 1740.

Tomkins, G. M., Gelehrter, T. D., Granner, D., Martin, D., Jr., Samuels, H. H., and Thompson, E. B. (1969). *Science* **166**, 1474.

Trachewsky, D., and Segal, S. J. (1968). *European J. Biochem.* **4**, 279.

Truong, H., and Baulieu, E. E. (1971). *Biochim. Biophys. Acta* **237**, 167.

Ui, H., and Mueller, G. C. (1963). *Proc. Natl. Acad. Sci. U. S.* **50**, 256.

Unhjem, O., Attramadal, A., and Sölna, J. (1968). *Acta Endocrinol.* **58**, 227.

Vonderhaar, B. K., and Mueller, G. C. (1969). *Biochim. Biophys. Acta* **176**, 626.

Vonderhaar, B. K., Kim, U. H., and Mueller, G. C. (1970a). *Biochim. Biophys. Acta* **208**, 517.

Vonderhaar, B. K., Kim, U. H., and Mueller, G. C. (1970b). *Biochim. Biophys. Acta* **215**, 125.

Wenzel, M., Mützel, W., and Hieronimus, B. (1970). *Biochem. J.* **120**, 899.

Wiest, W. G., and Rao, B. R. (1971). In "Advances in the Biosciences" (G. Raspé, ed.), Vol. 7, pp. 251–264. Pergamon, Oxford.

Williams-Ashman, H. G., and Reddi, A. H. (1971). *Ann. Rev. Physiol.* **33**, 31.

Wyss, R. H., Heinrichs, W. L., and Herrmann, W. L. (1968a). *J. Clin. Endocrinol. Metab.* **28**, 1227.

Wyss, R. H., Karsznia, R., Heinrichs, W. L., and Hermann, W. L. (1968b). *J. Clin. Endocrinol. Metab.* **28**, 1824.

Zimmering, P. E., Kahn, I., and Lieberman, S. (1970). *Biochemistry* **9**, 2498.

CHAPTER 8

Androgenic Regulation of Tissue Growth and Function

H. G. Williams-Ashman and A. H. Reddi

I. INTRODUCTION

Classification of vertebrate steroid sex hormones into the three principal classes of androgens, estrogens, and gestagens became generally
accepted well before the Second World War, and after concensus was
reached as to the validity of various quantitative bioassay methods for

these hormones.[1] The biological assay procedures for androgens commonly employed today depend on the growth or functions of male secondary sexual organs in immature or orchiectomized creatures, notably the accessory genital glands of rodents or the comb and wattles of chicks. Designation of androgens as "male sex hormones" rather than as "hormones of maleness" is altogether infelicitous, considering that androgenic steroids are not only elaborated and present in the blood stream in female as well as in male vertebrates, but also profoundly influence certain organs in normal genetic and gonadal females, especially heterosexual remnants such as clitoris and the female prostate gland.[2] There is, indeed, scarcely a tissue in the vertebrate body, regardless of the sex genotype, which is not affected in one way or another by androgen, although organs of the male reproductive tract or other tissues serving as sexual ornaments are obviously influenced most strikingly.

Most contemporary experimental attacks on the problem of the biochemical basis of hormone action rest on the assumptions that (1) the hormones must first recognize and interact with one or more types of "receptor" molecules in responsive cells, and (2) such hormone–receptor complexes then evoke trains of metabolic effects of orderly chronology which underlie gross alterations in cell growth and function. Obviously the niceties of the latter secondary biochemical processes will vary very much with the particular hormone-dependent tissue one chooses to study. As Hechter and Halkerston (1964) have pointed out, characterization of these "receptors" and of the physicochemical basis of their interaction with the hormones must lie at the heart of any postulates concerning the "molecular basis" of hormone action. There are reasons to believe that receptors for low molecular weight hormones such as steroids must be macromolecules, and that interaction with the steroids occurs via noncovalent forces (Hechter and Halkerston, 1964; Williams-Ashman, 1965a). Proteins of one form or another are, on a number of grounds, the most likely candidates for such receptors, although other macromolecules such as polynucleotides could conceivably serve such functions. In any event, postulation of discrete macromolecules as primary receptors for sex hormones implies that specific genes exist which are a repository of in-

---

[1] An intriguing illustrated summary of some of the great classical papers dealing with isolation and characterization of mammalian sex hormones is provided in a recent memoir by Raspé (1969).

[2] Szirmai (1962) has considered sex and species variations in the differential response of various epithelial, muscle, and connective tissue cells to androgens and estrogens in terms of the embryological origin, and the location in adult organisms, of these tissues.

formation for the synthesis of such receptors. Furthermore, expression of such genes in terms of the quantities, and even perhaps the intracellular locations, of their hormone–receptor products would likely be subject to regulation by all sorts of agencies, including direct feedbacks due to the hormones themselves.

Whether interaction with a single type of receptor can trigger off all subsequent biochemical responses, or whether a number of different types of receptor molecules are involved in the complex ensemble of metabolic processes set in motion by any particular hormone, are possibilities which immediately present themselves as guides to experimentation. Later we shall consider whether certain small molecules such as cyclic 3',5'-adenylic acid or polyamines such as spermidine and spermine may serve as intracellular "second messengers" for androgen action on certain cells. Like many other hormones, androgens evoke inhibitory as well as excitatory responses, examples of the former being inhibition of hypothalamic–hypophyseal mechanisms responsible for gonadotropin output, and depression of certain lymphoid tissues. From the standpoint of growth promotion, there exist some remarkable similarities in the sequences of biochemical happenings which occur as a result of the action of estrogens on female secondary sexual organs such as the uterus on the one hand, and following androgenic stimulation of the prostate gland or seminal vesicle on the other. Yet from a biological point of view, there appears to be a most fundamental difference in the androgenic regulation of many male reproductive organs as compared with the estrogen control of tissues of the female genital tract, at least in all of the mammalian orders, where the homogametic sex seems always to be female. This difference relates to the paramount role of androgens produced by the fetal testis in the initial embryonic differentiation of organs such as the prostate and seminal vesicles, and in the organization during fetal or early neonatal life of hypothalamic centers which in the postpubertal male dictate an acyclic style of gonadotropin production and male modes of copulatory behavior. Investigations on the hormonal control of the embryonic differentiation of male genital tract structures and on the development of sexual behavior patterns (Burns, 1961; Goy, 1964; Harris, 1964; Price and Ortiz, 1965; Young, 1961) have indicated that androgens exert two main classes of action: (1) "morphogenetic" or "organizational" effects which are evident only during restricted periods of early development and which are essentially irreversible; and (2) classic "activational" ("excitatory") or "inhibitory" actions which occur throughout the life span of postpubertal animals and which are often reversible. This is in marked contrast to the development of the mammalian female genital tract, the initial embryonic differentiation of which appears to a large extent to be anhormonal. The recent development of potent nonestrogenic steroidal antiandrogenic substances (Neumann *et al.*, 1967), and their application to mammalian fetuses, has provided strong independent evidence in support of the notion of two basic types of androgen action. Unfortunately, it has been very hard, for purely technical reasons, to study biochemical correlates of the initial morphogenetic actions of androgens in fetal life, although pioneer ultrastructural studies on the differentiation of mouse seminal vesicle (Deane and Wurzelmann, 1965) disclosed remarkable changes in cytoplasmic polyribosomes and endoplasmic reticulum membranes which may provide a pertinent starting point for further investigations. This article will perforce deal mainly with "activational" or "inhibitory" effects of androgens in postnatal life on structures whose initial differentiation was promoted by testicular hormones. But first we shall consider the disposition of androgens in responsive tissues, a subject which brings up, among other things, the nature of receptor macromolecules for androgens and possible "active forms" of these hormones in their target organs.

II. FATE OF ANDROGENIC STEROIDS IN RESPONSIVE CELLS

In male mammals, the principal circulating androgens of testicular origin are testosterone and androstenedione. The rates of production and plasma concentrations of these steroids are influenced by many factors, including age, diet, species, and gonadotropin output, in addition to being subject to individual, diurnal, and seasonal variations. In many mammalian species, the plasma levels of free testosterone in young postpuberal males are in the range of $1-3 \times 10^{-8}$ M. The binding of androgens to various components of blood was recently reviewed by Liao and Fang (1969). Testosterone and androstenedione are associated with erythrocytes to only a very small extent. These steroids can bind fairly tightly to plasma albumin, and much more firmly to a specific testosterone-binding globulin (Mercier *et al.*, 1965; Pearlman and Crépy, 1967; Vermeulen, 1969). Transcortin, the corticoid-binding protein of blood plasma, also shows a moderately high affinity for testosterone (Vermeulen, 1969). The physiological importance of these androgen-binding plasma proteins is rather obscure. It is easily imagined that they may serve either to protect androgens from enzymic inactivation, or as reservoirs from which androgens can be released gradually to their target organs (Liao and Fang, 1969).[3] It appears that none of the various plasma proteins with an affinity for androgens are identical with the intracellular C_{19}-steroid-binding proteins which are considered below. Early investigations on the fate of ^{14}C-labeled androgens of relatively low specific radioactivity (Barry *et al.,* 1952; Holmes, 1956; Greer, 1959; Harding and Samuels, 1962) can be largely discounted because of the unphysiologically high doses of androgens employed. With such very large doses of labeled androgens, the liver is swamped with the administered hormones, in which organ they are subject to a variety of transformations (notably hydroxylations of various positions in the molecule, 5α and 5β reduction of the double bond in ring A, reduction of the 3-keto group, oxidation at C-17, etc., in addition to conjugation of testosterone and some of its metabolites with the elements of glucuronic or sulfuric acid or other groups). Many of these reactions yield largely conjugated products with little or no biological activity and seem to be primarily involved in steroid homeostasis rather than in androgen action. An excellent account of dietary, hormonal, pharmacological, and other factors which influence hepatic metabolism of androgenic steroids is given by Schriefers (1967). Increases in the activity of liver enzymes that hydroxylate testosterone due to administration of phenobarbital or chlordane can profoundly depress the androgenic activity of exogenous testosterone (Levin *et al.,* 1969).

Pearlman and Pearlman (1961) infused tritiated androstenedione into rats and found some degree of selective concentration of radioactivity in the ventral prostate, in which organ 15% of the ether-soluble unconjugated steroid fraction was in the form of 5α-androstane-3,17-dione. Aliapoulios *et al.* (1965) infused the canine prostate *in vivo* with ^{14}C-labeled testosterone and observed that the gland contained a number of unconjugated metabolites, dihydrotestosterone (5α-androstane-17β-ol-3-one) and 5α-androstane-3α,17β-diol being the principal products. The conversion of testosterone to dihydrotestosterone and other unconjugated steroids by

---

[3] It is debatable whether specific steroid-binding proteins in blood plasma with such a high affinity for steroid hormones could actually act as transporters of the hormones to their target tissues, as it is hard to see how with such tight binding, the hormones could be released to their target tissues. On the contrary, the plasma steroid-binding proteins could act as steroid "buffers" or "chelators" in the bloodstream. These matters are considered thoughtfully with respect to transcortin by Fortier *et al.* (1970) and in the discussion appended to the latter article.

Testosterone   Dihydrotestosterone

prostatic tissue *in vitro* is exhaustively reviewed by Ofner (1969). Studies from various laboratories indicated the presence in this organ of various hydroxysteroid dehydrogenases and an NADPH-dependent testosterone 5α-reductase. The latter prostatic enzyme converts testosterone to dihydrotestosterone, one of the main transformation products of testosterone by prostatic tissue incubated *in vitro* as well as in the living animal. Farnsworth and Brown (1963) and Shimazaki *et al.* (1965a,b) were among the first to study the transformation of testosterone to dihydrotestosterone by the prostate. A critical analysis of Ofner (1969) casts considerable doubt on the hypothesis of Farnsworth (1965, 1966) that 19-nortestosterone may be an "active form" of testosterone in androgen-responsive tissues, and that the prostate gland can further aromatize 19-nortestosterone to estrogenic substances.

Wilson and Loeb (1965) found that radioactivity from ³H-testosterone injected into ducks became firmly associated with cell nuclei isolated from the uropygial (preen) gland, an organ under the tropic control of androgens. The nuclear-bound radioisotope was mainly bound to the euchromatin fraction, and apparently to protein components thereof, which were separated from the DNA by cesium chloride equilibrium density gradient centrifugation. Mangan *et al.* (1968) reported that tritiated testosterone injected directly into rat ventral prostates was taken up by the heterochromatin of the nuclei to a greater extent than by the euchromatin fraction, although the euchromatin exhibited a higher radioactivity per unit amount of DNA.

A. FORMATION OF DIHYDROTESTOSTERONE

Many publications over the last three years have indicated that dihydrotestosterone is the principal steroid retained in cell nuclei of some androgen-responsive tissues after administration of physiological doses of labeled testosterone. Bruchovsky and Wilson (1968a) state that dihydrotestosterone, 5α-androstanediols, and testosterone were detectable in rat prostate cytoplasm within 1 minute after injection of ³H-testosterone, whereas only dihydrotestosterone, and smaller amounts of testosterone as such, were recovered from prostatic cell nuclei for as long as 2 hours after injection of the hormone. *Free* dihydrotestosterone was found only in prostate, seminal vesicle, preputial gland, kidney, and (to a very small extent) in blood plasma in the rat given tritiated testosterone (Table I). Anderson and Liao (1968) and Fang *et al.* (1969) found that dihydro-testosterone formed from testosterone was retained by the rat ventral prostate for at least 6 hours, and long after virtually all radioactive steroids had disappeared from both blood and a number of tissues which are relatively insensitive to androgens. Tveter (1969) found that radio-active testosterone was, in comparison with muscle, selectively retained *in vivo* by all lobes of the rat prostate, the lateral lobe showing the greatest radioactivity. Very little of the tritium derived from the injected hormone was found in the prostatic secretion. Tveter and Unhjem (1969) observed selective uptake of radioactive testosterone by rat seminal vesicle. According to Tveter and Aakvaag (1969), 1 hour after adminis-tration of ^{3}H-testosterone, unchanged hormone represented only 3–17% of the total radioactivity in accessory sex organs, whereas dihydrotestoster-

TABLE I

DISTRIBUTION OF DIHYDROTESTOSTERONE-^{3}H IN TISSUES 5 MINUTES AFTER INTRAVENOUS ADMINISTRATION OF TESTOSTERONE-1,2-^{3}H[a]

Tissue	Amount analyzed (gm or ml)	Thin layer chromatography		Gas–liquid chromatography	
		Total activity (cpm)	Dihydro-testosterone (%)	Total activity (cpm)	Dihydrotes-tosterone (%)
Plasma	3.0	8,190	1.8		
Gut	1.4	—	—	37,234	<1.0
Liver	1.5	18,900	<1.0	4,136	<1.0
Heart	1.0	9,767	<1.0	—	—
Lungs	0.9	13,359	<1.0	—	—
Levator ani muscle	0.3	1,257	<1.0	—	—
Testis	1.7	13,531	<1.0	—	—
Kidney	1.0	18,019	5.3	13,694	3.3
Prostate	0.5	3,165	29.5	3,305	39.3
Seminal vesicles	0.5	4,000	29.1	2,341	44.2
Preputial gland	0.5	1,952	27.8	2,391	19.8

[a] Three normal rats were injected with 250 μCi of testosterone-1,2-^{3}H and killed 5 minutes later. Tissue extracts were assayed for steroid compounds either by thin layer or gas–liquid chromatography, and some samples were assayed by both methods. The percentage of the total counts per minute in the aliquots identified as dihydrotestoster-one-^{3}H by the different methods is shown. (From Bruchovsky and Wilson, 1968a.)

one accounted for as much as 70% of the radioactivity in prostate and seminal vesicles. Autoradiographic studies (Sar *et al.*, 1969; Tveter and Attramadal, 1969) show a distinctive labeling of the nuclei of accessory genital gland epithelial cells after injection of physiological doses of tritiated testosterone.

Bruchovsky and Wilson (1968a) and Anderson and Liao (1968) discovered a chromatin-bound steroid 5α-reductase in prostatic cell nuclei that catalyzes a reduction by NADPH of the double bond in ring A of testosterone to yield dihydrotestosterone. Earlier experiments by Shimazaki *et al.* (1965a,b) indicated that microsomes from rat ventral prostate also contain a similar C_{19}-steroid 5α-reductase. Shimazaki *et al.* (1969a) reported that 5α-reduction of testosterone in rat ventral prostate decreases with aging in postpubertal animals, whereas the oxidation of testosterone at C-17 did not diminish concomitantly. Castration reduced the 5α-reductase activity, which could be restored by androgen treatment. The precise nature and multiplicity of enzymes in androgen-sensitive cells which catalyze the 5α-reduction of testosterone and/or androstenedione needs to be clarified. Liver cytoplasm also contains active 5α- and 5β-reductases for C_{19}-steroids, but in this case the reaction products are readily subject *in vivo* to conjugation with glucuronide and other groups (Schriefers, 1967). Very recently, Frederiksen and Wilson (1971) have delineated many properties of the 5α-steroid reductase in rat ventral prostate cell nuclei that catalyzes the NADPH-dependent conversion of testosterone to 5α-dihydrotestosterone.

TABLE II

RETENTION OF RADIOISOTOPES BY ISOLATED NUCLEI OF MINCED RAT TISSUES INCUBATED WITH TESTOSTERONE-^{3}H FOR 30 MINUTES AT 37°C[a]

Tissues	Radioactivity of isolated nuclei (dpm/100 μg DNA)	Distribution of radioactivity[b] (%)		
		Testosterone	DHT[c]	Androstenedione
Brain	105	96.2	2.8	0.0
Thymus	78	93.5	0.0	2.1
Diaphragm	53	78.2	2.1	17.6
Liver	60	73.4	0.0	4.5
Ventral prostate	1250	17.3	78.2	1.0

[a] From Anderson and Liao (1968).

[b] Steroids extracted from nuclei were subjected to thin layer chromatography, and the percentage distribution of radioactivity associated with the three steroid spots was calculated.

[c] Dihydrotestosterone.

Anderson and Liao (1968) examined the fate of tritiated testosterone after incubation of the steroid at 37°C with minces of rat prostate. If the nuclei were isolated from such preparations at the end of the incubation period, a marked retention of radioactivity was observed, and only dihydrotestosterone and unchanged testosterone could be identified as the radioactive steroids. The cytoplasmic fraction contained at least five other unconjugated metabolites of testosterone in the labeled form. As shown in Table II, this selective retention of radioactivity (largely as dihydrotestosterone) by nuclei of minced prostate *in vitro* was not found with minces of thymus, liver, brain, and diaphragm.

It is well known that 5α-dihydrotestosterone exhibits an even greater potency than testosterone itself in a number of androgenic bioassay systems (Table III). This fact, together with the rapid formation of large amounts of dihydrotestosterone by androgen-responsive tissues and its retention in their nuclei, strongly hints that dihydrotestosterone may be an "active form" of testosterone in at least some androgen-sensitive

TABLE III

RELATIVE ANDROGENIC AND ANABOLIC ACTIVITIES OF SOME REPRESENTATIVE
ANDROSTANES AND ANDROSTENES[a]

Experimental animals	Chick comb[b]	Rat			
		VP	SV	LA	EL
Testosterone	100	100	100	100	100
5α-Dihydrotestosterone	228	268	158	152	74
17α-Methyltestosterone	300 (231)	103	100	108	162
17α-Methyl-5α-dihydrotestosterone	480	254	78	107	—
Androst-4-ene-3,17-dione	121 (262)	39	17	22	14
5α-Androstane-3,17-dione	115 (182)	33	13	11	—
5α-Androstane-3α,17β-diol	75	34	24	30	238
Androst-4-ene-3β,17β-diol	(76)	124	133	95	—
5α-Androstane-3β,17β-diol	2	—	10	—	5
Androst-4-ene-3-ol-17α-ol	—	8	2	3	—
5α-Androstan-3α-ol-17-one	115 (238)	53	8	10	46
19-Nortestosterone	(86)	—	10	180	52
19-Nordihydrotestosterone	118	—	—	—	—
17α-Methyl-19-nortestosterone	—	25	25	60	81
Testosterone propionate	(380)	161	146	187	195
5α-Androstan-17β-ol	128 (227)	—	—	—	5

[a] From Liao and Fang (1969).

[b] Comb tests are by inunction. Figures in parentheses are from different series of studies cited in Liao and Fang (1969).

[c] Rat tests are by injection. VP: ventral prostate, SV: seminal vesicle; SV: seminal vesicle; LA: levator ani muscle; EL: exorbital lacrimal gland tests.

cells.[4] A difficulty in the way of accepting the universal validity of this hypothesis is the finding that, after injection of labeled testosterone, hardly any dihydrotestosterone is found in various muscles, including levator ani muscles, which are well known (cf. Table III) to be very sensitive to androgenic hormones (Bruchovsky and Wilson, 1968a; Tveter, 1969). However, the growth response of muscles such as the levator ani in castrated rodents to exogenous testosterone is considerably more sluggish than that of male accessory glands. Furthermore, Shimazaki *et al.* (1965c) showed that 5α-androstane-3,17-dione is formed from labeled testosterone by dog gluteal muscles *in vivo*. The latter substance exhibits definite androgenic activity, albeit weaker than that of 5α-dihydrotestosterone (Table III).

B. Dihydrotestosterone-Binding Proteins

Recent investigations have revealed that rat ventral prostate contains macromolecules in both nuclei and cytosol which have a high and specific avidity for dihydrotestosterone and related steroids. These macromolecules seem to be proteids, inasmuch as their association with labeled steroids is uninfluenced by treatment with DNase or RNase, but is disrupted by proteolytic enzymes such as trypsin and Pronase. Gel filtration studies (Bruchovsky and Wilson, 1968b; Unhjem *et al.*, 1969) have provided some insight into these binding phenomena. An incisive series of experiments by Fang *et al.* (1969) have shown that a dihydrotestosterone-binding protein can be extracted from prostate cell nuclei with buffered 0.4 M KCl containing EDTA. Sucrose density gradient analyses indicated that this proteid has a sedimentation coefficient of about 3 S. The cytosol of rat ventral prostate also contains a dihydrotestosterone-binding proteid with a sedimentation coefficient which is slightly higher (3.5 S) from

---

[4] An interesting question which would readily be tractable to experimental scrutiny is whether the uterotropic actions of testosterone, and the ability of this steroid to cause proliferation of mucus-secreting cells of the vagina (Huggins *et al.*, 1954) involves conversion of testosterone to dihydrotestosterone in these tissues of the female genital tract. The unique ability of 5-androstene-3β,17β-diol among C_{19}-steroids to induce vaginal keratinization in a manner similar to phenolic estrogens, and evocation of stratification of the vaginal mucosa by substances such as 5α-androstane-3β,17β-diol and 5-androstene-3β-ol-17-one, should also be remembered in any consideration of structure–activity relationships of androstane derivatives (cf. Huggins and Jensen, 1954). The possible intermediary role of dihydrotestosterone or other 5α-androstane compounds in the regulation of spermatogenesis by testosterone (Steinberger and Duckett, 1967) would also be worthy of examination. Lostroh (1969) found that dihydrotestosterone as well as testosterone stimulated primary spermatocytes to complete meiosis in hypophysectomized rats.

that of its nuclear counterpart. If isolated prostatic cell nuclei from castrated rats were incubated with labeled testosterone or dihydrotestosterone, there was little or no retention of radioactive steroids by the nuclei in a bound form. However, addition of a cytosol fraction to the nuclei led to retention of dihydrotestosterone by the nuclei in the form of a 3 S proteid complex. The cytosol 3.5 S proteid interacts with dihydrotestosterone spontaneously at 0°C. Evidence was obtained for a two-step mechanism by which dihydrotestosterone first combines with the cytosol 3.5 S proteid, and only then can enter nuclei so as to be retained in the latter organelle in the form of a distinct 3 S proteid–dihydrotestosterone complex extractable with 0.4 M KCl. This is analogous to the two-step mechanism for uptake and retention of estradiol-17β in uterus which has been so thoroughly investigated by Jensen *et al.* (1968). There is evidence (Fang *et al.*, 1969) that at 37°C the dihydrotestosterone–proteid complex extracted from prostatic cell nuclei gradually releases bound dihydrotestosterone. Contrariwise, incubation of the cytosol 3.5 S proteid at temperatures between 15 and 50°C enhances its capacity to bind dihydrotestosterone. Neither testosterone nor cortisol interact firmly with the 3.5 S cytosol proteid from rat prostate, which can, however, bind progesterone and estradiol-17β to a significant extent. In a preliminary study, Mainwaring (1969) described a dihydrotestosterone-binding proteid in the cytoplasm of rat ventral prostate which, unlike the proteid investigated by Fang *et al.* (1969) appears to have a sedimentation coefficient of about 8 S. The possibility that cytosol androgen-binding proteids in male accessory glands are comprised of a number of subunits, and may perhaps exist in different states of aggregation, might account for this discrepancy. Fang and Liao (1971) have recently obtained evidence for the existence of two quite distinct 5α-dihydrotestosterone binding proteins in rat ventral prostate cytoplasm.

C. Possible Role of Dihydrotestosterone in the Androgenic Actions of Testosterone

These exciting new findings pointing to a role of dihydrotestosterone in the action of testosterone immediately raise a number of important questions. First, the retention of dihydrotestosterone by a specific proteid in accessory genital gland cell nuclei might be pertinent to the androgenic control of nuclear biochemical events, and particularly ribonucleic acid synthesis (cf. Williams-Ashman, 1969, 1970). As discussed by Fang *et al.* (1969) and Liao and Fang (1969) hardly any direct information is currently available which bears on this possibility, which will surely be the subject of much experimental work over the next few years. A very recent contribution by Bashirelahi *et al.* (1969) claims that incorporation of cytidine into acid-insoluble material by prostatic nuclei obtained from orchiectomized rats is increased by direct addition of low levels of dihydrotestosterone under conditions where testosterone is ineffective. Dihydrotestosterone in somewhat higher concentrations also depressed the entry of inorganic phosphate into ATP by the isolated nuclei, whereas testosterone showed only little inhibition. Bashirelahi and Villee (1970) have recorded similar stimulating effects of dihydro-testosterone on the entry of labeled cytidine into the RNA of nuclei isolated from the prostates of immature rats, under conditions where testosterone was ineffective.

Baulieu *et al.* (1968a,b) have concluded from prostate organ culture experiments that dihydrotestosterone formed in this organ is especially concerned with cell multiplication, whereas testosterone and its other metabolites are more involved in the regulation of epithelial cell height and secretory mechanisms. The evidence advanced in support of this conjecture can be subject to other interpretations. Gloyna and Wilson (1969) studied the conversion of testosterone to dihydrotestosterone by slices of various tissues from 11 mammalian species. They concluded that dihydrotestosterone formation was not an obligatory reaction for all of the effects of androgens, since it was not demonstrable in any of the muscles tested, was diminished with increasing age in the prostates of some species, and in the penis of man correlated best with the period of testosterone-induced growth. Gloyna and Wilson (1969) suggested that dihydrotestosterone may mediate the cell proliferative but not all other effects of testosterone. It can be seen from Table III, however, that 5α-dihydrotestosterone is even more effective than testosterone in promoting the growth of levator ani muscles in castrated rats. At least in neuter mice, the androgen-induced growth of levator ani muscles is almost solely due to hypertrophy of the muscle fibers, and involves virtually no division of cells (Venable, 1966).

It is easy to envision that the function of testosterone- and dihydro-testosterone-binding proteids may be to aid in the translocation of these steroids to nuclear sites at which they exert their action. Also it can be imagined that the dihydrotestosterone–nuclear 3 S proteid complex rather than dihydrotestosterone as such acts as the proximal "active form" of circulating androgens in the nuclei of responsive tissues, possibly to serve there as a "derepressor" of certain nuclear biochemical processes (cf. Fang *et al.*, 1969). Contrariwise, the androgen-binding proteids themselves may turn out to be the true effectors controlling certain nuclear functions, and their combination with dihydrotestosterone and/or testosterone may simply aid the translocation of these macro-molecules to regions of the cell nucleus where the proteids can be retained and exert regulatory actions for which the steroids as such are unnecessary. These hypotheses are discussed more fully by Williams-Ashman and Reddi (1971).

D. ACTION OF ANTIANDROGENS

The formation and binding to nuclear proteids of dihydrotestosterone in many androgen-sensitive organs appears to be related to the mechanism of action of a new class of antiandrogenic substances which includes the compounds cyproterone acetate and cyproterone. These are synthetic, nonestrogenic steroids which may exhibit powerful (cyproterone acetate) or only weak (cyproterone) progestational activity, but both of which inhibit the actions of endogenous testicular androgens and also of exogenous testosterone in fetal, immature, and castrated adult mammals (Neumann *et al.*, 1967). Fang and Liao (1969) showed that cyproterone acetate suppressed the uptake of radioactive androgens by rat ventral prostate *in vivo*. Cyproterone and its 17α-acetate also inhibited the formation of the nuclear dihydrotestosterone–proteid complex when minced prostate tissue was incubated with labeled testosterone or dihydrotestosterone. Noteworthy is the fact that estrogens such as estradiol-17β and diethylstilbestrol were much less active than cyproterone acetate in inhibiting the retention of dihydrotestosterone by prostatic cell nuclei.[5] Similar inhibition of testosterone uptake by accessory reproductive glands by the antiandrogen 17α-methyl-B-nortestos-

---

[5] There are certain biological situations in which estrogens appear to antagonize directly the actions of androgens (Huggins, 1947), notably the output of prostatic secretions by hypophysectomized dogs (Goodwin *et al.*, 1961; Tesar and Scott, 1963). But the effects of androgenic hormones on some other male secondary sexual organs in castrated animals are not so readily inhibited by estrogen treatment (Neumann *et al.*, 1967). Many of the dramatic "antiandrogenic" actions of estrogens in intact adult males are in fact due to depression of ICSH output by the anterior pituitary gland, resulting in a decline of androgen production by the Leydig cells of the testis (Huggins, 1947; Price and Williams-Ashman, 1961). Indeed, if androgens and estrogens are administered simultaneously to orchiectomized rats, ventral prostate weights (Tesar and Scott, 1963; Price and Williams-Ashman, 1961), as well as alkaline but not acid phosphatase activities (Shimazaki *et al.*, 1969b), may increase to a greater extent than observed with androgen solo. Huggins (1947) and Price and Williams-Ashman (1961) have reviewed the ability of estrogens to evoke fibromuscular cell growth and/or squamous metaplasia in certain male accessory glands. That natural and synthetic estrogens can inhibit the conversion of testosterone to androstenedione and 5α-dihydrotestosterone by prostatic tissue was demonstrated by Shimazaki *et al.* (1965a).

terone, as well as a lack of effort of estrogens *in vivo,* have been reported by Tveter and Aakvaag (1969). In confirmation of these studies on the action of antiandrogens, Stern and Eisenfeld (1969) showed that cyproterone reduces the accumulation of testosterone and dihydrotestosterone in seminal vesicles 30 minutes after intravenous injection of ³H-testosterone into castrated rats. Cyproterone also antagonized the binding of radioactivity from testosterone to macromolecules in the supernatant fluid of seminal vesicle homogenates. In general, compounds like cyproterone acetate seem to exert their action not by influencing the reduction of testosterone to dihydrotestosterone, but rather by inhibiting the combination of dihydrotestosterone and possibly testosterone with specific binding proteids in androgen-dependent cells or the uptake and retention of the dihydrotestosterone–proteid complexes by cell nuclei (Williams-Ashman and Reddi, 1971).

E. ANDROGEN-INSENSITIVITY SYNDROME

The experiments pointing to dihydrotestosterone being on "active form" of circulating androgens are of obvious interest from the standpoint of those anomalous organisms which appear to be refractory to the androgenic actions of endogenous and/or exogenous testosterone. This seems to be the case, for example, in the so-called human testicular feminization syndrome (Simmer *et al.,* 1965) which has been more aptly rechristened as the "androgen-insensitivity syndrome" by Money *et al.* (1968). In this condition there is abundant evidence (French *et al.,* 1965, 1966; Wade *et al.,* 1968) that the patients with abdominal testes, no ovaries, an almost normal female phenotypic appearance, and an uncomplicated XY sex genotype, are refractory to the androgenic actions of the androgens that their testes elaborate, and which in the circulation have fairly normal half-lives. Moreover, injection of testosterone or 17α-methyltestosterone into such patients, or local inunction of these androgens, is without effect. Two recent publications indicate that, in the androgen-insensitivity syndrome, there may be some impairment of enzymic conversion of testosterone to dihydrotestosterone (Mauvais-Jarvis *et al.,* 1969; Northcutt *et al.,* 1969). However, a defect in the reduction of testosterone to dihydrotestosterone does not seem to be the primary lesion in this disease. Wilson and Walker (1969) undertook an exhaustive study of the conversion of labeled testosterone to dihydrotestosterone by skin slices from various human anatomical sites. In patients with the androgen-insensitivity syndrome, formation of dihydrotestosterone by labia majora was indeed lower than in normal XX females, but no difference between the two groups was observed when the skin was excised from the mons veneris (which forms dihydro-testosterone at a slower rate than labial skin in normal women). More-over, Strickland and French (1969) showed quite unequivocally that injection of dihydrotestosterone did not elicit nitrogen retention or any other signs of androgenicity in patients with the androgen-insensitivity syndrome. In this disease, then, dihydrotestosterone was as inactive as testosterone; this speaks against a lack of dihydrotestosterone formation being the primary defect. It would be interesting to see whether in such patients various tissues which in normal women are clearly androgen-responsive are devoid or deficient in the dihydrotestosterone-binding proteids considered above. The studies of Mauvais-Jarvis et al. (1970) suggest that patients with the androgen-insensitivity syndrome are ab-normally sensitive to estrogens and may have increased levels of plasma androgen-binding proteins.

Stanley and Gumbreck (1964) have described a form of male pseudo-hermaphroditism in the rat which may provide a pertinent experimental model for the human androgen-insensitivity syndrome. The defect is a hereditary one which is passed by normal females to half of the male progeny, and may well be an X-linked recessive, although this is difficult to prove rigorously. The animals contain inguinal tests, but other struc-tures of the male genital tract such as the scrotum, seminal vesicles, prostate, and vas deferens are lacking. The phenotype, is, on the con-trary, female in character, with a short vagina, tiny phallus, and well-developed nipple lines. Bardin et al. (1969) showed that these creatures secrete about 25% as much testosterone as normal males. However, Bardin et al. (1970) found that treatment of these rats with testos-terone failed to produce the expected increases in weights of the preputial gland which are observed in intact females or castrated males. Similarly, testosterone administration did not alter the hexobarbital sleeping times in the pseudohermaphroditic rats, whereas the androgen decreased the time of sleep resulting from hexobarbital treatment in both females and castrated males. Yet the conversion of testosterone to di-hydrotestosterone by minced preputial glands in the presence of a NADPH-generating system was about the same in both normal and pseudohermaphroditic rats. This suggested that the insensitivity of the end organ to testosterone could not be accounted for by a defect in the transformation of testosterone into dihydrotestosterone. This view was corroborated by the finding (Bardin et al., 1970) that dihydrotestosterone as such failed to exhibit androgen-like effects on the preputial gland of the pseudohermaphrodite animals. Again, it seems possible that the latter rats may be defective in proteids responsible for the nuclear retention of dihydrotestosterone in organs which are normally androgen-responsive.

III. DO LOW MOLECULAR WEIGHT "SECOND MESSENGERS" MEDIATE THE ACTIONS OF ANDROGENS ON GENITAL TISSUES?

It is now well established that adenosine 3',5'-monophosphate (cyclic AMP) acts as an intracellular second messenger to mediate most if not all of the actions of a number of hormones, including glucagon, catecholamines, ACTH, vasopressin, and certain gonadotropins (Butcher et al., 1970). These hormones stimulate formation of cAMP by enhancing the activity of membrane-bound adenyl cyclase systems in responsive cells. Up to now, no evidence has been forthcoming that the actions of androgens are mediated by cAMP or other cyclic nucleoside monophosphates; however, experimental examination of this possibility has been limited. It may be pointed out in this connection that cAMP-stimulable protein kinase reactions involving histones and other substrates (Corbin and Krebs, 1969; Miyamoto et al., 1969), which have been proposed to play a central role in the control of gene expression by certain hormones which enhance cAMP formation (Langan, 1969), are demonstrable in androgen-sensitive tissues such as the prostate. Reddi et al. (1971) observed that rat ventral prostate histone phosphokinase activities are not strikingly affected by androgenic hormones in vivo. According to Rosenfeld and O'Malley (1970), testosterone does not stimulate adenyl cyclase activity of a rat prostate membrane fraction either in vitro or in vivo. However, Singhal et al. (1970) have stated that administration of cAMP elicits an androgen-like increase in prostatic enzyme activities in castrated rats. Liao et al. (1971) detected adenyl cyclase activity in purified prostatic cell nuclei, and suggested that certain hormones may regulate the local nuclear concentrations of cAMP directly.

Recent publications by Caldarera et al. (1968) and Moulton and Leonard (1969) summarize experiments which have been interpreted to mean that the polyamines spermidine and spermine may mediate some of the androgen-induced changes in RNA and protein synthesis known to occur in rat accessory genital glands. It has been shown (Pegg and Williams-Ashman, 1968a; Williams-Ashman et al., 1969; Pegg et al., 1970) that over the first 6 hours following injection of testosterone propionate into castrated adult rats, there indeed occur large increases in the activity of two soluble enzymes involved in spermidine biosynthesis (L-ornithine decarboxylase, and a putrescine-dependent S-adenosyl-L-methionine decarboxylase system which forms stoichiometric quantities of spermidine and 5′-methylthioadenosine). However, a detailed examination of the levels of putrescine, spermidine, and spermine in the ventral prostates of orchiectomized animals over the first 2 days of androgen treatment (Pegg *et al.*, 1970) revealed that the levels of spermidine did not change sufficiently to make it seem likely that this substance could serve as a mediator for the demonstrable enhancement of nuclear RNA synthesis and RNA polymerase activities, over this period. The levels of spermine remained essentially those found in the prostate of castrates, only to rise after longer androgen treatment. Rather than the polyamines serving a second messenger-like function with regard to ribonucleic acid and protein synthesis in androgen-sensitive tissues, the available evidence suggests that in organs such as the prostate and seminal vesicle, there occurs a coupling between RNA and polyamine (particularly spermidine) synthesis during the early phases of androgen-induced growth.

IV. ANDROGENIC CONTROL OF METABOLIC PROCESS PATTERNS

By far the majority of studies on biochemical concomitants of androgen action have been carried out on rodent male accessory glands over the first few days after injection of androgens into immature or orchiectomized adult animals. Most of the morphological and metabolic changes evoked by the androgens are reversible in castrates, so that if hormone administration is stopped and time is allowed for androgens to clear from the circulation, the glands begin to retrogress, with disappearance of the induced biochemical characteristics and secretory activities. Yet involution of these organs following androgen withdrawal proceeds only up to a certain point, so that even at long intervals after orchiectomy, the dwindled accessory glands do not shrivel up entirely. The biochemical events which underlie the involution of such androgen-dependent structures have not been investigated very thoroughly. Brandes and Bourne (1963) and Brandes *et al.* (1962) have offered histochemical and electron microscopic evidence for the presence of lysosome-like particles in rodent prostates. Studies by Lasnitzki *et al.* (1965) on the sedimentation characteristics and latency of acid protease, *p*-nitrophenol phosphate phosphatase (measured at pH 4.5), and arylsulfatase of rat prostate were consistent with association of these enzymes with lysosomal particles. Harkin (1963) also observed "electron dense bodies" in the supranuclear region of prostatic epithelial cells from castrated rats which seemed to be lysosomes. Inhibition of epithelial cell regression of rat ventral prostate in organ cultures by addition of testosterone or hydrocortisone was found by Lasnitzki *et al.* (1965) to be associated with less lysosomal acid phosphatase activity; they concluded that formation of modified lysosomes with increased hydrolytic enzyme activity may take place in the regressing prostate. Here it must be emphasized that tissue involution or cell death is an integral part of many embryonic developmental processes. Such tissue regressions may be quite complex in their biochemistry. Tata (1970) has discussed, for example, findings from his and other laboratories which indicate new ribonucleic acid and protein synthesis are necessary for tail regression during amphibian metamorphosis. Such tissue involutions may not result from direct hormonal activation of preexisting lysosomes and/or their enzymes, but may involve the production of new hydrolase molecules. These considerations may be germane to the postcastrate involution of androgen-dependent structures, a subject which has been reviewed by Swift and Hruban (1964), Brandes (1966), and Price and Williams-Ashman (1961).

Certain sex hormones can directly affect a number of enzyme systems under test tube conditions. For instance, low concentrations of some steroids exhibiting either estrogenic or androgenic activities can, by undergoing reversible oxidation of hydroxyl to ketone functions on the enzyme surfaces, serve as intermediary hydrogen carriers for pyridine nucleotide transhydrogenations catalyzed by certain mammalian hydroxy-steroid dehydrogenases (Jarabak *et al.*, 1962). And catalytic levels of phenolic estrogens may act as intermediary electron carriers for aerobic oxidations promoted by iron- and copper-containing oxidases (Williams-Ashman *et al.*, 1959). But as reviewed in detail elsewhere (Williams-Ashman and Liao, 1964; Williams-Ashman, 1965a), there is very little evidence in favor of these *in vitro* effects of sex hormones being related to their major physiological actions. The same may be said of other direct actions of sex hormones on various enzymic reactions which do not involve chemical transformations of the hormone molecules, some of which seem to be of an allosteric nature (Williams-Ashman, 1965a). The countless alterations in tissue enzyme activities now known to occur *in vivo* as a result of administration or deprival of androgens and estrogens are usually preceded by a lag period following the endocrine manipulations, and seem to reflect changes in the biosynthesis or degradation of the enzyme proteins (Kochakian, 1959, 1965, 1967; Williams-

Ashman *et al.*, 1964; Williams-Ashman, 1965a,b, 1969, 1970; Williams-Ashman and Shimazaki, 1967, 1968).

When about a decade ago it became appreciated that three major forms of ribonucleic acid—messenger, ribosomal, and transfer RNA's—represented the key intermediates in the flow of genetic information from DNA to protein, it was not altogether surprising that hypotheses were quickly put forward to the effect that hormones regulating tissue growth and function might primarily control the DNA-directed formation of messenger or other types of RNA (or perhaps the translocation of various ribonucleic acids from nucleus to the cytoplasmic sites of protein biosynthesis) in some sort of selective fashion, leading in turn to alterations in the rate of production of individual or groups of proteins. Simplistic interpretations of these ideas involving the notion that sex hormones might exert direct genotropic actions—in the sense that the steroids could recognize and interact with discrete loci of the nuclear DNA genome—appeared highly improbable from the start, considering the many pointers to the presence in all differentiated cells of the same complement of genes, and also in view of the remarkable tissue specificities for the action of gonadal hormones. It seemed more reasonable to postulate that sex hormones could somehow alter the functions of nuclear constituents (such as histones or other proteins) involved in the regulation of RNA transcription. In any event it is true that, regardless of their ultimate correctness, the hypothesis that early changes in RNA transcription and/or intracellular transport represent central mechanisms involved in sex hormone action has sparked a large amount of productive experimentation over the last decade. Nevertheless, it is still far from established that the majority of the effects of androgens on protein synthesis are due to primary regulation of transcriptional or RNA transport processes, and in no single instance has any chemically well-defined and incisive insight been obtained into the mechanism by which these hormones alter any type of macromolecular biosynthetic process. Indeed, preoccupation with nucleic acid and protein synthetic reactions has in recent years tended to overshadow other areas of the biochemical concomitants of androgen action. Before turning to a more detailed discussion of gene expression, we shall first consider some other metabolic effects of androgens.

A. Formation and Utilization of Adenosine Triphosphate and Pyridine Nucleotides

Thirty years ago, Barron and Huggins (1944) found that orchiectomy or diethylstilbestrol treatment reduced the oxygen consumption but not the anaerobic glycolysis of canine prostate slices. They hypothesized that "male sex hormones take part in regulation of the oxidative phase of carbohydrate metabolism of prostatic tissue, its absence or inhibition producing a decrease of this oxidative phase." The postcastrate diminution in the respiration but not the anaerobic lactate production of male accessory gland slices has been confirmed on many subsequent occasions (e.g., Rudolph and Samuels, 1949; Nyden and Williams-Ashman, 1953; Butler and Schade, 1958; Levey and Szego, 1955; Bern, 1953). The biochemistry of these effects of androgen withdrawal are undoubtedly very complex, involving, among other things, differential alterations in the activity of various respiratory as compared with glycolytic enzymes, and in the mitochondrial population densities and functions of accessory gland epithelial cells (Williams-Ashman, 1954, 1962; Price and Williams-Ashman, 1961; Edelman et al., 1963; Doeg, 1968). Another factor which is conceivably relevant to the decline in respiration but not of glycolysis which occurs in the prostate and seminal vesicles soon after castration is the increase in the ratio of nuclear to cytoplasmic volumes in the epithelial cells (Price and Williams-Ashman, 1961; Szirmai, 1962; Ritter, 1969). For there is evidence that glycolysis represents the major if not sole pathway for ATP production by mammalian cell nuclei, and that the contribution of the nuclei to the overall anaerobic lactate production in various cells is more or less proportional to the relative nuclear volumes (Siebert and Humphrey, 1965).

Ritter (1966) has reported that 2 weeks after castration, the concentration of ATP and pyridine nucleotides per unit wet weight of rat ventral prostate tissue is within the normal range. However, within 30 minutes after injection of castrates with free testosterone, Ritter observed a rapid decline in prostatic ATP levels, which was maximal within 1 hour, followed by a gradual rise in ATP toward normal. Ritter (1966) found oscillatory changes in the levels of prostatic NAD, NADH, and NADP over the first 10 hours after administration of testosterone which involved early increases in the total content of NAD and NADH. These effects of testosterone was stated to be similar in castrated rats that had been treated with either puromycin or actinomycin D, suggesting that new protein or RNA synthesis was not required for manifestation of these swift oscillations of NAD induced by testosterone. Ritter concluded that an increased biosynthesis of NAD represents an important early event in the action of androgens on the prostate.

Coffey et al. (1968b) confirmed Ritter's finding of a rapid lowering and subsequent restoration of total ATP levels in rat ventral prostate after administration of testosterone to castrated animals. However, Coffey et al. (1968b) were unable to confirm the large alterations in prostatic

NAD and NADH which Ritter (1966) had described under the same experimental conditions. The conclusion that an increased formation of NAD is a crucial early effect of testosterone on prostatic tissue can therefore be questioned. The physiological significance of androgen-induced changes in prostatic ATP and pyridine nucleotide content is at present quite obscure.

The transient lowering of prostatic ATP content following treatment of castrated rats with testosterone could conceivably be pertinent to the report of Farnsworth (1968) that very low levels (0.1 μM) of testosterone *in vitro* increased the $Mg^{2+} + Na^+ + K^+$-stimulated ATPase activity of microsomes isolated from rat ventral prostate. There is a considerable body of evidence that such sodium plus potassium activated ATPase systems are involved in the transport of these cations across cell membranes, and presumably these ATP-dependent ion translocating enzymes are important for the secretory functions of exocrine epithelial cells such as in prostate. Many attempts by Ahmed and Williams-Ashman (1969) to repeat the direct stimulation of prostatic microsomal $Na^+ + K^+$-activated ATPase by testosterone *in vitro* were uniformly unsuccessful, although enzyme preparations from castrated rats showed large decreases in the specific activity of the enzyme system which could be prevented by treatment of the castrates with testosterone propionate *in vivo*. Additional studies on more purified preparations of the ventral prostate $Mg^{2+} + Na^+ + K^+$-stimulated ATPase obtained by flotation of microsomal membranes in high-density sucrose solutions failed to reveal any effects of the *in vitro* addition of either testosterone or dihydro-testosterone at 0.1 μM to 10 μM concentrations under a number of different experimental conditions.

Arvill (1967) has given considerable attention to effects of testosterone on the entry of various labeled compounds into levator ani muscles of immature rats. The hormone stimulated intracellular accumulation of α-aminoisobutyric acid, xylose and glycine, but only when injected into the animals at least 6 hours before the *in vitro* measurements. Testosterone also enhanced incorporation of glycine and leucine into proteins, and of adenine into RNA, by the levator ani muscle preparations; no comparable effects of the hormone were observed in diaphragm muscle from the same rats. Phenomenological studies on effects of testosterone *in vivo* on transport of amino acids into cells have also been described by Riggs and Walker (1963) and Riggs and Wegrzyn (1966). There is no compelling evidence available (cf. Williams-Ashman *et al.*, 1964) to suggest that the profound effects of androgens on protein synthesis in various tissues are primarily due to alterations in amino acid transport.

Testosterone has a profound influence on glycogen metabolism in rat levator ani muscles. The glycogen levels in this tissue fall rapidly after orchiectomy. Bergamini *et al.* (1969) found that, after an irreducible time lag of 6 hours, muscle glycogen begins to increase following injection of testosterone. This is accompanied by increases in 2-deoxyglucose penetration and phosphorylation, and also in xylose penetration. Increases in hexokinase and glucose-6-phosphate-independent glycogen synthetase activities were also observed within 12 hours after giving testosterone. Administration of actinomycin D or puromycin completely inhibited the testosterone-induced glycogen synthesis. Under somewhat different experimental conditions, Mills and Spaziani (1968) found no increase in 2-deoxyglucose penetration into levator ani muscle cells as a result of testosterone treatment. Bergamini (1969) has reported additive effects of insulin and testosterone on glycogen content and 2-deoxyglucose phosphorylation, but not on xylose uptake, in rat levator ani muscle.

B. REGULATION OF GENE EXPRESSION

Many early considerations of the hormonal control of the genetically determined protein-synthesizing machinery of eucaryotic cells were influenced by the hypothesis of Jacob and Monod (1961) that in bacteria there exist specific regulator genes directing the synthesis of repressor proteins, which can in turn regulate the transcription of often unstable messenger RNA's (or polycistronic messengers) for the synthesis of specific proteins. That hormones might act as "derepressors" was an obvious possibility. A large body of evidence suggests, however, that protein synthesis in higher animal cells is subject to control at many other points besides mRNA production. Moreover, the steady-state levels of enzymes and other proteins in mammalian cells represents the net result of a balance between their rates of synthesis and degradation. The operon hypothesis of Jacob and Monod was formulated from experiments related to the mechanism of induced enzyme synthesis in bacteria—organisms which often need, in order to survive, to change their metabolism very quickly in response to drastic changes in the extracellular chemical environment. The mechanisms of gene expression in eucaryotic cells is now known to involve many attributes which differ profoundly from those operating in bacteria. Thus: (1) only a small fraction of all of the "DNA-like" RNA molecules formed in cell nuclei may ever resist intranuclear degradation, and reach the cytoplasmic sites of protein biosynthesis; (2) ribosomal RNA's are the principal products of gene transcription in nucleated cells (these rRNA's may turn over more swiftly, and many mRNA's may be relatively more stable, in animal as compared with bacterial cells; (3) the production of rRNA's in the nucleus entails complex "chopping up" processes whereby enormous (45 S) precursors are converted into smaller units; (4) translocation of mRNA's from nucleus to cytoplasm seems to occur via complexes with the smaller of the two ribonucleoprotein subunits; (5) membrane-bound rather than "free" polyribosomes in the cytoplasm seem to be the major sites of protein biosynthesis in mammalian cells; the lipoprotein membranes of the endoplasmic reticulum may turn over at rates commensurate with the formation and degradation of the ribosomes themselves.

Several recent theories of gene regulation in higher organisms, notably that advanced by Britten and Davidson (1969) have tried to take into account these considerations, together with the fact that the genome of mammalian as compared with bacterial cells is very large indeed, and appears to contain repetitive nucleotide sequences scattered throughout the nuclear DNA. But none of these hypotheses have as yet provided any clear cut insight into the control of RNA or protein biosynthesis by any hormone. It is noteworthy that Tomkins *et al.* (1969) have recently postulated that adrenocortical hormones can affect the synthesis of certain specific enzymes in liver by influencing the production of "cytoplasmic repressors" which regulate the translation of their corresponding mRNA's.

Studies on the androgenic control of nuclear RNA polymerase reactions and amino acid incorporation by polyribosomal systems in the prostate and seminal vesicle have been documented extensively (Williams-Ashman *et al.*, 1964; Williams-Ashman, 1965a,b, 1969, 1970; Liao and Fang, 1969; Fujii and Villee, 1969; Mangan *et al.*, 1968; Kochakian, 1965), and only a brief summary of the principal findings will be re-iterated here. First it should be underscored that in all of the reported experiments, incorporation of labeled precursors into only relatively crude RNA and protein fractions was determined, and in particular, no reliable estimates have been made of the formation of translation of *specific* mRNA's cognate to individual enzymes or other proteins. The large fall in accessory gland total RNA which results from castration and can be restored by androgen treatment reflects in the main gross changes in the cytoplasmic ribosomal population density. After injection of androgens into castrated rats, there occur rapid elevations in the entry of labeled precursors *in vivo* into seminal vesicle RNA's, but with no pronounced differential effects of the hormones on labeling of any particular class of RNA molecules (Greenman *et al.*, 1965; Fujii and Villee, 1968). In rat ventral prostate, androgen treatment also re-

TABLE IV

<small>Effect of Testosterone on the RNA Polymerase Activities of Rat Liver, Thymus, and Ventral Prostate[a]</small>

		RNA polymerase activity[b]	
Sources of nuclei	Assay conditions	Control castrates	Testosterone-treated castrates
Ventral prostate	complete	16.7 ± 0.8	30.4 ± 0.9
	+ actinomycin D	2.6 ± 0.3	4.8 ± 0.7
Thymus	complete	7.8 ± 0.9	7.0 ± 1.2
	+ actinomycin D	1.5 ± 0.6	2.0 ± 0.8
Liver	complete	58.2 ± 10.5	52.9 ± 4.1
	+ actinomycin D	11.1 ± 2.4	9.7 ± 1.8

[a] From Liao *et al.* (1965).

[b] Sixteen rats were castrated for 70 hours and testosterone propionate was administered to two groups of the animals (4 rats/group) 15 hours before sacrifice. The average values and the ranges of duplicate experiments are tabulated. The numbers represent the amount of P-UMP (in pmoles) incorporated by an amount of nuclei containing 100 μg of DNA. If added, 4 μM of actinomycin D was used in each reaction tube.

sults within a few hours in enhancement of RNA polymerase activities directed by the endogenous DNA of nuclear preparations; the effects of androgens were most marked when the reactions were examined in media of fairly low ionic strength (Table IV). Studies in Shutsung Liao's laboratory (reviewed by Liao and Fang, 1969) established that the RNA polymerase reactions catalyzed by prostatic cell nuclei which were sensitive to androgen *in vivo* were: (1) especially sensitive to the in-

TABLE V

<small>Nucleotide Composition of ^{32}P-RNA Synthesized by Prostatic Nuclei of Rats[a]</small>

	Castrated (mole %)		Testosterone-treated castrates (mole %)		Prostatic ribosomal (or nuclear) RNA (mole %)	Rat liver DNA (mole %)
Base	Control	Actinomycin D	Control	Actinomycin D		
C	29.7	28.8	32.4	26.9	24 (26)	21.5
A	20.9	21.6	16.1	22.5	18 (16)	28.7
G	27.7	26.1	31.2	28.8	38 (36)	21.4
U(T)	21.7	23.5	20.3	21.8	20 (22)	28.4
C + G:A + U(T)	1.35	1.22	1.75	1.26	1.63	0.75

[a] From Liao *et al.* (1966a).

hibitory action of actinomycin D both *in vivo* and *in vitro* (Tables IV and V); (2) differentially labile after orchiectomy of adult animals (Liao and Fang, 1969); and (3) producing products rich in guanine and cytosine that resembled rRNA's or their precursors (Table V). These and other studies led Liao *et al.* (1966b) to conclude that the normal function of prostatic nucleoli to synthesize rRNA's is particularly sensitive to androgenic hormones, which was borne out by radioautographic studies (Liao and Stumpf, 1968). In this connection, it may be mentioned that Brown and Dawid (1968) were unable to obtain evidence for any differential amplification of cistrons directing the synthesis of rRNA molecules in prostatic DNA. Direct determinations of the binding of actinomycin D to prostatic nuclear preparations, as well as studies on the synthesis of RNA by such preparations in the

TABLE VI

RNA SYNTHESIS AND ACTINOMYCIN D BINDING BY RAT DNA AND PROSTATIC
NUCLEAR PREPARATIONS[a]

DNA or nuclei	*Micrococcus* polymerase	^{32}P-UMP incorporation (pmoles/100 μg DNA)	%
Rat liver DNA	+	4300	100.0
Prostatic nuclei			
C	+	1080	25.1
T	+	1010	23.5
C	−	50	1.2
T	−	104	2.4
		Actinomycin D-binding (μg/100 μg DNA)	
Rat liver DNA	−	30–40	100
Prostatic nuclei (C or T)	−	7–10	20–30

[a] Prostatic nuclei were isolated from rats castrated for 60 hours and pressure-disrupted just before the addition. C: control castrates; T: castrated rats injected with testosterone at 0, 24, and 48 hours. Reactions were carried out in the presence of 2–6 μg rat liver DNA or prostatic nuclei which contain 10–30 μg DNA and an excess amount of *Micrococcus* polymerase (10 μg) if added. They were incubated under the standard conditions for 15 minutes. Under these conditions the amount of UMP incorporated was proportional to the amount of DNA used. Addition of twice the amount of *Micrococcus* polymerase resulted in only about 20% increase in RNA synthesis in the tube which already had the bacterial polymerase. Binding of actinomycin D was analyzed spectrophotometrically under conditions where the amount of antibiotic bound was proportional to the amount of nuclei or DNA present and DNase pretreatment of nuclei or DNA abolished such binding. (From Liao and Lin, 1967.)

absence and presence of exogenous bacterial RNA polymerases (Table VI) did not point to any gross "unmasking" of DNA templates, but rather to increases in the synthesis of RNA molecules complementary to very restricted regions of the nuclear DNA genome. The manner by which androgens induce swift increases in nuclear RNA synthesis in male accessory glands, and the relation of the nuclear dihydrotestosterone-binding proteins considered above to such effects, remains very mysterious at the moment, as Liao and Fang (1969) discuss. A major difficulty currently in way of interpretation of studies on RNA synthesis by nuclear preparations is that the precise multiplicity of mammalian RNA polymerases is still uncertain (Widnell and Tata, 1966; Roeder and Rutter, 1969; Liao et al., 1969). Moreover, in most in vitro experiments on nuclear RNA polymerase activities as influenced by hormones, no distinction has been made experimentally between the initiation of new RNA chains and elongation of preexisting ones. Factors such as the "σ" RNA polymerase subunit concerned with chain initiation, and others which may control termination of RNA synthesis, are well known to occur in bacteria (Geiduschek and Haselkorn, 1969); similar entities could well play a role in the hormonal control of RNA synthesis in nucleated cells.

The early increases in nuclear RNA synthesis due to androgen treatment in male accessory glands are followed by later enhancement of cytoplasmic protein synthesis (Liao and Williams-Ashman, 1962; Fujii and Villee, 1969) which seem to depend upon an increased number of new cytoplasmic ribosomes with a greater capacity for amino acid incorporation, possibly as a result of production of new mRNA molecules. The same sort of train of macromolecular biosynthetic events, i.e., early increases in synthesis of nuclear RNA which appears to be predominantly rRNA (Avdalovic and Kochakian, 1969), followed by elevated cytoplasmic polyribosomal protein synthesis, were observed by Kochakian (1969) and Kochakian et al. (1969) with respect to the androgen-dependent growth of mouse kidney. Neither castration nor androgen treatment affected the rather marked lability of the amino acid incorporating system of postmitochondrial fractions of mouse kidney homogenates (Kochakian and Hama, 1969). However, the effects of androgen administration on the degradation of various RNA's involved in protein biosynthesis (cf. Kochakian et al., 1969) require more thorough investigation.

Breuer and Florini (1965, 1966) found that testosterone increased the template activity of DNA in chromatin and also protein synthesis in rat skeletal muscle. Very recently, Florini (1970) attempted to see whether androgens caused increased synthesis of any specific muscle proteins by measuring the entry of labeled amino acids into various proteins of muscle extracts that were separated by disc electrophoresis and isoelectric focusing on polyacrylamide gels. No appreciable differences in the profiles of radioactive proteins were detected under conditions in which the total synthesis of both RNA and proteins were stimulated about 60% by testosterone administration. That androgens can, in certain tissues, enhance the synthesis of certain specific proteins is, however, evident from studies on an isoenzyme of esterase in mouse kidney (Shaw and Koen, 1963) and a sex-associated bulk protein in male rat liver (Bond, 1962).

It is now generally accepted that the mitochondria of eukaryotic cells contain unique circular DNA molecules which are not only replicated independently of the nuclear DNA genome, but may also play a directive role in the synthesis of certain mitochondrial RNA's, some of which may participate in the synthesis of certain (although by no means all) mitochondrial proteins. Pegg and Williams-Ashman (1968b) found that the incorporation of labeled isoleucine and pheylalanine into proteins by isolated rat ventral prostate mitochondria was enhanced by testosterone *in vivo*. These investigations were conducted under conditions where the ATP necessary for mitochondrial "protein synthesis" was supplied externally, so that the reactions were independent of any effects of androgens on energy transductions by the electron transport chain of the particles. However, no effects of testosterone treatment of orchiectomized rats on prostate mitochondrial amino acid incorporations could be observed at less than 12 hours after injection of the hormone, that is, over a period when increases in nuclear RNA polymerase activities are already very marked. It therefore seems possible that alterations in the cytoplasmic environment due to testosterone administration may be a major factor in these relatively slow changes in mitochondrial protein synthesis.

Fujii and Villee (1967) instilled RNA's isolated from various tissues by the phenol–sodium dodecyl sulfate procedure into the lumens of seminal vesicle of immature rats. RNA from the seminal vesicle of testosterone-treated immature rats, and from seminal vesicle, prostate, liver, and kidney of adult male untreated animals, enhanced the wet weight and protein content of the seminal vesicles of the recipients. Preparations of RNA from tissues of untreated immature rats were ineffective. Treating the active RNA preparations with ribonuclease or by boiling removed the "growth-promoting" activity. Evidence was obtained that the active RNA fractions were not contaminated with testosterone. Fujii and Villee (1969) fractionated preparations of RNA from adult male rats on sucrose density gradients. The material in a peak sedimenting at about 18 S caused a 22% increase in the wet weight when instilled into the seminal vesicles of immature animals; other RNA fractions obtained from the sucrose density gradient experiments as well as some preparations of liver soluble RNA were inactive. The physiological significance of the experiments of Fujii and Villee (1967, 1969) is very difficult to evaluate in the absence of further data. These studies might be construed to mean that RNA isolated from seminal vesicle and liver of adult male rats contains expressible information for the synthesis of proteins which are normally formed in seminal vesicle tissue of immature rats after androgenic stimulation. It appears at least equally possible that such active RNA preparations might trigger off various macromolecular synthetic events (e.g., RNA and subsequent protein synthesis) in seminal vesicle which resemble those occurring within the tissue as a result of androgen administration. As Fujii and Villee (1969) point out, unspecific effects of RNA on certain protein biosynthetic reactions have been recorded, e.g., the finding of Hunt and Wilkinson (1967) that liver RNA as well as reticulocyte RNA preparations enhance hemoglobin synthesis by cell-free extracts of reticulocytes, possibly by virtue of stimulating translation of endogenous globin mRNA on reticulocyte polyribosomes rather than the liver RNA preparations serving a true messenger RNA function.

As might be expected, administration of actinomycin D can depress many of the actions of testosterone on responsive tissues (Angeletti et al., 1964; Williams-Ashman, 1965b; Breuer and Florini, 1965; Singhal and Valadares, 1968). Problems in the interpretation of such experiments are discussed by Williams-Ashman (1965a, 1970). Talwar et al. (1965) have concluded that development of the chick's comb under the influence of testosterone may not require prior stimulation of DNA-dependent RNA synthesis. This conclusion was drawn from experiments in which the growth response was not modified by application of actinomycin D to the combs. In these investigations, however, no measurements were made of the degree to which the actinomycin D was actually inhibiting RNA synthesis in the comb tissue. Frieden et al. (1964) found in experiments of some day's duration that injection of actinomycin D prior to and concurrently with testosterone virtually nullified the androgen-induced enhancement of β-glucuronidase activity in mouse kidney. But the increase of leucine incorporation into proteins by kidney slices due to testosterone administration was not affected by the antibiotic over this period, even though actinomycin D depressed the baseline leucine incorporations. Similar results were obtained when either glycine or arginine were employed as labeled substrates. Frieden et al. (1964) also found that actinomycin D had little influence on mouse renal β-

glucuronidase response to androgens if the antibiotic was given after the first injection of testosterone. Frieden and Fishel (1968) observed that DL-ethionine inhibited the androgen-dependent stimulation of mouse kidney arginase and β-glucuronidase. The elevation in arginase activity by testosterone was insensitive to actinomycin D, unlike the increase in β-glucuronidase. Frieden and Fishel (1968) suggested that this might be due to a "difference in the sensitivity of the two DNA primers" to actinomycin D. These authors appear to overlook the possibility that the levels of mouse kidney arginase may be perturbed by altering the rate of degradation as well as of the synthesis of the enzyme, as Schimke *et al.* (1968) has shown for liver arginase.

Studies by Lostroh (1968) on organ cultures of prostates from gonadectomized mice revealed that direct addition of testosterone or 5α-dihydrotestosterone augmented both citrate formation and incorporation of tritiated leucine into proteins. No effect of androgen *in vitro* on either of these parameters measured with cultures of regressed prostates could be demonstrated unless insulin was added to the culture medium. It was shown that insulin did not influence the uptake of radioactive testosterone by the explants. If the prostate tissue was excised from orchiectomized mice which had been treated *in vivo* with submaximal doses of testosterone, however, the addition of insulin was not necessary for an enhancing action of testosterone *in vitro* on leucine incorporation.

C. Cell Proliferation, DNA Replication, and Androgen Action

There is clear-cut evidence that in adult mammals, steroid hormones can evoke marked changes in the expression of certain genes in many types of nondividing cells (Williams-Ashman, 1965a; Tomkins *et al.*, 1969). Yet hormone-dependent functional differentiations in some cell types does necessitate rounds of DNA synthesis, cell division, and appearance of new gene products only in daughter cells. This is illustrated, for example, by the studies of Lockwood *et al.* (1967) on the promotion by combinations of insulin, hydrocortisone, and prolactin of the differentiation of milk-secreting cells in mouse mammary gland grown in organ culture.

The initial morphogenesis of many androgen-dependent structures is, as already considered, under the control of fetal testicular androgens, and obviously involves extensive multiplication of cells. The growth of androgen-sensitive structures in castrated postpubertal mammals resulting from androgen administration is more complex, and the extent to which true hyperlasia contributes to the overall increase in mass varies very much from one particular organ to another in any given species. For instance, the levator ani muscles (Venable, 1966) and kidneys (Kochakian and Harrison, 1962) of neuter mice, and the masseter muscles of castrated guinea pigs (Kochakian et al., 1964), grow in response to androgen very largely as a result of hypertrophy of cells, although there may be some fabrication of new blood vessels. On the contrary, testosterone-induced growth of organs such as the prostate and seminal vesicles in orchiectomized rodents involves not only hypertrophy of epithelial cells and formation and retention of secretory products, but also extensive hyperplasia of various cellular elements. There is, nevertheless, no evidence that the very early increases in nuclear RNA synthesis and subsequent enhancement of protein synthesis in these organs requires any prior replication of nuclear DNA. Rather the onset of DNA synthesis, and subsequent mitoses are relatively late events in the growth of male accessory glands promoted by androgens. Some studies by Coffey et al. (1968a) on the synthesis of DNA and enzymes concerned with this event were conducted in adult rats that had been orchiectomized for 7 days, and to which were then injected hyperphysiological daily doses of testosterone propionate, so that within a period of 2 weeks, ventral prostate growth attained a stable plateau. Particular attention was given to a "replicative" type of prostatic DNA polymerase which preferentially utilized single-stranded DNA's as primers, required all four major deoxyribonucleoside triphosphates, and was activated by fairly high concentrations of glycerol ($1.7 M$) in the incubation medium. This DNA polymerase appeared in the soluble fraction obtained by ultracentrifugation of prostate homogenates prepared in dilute buffers or $0.25 M$ sucrose, but was retained in the nuclei to an extent of about 50% of the total cellular activity when the tissue was homogenized in more concentrated ($2.2 M$) sucrose solutions (Table VII). Orchiectomy as such caused only a modest decline in the low DNA polymerase activity of resting prostate. Following the daily (or single) injections of 2 mg of testosterone propionate, no change was observed over the first 24 hours in either soluble DNA polymerase activity, or in the incorporation of labeled thymidine into ventral prostate DNA measured in vivo or with intact cell preparations in vitro. By 48 hours prostatic DNA polymerase levels rose many fold, and reached a maximum of up to 30-fold at about 3–5 days after the hormone was first injected. Despite continued daily injection of the androgen, prostatic DNA polymerase levels subsequently declined. The alterations in DNA polymerase activity largely paralleled changes in the entry of thymidine into DNA as determined either in vivo or in vitro. Qualitatively similar changes in prostatic DNA polymerase activities

TABLE VII

Effects of Androgen on Distribution of DNA Polymerase Activity in Fractions of Homogenates Prepared in 2.2 M Sucrose[a]

			Rat ventral prostate characteristics				DNA polymerase activity[c] (pmoles dAMP ^{14}C/hour/100 μg equivalent of tissue DNA)		
Treatment	Total days castrated	Cumulative days of testosterone propionate treatment[b]	Total weight ventral prostate (mg/100 gm body weight)	Total DNA of ventral prostate (μg/100 gm body weight)	Total RNA of ventral prostate (μg/100 gm body weight)	RNA/ DNA	"Soluble"	"Nuclear"	Total
Normal	0	0	128	276	661	2.4	180	123	303
Castrate	7	0	20	85	50	0.6	48	6	54
Castrate treated with	9	2	41	106	192	1.8	300	24	324
testosterone	12	5	84	192	368	1.9	3880	166	4046
propionate	16	9	121	255	571	2.2	191	202	393
	19	12	188	315	835	2.7	157	165	322
Normal treated with	0	2	184	368	1130	3.1	250	220	470
testosterone	0	5	203	362	910	2.5	484	110	594
propionate	0	12	251	372	1200	3.2	279	138	417

[a] From Coffey et al. (1968a).

[b] On the seventh day after castration daily subcutaneous injections of 0.2 ml sesame oil containing 2 mg testosterone propionate were initiated.

[c] Ventral prostate tissue was homogenized at 2°C in 10 volumes of 2.2 M sucrose, 1 mM MgSO$_4$, and 5 mM β-mercaptoethanol. The homogenate was filtered through a silk cloth and then centrifuged for 1 hour at 50,000 g.

resulted from treatment of hypophysectomized as well as of castrated rats with androgen, indicating that pituitary hormones were not involved in any major fashion in the response.[6] The massive yet transitory increases in prostatic DNA polymerase: (1) occurred largely in the soluble cytoplasmic rather than nuclear fraction of prostate homogenates prepared in 2.2 M sucrose (Table VII), (2) could not be accounted for by removal or inactivation of polymerase reaction inhibitors from the prostates of castrates. These findings are in line with observations made on many other mammalian cells that large quantities of enzymes involved in DNA replication may be elaborated only near to or during the "S" phase of the cell cycle. The soluble prostatic DNA polymerase may, however, be mainly involved in "repair" rather than net synthesis of DNA.

The growth and total DNA content of rat male accessory glands cannot be increased beyond a value of about twofold that found in corresponding normal adult animals even by very prolonged treatment of normal or castrated animals with excessive amounts of testosterone. The effects of the hormone on DNA synthesis and cell multiplication eventually come to a halt under conditions where there is no "wearing off" of the ability of androgens to stimulate and maintain RNA and protein biosynthesis and secretory functions in these organs (Coffey et al., 1968a). Recent speculations considered above concerning the possible control by 5α-dihydrotestosterone of cell hyperplasia in androgen-sensitive tissues suggest that it may be enlightening to examine the effects of prolonged treatment with dihydrotestosterone on male genital gland growth. Nevertheless, the factors which determine, in the absence of frank neoplasia, the ultimate restrictions on the dimensions these organs can attain in adult animals regardless of the intensity and duration of the androgenic stimulus remain extremely obscure. Some of the complexities of this problem are illustrated by some recent experiments of Whalen (1968) on the size of the penis in adult rats which had been subject to various hormonal manipulations after birth. If the rats were castrated neonatally, they exhibited reduced penile development even if they were injected with testosterone propionate in infancy. Stimulation of these animals in adulthood with testosterone caused an increase in shaft and glans length and

---

[6] As reviewed by Price and Williams-Ashman (1961) and Reddi (1969), growth hormone and prolactin can to some degree enhance the stimulatory effects of androgens on the growth of certain male accessory glands in castrated or hypophysectomized animals of some species. The size of these organs in such animals is not increased by growth hormone or prolactin in the absence of androgens. Nothing is known about the mechanism of these synergistic effects of anterior pituitary hormones on the androgen-induced growth of certain tissues. Whether growth hormone or prolactin can influence the uptake and/or metabolic transformations of testosterone by androgen-responsive tissues does not seem to have been examined.

in the total weight of the phallus. However, this enhancement of penile growth evoked by administration of testosterone to the adults was much greater in the rats which had received a single dose of androgen on day 1 or day 4 of life, and after the neonatal orchiectomy. Evidently the penis goes through a critical period of differentiation very soon after birth which has a most profound influence on the extent to which penile size can be increased by androgens in adult rodents. Such considerations may well apply to the androgenic regulation of the dimensions of other male secondary sexual organs. In a few mammalian species, the prostate can attain a very large size as a result of benign or malignant growths; some of these tumors appear to be androgen-dependent and may shrink at least temporarily following orchiectomy and/or estrogen treatment (Huggins, 1947; Price and Williams-Ashman, 1961). The horrendous clinical consequences of many human prostatic neoplasms should serve as a strong impetus for further investigations on the androgenic control of cell division. Recent investigations of Siiteri and Wilson (1970) and Gloyna *et al.* (1970) indicating that 5α-dihydrotestosterone accumulation may be related to the development of prostatic tumors in men and dogs represent an important new facet of this problem.

ACKNOWLEDGMENT

Recent work from the senior author's laboratory discussed in this review was supported in part by a research grant (HD-01453) from the United States Public Health Service.

REFERENCES

Ahmed, K., and Williams-Ashman, H. G. (1969). *Biochem. J.* 113, 829.
Aliapoulios, M. A., Chamberlain, J., Jagarinec, N., and Ofner, P. (1965). *Biochem. J.* 98, 15P.
Anderson, K. M., and Liao, S. (1968). *Nature* 219, 277.
Angeletti, P. U., Salvi, M. L., and Tacchini, G. (1964). *Experientia* 20, 612.
Avdalovic, N., and Kochakian, C. D. (1969). *Biochim. Biophys. Acta* 182, 382.
Arvill, A. (1967). *Acta Endocrinol. Suppl.* 122, 1.
Bardin, C. W., Allison, J. E., Stanley, A. J., and Gumbreck, L. G. (1969). *Endocrinology* 84, 435.
Bardin, C. W., Bullock, L., Schneider, G., Allison, J. E., and Stanley, A. J. (1970). *Science* 167, 1136.
Barron, E. S. G., and Huggins, C. (1944). *J. Urol.* 51, 630.
Barry, M. C., Eidinoff, M. L., Dobriner, K., and Gallagher, T. F. (1952). *Endocrinology* 50, 587.
Barton, R. W., and Liao, S. (1967). *Endocrinology* 81, 409.

Bashirelahi, N., and Villee, C. A. (1970). *Biochim. Biophys. Acta* **202**, 192.

Bashirelahi, N., Chader, G. J., and Villee, C. A. (1969). *Biochem. Biophys. Res. Commun.* **37**, 976.

Baulieu, E-E., Lasnitzki, I., and Robel, P. (1968a). *Biochem. Biophys. Res. Commun.* **32**, 575.

Baulieu, E-E., Lasnitzki, I., and Robel, P. (1968b). *Nature* **219**, 1155.

Bergamini, E. (1969). *Biochim. Biophys. Acta* **177**, 235.

Bergamini, E., Bombara, G., and Pellegrino, C. (1969). *Biochim. Biophys. Acta* **177**, 220.

Bern, H. A. (1953). *J. Endocrinol.* **9**, 312.

Bond, H. E. (1962). *Nature* **196**, 242.

Brandes, D. (1966). *Intern. Rev. Cytol.* **20**, 207.

Brandes, D., and Bourne, G. H. (1963). *Natl. Cancer Inst. Monograph* **12**, 29.

Brandes, D., Groth, D. P., and Györkey, F. (1962). *Exptl. Cell Res.* **28**, 61.

Breuer, C. B., and Florini, J. R. (1965). *Biochemistry* **4**, 1544.

Breuer, C. B., and Florini, J. R. (1966). *Biochemistry* **5**, 3857.

Britten, R. J., and Davidson, E. H. (1969). *Science* **165**, 349.

Brown, D. D., and Dawid, I. B. (1968). *Science* **160**, 272.

Bruchovsky, N., and Wilson, J. D. (1968a). *J. Biol. Chem.* **243**, 2012.

Bruchovsky, N., and Wilson, J. D. (1968b). *J. Biol. Chem.* **243**, 5953.

Burns, R. K. (1961). In "Sex and Internal Secretions" (W. C. Young, ed.), Vol. I, pp. 76–158. Williams & Wilkins, Baltimore, Maryland.

Butcher, R. W., Robison, G. A., and Sutherland, E. W. (1970). *Ciba Found. Symp., Control Processes Multicellular Org.* pp. 64–85.

Butler, W. W. S., III, and Schade, A. L. (1958). *Endocrinology* **63**, 271.

Caldarera, C. M., Moruzzi, M. S., Barbiroli, B., and Moruzzi, G. (1968). *Biochem. Biophys. Res. Commun.* **33**, 266.

Coffey, D. S., Shimazaki, J., and Williams-Ashman, H. G. (1968a). *Arch. Biochem. Biophys.* **124**, 184.

Coffey, D. S., Ichinose, R. R., Shimazaki, J., and Williams-Ashman, H. G. (1968b). *Mol. Pharmacol.* **4**, 580.

Corbin, J. D., and Krebs, E. G. (1969). *Biochem. Biophys. Res. Commun.* **36**, 328.

Deane, H. W., and Wurzelmann, S. (1965). *Am. J. Anat.* **117**, 91.

Doeg, K. A. (1968). *Endocrinology* **82**, 535.

Edelman, J. C., Brendler, H., Zorgniotti, A. W., and Edelman, P. M. (1963). *Endocrinology* **72**, 853.

Fang, S., and Liao, S. (1969). *Mol. Pharmacol.* **5**, 428.

Fang, S., and Liao, S. (1971). *J. Biol. Chem.* **246**, 16.

Fang, S., Anderson, K. M., and Liao, S. (1969). *J. Biol. Chem.* **244**, 6584.

Farnsworth, W. E. (1965). *Steroids* **6**, 519.

Farnsworth, W. E. (1966). *Steroids* **8**, 825.

Farnsworth, W. E. (1968). *Biochim. Biophys. Acta* **150**, 446.

Farnsworth, W. E., and Brown, J. R. (1963). *Natl. Cancer Inst. Monograph* **12**, 323.

Florini, J. R. (1970). *Biochemistry* **9**, 909.

Fortier, C., Labrie, F., Pelletier, G., Raynaud, J-P., Ducommun, P., Delgado, A., Labrie, R., and Ho-Kim, M-A. (1970). *Ciba Found. Symp., Control Processes Multicellular Org.* pp. 178–209.

Frederiksen, D. N., and Wilson, J. D. (1971). *J. Biol. Chem.* **246**, 2584.

French, F. S., Baggett, B., Van Wyk, J. J., Talbert, L. M., Hubbard, W. R., Johnston,

F. R., Weaver, W-P., Forchielli, E., Rao, G. S., and Sarda, I. R. (1965). *J. Clin. Endocrinol.* **25**, 661.

French, F. S., Van Wyk, J. J., Baggett, B., Easterling, W. E., Talbert, L. M., Johnston, F. R., Forchielli, E., and Dey, A. C. (1966). *J. Clin. Endocrinol.* **26**, 493.

Frieden, E. H., and Fishel, S. S. (1968). *Biochem. Biophys. Res. Commun.* **31**, 515.

Frieden, E. H., Harper, A. A., Chin, F., and Fishman, W. H. (1964). *Steroids* **4**, 777.

Fujii, T., and Villee, C. A. (1967). *Proc. Natl. Acad. Sci. U. S.* **57**, 1468.

Fujii, T., and Villee, C. A. (1968). *Endocrinology* **82**, 463.

Fujii, T., and Villee, C. A. (1969). *Proc. Natl. Acad. Sci. U. S.* **62**, 836.

Geiduschek, E. P., and Haselkorn, R. (1969). *Ann. Rev. Biochem.* **38**, 647.

Gloyna, R. E., and Wilson, J. D. (1969). *J. Clin. Endocrinol.* **29**, 970.

Gloyna, R. E., Siiteri, P. K., and Wilson, J. D. (1970). *J. Clin. Invest.* **49**, 1746.

Goodwin, D. A., Rusmussen-Taxdal, D. S., Ferrerira, A. A., and Scott, W. W. (1961). *J. Urol.* **86**, 134.

Goy, R. W. (1964). In "Human Reproduction and Sexual Behavior" (C. W. Lloyd, ed.), pp. 409–441. Lea & Febiger, Philadelphia, Pennsylvania.

Greenman, D. L., Wicks, W. D., and Kenney, F. T. (1965). *J. Biol. Chem.* **240**, 4420.

Greer, D. S. (1959). *Endocrinology* **64**, 898.

Harding, B. W., and Samuels, L. T. (1962). *Endocrinology* **70**, 109.

Harkin, J. C. (1963). *Natl. Cancer Inst. Monograph* **12**, 85.

Harris, G. W. (1964). *Endocrinology* **75**, 627.

Hechter, O., and Halkerston, I. D. K. (1964). In "The Hormones" (G. Pincus, K. V. Thimann, and E. B. Astwood, eds.), Vol. 5, pp. 697–825. Academic Press, New York.

Holmes, W. N. (1956). *Acta Endocrinol.* **23**, 89.

Huggins, C. (1947). *Harvey Lectures* **42**, 148.

Huggins, C., and Jensen, E. V. (1954). *J. Exptl. Med.* **100**, 241.

Huggins, C., Jensen, E. V., and Cleveland, A. S. (1954). *J. Exptl. Med.* **100**, 225.

Hunt, J. A., and Wilkinson, B. R. (1967). *Biochemistry* **6**, 1688.

Jacob, F., and Monod, J. (1961). *J. Mol. Biol.* **3**, 318.

Jarabak, J., Adams, J. A., Williams-Ashman, H. G., and Talalay, P. (1962). *J. Biol. Chem.* **237**, 345.

Jensen, E. V., Suzuki, T., Kawashima, T., Stumpf, W. E., Jungblut, P. W., and DeSombre, E. R. (1968). *Proc. Natl. Acad. Sci. U. S.* **59**, 632.

Kochakian, C. D. (1959). *Lab. Invest.* **8**, 538.

Kochakian, C. D. (1965). In "Mechanisms of Hormone Action" (P. Karlson, ed.), pp. 192–213. Thieme, Stuttgart.

Kochakian, C. D. (1967). In "Conferences on Cellular Dynamics" (L. D. Peachey, ed.), pp. 186–197. N. Y. Acad. Sci., New York.

Kochakian, C. D. (1969). *Gen. Comp. Endocrinol.* **13**, 146.

Kochakian, C. D., and Hama, T. (1969). *Acta Endocrinol.* **62**, 328.

Kochakian, C. D., and Harrison, D. G. (1962). *Endocrinology* **70**, 99.

Kochakian, C. D., Hill, J., and Harrison, D. G. (1964). *Endocrinology* **74**, 635.

Kochakian, C. D., Nishida, M., and Hirone, T. (1969). *Am. J. Physiol.* **217**, 383.

Langan, T. A. (1969). *Proc. Natl. Acad. Sci. U. S.* **64**, 1276.

Lasnitzki, I., Dingle, J. T., and Adams, S. (1965). *Exptl. Cell Res.* **43**, 120.

Levey, H. A., and Szego, C. M. (1955). *Am. J. Physiol.* **183**, 371.

Levin, W., Welch, R. M., and Conney, A. H. (1969). *Steroids* **13**, 155.

Liao, S., and Fang, S. (1969). *Vitamins Hormones* **27**, 17.

Liao, S., and Lin, A. H. (1967). *Proc. Natl. Acad. Sci. U. S.* **57**, 379.

Liao, S., and Stumpf, W. E. (1968). *Endocrinology* **83**, 629.

Liao, S., and Williams-Ashman, H. G. (1962). *Proc. Natl. Acad. Sci. U. S.* **48**, 1956.

Liao, S., Leininger, K., Sagher, D., and Barton, R. W. (1965). *Endocrinology* **77**, 763.

Liao, S., Lin, A. H., and Barton, R. W. (1966a). *J. Biol. Chem.* **241**, 3869.

Liao, S., Barton, R. W., and Lin, A. H. (1966b). *Proc. Natl. Acad. Sci. U. S.* **55**, 1593.

Liao, S., Sagher, D., Lin, A. H., and Fang, S. (1969). *Nature* **223**, 297.

Liao, S., Lin, A. H., and Tymoczko, J. L. (1971). *Biochim. Biophys. Acta* **230**, 535.

Lockwood, D. H., Voytovich, A. E., Stockdale, F. E., and Topper, Y. J. (1967). *Proc. Natl. Acad. Sci. U. S.* **58**, 658.

Lostroh, A. J. (1968). *Proc. Natl. Acad. Sci. U. S.* **60**, 1312.

Lostroh, A. J. (1969). *Endocrinology,* **85**, 438.

Mainwaring, W. I. P. (1969). *J. Endocrinol.* **45**, 531.

Mangan, F. R., Neal, G. E., and Williams, D. C. (1968). *Arch. Biochem. Biophys.* **124**, 27.

Mauvais-Jarvis, P., Bercovici, J. P., and Gauthier, F. (1969). *J. Clin. Endocrinol.* **29**, 417.

Mauvais-Jarvis, P., Bercovici, J. P., Crepy, O., and Gauthier, F. (1970). *J. Clin. Invest.* **49**, 31.

Mercier, C., Alfsen, A., and Baulieu, E-E. (1965). *In* "Androgens in Normal and Pathological Conditions" *Intern. Congr. Ser.* No. 101, p. 212. Excerpta Med. Found., Amsterdam.

Mills, T. M. and Spaziani, E. (1968). *Biochim. Biophys. Acta* **150**, 435.

Miyamoto, E., Kuo, J. F., and Greengard, P. (1969). *J. Biol. Chem.* **244**, 6395.

Money, J., Ehrhardt, A. A., and Masica, D. N. (1968). *Johns Hopkins Med. J.* **123**, 105.

Moulton, B. C., and Leonard, S. L. (1969). *Endocrinology* **84**, 1461.

Neumann, F., von Berswordt-Wallrabe, R., Elger, W., and Steinbeck, H. (1967). *Colloq. Ges. Physiol. Chem.* **18**, 218.

Northcutt, R. C., Island, D. P., and Liddle, G. W. (1969). *J. Clin. Endocrinol.* **29**, 422.

Nyden, S. J., and Williams-Ashman, H. G. (1953). *Amer. J. Physiol.* **172**, 688.

Ofner, P. (1969). *Vitamins Hormones* **26**, 237.

Pearlman, W. H., and Crépy, O. (1967). *J. Biol. Chem.* **242**, 182.

Pearlman, W. H., and Pearlman, M. R. J. (1961). *J. Biol. Chem.* **236**, 1321.

Pegg, A. E., and Williams-Ashman, H. G. (1968a). *Biochem. J.* **109**, 32p.

Pegg, A. E., and Williams-Ashman, H. G. (1968b). *Endocrinology* **82**, 603.

Pegg, A. E., Lockwood, D. H., and Williams-Ashman, H. G. (1970). *Biochem. J.* **116**, 000.

Price, D., and Ortiz, E. (1965). *In* "Organogenesis" (R. L. DeHaan and H. Ursprung, eds.), pp. 620–652. Holt, New York.

Price, D., and Williams-Ashman, H. G. (1961). *In* "Sex and Internal Secretions" (W. C. Young, ed.), pp. 366–388. Williams & Wilkins, Baltimore, Maryland.

Raspé, G. (1969). *In* "Advances in the Biosciences" (G. Raspé, ed.), Vol. 1, pp. 1–13. Pergamon Press, Oxford.

Reddi, A. H. (1969). *Gen. Comp. Endocrinol. Suppl.* **2**, 81.

Reddi, A. H., Ewing, L. L., and Williams-Ashman, H. G. (1971). *Biochem. J.* **122**, 333.

Riggs, T. R. and Walker, L. M. (1963). *Endocrinology* **73**, 781.

Riggs, T. R. and Wegrzyn, S. W. (1966). *Endocrinology* **78**, 137.

Ritter, C. (1966). *Mol. Pharmacol.* **2**, 125.

Ritter, C. (1969). *Endocrinology* **84**, 844.

Roeder, R. G., and Rutter, W. J. (1969). *Nature* **224**, 234.

Rosenfeld, M. G., and O'Malley, B. W. (1970). *Science* **168**, 253.

Rudolph, G. G., and Samuels, L. T. (1949). *Endocrinology* **44**, 190.

Sar, M., Liao, S., and Stumpf, W. E. (1969). *Federation Proc.* **28**, 707.

Schimke, R. T., Ganschow, R., Doyle, D., and Arias, I. M. (1968). *Federation Proc.* **27**, 1223.

Schriefers, H. (1967). *Vitamins Hormones* **25**, 271.

Shaw, C. R., and Koen, A. L. (1963). *Science* **140**, 70.

Shimazaki, J., Kurihara, H., Ito, Y., and Shida, K. (1965a). *Gunma J. Med. Sci.* **14**, 313.

Shimazaki, J., Kurihara, H., Ito, Y., and Shida, K. (1965b). *Gunma J. Med. Sci.* **14**, 326.

Shimazaki, J., Kurihara, H., Ito, Y., and Shida, K. (1965c). *Gunma J. Med. Sci.* **14**, 100.

Shimazaki, J., Matsushita, I., Furuya, N., Yamanaka, H., and Shida, K. (1969a). *Endocrinol. Japan.* **16**, 453.

Shimazaki, J., Furuya, N., Yamanaka, H., and Shida, K. (1969b). *Endocrinol. Japon.* **16**, 163.

Siebert, G., and Humphrey, G. B. (1965). *Advan. Enzymol.* **27**, 239.

Siiteri, P. K., and Wilson, J. D. (1970). *J. Clin. Invest.* **49**, 1737.

Simmer, H. H., Pion, R. J., and Dignam, W. J. (1965). "Testicular Feminization: Endocrine Function of Feminizing Testes: Comparison with Normal Testes." Thomas, Springfield, Illinois.

Singhal, R. L., and Valadares, J. R. E. (1968). *Biochem. J.* **110**, 703.

Singhal, R. L., Vijayvargiya, R., and Ling, G. M. (1970). *Science* **168**, 261.

Stanley, A. J., and Gumbreck, L. G. (1964). *Program 46th Meeting of Am. Endocrine Soc., San Francisco* p. 40.

Steinberger, E., and Duckett, G. E. (1967). *J. Reprod. Fertility Suppl.* **2**, 75.

Stern, J. M., and Eisenfeld, A. J. (1969). *Science* **166**, 233.

Strickland, A. L., and French, F. S. (1969). *J. Clin. Endocrinol.* **29**, 1284.

Swift, H., and Hruban, Z. (1964). *Federation Proc.* **23**, 1026.

Szirmai, J. A. (1962). *In* "Protein Metabolism" (F. Gross, ed.), pp. 45–74. Springer, Berlin.

Talwar, G. P., Modi, S., and Rao, K. N. (1965). *Science* **150**, 1315.

Tata, J. R. (1970). *Ciba Found. Symp., Control Processes Multicellular Org.* pp. 131–157.

Tesar, C., and Scott, W. W. (1963). *Invest. Urol.* **1**, 482.

Tomkins, G. M., Gelehrter, T. D., Granner, D., Martin, D., Jr., Samuels, H. H., and Thompson, E. B. (1969). *Science* **166**, 1474.

Tveter, K. J. (1969). *Acta Endocrinol.* **60**, 60.

Tveter, K. J., and Aakvaag, A. (1969). *Endocrinology* **85**, 683.

Tveter, K. J., and Attramadal, A. (1969). *Endocrinology* **85**, 350.

Tveter, K. J., and Unhjem, O. (1969). *Endocrinology* **84**, 963.

Unhjem, O., Tveter, K. J., and Aakvaag, A. (1969). *Acta Endocrinol.* **62**, 153.

Venable, J. H. (1966). *Am. J. Anat.* **119**, 263.

Vermeulen, A. (1969). *In* "Advances in the Biosciences" (G. Raspé, ed.), Vol. 2, pp. 103–112. Pergamon Press, Oxford.

Wade, A. P., Wilkinson, G. S., Davis, J. C., and Jeffcoate, T. N. A. (1968). *J. Endocrinol.* **42,** 391.

Whalen, R. E. (1968). *In* "Perspectives in Reproduction and Sexual Behavior" (M. Diamond, ed.), pp. 303–340. Indiana Univ. Press, Bloomington, Indiana.

Widnell, C. C., and Tata, J. R. (1966). *Biochim. Biophys. Acta* **123,** 478.

Williams-Ashman, H. G. (1954). *Endocrinology* **54,** 121.

Williams-Ashman, H. G. (1962). *In* "On Cancer and Hormones: Essays in Experimental Biology," pp. 325–346. Univ. of Chicago Press, Chicago, Illinois.

Williams-Ashman, H. G. (1965a). *Cancer Res.* **25,** 1096.

Williams-Ashman, H. G. (1965b). *J. Cellular Comp. Physiol.* **66,** Suppl. 1, 111.

Williams-Ashman, H. G. (1969). *In* "Advances in the Biosciences" (G. Raspé, ed.), Vol. 2, pp. 200–221. Pergamon Press, Oxford.

Williams-Ashman, H. G. (1970). *In* "The Androgens of the Testis" (K. B. Eik-Nes, ed.), pp. 117–144. Dekker, New York.

Williams-Ashman, H. G., and Liao, S. (1964). *In* "Actions of Hormones on Molecular Processes" (G. Litwack and D. Kritchevsky, eds.), pp. 482–508. Wiley, New York.

Williams-Ashman, H. G., and Reddi, A. H. (1971). *Annu. Rev. Physiol.* **33,** 31.

Williams-Ashman, H. G., and Shimazaki, J. (1967). *In* "Endogenous Factors in Tumor-Host Balance" (R. W. Wissler, T. Dao, and S. Woods, eds.), pp. 31–41. Univ. of Chicago Press, Chicago, Illinois.

Williams-Ashman, H. G., and Shimazaki, J. (1968). *In* "Perspectives in Reproduction and Sexual Behavior" (M. Diamond, ed.), pp. 241–260. Indiana Univ. Press, Bloomington, Indiana.

Williams-Ashman, H. G., Cassman, M., and Klavins, M. (1959). *Nature* **184,** 427.

Williams-Ashman, H. G., Liao, S., Hancock, R. L., Jurkowitz, L., and Silverman, D. A. (1964). *Recent Progr. Hormone Res.* **20,** 247.

Williams-Ashman, H. G., Pegg, A. E., and Lockwood, D. H. (1969). *Advan. Enzyme Regulation* **7,** 291–323.

Wilson, J. D., and Loeb, P. M. (1965). *J. Clin. Invest.* **44,** 1111.

Wilson, J. D., and Walker, J. D. (1969). *J. Clin. Invest.* **48,** 371.

Young, W. C. (1961). *In* "Sex and Internal Secretions" (W. C. Young, ed.), 3rd Ed., Vol. 2, pp. 1173–1239. Williams & Wilkins, Baltimore, Maryland.

CHAPTER 9

Mechanism of Action of Gonadotropins and Prolactin

Ralph I. Dorfman

I. INTRODUCTION

Gonadotropins regulate three functions of gonads: (1) the growth and maintenance of the tissue structure, (2) the formation of spermatozoa and ova, and (3) the biosynthesis of steroid hormones including progesterone, androgens, and estrogens. This review is directed toward a discussion of the biochemical mechanisms involved in steroid hormonal biosynthesis in the ovaries and testes. The general plan is to discuss the action of the gonadotropins and prolactin on the ovary, the testes, and certain accessory sexual tissues.

Following are the definitions of those pituitary principles which are the subject of this paper.

FHS (*Follicle Stimulating Hormone*)

This is a hormone of the anterior pituitary which produces ovarian follicular stimulation, probably has a role in ovulation in combination with the luteinizing hormone, and is responsible for the growth and maintenance of the seminiferous tubules and spermatogenesis.

LH (*Luteinizing Hormone, also called ICSH or Interstitial Cell Stimulating Hormone*)

This is a hormone of the anterior pituitary which probably, in association with FSH, induces ovulation, forms the corpus luteum, and controls, at least in part, the biosynthesis of estrogens, androgens, and progesterone by the ovary and stimulates the interstitial cells of the testis to biosynthesize and secrete androgens and estrogens.

HCG (*Human Chorionic Gonadotropin*)

This is a hormonal material that is produced in the placenta, is isolated from urine and is similar in its biological properties to LH.

PMS (*Pregnant Mare's Serum Gonadotropin*)

This is a hormonal material of placental origin having the biological properties of a mixture of LH and FSH.

LTH (*Luteotropic Hormone; Prolactin*)

This is a hormone of the anterior pituitary having a primary function in lactation. In some species such as the rat it appears to prolong estrus and the functioning corpus luteum.

II. OVARY

A. Ovarian Steroids and Biosynthetic Pathways

The biosynthetic pathways leading to ovarian steroid hormones has been described in reasonable detail (Dorfman and Ungar, 1965).

Ovarian tissue contains C_{27}, C_{21} (progesterone and related steroids), C_{19} (androgens), a neutral C_{18}, and phenolic C_{18} steroids (estrogens). The C_{27} steroids include cholesterol, 20α-hydroxycholesterol, and 20α, 22R-dihydroxycholesterol. It is likely but not yet demonstrated that 22Rhydroxycholesterol is present in adrenal tissue. Cortisol may be formed by certain tumor-bearing ovaries but it is quite unlikely that this corticoid is a normal biosynthetic product. Normally, the following C_{21} steroids are produced: progesterone, 17α-hydroxyprogesterone, pregnenolone, 17α-hydroxypregnenolone, 16α-hydroxyprogesterone, 20α-hydroxypregn-4-en-3-one, 20β-hydroxypregn-4-en-3-one, and 3β-hydroxy-5α-pregnan-20-one. The C_{19} steroids of ovaries include testosterone, androst-4-ene-3,17-dione, androsterone, dehydroepiandrosterone, and epitestosterone. Certain ovarian tumors biosynthesize 11β-hydroxyandrost-4-ene-3,17-dione, but it is unlikely that this 11-oxygenated steroid is produced in significant amounts by normal ovaries. The C_{18} steroids of the ovary include the estrogens 17β-estradiol, estrone, estriol, and 6β-hydroxy-17β-estradiol and one neutral C_{19} steroid, 19-norandrost-4-ene-3,17-dione.

The biosynthetic pathways indicated by overall studies include acetate to cholesterol, cholesterol to pregnenolone, possibly a pathway involving 20α-hydroxycholestenone to progesterone, pregnenolone and/or progesterone to androgens and, finally, androgens to estrogens.

The biosynthetic pathway cholesterol to pregnenolone has been established with considerable certainty for both bovine adrenal and corpus luteum. Indicated is the route(s) cholesterol → 20α-hydroxycholesterol (or 22R-hydroxycholesterol) → 20α,22R-dihydroxycholesterol → pregnenolone and isocaproaldehyde.

A number of reports have appeared on the pathways of progesterone, androgen, and estrogen formation from pregnenolone. For a detailed consideration of the literature, the reader is referred to Dorfman and Ungar (1965). Only selected references will be presented here. Ryan and Smith have reported (1961a) that human ovaries incubated with 1-^{14}C-acetate form ^{14}C-labeled cholesterol and estrogens. The same authors (Ryan and Smith, 1961b) demonstrated that ^{14}C-progesterone incubated with the same human ovarian preparation yielded estrogens and that 4-^{14}C-cholesterol under the same conditions yields estrone (Ryan and Smith, 1961c). In a fourth study by Ryan and Smith (1961d), the human ovarian tissue *in vitro* converted acetate to the neutral steroids, progesterone, 17α-hydroxyprogesterone, androst-4-ene-3,17-dione, pregnenolone, 17α-hydroxypregnenolone, and dehydroepiandrosterone, in addition to estrogens.

Additional biosynthetic studies which may be mentioned here include the formation of testosterone and androstene-3,17-dione by the normal human ovary (Kase *et al.*, 1961) and the secretion of testosterone by normal human ovaries. This latter study was consistent with the report of Simmer (1964) who found a mean difference of +0.09 μg testosterone/100 ml ovarian vein plasma and ovarian or iliac artery plasma.

B. LH Stimulation of Biosynthetic Pathways

That gonadotropins stimulate ovarian hormonal biosynthesis has been established by *in vitro* and *in vivo* methods. Some of the reported studies involve *in vivo* stimulation followed by removal of the gland and assessment of steroid biosynthetic capability by *in vitro* methods.

Data on direct *in vitro* effects of gonadotropin have been reported using ovarian tissue of various species but always systems where cell structure was preserved. No clear-cut effect of gonadotropins in a cell-free system is known. The earlier report of Ichii *et al.* (1963) has not been confirmed (Yago *et al.*, 1967). Among the earlier studies are the influence of PMS to stimulate the production of progesterone and androst-4-ene-3,17-dione, demonstrated by Legault-Démare *et al.* (1960). Somewhat later, Savard and co-workers made important contributions to the influence of gonadotropins on luteal tissue.

Addition of the gonadotropins LH, HCG, and FSH, contaminated with LH, but not serum albumin, prolactin, or ACTH to bovine luteal slices stimulated the production of progesterone using corpus luteum tissue (Mason *et al.*, 1962; Savard *et al.*, 1965; Armstrong and Black, 1966; Koritz and Hall, 1965).

In addition to bovine corpus luteum slices being stimulated by LH, the corpora lutea from porcine (Cook *et al.*, 1967), rat (Armstrong *et al.*, 1964), rabbit (Gorski *et al.*, 1965), opossum (Cook and Nalbandov, 1968), and human (Savard *et al.*, 1965) have been shown to be responsive to this gonadotropin. The addition of cAMP (cyclic adenosine 3′,5′-monophosphate) to slices of bovine corpora lutea stimulates steroid biosynthesis (Marsh and Savard, 1966). Savard and Casey (1963, 1964) have demonstrated an intense LH stimulation in the formation of progesterone from acetate by corpus luteum slices.

1. Haynes-Berthet Hypothesis

As a background for studies on the mechanism of LH stimulation of ovarian biosynthesis, the ACTH studies of Haynes and Berthet (1957) must be considered. The action of ACTH on the adrenal, according to the Haynes-Berthet hypothesis is dependent upon an increased supply of NADPH. This in turn is dependent on the production of cAMP from ATP and the theory holds that the former compound activates phosphorylase, which increases glucose phosphate for the hexose monophosphate shunt (Haynes and Berthet, 1957; Haynes, 1958; Haynes *et al.*, 1959, 1960).

There is strong evidence that at least one mechanism of action of LH on the ovary is similar to that of ACTH on the adrenal as indicated by the Haynes-Berthet hypothesis. This evidence is based on the following studies. Phosphorylase activity has been demonstrated in the bovine corpus luteum by Williams *et al.* (1961). LH activates corpus luteum phosphorylase (Marsh and Savard, 1964). Stansfield and Robinson (1965) reported the presence of phosphorylase and glycogen in the rat and cow corpora lutea. When LH was administered to rats, luteal phosphorylase was increased and a slight but significant decrease in total glycogen was observed.

LH stimulation of progesterone biosynthesis in bovine corpus luteum slices was correlated with the extent of phosphorylase stimulation when both parameters were measured simultaneously (Marsh and Savard, 1964).

Marsh *et al.* (1966) not only demonstrated the presence of cAMP in bovine corpus luteum but have also shown that it was increased many fold by LH and the effect seen was specific for LH. Furthermore, addition of puromycin to the system inhibited steroidogenesis but had no effect on the increased synthesis of cAMP produced by LH. They postulated that the cyclic nucleotide acts as the intracellular mediator of the action of LH upon the progesterone biosynthetic pathway.

A provocative relationship between LH and NADP and glucose-6-phosphate stimulation in the bovine corpus luteum has been reported. In the bovine corpus luteum Armstrong and Black (1966) demonstrated that progesterone biosynthetic activity per gram of tissue was greatest in the young corpora lutea and decreased gradually until about 18 days postestrum when the biosynthetic capability of the corpora lutea decreased to undetectable levels. LH stimulated biosynthesis prior to the 19th day. NADP and glucose-6-phosphate was active minimally in the youngest corpora lutea and became more effective as the age of the corpora lutea increased. Particularly striking was the effectiveness of this coenzyme in stimulating corpora lutea which were inactive to LH. Since progesterone could still be formed from pregnenolone and since the LH-inactive corpora lutea still had approximately normal sterol concentrations, it appears that the inactive corpora lutea have an impaired ability to form pregnenolone and this in turn may be the failure of the old corpora lutea to produce adequate quantities of NADPH in response to LH.

2. *Cholesterol Esterase*

The Haynes-Berthet effect of LH is a means by which NADPH, an obligatory cofactor for ovarian biosynthesis, is made available and is one mechanism of action of LH. Behrman and Armstrong (1969) suggested a second mechanism when they demonstrated a role for LH related to the availability of cholesterol for steroid hormone biosynthesis. Experimentally this was achieved by administering LH by the intravenous route and demonstrating a highly significant increase in esterase activity. The increase in the enzyme activity converts a greater amount of the cholesterol ester to free mitochondrial cholesterol which is now more readily available for conversion to pregnenolone. The LH effect is rapid, occurring as early as 15 minutes after injection and does not appear to be directly mediated by cAMP.

3. Ovarian Cholesterol

Ovarian cholesterol is depleted by LH (Bell *et al.*, 1964; Herbst, 1967; Clark and Zarrow, 1968). This response appears to be related to ovarian steroid biosynthesis.

Studies by Zarrow and Clark (1969) demonstrated that, although LH treatment of the intact rat depleted ovarian cholesterol and stimulated estrogen formation, these events did not take place in the presence of aminoglutethimide phosphate, a compound which prevents the conversion of cholesterol to pregnenolone. In the presence of this inhibitor cholesterol was accumulated in the ovarian interstitial tissue.

4. LH and 20α-Hydroxypregn-4-en-3-one (20α-OH)

20α-Hydroxypregn-4-en-3-one has been detected in ovarian tissue as a result of LH stimulation and has been assigned a special positive feedback role in corpus luteum maintenance in the rabbit. A more generalized role in reproductive physiology of other species has not been established.

The interstitial tissue of rabbit ovaries were found to contain a relatively high concentration of free and esterified cholesterol (Claesson *et al.*, 1953) and Δ^5-3β-ol-dehydrogenase (Rubin *et al.*, 1963). On LH stimulation 20α-OH synthesis and release was stimulated. This has been demonstrated both by *in vivo* and *in vitro* methods (Hilliard and Sawyer, 1964; Simmer *et al.*, 1963; Armstrong, 1967; Solod *et al.*, 1966). A corresponding decrease was observed for the ovarian cholesterol.

Hillard *et al.* (1964) discovered that the rabbit pituitary discharges LH immediately after coitus and an elevated level continues to be secreted for about 6 hours. A reasonably long period of continuous LH secretion was necessary for ovulation to take place. Hilliard *et al.* (1964) indicated that the postcoital release of pituitary gonadotropin continues for about 2 hours and that the hormone remains in circulation for 4 additional hours. In the same species, Hilliard *et al.* (1967) showed that coitus increased the secretion of 20α-OH some 10 to 20 times during the first 8 hours after contact. The release of 20α-OH from the ovarian interstitial tissue prolongs the LH discharge from the pituitary. This is inferred from the studies of Hilliard *et al.* (1967) who demonstrated that if the rabbit is ovariectomized, the estrogen-primed animal releases only small amounts of LH following coitus, which disappears from circulation within 2 hours rather than the normal 6-hour period. The LH plasma levels in the mated ovariectomized rabbits can be maintained by injecting 20α-OH immediately after mating. Thus a positive feedback system has been established in the rabbit in which coitus triggers release of LH, LH stimulates biosynthesis and release of 20α-OH from ovarian interstitial tissue, and finally, 20α-OH stimulates LH biosynthesis and/or release.

C. Influence of FSH

Savard (1968) summarized his extensive experiences on the influence of various FSH preparations on bovine corpora lutea slices. Whereas LH invariably gave excellent stimulation, FSH preparations were inactive except when contaminated with LH and in the latter case the potency is directly related to the quantity of the LH contaminant.

D. Influence of Prolactin (Luteotropin; LTH)

Prolactin has a growth-promoting action on the mammary gland and has an important control over lactation. The growth effect is dependent upon a combination of somatotropin and LTH which can induce full mammary lobuloalveolar growth in the apparent absence of ovarian hormones in the rat (Meites and Nicoll, 1966). This section will not deal further with the mammary gland action of prolactin but rather will examine possible functions of the hormone related to steroid hormone biosynthesis.

Prolactin is ineffective as an *in vitro* stimulator of steroid hormone biosynthesis in corpora lutea from the porcine (Duncan *et al.*, 1961), rat (Huang and Pearlman, 1962), women (Savard *et al.*, 1965), and bovine (Mason *et al.*, 1962). Similar negative *in vivo* data have been reported in rats (Marsh *et al.*, 1966), rabbits (Hilliard *et al.*, 1963), and ovine (Short *et al.*, 1963).

1. LH, LTH, and Cholesterol Biosynthesis

Gospodarowicz and Legault-Démare (1963) reported that HCG and LTH singly did not stimulate the incorporation of ^{14}C-acetate into cholesterol in the normal rat corpus luteum *in vitro*. When the incubation experiment was repeated with a combination of HCG and LTH an increase of 90% in cholesterol labeling was found.

2. LTH and Stores of Steroid Precursors

Hilliard and Sawyer (1966) reported in abstract form that prolactin maintains cholesterol stores in the corpus luteum. These studies suggested that prolactin effects steroid biosynthesis by making steroid precursor available. In the full paper Hilliard et al. (1968) demonstrated that prolactin treatment promotes the cholesterol storage in ovaries which have been depleted of cholesterol by large doses of LH. Prolactin treatment also restored the secretion of the 20α-OH and made the ovary sensitive to LH.

Hypophysectomy of rabbits within 24 hours of LH treatment exhibited atrophied interstitial tissue and corpora lutea. Cholesterol levels remained low and neither 20α-OH nor progesterone could be detected. Prolactin treatment of these animals stimulates the ovarian interstitial tissue, elevates the cholesterol stores but does not release the progesterone or 20α-OH. For the latter effect, estrogens or LH are needed.

If the corpora lutea are maintained with estrogen, release of progesterone exceeds that of 20α-OH but the interstitial tissue is not stimulated. If prolactin and estrogen are administered together, the interstitial tissue and corpora lutea are hypertrophied and 20α-OH release exceeds the secretion of progesterone. On the basis of these data, Hilliard et al. (1968) concluded that prolactin acts on the rabbit ovary to maintain the interstitial tissue and the steroid-producing capacity.

3. Permissive Action of LTH

Armstrong et al. (1969) used a rat model in which the animals were prolactin-deficient without being deficient in other pituitary hormones. This is different from the effects of hypophysectomy, and has advantages over the surgical model, in which many pituitary principles are severely decreased. The superior model was accomplished by the subcutaneous injection of PMS between 8 and 9 A.M. at 30 days of age. This treatment resulted in ovulation and corpus luteum formation about 72 hours after injection. The experimental design has the further advantage that the ovaries contained this single crop of corpora lutea of known age.

Prolactin treatment of these specially prepared corpora lutea bearing rats prevented the reduction of progesterone to 20α-OH. This finding is in harmony with that of Wiest (1959) and Wiest et al. (1968) which indicated that the appearance of 20α-OH steroid dehydrogenase in corpora lutea can be inhibited by cervical stimulation or prolactin injection.

In the presence of prolactin, LH produces a greater stimulation of progesterone biosynthesis (Armstrong *et al.*, 1969). Armstrong *et al.* (1969) described this effect as a permissive action of prolactin and pointed out that this is somewhat analogous to the permissive actions of prolactin on the ovarian ascorbic acid depletion produced by LH (Guillemin and Sakiz, 1963). Armstrong *et al.* (1969) also quotes from unpublished studies by Piacsek and Armstrong of a similar relationship between prolactin and LH effects with the ovarian endpoint of decrease in concentration of cholesterol esters.

Prolactin seems to have increased the rates of cholesterol biosynthesis in corpora lutea on the basis of accumulation of radioactivity from acetate-1-^{14}C in cholesterol and in the biosynthetic products progesterone and 20α-OH.

Ovarian ascorbic acid sensitivity to LH decreased following hypophysectomy (McCann *et al.*, 1960; Baird *et al.*, 1961). The latter group suggested that prolactin was probably responsible for this permissive action. Guillemin and Sakiz (1963) restudied this question and demonstrated that the ovarian ascorbic content of the luteinized ovary falls markedly as early as 4½ hours after hypophysectomy and that this test animal does not respond to doses of LH that produce significant responses in the intact animal. Treatment of the hypophysectomized animal with prolactin at the time of surgery maintains the ovarian ascorbic acid concentration and preserves the responsivity to LH.

III. TESTIS

The biosynthetic capacity and secretory function of the testis has been reviewed (Dorfman and Ungar, 1965; Eik-Nes, 1964).

The pathways leading to testicular androgen biosynthesis have important similarities to those already described for ovarian steroid biosynthesis. In general the testicular steroid hormones are derived principally from cholesterol by a pathway(s) which involves cholesterol → 20α-hydroxycholesterol (or 22R-hydroxycholesterol) → 20α,22R-dihydroxycholesterol → pregnenolone + isocaproaldehyde. In a typical experiment incubation of cholesterol, labeled with ^{3}H in ring B and ^{14}C at carbon-26, with a rat testis homogenate preparation yielded 5.2% as isocaproic acid, the oxidation product of isocaproaldehyde, and 3.73% as steroids. This latter fraction consisted of testosterone 0.48%, pregnenolone 0.35%, progesterone 1.31%, 17α-hydroxyprogesterone 1.31% and

20α-hydroxycholesterol 0.28% (Toren *et al.*, 1964; Menon *et al.*, 1965a). The incubation of 20α-hydroxycholesterol and 20α,22R-dihydroxycholesterol yields C_{21} and C_{19} steroids similar to those found after cholesterol incubation.

The control of androgen may be considered to be initiated with a stimulus, in the form of a releasing factor, from the hypothalamus which impinges upon the anterior pituitary to release LH. The latter substances stimulate the testis to secrete steroids and this action will be the main subject of our review of the mechanism of tropic hormone action on the testis.

The steroid hormones of the testis, androgens and estrogens, control the biosynthesis and/or secretion of the releasing factor(s) of the hypothalamus and pituitary via negative feedback. Direct control also is manifested by inhibitory action of substrates, biosynthetic intermediates, and steroidal hormonal products of the various enzyme systems involved in steroidogenesis (Dorfman *et al.*, 1967). This area will not be discussed further in this review.

A. LH Action on Testis

Brady (1956) reported one of the earliest studies on the biosynthetic role of the testis and demonstrated that HCG stimulated steroid hormone biosynthesis by intact testis cells *in vitro*. More specifically hog, rabbit, and human testicular slices converted 1-^{14}C-acetate to ^{14}C-testosterone and addition of human chorionic gonadotropin *in vitro* to testis slices resulted in a marked stimulation of ^{14}C-acetate incorporation into testosterone. These observations have been confirmed and extended (Dorfman and Ungar, 1965).

Brady (1956) further noted that the addition of HCG to the testis slice incubate enhanced incorporation of radioactivity from ^{14}C-acetate into testosterone without influencing the incorporation of radioactivity into cholesterol. On the basis of this negative result the author suggested that cholesterol may not be an important precursor of testosterone. Hall (1963) reported the same experimental observation. During the course of these incubation studies, that is, in the presence of LH and acetate the specific activity of testosterone increased, whereas that of cholesterol decreased with time. Hall (1963) considered the following possibilities to explain that the bulk of the testicular cholesterol is not involved in steroid biosynthesis; LH stimulation might result in a rate of ^{14}C-cholesterol conversion to ^{14}C-testosterone greater than that at which ^{14}C-acetate is converted to ^{14}C-cholesterol and that precursor cholesterol is associated with a pool of high specific activity which is depleted rapidly under the influence of LH.

Rabbit testicular slices exposed to triparanol (1-p-β-diethylamino-ethoxy-phenyl-1-(p-tolyl)-2-(p-chlorophenyl) ethanol), a substance which is known to inhibit the conversion of acetate to cholesterol, are not significantly influenced when conversion of acetate to testosterone is assessed. The triparanol treated slices may be stimulated by LH to produce an increased amount of testosterone. Similar results were observed when the LH was administered by intravenous injection. Hall (1964) interpreted these data to indicate that there is only a limited specificity of the enzymes which convert cholesterol to pregnenolone. More specifically this could indicate that desmosterol, the cholesterol biosynthetic intermediate, known to accumulate in the presence of triparanol, may serve as a steroid hormone biosynthetic intermediate in place of or as well as cholesterol.

The cholesterol biosynthesis inhibitor AY9944 (trans-1,4-(bis-2-chlorobenzylaminomethyl)cyclohexane dihydrochloride) was employed to study the roles of cholesterol and LH in steroid biosynthesis in testis tissue (Menon *et al.*, 1965a). In experiments with rabbit testis slices inhibition of ^{14}C-acetate incorporation into cholesterol by AY9944 concomitant with inhibition of ^{14}C-testosterone formation was observed. Also, when ^{14}C-acetate incorporation into cholesterol is inhibited, the stimulatory effect of LH added *in vitro* on radioactive testosterone biosynthesis also was abolished.

It is of importance to compare the Hall (1964) and Menon *et al.* (1965b) data on the influence of inhibitors on cholesterol and testosterone formation in rabbit testis slices. Hall (1964) used triparanol which produces a decrease in cholesterol formation and an increase in desmosterol, a steroid convertible to C_{21} and C_{19} steroids. On the other hand, Menon *et al.* (1965b) used an inhibitor which decreases cholesterol biosynthesis and increases Δ^7-dehydrocholesterol formation. This latter compound apparently is not significantly converted to C_{21} and C_{19} steroids. The difference between the Hall (1964) and Menon *et al.* (1965b) studies seems to be related to the efficiency with which the sterol intermediates are able to undergo enzymic side-chain cleavage. The prediction from these results of Hall (1964) and Menon *et al.* (1965b) is that desmosterol can be converted and that Δ^7-dehydrocholesterol cannot undergo this transformation.

Gonadotropic hormone, either LH or HCG, stimulated rabbit testis slices production of pregnenolone from acetate when the incubations were carried out in the presence of the 17α-hydroxylase inhibitor SU-8000 (3-(6-chloro-3-methyl,2-indenyl)-pyridine). Pregnenolone was not found in similar incubates in the absence of LH. The authors of these studies (Hall and Eik-Nes, 1964) offer these studies as being consistent with the idea that LH stimulation occurs before pregnenolone.

LH added to rabbit testis slices stimulated testosterone formation from cholesterol. In the same experiment LH produced a decrease in testosterone from 20α-hydroxycholesterol (Hall and Young, 1968). These data are consistent with the idea that LH acts between cholesterol and 20α-hydroxycholesterol. Similar results were obtained by these investigators for ACTH stimulation of bovine adrenal slices and LH stimulation of slices of bovine corpora lutea.

LH stimulates rabbit testis slices to produce testosterone in an amount about equal to that of testosterone production by testis homogenates. As Hall and Eik-Nes (1963) point out, this is similar to the findings with respect to the steroid biosynthetic effect of ACTH on adrenal slices (Macchi and Hechter, 1954) and the rate of formation of corticoids in adrenal homogenates (Schonbaum, 1954). LH does not appear to stimulate testis steroid formation in the absence of intact testicular cells.

B. Cholesterol Side-Chain Cleavage by Rat Testis Mitochondrial Enzyme Preparation

The control of steroid hormone biosynthesis in the testis was studied by an examination of the factors that influenced the rate of cholesterol side-chain cleavage (conversion of cholesterol to pregnenolone) by the rat testis. This appeared to be a reasonable approach since indirect evidence placed the action of LH between cholesterol and pregnenolone.

Optimal conditions were established for a mitochondrial preparation of rat testis for the cleavage of 26-^{14}C-cholesterol to ^{14}C-isocaproic acid and C_{21} and C_{19} steroids. Quantitation of liberated ^{14}C-isocaproic acid was used as a good indicator of overall neutral steroid biosynthesis by the testis preparation (Toren *et al.*, 1964; Menon *et al.*, 1965a).

Treatment of immature male rats with LH increased the rate of cholesterol side-chain cleavage *in vitro* by the mitochondrial enzyme system prepared from the testis of the treated rats. This effect was dose-related. LH pretreatment of hypophysectomized immature male rats yielded testicular enzyme preparations with a tenfold increase in the *in vitro* rate of cholesterol side-chain cleavage.

The marked dependency of this enzyme system on LH is emphasized in ablation experiments with mature male rats. The rate of cholesterol side-chain cleavage in testes preparations obtained from animals 3 days after hypophysectomy decreased to about 15% of the activity seen in preparations from sham-operated control rats and the effect of hypophysectomy was reversed by LH treatment.

Comparisons were made of the enzyme activity of mitochondrial preparations obtained from immature and mature rat testis using the substrate 20α-hydroxycholesterol as well as cholesterol. Testis preparations from mature rats cleaved the side chain of cholesterol at a significantly greater rate than that from immature animals but no difference was seen in the rate of cleavage of the biosynthetic intermediate 20α-hydroxycholesterol. Since the rate of cleavage of 20α-hydroxycholesterol was the same in the preparations from both the immature and mature rats, the assumption can be made that the subsequent steps in the sequence, hydroxylation at C-22 and scission of the C-20—C-22 bond, will also proceed at essentially the same rate in both preparations. Then the slowest step and the rate-limiting one would be 20α-hydroxylation of cholesterol and this step might well represent the locus of action of LH (Menon *et al.*, 1965a).

To test this hypothesis, immature 21-day-old male rats were treated with HCG. Testis mitochondrial preparations were studied *in vitro* for side-chain cleavage activity with the substrates cholesterol and 20α-hydroxycholesterol. The HCG treatment produced a marked increase in rate of cholesterol side-chain cleavage while being without effect on the ability of these two preparations to cleave the side chain of 20α-hydroxycholesterol. This strongly suggested that the gonadotropin, probably LH component, influences 20α-hydroxylation (Menon *et al.*, 1965a) in a manner which still awaits elucidation.

Sandler and Hall (1966) suggested that the LH effect on testicular testosterone production was mediated through cAMP. This suggestion has been demonstrated in testis (Kuehl *et al.*, 1970). LH stimulates adenyl cyclase in the testis as measured by the increase in newly formed nucleotide cAMP.

Kuehl *et al.* (1970) further demonstrated that FSH stimulated cAMP production in the testis of intact rats less than 21 days of age or in the hypophysectomized animal.

C. LTH Action on Testis

Bartke (1969) presented the hypothesis that prolactin may increase mouse testicular androgen biosynthesis by making more cholesterol available for this conversion. This concept is consistent with studies in the rat (Armstrong, 1968; Zarrow and Clark, 1969) and in the rabbit

(Hilliard *et al.*, 1968) which indicated that prolactin effects ovarian steroid biosynthesis by changes in cholesterol storage.

In Bartke's study (1969) ovine prolactin was administered intraperitoneally and produced a significant increase in the concentration of total cholesterol and the percentage of esterified cholesterol.

IV. EFFECT OF ANTERIOR PITUITARY HORMONES ON SEXUAL TISSUES

The fact that hypophysectomy produces a more severe prostatic atrophy than castration in the rat (Grayhack *et al.*, 1955) and in the dog (Huggins and Russell, 1946) suggested that a pituitary factor may have a role in growth and/or maintenance of the prostate gland. Segaloff *et al.* (1956) reported pertinent data in this area and concluded that "prolactins obtained from hogs, sheep, and cows sensitize the hypophysectomized rat ventral prostate to the action of androgens produced by the administration of luteinizing hormone."

Pasqualini (1953) and Antliff *et al.* (1960) described similar activity of LTH on the seminal vesicles of the hypophysectomized rat. In the Antliff *et al.* report (1960) LTH was inactive in stimulating the seminal vesicles of the castrated guinea pig. However, LTH together with a subminimal amount of testosterone propionate resulted in significant seminal vesicle stimulation in both castrated and hypophysectomized guinea pigs.

Chase *et al.* (1957) used the model of the hypophysectomized-castrated male rat and studied the influence of growth hormone (STH) and LTH on the weights and histology of the ventral prostate, anterior prostate, and seminal vesicles. LTH produced a small but significant increase in seminal vesicle weight. When LTH was administered with testosterone propionate an increase in glandular tissue was found in the ventral prostate. Although STH alone or together with testosterone propionate did not produce any significant increase in the weights of the accessories, the three-component system of TP, LTH, and STH produced changes in accessory weight responses greater than that of TP alone.

Okamoto *et al.* (1967) reported that prolactin increased prostate but not seminal vesicle weight of the hypophysectomized or hypophysectomized–castrated rat. Bengmark and Hesselsjö (1963, 1964) reported a stimulating effect of prolactin on the seminal vesicle growth in tissue culture.

In their review on prolactin Meites and Nicoll (1966) include the following statement:

> An additional observation which indicates that prolactin may stimulate the sex accessories of males has been provided by observations on the action of a "mammotropic" pituitary tumor in mice (Haran-Ghera, personal communication). She observed that a pituitary tumor which stimulated full mammary development and milk secretion in female mice did not exert a mammotropic action in males of the same strain; however, the "mammotropic" tumor produced huge seminal vesicles in the male mice.

Huggins *et al.* (1955) studied the control of growth and/or maintenance of the rat preputial glands. They clearly demonstrated that the gland is sensitive to androgens, marginally sensitive to progesterone and insensitive to estrogens. In spite of these facts females had larger preputial glands than those found in the males. Since males have higher plasma levels of androgens it is obvious that some factor other than androgens must be of considerable importance in the growth and maintenance of the preputial gland.

The following data of Huggins *et al.* (1955) strongly suggest some pituitary involvement. Intact females had mean preputial gland ratios (mg/100 gm body weight) of 53.6 ± 8.8 SE). Ovariectomy resulted in a ratio of 43.5 ± 4.5, not significantly lower than that found for the intact females. The corresponding values for the adrenalectomized, adrenalectomized–ovariectomized, and hypophysectomized females were, respectively, 57.7 ± 11.3, 41.4 ± 4.9, and 16.4 ± 2.5. Only hypophysectomy significantly lowered the preputial gland ratio.

Most of the data of Huggins *et al.* (1955) may be explained on the basis of a pituitary factor synergizing an androgen. Thus the ovariectomized rat has "large" preputial glands because the pituitary factor synergizes the adrenal androgens. The hypophysectomized animal has a small preputial gland because androgens of the ovaries and adrenals are very low and in fact the synergizing factor of the pituitary is absent. The female preputial gland is larger than that of the male perhaps because of the excessively high content of the "synergizing" pituitary factor on the small but adequate concentration of androgens.

The fact that the preputial glands of the adrenalectomized–ovariectomized animal were maintained at a ratio not significantly lower than the intact animal needs consideration. The explanation could invoke the possibility of incomplete adrenalectomy and therefore androgens are still being secreted. This is unlikely in the Huggins *et al.* studies (1955) since adrenalectomy at 24 days of age is complete without the complications of adrenal rests. Another possibility is that the preputial gland has a small but significant androgen biosynthetic capacity and the androgens so formed are synergized by the active pituitary principle. This possibility is admittedly a difficult one to accept since steroid hormone biosynthesis from cholesterol in such a tissue has yet to be demonstrated.

Huggins *et al.* (1955) reported that bovine growth hormone induced preputial gland weight stimulation in the castrated–hypophysectomized rat and that the growth hormone seemed to synergize the effect of testosterone on the preputial glands of the same test animals. These responses are reminiscent of the effects reported by Segaloff *et al.* (1956).

Tullner (1963) studied the weight and histological ventral prostate response of the castrated, castrated–adrenalectomized, and hypophysectomized–castrated rats to prolactin alone and in combination with ACTH. The mean weight of ventral prostate of untreated castrate rats was 9 ± 1 (SD) mg, whereas 20 USP units daily dose of ACTH resulted in a mean ventral prostate weight of 14 ± 2 mg. Whereas a daily dose of 1 mg of prolactin alone did not stimulate the ventral prostate, when combined with a minimum effective dose of 20 USP units of ACTH the mean ventral prostate weight was 21 ± 5 mg. A second study using castrated rats and a sub-threshold dose of ACTH of 5 USP units combined with prolactin, 1 mg/day, resulted in a highly significant increase in the ventral prostate weight.

In the hypophysectomized–castrated male rats no ventral prostate response could be elicited by ACTH or prolactin administered singly or by administration of ACTH plus prolactin. Treatment of these doubly operated rats with ACTH, prolactin, and *dl*-thyroxine produced a change in ventral prostate weight from 7.1 ± 0.8 mg (SD) to 14.3 ± 1.2.

When the interval between the double surgery of hypophysectomy and castration was shortened, the stimulation by the combination of ACTH plus prolactin produced a fourfold increment in ventral prostate weight from the control no-treatment value of 4.1 ± 0.02 to 16.5 ± 1.6 mg.

The studies of Tullner (1963) clearly indicate that the rat ventral prostate responds to large doses of ACTH and that this response is adrenal-dependent. Prolactin augments the ACTH effect with respect to prostate weight and secretory activity. It is quite likely that all these responses are dependent upon a base secretion of androgens.

Woodbury *et al.* (1965a,b) devised a sensitive assay method for the determination of sebotropic activity in the rat and studied, in some detail, the influence of steroids in the young adult hypophysectomized–

castrated rat. The bioassay parameters were changes in preputial gland weight and β-glucuronidase content of the gland. Testosterone and dehydroepiandrosterone stimulated the sebaceous gland of the doubly operated rats. Progesterone, androst-4-ene-3,17-dione, and 17-hydroxyprogesterone produced a significant weight increase on the sebaceous glands only when administered in combination with an anterior pituitary fraction. On the basis of these findings the authors suggested a sebotropic factor which "may promote the generation of androgens from 17-hydroxyprogesterone and its precursors."

Ebling (1964) refers to a pituitary principle, not defined, as having a permissive role for the action of androgens on the sebaceous glands. This conclusion was based on the fact that castration reduced the mean volume of the sebaceous glands and testosterone corrected this. No significant increase in mean volume was produced, however, when the hypophysectomized–castrated rat was treated with testosterone. In another report Ebling (1970) demonstrated that the response of the sebaceous glands of the hypophysectomized rats to testosterone could be restored by a prolactin preparation or a thyrotropic hormone preparation, both free of growth hormone.

Eisenberg and Gordan (1950) demonstrated that a crude preparation of growth hormone increased the levator ani of the castrated rat from 33 ± 2.9 (SE) to 53 ± 6.5 mg, while the seminal vesicles of the same animal actually decreased from 14 ± 1.2 (SE) to 10 ± 1.1. Admittedly, the growth hormone was impure and the active pituitary component is not rigidly defined. However, in these studies the adrenal could supply the base androgen.

A recent study by Krähenbühl and Desaulles (1969) was reported indicating that α-MSH at 0.3 mg/kg produced a 100% increase in preputial gland size in the intact female rat. This effect was increased to 250% growth when the 0.3 mg/kg α-MSH was combined with 10 mg/kg of progesterone. The stimulatory effect was reduced in the absence of the ovary. This α-MSH stimulation was dependent upon the presence of the adrenal and of the pituitary.

Incubation of various preparations of prolactin increased the β-glucuronidase activity of a mouse or rat testis homogenate (Evans, 1962; Evans et al., 1962). Twenty other hormonal and related substances including ACTH, TSH, HCG, growth hormone (bovine and human), testosterone, estradiol-17β, and dl-thyroxine were inactive in this test. Evans (1962) has suggested that "prolaction releases bound β-glucuronidase from within subcellular granules thus making it accessible to substrate."

The report of Evans (1962) may be a clue to the mechanism by which prolactin or other active material of the anterior pituitary could influence the action of androgens on accessory sexual tissues.

These anterior pituitary principles may increase the accessory tissue response to a given dose of androgen by increasing the effective tissue concentration of enzymes such as sulfatase and/or glucuronidase, which in turn convert the relatively inactive esterified form of the steroid hormone to an active form in the target tissue. The Evans studies (1962) have indicated such a possibility for the rat and mouse testis.

V. CONCLUSIONS

Significant progress has been made in the elucidation of the stimulatory effect of LH on ovarian steroid hormone biosynthesis. FSH is ineffective and LH acts only on the intact ovarian cell. LH action on the ovary, particularly the corpus luteum, acts through the Haynes-Berthet mechanism originally described for the action of ACTH on the adrenal. This sequence involves progressively the adenylic acid cyclase → formation of cAMP → increase in phosphorylase activity → increase in glucose-6-phosphate from glycogen → increase in NADPH. The cofactor NADPH is a requirement for many of the biosynthetic steps leading to the ovarian steroid hormones.

In the rabbit, LH stimulates the formation and secretion of 20α-OH which specifically stimulates the biosynthesis and release of LH, thus completing a positive feedback circuit.

LH stimulates the effective concentration of cholesterol esterase which makes cholesterol available for steroid hormone biosynthesis. The final function of LH relates to a stimulatory process between cholesterol and pregnenolone.

Unlike LH, the luteotrophic hormone prolactin has no direct influence on ovarian steroid hormone biosynthesis. Indirect effects of prolactin include stimulation of cholesterol formation from acetate, maintenance of cholesterol stores for biosynthetic reactions, and sensitizes the ovary to the action of prolactin including facilitation of progesterone biosynthesis.

LH acts on the interstitial cells of testis to stimulate androgen production. The main action appears to be on the 20α-hydroxylation of cholesterol leading successively to C_{21} and C_{19} steroids. This action is probably in addition to the action of LH in increasing NADPH according to the Haynes-Berthet mechanism.

LH acts only on intact testis cells and FSH appears to stimulate testicular cAMP in rats less than 21 days old or in hypophysectomized animals.

Prolactin increases the cholesterol stores and may play an indirect role in steroid hormone biosynthesis by making substrate available.

The presence of prolactin and/or other anterior pituitary factors may play a role in the maintenance of sexual tissues. The fact that castration produces a less severe atrophy of the prostate than hypophysectomy seems to indicate that a pituitary material has a role in the growth and maintenance of this accessory tissue.

Other studies indicate that the action of androgens on accessory tissue is intensified by the various anterior pituitary principle(s). The action of these pituitary factors may be an augmentation or synergism of the pituitary hormone of the androgenic action on the prostate, the seminal vesicles, the preputial glands or the levator ani. The anterior pituitary preparations used in reported studies are in all cases crude and activities of this nature have been associated with prolactin and/or growth hormone or combinations of the two.

It is suggested that the augmentative, synergistic, and/or permissive action of the anterior pituitary hormones (or fractions) may be related to their ability to increase the effective concentration of β-glucuronidase and/or sulfatase. The effective increase in these enzymes could theoretically increase the effective androgen concentration at the target site resulting in a proportionally greater stimulation for a given supply of androgens.

REFERENCES

Antliff, H. R., Prasad, M. R. N., and Meyer, R. K. (1960). *Proc. Soc. Exptl. Biol. Med.* **103**, 77.

Armstrong, D. T. (1967). *Proc. 2nd Intern. Congr. Hormonal Steroids, Milan, 1966* Intern. Congr. Ser. No. 132, p. 262. Excerpta Med. Found., Amsterdam.

Armstrong, D. T. (1968). *Recent Progr. Hormone Res.* **24**, 255.

Armstrong, D. T., and Black, D. C. (1966). *Endocrinology* **78**, 937.

Armstrong, D. T., O'Brien, J., and Greep, R. O. (1964). *Endocrinology* **75**, 488.

Armstrong, D. T., Miller, L. S., and Knudsen, K. A. (1969). *Endocrinology* **85**, 393.

Baird, J. M., Wolf, R. O., and Rennels, E. G. (1961). *Proc. Soc. Exptl. Biol. Med.* **106**, 362.

Bartke, A. (1969). *Nature* **224**, 700.

Behrman, H. R., and Armstrong, D. T. (1969). *Endocrinology* **85**, 474.

Bell, E. T., Mukerji, S., and Loraine, J. A. (1964). *Endocrinology* **28**, 321.

Bengmark, S. B., and Hesselsjö, R. H. (1963). *Urol. Intern.* **16**, 387.

Bengmark, S. B., and Hesselsjö, R. H. (1964). *Urol. Intern.* **17**, 84.

Brady, R. O. (1956). *J. Biol. Chem.* **193**, 145.

Chase, M. O., Geshwind, I. I., and Bern, H. A. (1957). *Proc. Soc. Exptl. Biol. Med.* **94**, 680.

Claesson, L., Hillarp, N., and Högberg, B. (1953). *Acta Physiol. Scand.* **29**, 329.

Clark, J. H., and Zarrow, M. X. (1968). *Proc. Soc. Exptl. Biol. Med.* **127**, 626.

Cook, B., and Nalbandov, A. V. (1968). *J. Reprod. Fertility* **15**, 267.

Cook, B., Kaltenbach, C. C., Norton, H. W., and Nalbandov, A. V. (1967). *Endocrinology* **81**, 573.

Dorfman, R. I., and Ungar, F. (1965). "Metabolism of Steroid Hormones." Academic Press, New York.

Dorfman, R. I., Sharma, D. C., Menon, K. M. J., and Forchielli, E. (1967). *Proc. 2nd Intern. Congr. Hormonal Steroids, Milan, 1966* Intern. Congr. Ser. No. 132, pp. 391–396. Excerpta Med. Found., Amsterdam.

Duncan, G. W., Bowerman, A. M., Anderson, L. L., Hearn, W. R., and Melampy, R. M. (1961). *Endocrinology* **68**, 199.

Ebling, F. J. (1964). *In* "Hormonal Steroids" (L. Martini and A. Pecile, eds.), Vol. 1, p. 540. Academic Press, New York.

Ebling, F. J. (1970). *Brit. J. Dermatol.* **82**, Suppl. 6, 9.

Eik-Nes, K. B. (1964). *Physiol. Rev.* **44**, 609.

Eisenberg, E., and Gordan, G. S. (1950). *J. Pharmacol. Exptl. Therap.* **99**, 38.

Evans, A. J. (1962). *J. Endocrinol.* **24**, 233.

Evans, A. J., Ferguson, K. A., and Kovačić, N. (1962). *J. Endocrinol.* **24**, 245.

Gorski, J., Padnos, D., and Nelson, N. J. (1965). *Life Sci.* **4**, 713.

Gospodarowicz, D., and Legault-Démare, J. (1963). *Acta Endocrinol.* **42**, 509.

Grayhack, J. T., Bunce, P. L., Kearns, J. W., and Scott, W. W., (1955). *Bull. Johns Hopkins Hosp.* **96**, 154.

Guillemin, R., and Sakiz, E. (1963). *Endocrinology* **72**, 813.

Hall, P. F. (1963). *Biochemistry* **2**, 1232.

Hall, P. F. (1964). *Endocrinology* **74**, 201.

Hall, P. F., and Eik-Nes, K. B. (1963). *Proc. Soc. Exptl. Biol. Med.* **114**, 7991.

Hall, P. F., and Eik-Nes, K. B. (1964). *Biochim. Biophys. Acta* **86**, 604.

Hall, P. F., and Young, D. G. (1968). *Endocrinology* **82**, 559.

Haynes, R. C., Jr. (1958). *J. Biol. Chem.* **233**, 1220.

Haynes, R. C., Jr., and Berthet, L. (1957). *J. Biol. Chem.* **225**, 115.

Haynes, R. C., Jr., Koritz, S. B., and Péron, F. G. (1959). *J. Biol. Chem.* **234**, 421.

Haynes, R. C., Jr., Sutherland, E. W., and Rall, T. W. (1960). *Recent Progr. Hormone Res.* **16**, 121.

Herbst, A. L. (1967). *Endocrinology* **81**, 54.

Hilliard, J., and Sawyer, C. H. (1964). *In* "Hormonal Steroids" (L. Martini and A. Pecile, eds.), Vol. 1, p. 263. Academic Press, New York.

Hilliard, J., and Sawyer, C. H. (1966). *Excerpta Med. Found. Intern. Congr. Ser.* **111**, 195.

Hilliard, J., Archibald, D., and Sawyer, C. H. (1963). *Endocrinology* **72**, 59.

Hilliard, J., Hayward, J. N., and Sawyer, C. H. (1964). *Endocrinology* **75**, 957.

Hilliard, J., Penardi, R., and Sawyer, C. H. (1967). *Endocrinology* **80**, 901.

Hilliard, J., Spies, H. G., Lucas, L., and Sawyer, C. H. (1968). *Endocrinology* **82**, 122.

Huang, W. Y., and Pearlman, W. H. (1962). *J. Biol. Chem.* **237**, 1060.

Huggins, C., and Russell, P. S. (1946). *Endocrinology* **39**, 1.

Huggins, C., Parsons, F. M., and Jensen, E. V. (1955). *Endocrinology* **57**, 25.

Ichii, S., Forchielli, E., and Dorfman, R. I. (1963). *Steroids* **2**, 631.

Kase, N., Forchielli, E., and Dorfman, R. I. (1961). *Acta Endocrinol.* **37**, 19.

Koritz, S. B., and Hall, P. F. (1965). *Biochemistry* **4**, 2740.

Krähenbühl, C., and Desaulles, P. A. (1969). *Acta Endocrinol. Suppl.* **138**, 241.

Kuehl, F. A., Jr., Patanelli, D. J., Tarnoff, J., and Humes, J. L. (1970). *Biol. Reprod.* **2**, 154.

Legault-Démare, J., Mauléon, P., and Suarez-Soto, M. (1960). *Acta Endocrinol.* **34**, 163.

McCann, S. M., Taleisnik, S., and Friedman, H. M. (1960). *Proc. Soc. Exptl. Biol. Med.* **104**, 432.

Macchi, A., and Hechter, O. (1954). *Arch. Biochem. Biophys.* **53**, 305.

Marsh, J. M., and Savard, K. (1964). *J. Biol. Chem.* **239**, 1.

Marsh, J. M., and Savard, K. (1966). *Steroids* **8**, 133.

Marsh, J. M., Telegdy, G., and Savard, K. (1966). *Nature* **212**, 950.

Mason, N. R., Marsh, J. M., and Savard, K. (1962). *J. Biol. Chem.* **237**, 1801.

Meites, J., and Nicoll, C. S. (1966). *Ann. Rev. Physiol.* **28**, 57.

Menon, K. M. J., Dorfman, R. I., and Forchielli, E. (1965a). *Steroids* Suppl. 2, 165.

Menon, K. M. J., Drosdowsky, M., Dorfman, R. I., and Forchielli, E. (1965b). *Steroids* Suppl. 1, 95.

Okamoto, R., Kawashima, K., and Fujii, K. (1967). *Bull. Tokyo Med. Dental Univ.* **14**, 37.

Pasqualini, R. (1953). *Prensa Med. Arg.* **40**, 2658.

Rennels, E. G., Anigstein, D. M., and Anigstein, L. (1961). *Texas Rept. Biol. Med.* **19**, 159.

Rubin, B. L., Deane, H. W., and Hamilton, J. A. (1963). *Endocrinology* **73**, 748.

Ryan, K. J., and Smith, O. W. (1961a). *J. Biol. Chem.* **236**, 705.

Ryan, K. J., and Smith, O. W. (1961b). *J. Biol. Chem.* **236**, 710.

Ryan, K. J., and Smith, O. W. (1961c). *J. Biol. Chem.* **236**, 2204.

Ryan, K. J., and Smith, O. W. (1961d). *J. Biol. Chem.* **236**, 2207.

Sandler, R., and Hall, P. F. (1966). *Endocrinology* **79**, 647.

Savard, K. (1968). *In* "Ovary" (H. C. Mack, ed.), pp. 10–26. Thomas, Springfield, Illinois.

Savard, K., and Casey, P. J. (1963). *Federation Proc.* **22**, 530.

Savard, K., and Casey, P. J. (1964). *Endocrinology* **74**, 599.

Savard, K., Marsh, J. M., and Rice, B. F. (1965). *Recent Progr. Hormone Res.* **21**, 285.

Schonbaum, E. (1954). *Rev. Can. Biol.* **13**, 495.

Segaloff, A., Stellman, S. L., and Flores, A. (1956). *Endocrinology* **59**, 233.

Short, R. V., McDonald, M. F., and Rowson, J. E. A. (1963). *J. Endocrinol.* **26**, 155.

Simmer, H. H. (1964). *Recent Progr. Hormone Res.* **20**, 341 (in discussion of V. B. Mahesh and R. B. Greenblatt).

Simmer, H. H., Hilliard, J., and Archibald, D. (1963). *Endocrinology* **72**, 67.

Solod, E. A., Armstrong, D. T., and Greep, R. O. (1966). *Steroids* **7**, 607.

Stansfield, D. A., and Robinson, J. W. (1965). *Endocrinology* **76**, 390.

Toren, D., Menon, K. M. J., Forchielli, E., and Dorfman, R. I. (1964). *Steroids* **3**, 381.

Tullner, W. W. (1963). *Natl. Cancer Inst. Monograph* **12**, 211.

Wiest, W. G. (1959). *J. Biol. Chem.* **234**, 3115.

Wiest, W. G., Kidwell, W. R., and Balogh, K. (1968). *Endocrinology* **82**, 844.

Williams, H. E., Johnson, P. L., and Field, J. B. (1961). *Biochem. Biophys. Res. Commun.* **6**, 129.

Woodbury, L. P., Lorincz, A. L., and Ortega, P. (1965a). *J. Invest. Dermatol.* **45**, 362.

Woodbury, L. P., Lorincz, A. L., and Ortega, P. (1965b). *J. Invest. Dermatol.* **45**, 364.

Yago, N., Nightingale, M. S., Dorfman, R. I., and Forchielli, E. (1967). *J. Biochem. (Tokyo)* **62**, 274.

Zarrow, M. X., and Clark, J. H. (1969). *Endocrinology* **84**, 340.

CHAPTER 10

The Mechanism of Action of Adrenocorticotropic Hormone

James J. Ferguson, Jr.

I. INTRODUCTION

Steroidogenesis, which is the most evident physiological effect of ACTH on the adrenal cortex, can easily be reproduced *in vitro*. It is perhaps the simplicity of the experimental model which has prompted such extensive study of this phenomenon. To date there is no single comprehensive and incontrovertible explanation for the actions of ACTH on the adrenal cortex. In fact, there exists much more controversy on the topic than is suggested in most standard physiological, biochemical, and clinical texts. But in a broader sense, work from many groups is now converging on the elusive "mechanism of action" answer. The current state of progress in these studies prompts this brief analysis of the subject. It will rapidly become evident that this essay is not meant to be an encyclopedic review of all important contributions in the field of ACTH research. Rather, it reflects the personal and surely biased views of the author concerning progress in the subject of how ACTH induces adrenal steroidogenesis.

II. THE ACTH MOLECULE

ACTH is a linear peptide containing 39 amino acids. The chemical structure of ACTH was elucidated in the mid-1950's (cf. Hofmann and Yajima, 1962; Li, 1962). The conformation of the molecule *in vivo* is unknown, but estimates of its helicity have been made (Squire and Bewley, 1965). Other approaches to conformational analysis have yielded limited information (Botre and Salinas, 1964). Functional specificity resides in the N-terminal sequence of amino acids. The observed species differences in amino acid sequence have been noted in amino acids numbers 25 to 33, that is, in the C-terminal portion of the molecule. These latter amino acids are not required for functional effectiveness of the peptide hormone. While the 17-amino acid N-terminal sequence is about 5% as effective physiologically as the naturally occurring molecule (Li *et al.*, 1962), the 23-amino acid N-terminal sequence is fully as active on a molar basis (Hofmann *et al.*, 1962). Efforts in the recent past have successfully been directed toward the chemical synthesis of peptides more potent than natural ACTH. For example, D-serine^1-dilysine-17,18-β^{1-18}corticotropin-18-amide, synthesized in the Ciba Laboratories, has been found to be considerably more potent than β^{1-24}-corticotropin on a weight-for-weight basis, with a longer duration of action (Desaulles *et al.*, 1968).

A structural feature to be noted in natural ACTH, as well as various effective synthetic analogs of ACTH, is the requirement for a sequence of basic amino acids at positions 15 to 18. It has been suggested that this "basic core" in ACTH is involved in ionic bonding of hormone to a receptor site in the adrenal cortex (Li and Oelofsen, 1967).

III. SITE OF ACTION OF ACTH

A. ANATOMICAL LOCUS

Richards and Sayers (1951) were the first to point out that ACTH is concentrated within the adrenal cortex. But beyond this, little is known of the mechanism of interaction of ACTH and the adrenocortical cell. Schimmer *et al.* (1968), using ACTH conjugated to insoluble cellulose, have found evidence that the physiological effects of ACTH occur without the peptide penetrating the adrenal cell. Scriba and Müller (1968) found rapid labeling of all subcellular fractions of adrenals from rats injected intraarterially with tritiated ACTH. Studies by others (Taunton *et al.*, 1967a) have demonstrated the rapid concentration of ACTH on the surface of adrenal cells. Lefkowitz *et al.* (1970) have investigated the binding of ACTH to a high molecular weight protein derived from a membrane fraction of mouse adrenal tumor cells. The specificity and sensitivity of this technique hold promise as a method of assay for ACTH, as well as providing a new approach to study of the interaction between hormone and target tissue.

B. CHEMICAL LOCUS

The perfusion studies of Hechter (1951), and Stone and Hechter (1954) first indicated that the steroidogenic effect of ACTH in the adrenal is localized to reactions involved in the conversion of cholesterol to pregnenolone. To date, no conclusive evidence has suggested another locus, and corroborative data have been reported (Karaboyas and Koritz, 1965). It has since been found, however, that the conversion of cholesterol to pregnenolone is itself a complex, multistep reaction sequence, with the probable intermediate formation of 20α-hydroxycholesterol and 20α-22ϵ-dihydroxycholesterol, followed by a cleavage of the side chain to form pregnenolone and isocapraldehyde (cf. Tchen, 1968). The participation of 20α-hydroxycholesterol in the sequence has been questioned by Burstein *et al.* (1969) on the basis of the kinetics of radioactive labeling of intermediate pools. The validity of this methodology must be viewed with reserve, however, in that rate constants for steroid interconversions were calculated on the basis of the velocity of reactions under conditions of first-order kinetics, with only tracer concentrations of intermediates present.

The failure by many investigators to identify free sterol intermediates (e.g., 20α-hydroxycholesterol) in the conversion of cholesterol to preg-nenolone remains an enigma in this area of study. This failure has been interpreted to mean that intermediate compounds are tightly—perhaps covalently—bound to the involved enzymes. Liebman *et al.* (1969) have logically suggested that alkoxy free radicals are the true inter-mediates in this sequence, accounting for the failure to isolate free sterol intermediates. In any event, it is clear that identification of the cholesterol-to-pregnenolone conversion as the metabolic site of ACTH action only begs the question of what precise biochemical event in this complex sequence is accelerated by ACTH.

IV. HYDROXYLATION REACTIONS IN STEROIDOGENESIS

The studies of Simpson and Boyd (1967a) have established the par-ticipation of mixed-function oxidases in the conversion of cholesterol to pregnenolone. Pioneering studies by Cooper *et al.* (1962), Estabrook *et al.* (1963), Omura and Sato (1964), and Kimura and Suzuki (1967) have vastly increased our knowledge of the mechanisms of such hy-droxylations. More specifically, it has been recognized that there exists a unique electron transport pathway involved in steroid hydroxylation reactions. Ryan and Engel (1957) had originally established the partici-pation of NADPH and molecular oxygen in 21-hydroxylation of 17α-hydroxyprogesterone by adrenal microsome preparations. These same investigators also demonstrated the sensitivity of the system to carbon monoxide inhibition and the reversibility of this inhibition by light. Cytochrome P_{450} was found to be the carbon monoxide-sensitive moiety (Estabrook *et al.*, 1963), and soon was recognized to be the oxygen-activating component of this system. 11β-hydroxylation in adrenal mito-chondria requires the participation of a similar cytochrome P_{450} (Harding *et al.*, 1964). This system proves to be experimentally advantageous in that the components of this electron transport sequence can be isolated from adrenal mitochondria and separately characterized (Omura *et al.*, 1966), while the microsomal 21-hydroxylase system has not yet suc-cessfully been fractionated.

Figure 1 illustrates the probable path of electron flow from NADPH to steroid in 11β-hydroxylation. A flavoprotein is the first acceptor, transferring electrons on to adrenodoxin, a nonheme iron protein. This latter component has been characterized in detail by Kimura (1968). Cytochrome P_{450} is the penultimate electron acceptor, but not yet clear

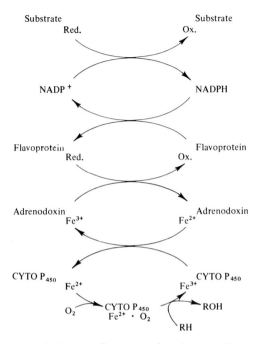

Fig. 1. Possible path of electron flow in hydroxylations. The sequence of interactions between cytochrome P_{450}, O_2, and steroid in the final step is unknown. It has been suggested (Sih, 1969) that NADPH also participates at this step.

is the precise sequence in which P_{450} interacts with oxygen, electrons, and steroid substrate. Sih (1969) has suggested that NADPH participates directly in this terminal step of electron transfer, as well as in maintaining the ferrous cytochrome P_{450} in a reduced state by means of electron flow through flavoprotein and adrenodoxin. Adrenal cytochrome P_{450} has not yet been purified to any great extent, and as a consequence is neither functionally nor physiologically well-characterized.

An analogous participation of NADPH, flavoprotein, adrenodoxin, and cytochrome P_{450} has been shown to occur in the cleavage of the side chain of cholesterol (Simpson and Boyd, 1967b). In addition, studies by Whysner and Harding (1968) have demonstrated the development of distinguishable binding spectra when deoxycorticosterone or 20α-hydroxycholesterol are added to adrenal cortical preparations in the absence of NADPH. Spin resonance studies (Whysner *et al.*, 1969) indicate that these spectral differences are associated with, and possibly caused by, a shift in spin state of cytochrome P_{450}. Recombination of mitochondrial flavoprotein, adrenodoxin, and cytochrome P_{450} fractions will hydroxylate deoxycorticosterone, cholesterol, and 20α-hydroxycholesterol simultaneously, with no evidence of competition between the substrates (Ferguson, 1969). Ramseyer and Harding (1970) have described the isolation of a species of cytochrome P_{450} from bovine adrenal mitochondria which, in a reconstituted system, allows side-chain cleavage, but not 11β-hydroxylation. If cytochrome P_{450} is the moiety which recognizes substrate steroid, as these observations would suggest, it would then appear that there exist multiple forms of this cytochrome which function independently. Leibman *et al.* (1969) have shown that cytochrome P_{450} of rat liver microsomes exists as a mixture of two proteins, with absorbance peaks at 446 and 454 mμ.

Tchen reported (1968) that the administration of ACTH to hypophysectomized animals· results in a very slow restoration of the ability of adrenal homogenates from these animals to cleave the side chain of cholesterol. At present it is not known if an enzyme component in the system physiologically limits the overall rate of hydroxylation, or if, *in vivo*, the rate of steroid hydroxylation is limited by inaccessibility of substrate (steroid, oxygen or NADPH, or homo- or heterotropic effector molecule). It would seem that identification of that rate-limiting participant would allow a very precise localization of the metabolic events which are enhanced by ACTH. It would be difficult to imagine this control to occur at any but the slowest, rate-determining reaction in the sequence.

V. SOURCES OF REDUCING EQUIVALENTS IN STEROIDOGENESIS

A number of laboratories have systematically studied the origins of the reducing equivalents involved in steroid hydroxylations. To be sure, if the rate at which NADPH is made available in the cell limits the rate of pregnenolone formation, ACTH control could be sought in the regulation of NADPH generation, or in the control of its accessibility to a subcellular compartment. Criss and McKerns (1968) have described a direct effect of ACTH—but not cyclic AMP (cAMP)—on purified bovine adrenal glucose-6-phosphate dehydrogenase, this resulting in an approximate halving of the apparent K_m of the enzyme for glucose-6-phosphate and $NADP^+$. The effect of such an activation of the dehydrogenase would be the enhancement of NADPH production under conditions of restricted concentrations of $NADP^+$. The major reservation in interpreting these observations lies in the apparent lack of physiological specificity of such an effect. An increase in NADPH production would seem to be a rather coarse and nonspecific cellular effect of ACTH. It is curious that cAMP is without effect on the dehydrogenase, in that it is well recognized as an agent capable of mimicking the steroidogenic effect of ACTH. It is possible that the effect of ACTH on glucose-6-phosphate dehydrogenase represents one of several related effects of the tropic hormone on the adrenal cell, although not an effect essential to the triggering of enhanced steroidogenesis.

The observations of Kahnt and Wettstein (1951), Hayano and Dorfman (1953), and Brownie and Grant (1954), have directed attention to the Krebs cycle intermediates as potential sources of reducing equivalents in the adrenal cortex. The more recent studies of Simpson and Estabrook (1969) have embellished these observations by pointing up the unique potentials of malate oxidation by malic enzyme as a mechanism for intramitochondrial NADPH production. This enzyme catalyzes the reversible oxidation of malate by $NADP^+$, yielding pyruvate, CO_2, NADPH, and hydrogen ion. Their studies have demonstrated, in the adrenal cortex, the existence of a mitochondrial form of the enzyme, as well as the more typical cytoplasmic form. The occurrence of these two enzyme forms suggest the possibility that malate is the transport form of reducing equivalents, allowing intramitochondrial hydroxylation at the ultimate expense of cytoplasmic NADPH. Such a mechanism would of course permit the utilization of NADPH generated in the cytoplasm from glucose-6-phosphate, as suggested by Criss and McKerns (1968).

The importance of mitochondrial malic enzyme as the source of NADPH under physiological conditions rates further scrutiny. In beef adrenal mitochondria, Simpson and Estabrook (1969) have demonstrated the appropriate formation and release of pyruvate when deoxycorticosterone is hydroxylated in the presence of malate or succinate and further metabolism of pyruvate is inhibited. Peron (1969) has not been able to demonstrate such a stoichiometric production of pyruvate in rat adrenal mitochondria. In fact, the inhibition of pyruvate transformations in Peron's system results in a diminution in 11β-hydroxylation. He appropriately suggests that the malic enzyme may be but one of several sources of NADPH, these including the NADP-specific mitochondrial isocitrate dehydrogenase of the adrenal cortex. It is not evident that different hydroxylations (e.g., in the 11β position versus the 20α position) utilize NADPH from different metabolic sources.

Birmingham (1968) first described the rapid accumulation of lactate in adrenals exposed to ACTH in the presence of glucose. Kowal (1969a) has extended these studies and has demonstrated more directly enhanced glycolysis under these conditions. In that the steroidogenic effect of ACTH can be observed in the presence of inhibitors which block this effect on glycolysis, it would seem as though the glycolytic effect is ancillary, rather than causative in the production of steroidogenesis.

If it is NADPH availability which limits the rate of pregnenolone formation *in vivo*, one would have to presume that side-chain hydroxylations utilize NADPH more avidly than do other mitochondrial hydroxylases. Otherwise, one would expect added ACTH to increase the rate of all hydroxylations in the adrenal. It is pertinent to note that there is no stimulatory effect of ACTH on the conversion of pregnenolone to hydroxylated corticosteroid products (Karaboyas and Koritz, 1965). The effect is quite clearly limited to side-chain cleavage.

VI. SUBSTRATES FOR STEROIDOGENESIS

The adrenal cortex has abundant stores of esterified cholesterol which are depleted in the course of steroidogenesis (Sayers *et al.*, 1944). It is difficult to quantitate the contribution of circulating cholesterol to these stores, but it is known that cholesterol is also synthesized *de novo* from acetate in the adrenal cortex (Morris and Chaikoff, 1959). Dexter *et al.* (1967) have shown that the adrenal stimulated by ACTH will actively accumulate cholesterol, even when steroidogenesis has been blocked. Evidence exists that free cholesterol can be esterified in the adrenal (Shyamala *et al.*, 1966).

Davis and Garren (1966) have demonstrated a direct effect of ACTH on the hydrolysis of cholesterol esters in the adrenal cortex under conditions wherein steroidogenesis was inhibited, thus allowing liberated free cholesterol to accumulate. Other studies by their group (Davis *et al.*, 1968) have shown that cholesterol is depleted from all subcellular fractions, but especially from the cytoplasmic lipid granules, in response to ACTH. This has prompted the suggestion that ACTH initiates the translocation of cytoplasmic cholesterol to the mitochondrion for further metabolism. It must be recognized, however, that this depletion of cytoplasmic cholesterol may be a result of increased steroid synthesis, rather than a direct effect of ACTH. It would also be of interest to know if cAMP can produce these effects.

VII. EFFECTS OF ACTH

Haynes' original description of the accumulation of cAMP in the adrenal after exposure to ACTH (1958) has been amply confirmed (e.g., Grahame-Smith *et al.*, 1967). This observation, coupled with the recognition that cAMP can mimic the steroidogenic effects of ACTH (Haynes *et al.*, 1959) has provided a milepost in studies on the mechanism of ACTH action. In fact, a great part of current studies on ACTH is based on the reasonable premise that cAMP mediates steroidogenesis in response to ACTH. As a consequence, much effort is currently being expended to determine (1) how cAMP is produced in response to ACTH, and (2) how cAMP causes steroidogenesis. While discretion might dictate the use of conditional clauses and other disclaimers, it seems fair to say that most workers in this field accept the idea that cAMP is involved in the steroidogenic response to ACTH. It is also possible that other nucleoside 3′,5′-cyclic monophosphates may be involved (Mahaffee *et al.*, 1970).

A. cAMP PRODUCTION

Grahame-Smith *et al.* (1967) and Taunton *et al.* (1967b) have rather clearly demonstrated that ACTH specifically activates the particulate adenyl cyclase of the adrenal cell. This observation is most interesting in that it is the only well-documented effect of ACTH that can be demonstrated in subcellular preparations of the adrenal cortex. Like the hormone-responsive adenyl cyclase of other tissues, this enzyme has not yet been significantly characterized aside from demonstration of its particulate nature. Taunton *et al.* (1969) report that ACTH at $1.5 \times 10^{-8} M$ is sufficient to evoke a stimulation of the cyclase. By time course studies, Grahame-Smith *et al.* (1967) showed that activation of the cyclase by ACTH produces increased concentrations of cAMP, this preceding the onset of increased steroidogenesis. Of further interest is the fact that the enhancement of cAMP production by ACTH is not hindered by the presence of inhibitors (e.g., cycloheximide and puromycin) which block the steroidogenic effect of cAMP. Bär and Hechter (1969) have studied further the activation of adenyl cyclase by ACTH in the bovine adrenal cortex. They found this response to be abolished by the addition of calcium complexing agents, and restored on restoring the calcium concentration. These authors, incidentally, identify ACTH-stimulated cyclase in their so-called "mitochondrial fractions" obtained by differential centrifugation. This would be novel if verified, in that cyclases from other tissues are thought to be in the plasma membrane rather than in mitochondria (Marinetti *et al.*, 1969). Also, the presence of an ACTH-sensitive cyclase within mitochondria would suggest that ACTH has anatomical access to the adrenal mitochondrion.

B. The Steroidogenic Response to cAMP

The steroidogenic responsiveness of the adrenal cortex to cAMP as originally reported by Haynes *et al.* (1959), has been demonstrated both *in vivo* and *in vitro*. There is thus no doubt that the cyclic nucleotide can mimic the physiological effect of ACTH. But how this is accomplished remains unknown. Haynes and Berthet (1957) first suggested that adrenal steroidogenesis is the end result of a demonstrable activation of phosphorylase, which presumably causes, in turn, glycogenolysis, increased production of glucose phosphate, and increased availability of NADPH generated by the action of glucose-6-phosphate dehydrogenase. Several observations have tended to cast doubt on this hypothesis, though none have really disproved it. In the presence of the antibiotic puromycin, which inhibits the steroidogenic response of beef adrenal cortex to both ACTH and cAMP (Ferguson, 1963), there is still observed an activation of phosphorylase. This result dissociates the steroidogenic effect from phosphorylase activation, but of course the antibiotic may inhibit at some essential step after phosphorylase activation. A specific inhibitor of phosphorylase activation would be a useful tool. Phosphorylase activation by ACTH has not been demonstrated in rat adrenal. Vance *et al.* (1962) could demonstrate no change in adrenal glycogen content in hypophysectomized rats exhibiting steroidogenesis in response to ACTH, but others (e.g., Greenberg and Glick, 1962) claim glycogenolysis under these conditions. Field *et al.* (1960) were unable to demonstrate evidence for an increase in intracellular glucose-6-phosphate after ACTH administration. Finally, and this again a negative argument, there is no evidence that NADPH availability in any way limits steroidogenesis *in vivo*. To the contrary, the findings of Chance *et al.* (1962) suggest that ACTH-supported steroidogenesis is associated with a rapid depletion of reduced pyridine nucleotide *in vivo*, rather than an excessive production, as the Haynes-Berthet hypothesis would predict. These studies unfortunately could not distinguish between NADH and NADPH, however. A haunting problem in the study of how cAMP causes steroidogenesis lies in the difficulty of demonstrating a steroid response to the cyclic nucleotide in broken-cell preparations. Numerous authors have reported failure in such efforts. However, one group (Roberts *et al.*, 1965; Roberts and Creange, 1968) has described responsiveness to cAMP in homogenates, and in fact in particles from sonicated adrenal mitochondria (Roberts *et al.*, 1967). The later study describes enhanced incorporation of radioactivity from precursor cholesterol into pregnenolone in the presence of cAMP. However, Koritz *et al.* (1968) have found, and McCune *et al.* (1969) have verified that cAMP inhibits the conversion of pregnenolone to progesterone in such preparations. This raises the possibility that the reported enhancement of incorporation of label into pregnenolone merely represents an artifactual expansion of the size of the pregnenolone pool by blocking its further metabolism, rather than by increasing the rate of its synthesis. The matter certainly warrants further study. If such a direct stimulatory effect of cAMP on subcellular particles can be demonstrated, there remains the question of the precise metabolic reaction affected by cAMP.

The recently described activation of protein kinases by cAMP may have relevance in this problem. Experiments in the laboratory of Edwin Krebs (De Lange *et al.*, 1968; Walsh *et al.*, 1968) have demonstrated the existence of a cAMP-dependent protein kinase in skeletal muscle. Similar protein kinases, which transfer phosphate from ATP to an acceptor protein and are activated to varying degrees by low concentrations of cAMP, have since been described in liver (Langan, 1968), brain (Miyamoto *et al.*, 1969), *E. coli* (Kuo and Greengard, 1969), and adipose tissue (Corbin and Krebs, 1969). Basic proteins such as histone have generally been found to be the most efficient phosphate acceptors in these partially purified preparations. The protein kinase from skeletal muscle (Walsh *et al.*, 1968) also catalyzes the phosphorylation and enzymic activation of phosphorylase kinase.

Studies by Gill and Garren (1970) and in the author's laboratory (Ferguson, 1970) have demonstrated the existence of a similar cAMP-stimulated protein kinase in extracts of rat and beef adrenal cortex, using either histone or protamine as an acceptor protein. Gill and Garren (1971) have extended these studies and neatly explained the stimulation of adrenal protein kinase by cAMP. In purifying this enzyme, they found that it existed associated with a cAMP binding protein which they had previously studied (Gill and Garren, 1969). The two proteins could be separated by ion exchange chromatography and by electrophoresis or centrifugation in the presence of cAMP. After separation, the protein kinase no longer was stimulated by cAMP, and rather was inhibited by adding back binding protein. These observations prompted the very logical suggestion that when associated with binding protein, protein kinase exists in an inhibited state. In the presence of cAMP, binding protein dissociates from protein kinase, leaving the latter fully activated. Similar phenomena have also been described by Kumon *et al.* (1970) in liver and by Reiman *et al.* (1971) in skeletal muscle, as well as by Tao *et al.* (1970) in rabbit reticulocytes.

The natural phosphate acceptor(s) and the physiological function(s) of adrenal protein kinase are as yet unknown, and the phenomenon may simply be related to the activation of phosphorylase in the adrenal in response to cAMP. But it is equally possible that it represents a mechanism for the direct or indirect activation (by phosphorylation) of enzymes involved in cholesterol side-chain cleavage, and so clearly warrants further study. In addition to steroidogenesis and phosphorylase activation, cAMP is known to produce other effects in the adrenal cortex, e.g., ascorbate depletion (Earp *et al.*, 1969). Each of these effects could reasonably be expected to involve cAMP binding to one or more effector proteins, and possibly the action of a protein kinase, all within a single cell. Thus the question of multiple specificities of cAMP remains to be explored with profit. The promise of this line of investigation lies in the fact that protein kinase activation by cAMP is a molecular phenomenon that can be demonstrated in broken-cell preparations, which is not the case with other responses to cAMP.

VIII. THE INVOLVEMENT OF MACROMOLECULES IN ACTH RESPONSIVENESS

Several years ago it was found (Ferguson, 1962) that puromycin, an inhibitor of amino acid incorporation into protein, also inhibits the enhancement of steroidogenesis in response to ACTH. It does not inhibit basal steroid biosynthesis. This observation prompted the suggestion that concomitant protein synthesis is required for ACTH responsiveness, and further that ACTH may cause the synthesis of a protein which is directly or indirectly rate-limiting in steroidogenesis (Ferguson, 1963). As part of these studies, it was noted that puromycin also blocks the steroidogenic response to cAMP, but does not interfere with the activation of beef adrenal phosphorylase by ACTH. The implication was that puromycin does not interfere with cAMP production, but rather with one of its effects, i.e., steroidogenesis. The passage of time has not added much to our understanding of the role of protein synthesis in the adrenal response to ACTH, but several observations have at least thickened the plot. In rat adrenal it was found that inhibition of RNA synthesis with actinomycin was without inhibitory effect on ACTH responsiveness (Ferguson and Morita, 1964). This has been interpreted to mean that ACTH mediates a translational (rather than transcriptional) control of adrenal protein synthesis. A number of other chemically unrelated antibiotic compounds which block amino acid incorporation into protein have also been shown to inhibit ACTH responsiveness. Cycloheximide has been shown to have this dual effect *in vivo* (Garren *et al.*, 1965). Additionally, Sato *et al.* (1965), using ACTH-sensitive mouse adrenal tumor cells has reported that when depleted of glutamine, these cells will neither respond to ACTH nor incorporate amino acid into protein unless the medium is supplemented with glutamine. Interestingly, the increased adrenal steroidogenesis reported to occur in the presence of prostaglandins is also prevented by inhibition of protein synthesis (Flack *et al.*, 1969).

There thus seems to be reasonably good evidence that the adrenal cell must be capable of protein synthesis if ACTH is to be effective in eliciting a steroid response. The question then arises: what is the function of the synthesized protein and how can it be detected experimentally? There is ordinarily no measurable increase in total protein synthesis in the ACTH-stimulated adrenal. In fact, more typically, amino acid incorporation into total adrenal protein *decreases* after ACTH, presumably due to an inhibitory local effect of the corticosterone elaborated (Morrow *et al.*, 1967; Ferguson *et al.*, 1967). Increased amino acid incorporation into adrenal protein can be demonstrated after ACTH if steroid biosynthesis is inhibited by aminoglutethimide (Farese, 1969). Efforts to identify unique proteins synthesized in response to ACTH, using double-labeling chromatographic techniques, have thus far been unsuccessful (Ferguson, 1969). Grower and Bransome (1969), however, report the identification of such unique proteins on the basis of alterations in the radioactivity/densitometry ratios of adrenal proteins separated by disc gel electrophoresis.

Farese (1967) has studied the accumulation in the ACTH- and cAMP-stimulated adrenal of a cytoplasmic material with the characteristics of a protein. This material enhances steroidogenesis in homogenates from nonstimulated adrenals, and has been shown to have a fairly localized effect on cholesterol side-chain cleavage. It does not accumulate in adrenals in which protein synthesis has been inhibited. Cytoplasmic protein extracts from adrenals not exposed to ACTH or cAMP inhibit cholesterol side-chain cleavage in adrenal mitochondria, suggesting the possible interplay of opposing stimulating and inhibiting materials in ACTH regulation.

If the material described by Farese proves to be an ACTH- and cAMP-induced regulatory protein, the precise function of this protein remains to be demonstrated. Parenthetically, a number of authors have described the synthesis of new enzyme protein in nonadrenal animal tissues exposed to cAMP. For instance, Wicks (1968) has described the appearance of tyrosine-α-ketoglutarate transaminase in fetal rat liver explants, and Jost *et al.* (1969) have reported the synthesis of serine dehydratase in liver, following cAMP. How this "induction" is accomplished remains to be determined, but at least the precedent exists. Kairallah and Pitot (1967) and Lissitzky *et al.* (1969) have reported a direct effect of cAMP on protein assembly on the ribosome, as have Malkin and Lipmann (1969). Walton *et al.* (1971) have very recently presented evidence that a cAMP-responsive protein kinase isolated from the adrenal microsome fraction can phosphorylate a protein associated with adrenal ribosomes. These authors postulate that this event may have a regulatory function in hormone-mediated control of adrenal protein synthesis at the translational level. This hypothesis is most attractive in relating cAMP and protein synthesis. However, some reserve is indicated, in that Traugh and Traut (1971) have shown that skeletal muscle protein kinase is capable of phosphorylating ribosomal proteins isolated from *E. coli*, pointing up an impressive lack of specificity for these enzymes.

Studies by Koritz (1968) have demonstrated the fact that cholesterol side-chain cleavage is sensitive to the accumulation of pregnenolone, the product of this complex reaction sequence. There then emerges the attractive hypothesis that ACTH might regulate steroidogenesis by altering the rate by which inhibitory pregnenolone emerges from the mitochondrial compartment. If cleared rapidly, there would be a rapid and continuing synthesis and further transformation of pregnenolone. This formulation has been found compatible with simulated mathematical models (Urquhart *et al.*, 1969), but thus far it lacks direct supporting evidence as a physiologically important mechanism. Coupling this with ideas on the participation of newly synthesized protein in this process, ACTH, or its mediator cAMP, might specifically alter permeability by allowing the assembly of a specific carrier protein which functions in the transport of steroids into and out of the mitochondrion.

The tantalizing closeness of the solution of the riddle of how ACTH alters adrenal steroidogenesis has perhaps distracted attention of many investigators from the study of an equally intriguing effect of ACTH: its "trophic" effect in sustaining the anatomical and functional integrity of the adrenal cortex. There can be no doubt that RNA and protein synthesis are involved in this phenomenon, as demonstrated by early studies in Reddy's laboratory (Farese and Reddy, 1963; Scriba and

Reddy, 1965). This ACTH–adrenal interrelationship then becomes an attractive model system for the investigation of the regulation of mammalian RNA and protein metabolism (e.g., Ney *et al.*, 1966). The observation that cAMP may mediate some of the "trophic" effects of ACTH (Ney, 1969) adds to the attractiveness of this model for further study.

As stated initially, this article is not addressed to the total biology of ACTH. In recent years a number of reviews and reports have appeared which provide the interested reader with a view of ACTH much broader than intended herein. Foremost among these are the detailed reviews by Bransome (1968) and Garren (1968). The symposium on Functions of the Adrenal Cortex (McKerns, 1968) catalogs in two volumes an immense amount of experimental work in this area. In like fashion, the symposium on Protein and Polypeptide Hormones (Margoulies, 1968) includes succinct reviews by a number of workers active in the field. The development of our understanding of adrenal hydroxylation reactions is lucidly reviewed by Simpson *et al.* (1969). Finally, in reviewing his extensive experience using the ACTH-responsive mouse adrenal cell line developed in Sato's laboratory (Buonassisi *et al.*, 1962), Kowal (1970b) has documented the unique promise of this methodology in approaching the problem of steroidogenic mechanisms.

IX. SUMMARY

It must be acknowledged that the precise mechanism by which ACTH causes steroidogenesis in the adrenal cortex is still unclear in detail. This mechanism almost surely utilizes cAMP as an intermediary effector. Protein synthesis seems to be obligatorily involved in this process, while RNA synthesis is not. This protein synthesis may be a result of cAMP accumulation, or merely be necessary for the expression of the effect of the cyclic nucleotide.

Enhanced steroidogenesis is limited by the rate at which cholesterol is converted to pregnenolone. This process may be controlled either by the availability of substrate (cholesterol, NADPH, reducing equivalents, etc.) or by controlling the effectiveness of those protein catalysts directly involved in steroid transformations. This latter could be accomplished by the regulation of enzyme concentration, or by the regulation of the catalytic efficiency of a rate-limiting enzyme by various heterotropic inhibitory mechanisms. Such regulation of enzyme concentration or catalytic efficiency may be effected by cAMP-responsive protein kinase(s).

It can reasonably be anticipated that the mechanism of ACTH action in the adrenal cortex will be similar to the mechanism of action of other steroidogenic tropic hormones.

ACKNOWLEDGMENTS

Original investigations from the author's laboratory have been supported by Grant AM-07207 from the National Institutes of Health. The author is a recipient of a Research Career Development Award from this agency.

REFERENCES

Bär, H., and Hechter, O. (1969). *Biochem. Biophys. Res. Commun.* **35**, 681.

Birmingham, M. (1968). *In* "Protein and Polypeptide Hormones" (M. Margoulies, ed.), Intern. Congr. Ser. No. 161, p. 458. Excerpta Med. Found. Amsterdam.

Botre, C., and Salinas, M. (1964). *Biochim. Biophys. Acta* **88**, 415.

Bransome, E. D., Jr. (1968). *Ann. Rev. Physiol.* **30**, 171.

Brownie, A. C., and Grant, J. K. (1954). *Biochem. J.* **57**, 255.

Buonassisi, V., Sato, G. H., and Cohen, A. I. (1962). *Proc. Natl. Acad. Sci. U. S.* **48**, 1184.

Burstein, S., Kimball, H. L., Chaudhuri, N. K., and Gut, M. (1969). *Federation Proc.* **28**, 666.

Chance, B., Schoener, B., and Ferguson, J. J., Jr. (1962). *Nature* **195**, 776.

Cooper, D. Y., Estabrook, R. W., and Rosenthal, O. (1962). *J. Biol. Chem.* **238**, 1320.

Corbin, J. D., and Krebs, E. G. (1969). *Biochem. Biophys. Res. Commun.* **36**, 328.

Criss, W. E., and McKerns, K. W. (1968). *Biochemistry* **7**, 2364.

Davis, W. W., and Garren, L. D. (1966). *Biochem. Biophys. Res. Commun.* **24**, 805.

Davis, W. W., Moses, H. L., Rosenthal, A. S., and Garren, L. D. (1968). *J. Clin. Invest.* **47**, 25a.

De Lange, R. J., Kemp, R. G., Riley, W. D., Cooper, R. A., and Krebs, E. G. (1968). *J. Biol. Chem.* **243**, 2200.

Desaulles, P. A., Riniker, B., and Rittel, W. (1968). *In* "Protein and Polypeptide Hormones" (M. Margoulies, ed.), Intern. Congr. Ser. No. 161, Vol. II, pp. 489–491. Excerpta Med. Found., Amsterdam.

Dexter, R. N., Fishman, L. M., Ney, R. L., and Liddle, G. W. (1967). *Endocrinology* **81**, 1185.

Earp, H. S., Watson, B. S., and Ney, R. L. (1969). *Clin. Res.* **17**, 22.

Estabrook, R. W., Cooper, D. Y., and Rosenthal, O. (1963). *Biochem. Z.* **338**, 271.

Farese, R. V. (1967). *Biochemistry* **6**, 2052.

Farese, R. V. (1969). *Endocrinology* **85**, 1209.

Farese, R. V., and Reddy, W. J. (1963). *Endocrinology* **73**, 294.

Ferguson, J. J., Jr. (1962). *Biochim. Biophys. Acta* **57**, 616.
Ferguson, J. J., Jr. (1962). *Biochim. Biophys. Acta* **57**, 616.
Ferguson, J. J., Jr. (1963). *J. Biol. Chem.* **238**, 2754.
Ferguson, J. J., Jr. (1969). Unpublished data.
Ferguson, J. J., Jr. (1970). *J. Clin. Invest.* **49**, 28a.
Ferguson, J. J., Jr., and Morita, Y. (1964). *Biochim. Biophys. Acta* **87**, 348.
Ferguson, J. J., Jr., Morita, Y., and Mendelsohn, L. (1967). *Endocrinology* **80**, 521.
Field, J. B., Pastan, I., Herring, B., and Johnson, P. (1960). *Endocrinology* **67**, 801.
Flack, J. D., Jessup, R., and Ramwell, P. W. (1969). *Science* **163**, 691.
Garren, L. D. (1968). *Vitam. Horm. (New York)*, **26**, 119.
Garren, L. D., Ney, R. L., and Davis, W. W. (1965). *Proc. Natl. Acad. Sci. U. S.* **53**, 1443.
Gill, G. N., and Garren, L. D. (1969). *Proc. Natl. Acad. Sci. U. S.* **63**, 512.
Gill, G. N., and Garren, L. D. (1970). *J. Clin. Invest.* **49**, 34a.
Gill, G. N., and Garren, L. D. (1971). *Proc. Natl. Acad. Sci. U. S.* **68**, 786.
Grahame-Smith, D. G., Butcher, R. W., Ney, R. L., and Sutherland, E. W. (1967). *J. Biol. Chem.* **242**, 5535.
Greenberg, L. J., and Glick, D. (1962). *Biochemistry* **1**, 452.
Grower, M. F., and Bransome, E. D., Jr. (1969). *Federation Proc.* **28**, 701.
Harding, B. W., Wong, S. H., and Nelson, D. H. (1964). *Biochim. Biophys. Acta* **92**, 415.
Hayano, M., and Dorfman, R. I. (1953). *J. Biol. Chem.* **201**, 175.
Haynes, R. C., Jr. (1958). *J. Biol. Chem.* **233**, 1220.
Haynes, R. C., Jr., and Berthet, L. (1957). *J. Biol. Chem.* **225**, 115.
Haynes, R. C., Jr., Peron, F. G., and Koritz, S. B. (1959). *J. Biol. Chem.* **234**, 1421.
Hechter, O. (1951). *In* "Transactions of the 3rd Conference on the Adrenal Cortex" (E. P. Ralli, ed.), p. 115. Josiah Macy, Jr., Found., New York.
Hofmann, K., and Yajima, H. (1962). *Recent Progr. Hormone Res.* **18**, 41.
Hofmann, K., Yajima, H., Liu, T. Y., and Yanaihara, N. (1962). *J. Am. Chem. Soc.* **84**, 4475.
Jost, J., Hsie, A. W., and Rickenberg, H. V. (1969). *Biochem. Biophys. Res. Commun.* **34**, 748.
Kahnt, F. W., and Wettstein, A. (1951). *Helv. Chim. Acta* **34**, 1790.
Kairallah, E. A., and Pitot, H. C. (1967). *Biochem. Biophys. Res. Commun.* **29**, 269.
Karaboyas, G. C., and Koritz, S. B. (1965). *Biochemistry* **4**, 462.
Kimura, T. (1968). *In* "Functions of the Adrenal Cortex" (K. W. McKerns, ed.), Vol. II, pp. 993–1006. Appleton, New York.
Kimura, T., and Suzuki, K. (1967). *J. Biol. Chem.* **242**, 485.
Koritz, S. B. (1968). *In* "Functions of the Adrenal Cortex" (K. W. McKerns, ed.), Vol. I, pp. 27–48. Appleton, New York.
Koritz, S. B., Yun, J., and Ferguson, J. J., Jr. (1968). *Endocrinology* **82**, 620.
Kowal, J. (1969). *Abstr. 51st Meeting Endocrine Soc., New York*, p. 74.
Kowal, J. (1970). *Recent Progr. Hormone Res.* **26**, 623.
Kumon, A., Yamamura, H., and Nishizuka, Y. (1970). *Biochem. Biophys. Res. Commun.* **41**, 1290.
Kuo, J. F., and Greengard, P. (1969). *J. Biol. Chem.* **244**, 3417.
Langan, T. A. (1968). *Science* **162**, 579.
Lefkowitz, R. J., Roth, J., Pricer, W., and Pastan, I. (1970). *Proc. Natl. Acad. Sci. U. S.* **65**, 745.

Leibman, K. C., Hildebrandt, A. G., and Estabrook, R. W. (1969). *Biochem. Biophys. Res. Commun.* **36**, 789.

Li, C. H. (1962). *Recent Progr. Hormone Res.* **18**, 1.

Li, C. H., and Oelofsen, W. (1967). *In* "The Adrenal Cortex" (A. B. Eisenstein, ed.), pp. 185–201. Little, Brown, Boston, Massachusetts.

Li, C. H., Ramachandran, J., Chung, D., and Gorup, B. (1962). *J. Am. Chem. Soc.* **84**, 2460.

Lieberman, S., Bandy, L., Lippman, V., and Roberts, K. D. (1969). *Biochem. Biophys. Res. Commun.* **34**, 367.

Lissitzky, S., Mante, S., Attali, J., and Cartouzou, G. (1969). *Biochem. Biophys. Res. Commun.* **35**, 437.

McCune, R. W., Roberts, S., and Young, P. L. (1969). *Abstr. 51st Meeting Endocrine Soc., New York*, p. 96.

McKerns, K. W., ed. (1968). "Functions of the Adrenal Cortex." Appleton, New York.

Mahaffee, D., Watson, B. S., and Ney, R. L. (1970). *Clin. Res.* **18**, 73.

Malkin, M., and Lipmann, F. (1969). *Proc. Natl. Acad. Sci. U. S.* **64**, 973.

Margoulies, M., ed. (1968). "Protein and Polypeptide Hormones," Intern. Congr. Ser. No. 161. Excerpta Med. Found., Amsterdam.

Marinetti, G. V., Ray, T. K., and Tomasi, V. (1969). *Biochem. Biophys. Res. Commun.* **36**, 185.

Miyamoto, E., Kuo, J. F., and Greengard, P. (1969). *Science* **165**, 63.

Morris, M. D., and Chaikoff, I. L. (1959). *J. Biol. Chem.* **234**, 1095.

Morrow, L. B., Burrow, G. W., and Mulrow, P. J. (1967). *Endocrinology* **80**, 883.

Ney, R. L. (1969). *Endocrinology* **84**, 168.

Ney, R. L., Davis, W. W., and Garren, L. D. (1966). *Science* **153**, 896.

Omura, T., and Sato, R. (1964). *J. Biol. Chem.* **239**, 2370.

Omura, T., Sanders, E., Estabrook, R. W., Cooper, D. Y., and Rosenthal, O. (1966). *Arch. Biochem. Biophys.* **117**, 660.

Peron, F. G. (1969). *Biochim. Biophys. Acta* **180**, 445.

Ramseyer, J., and Harding, B. W. (1970). *Clin. Res.* **18**, 124.

Reiman, E. M., Brostrom, C. O., Corbin, J. D., King, C. A., and Krebs, E. G. (1971). *Biochem. Biophys. Res. Commun.* **42**, 187.

Richards, J. B., and Sayers, G. (1951). *Proc. Soc. Exptl. Biol. Med.* **77**, 87.

Roberts, S., and Creange, J. E. (1968). *In* "Functions of the Adrenal Cortex" (K. W. McKerns, ed.), Vol. I, pp. 339–397.

Roberts, S., Creange, J. E., and Young, P. L. (1965). *Biochem. Biophys. Res. Commun.* **20**, 446.

Roberts, S., McCune, R. W., Creange, J. E., and Young, P. L. (1967). *Science* **158**, 372.

Ryan, K. J., and Engel, L. L. (1957). *J. Biol. Chem.* **225**, 103.

Sato, G. H., Rossman, T., Edelstein, L., Holmes, S., and Bounassisi, V. (1965). *Science* **148**, 1733.

Sayers, G., Sayers, M. A., Fry, E. G., White, A., and Long, C. N. H. (1944). *Yale J. Biol. Med.* **16**, 361.

Schimmer, B. P., Ueda, K., and Sato, G. H. (1968). *Biochem. Biophys. Res. Commun.* **32**, 806.

Scriba, P. C., and Müller, O. A. (1968). *In* "Protein and Polypeptide Hormones" (M. Margoulies, ed.), Intern. Congr. Ser. No. 161, Vol. II, pp. 472–474. Excerpta Med. Found., Amsterdam.

Scriba, P. C., and Reddy, W. J. (1965). *Endocrinology* **76**, 745.

Shyamala, G., Lossow, W. J., and Chaikoff, I. L. (1966). *Biochim. Biophys. Acta* **116**, 543.

Sih, C. J. (1969). *Science* **163**, 1297.

Simpson, E. R., and Boyd, G. S. (1967a). *Biochem. Biophys. Res. Commun.* **28**, 945.

Simpson, E. R., and Boyd, G. S. (1967b). *European J. Biochem.* **2**, 275.

Simpson, E. R., and Estabrook, R. W. (1969). *Arch. Biochem. Biophys.* **129**, 384.

Simpson, E. R., Cooper, D. Y., and Estabrook, R. W. (1969). *Recent Progr. Hormone Res.* **25**, 523.

Squire, P. G., and Bewley, T. (1965). *Biochim. Biophys. Acta* **109**, 234.

Stone, D., and Hechter, O. (1954). *Arch. Biochem. Biophys.* **51**, 457.

Tao, H., Salus, M. L., and Lipmann, F. (1970). *Proc. Natl. Acad. Sci. U. S.* **67**, 408.

Taunton, O. D., Roth, J., and Pastan, I. (1967a). *J. Clin. Invest.* **46**, 1122.

Taunton, O. D., Roth, J., and Pastan, I. (1967b). *Biochem. Biophys. Res. Commun.* **29**, 1.

Taunton, O. D., Roth, J., and Pastan, I. (1969). *J. Biol. Chem.* **244**, 247.

Tchen, T. T. (1968). *In* "Functions of the Adrenal Cortex" (K. W. McKerns, ed.), Vol. I, pp. 3–26. Appleton, New York.

Traugh, J., and Traut, R. R. (1971). *Federation Proc.* **30**, 1204 Abs.

Urquhart, J., Li, C. C., and Gall, D. A. (1969). *Federation Proc.* **28**, 701.

Vance, V. K., Girard, F., and Cahill, G. F., Jr. (1962). *Endocrinology* **71**, 113.

Walsh, D. A., Perkins, J. P., and Krebs, E. G. (1968). *J. Biol. Chem.* **243**, 3763.

Walton, G. M., Gill, G. N., Abrass, I. B., and Garren, L. D. (1971). *Proc. Natl. Acad. Sci. U. S.* **68**, 88D.

Whysner, J. A., and Harding, B. W. (1968). *Biochem. Biophys. Res. Commun.* **32**, 921.

Whysner, J. A., Ramseyer, J., Kazmi, G. M., and Harding, B. W. (1969). *Biochem. Biophys. Res. Commun.* **36**, 795.

Wicks, W. D. (1968). *Science* **160**, 997.

CHAPTER 11

25-Hydroxycholecalciferol:
A Hormonal Form of Vitamin D[1]

Hector F. DeLuca and Mark J. Melancon, Jr.

[1] Some of the investigations reported were made possible by U. S. Atomic Energy Commission Contract number AT(11-1)-1668, by a U.S.P.H.S. grant number AMO 5800-8, and the Steenbock Research Fund of the Wisconsin Alumni Research Foundation.

I. INTRODUCTION AND HISTORY

The disease characterized by improper bone formation, which later became known as rickets, probably appeared in the human population at the dawn of civilization. Although this is conjecture, there is evidence in the literature that even in antiquity a disease was described which could have easily been considered rickets (Griffenhagen, 1952). In effect, what the human population in becoming "urbanized" did was to convert a hormone into a dietary essential, or a vitamin. We now know that an extremely important reaction was not occurring in the skin of those people who chose to spend most of their time in dwellings they had constructed and under circumstances wherein their bodies were covered almost entirely with clothing they had devised. Thus, the conversion of 7-dehydrocholesterol to vitamin D_3 by ultraviolet irradiation was no longer occurring in the skin, resulting in the failure of formation of the "hormone" 25-hydroxycholecalciferol.[2]

The disease rickets was continually described in increasing detail throughout the course of civilization in the western world, and, undoubtedly by means of random trials, reports occasionally appeared regarding the effectiveness of either sunlight or of cod liver oil in the prevention of the disease. An interesting hypothesis has been advanced by Loomis (1967) which encompasses the skin reaction for the produc-

---

[2] *Abbreviations used:* 25-HCC, 25-hydroxycholecalciferol; 25-HEC, 25-hydroxyergocalciferol; 25-OHDHT, 25-hydroxydihydrotachysterol; 25-OHDHT$_3$, 25-hydroxydihydrotachysterol$_3$; DHT, dihydrotachysterol; DHT$_2$, dihydrotachysterol$_2$; DHT$_3$, dihydrotachysterol$_3$; CT, calcitonin; PTH, parathyroid hormone; ATP, adenosine triphosphate.

tion of vitamin D as the mechanism involved in the selection of the black and white races. The theory suggests that light-skinned individuals could not have survived the large amounts of sunlight or ultraviolet irradiation in the tropics because of the production of toxic quantities of vitamin D. Thus, there was a natural selection for the heavily pigmented skins in this region. On the other hand, individuals of the dark races in the temperate zones would not be able to reproduce themselves because of the bony deformities of rickets resulting in their failure to convert adequate amounts of 7-dehydrocholesterol to vitamin D_3 with the minimal irradiation in the temperate zones. Dark skin would, of course, prevent the penetration of the ultraviolet light to the regions of the epidermis where the 7-dehydrocholesterol is found. Although this theory has some merit and has attractive aspects, quantitative information regarding the amount of vitamin D produced in the skin is lacking. Furthermore, it does not take into account other possible toxic phenomena which might be associated with excessive ultraviolet irradiation of skin.

The unraveling of the vitamin D and rickets mystery did not really begin until 1919 when Sir Edward Mellanby produced the first experimental demonstration of rickets in dogs by means of dietary manipulation (Mellanby, 1919a,b). This disease in dogs, which was produced by the feeding of oatmeal in the absence of sunlight, resembled in all respects rickets, the disease rampant in the human population at that time. Sir Edward Mellanby was able to prevent this disease by the administration of cod liver oil, and he incorrectly concluded that this must be due to the then newly discovered fat soluble vitamin A of McCollum. McCollum was very quick to realize that this perhaps represented another fat soluble material and by means of stability tests showed that the vitamin A activity could be destroyed, whereas the antirachitic activity remained (McCollum *et al.*, 1922a). He therefore concluded correctly that the antirachitic activity was due to another fat soluble vitamin, which he named vitamin D (McCollum *et al.*, 1922b, 1925).

At about this time, Huldshinsky (1919) noted that rickets in children could be cured by exposing them to sunlight or ultraviolet light. This was an outgrowth of the work of the Vienna school of physicians, who used a number of different cures for the disease. Another important fundamental observation was that of Goldblatt and Soames (1923), who demonstrated that the livers of rats irradiated with ultraviolet light when fed to vitamin D-deficient rats would cure their rickets. This undoubtedly led to the discovery by Steenbock and his co-workers that irradiation, not only of the skins of animals but also of their diet, could prevent or cure rickets (Steenbock, 1924; Steenbock and Black, 1924; Steenbock and Nelson, 1924). Thus, it appeared that ultraviolet irradiation of the diet was equivalent to supplementing it with cod liver oil. Hess and Weinstock confirmed these results (Hess and Weinstock, 1924a,b), and the two groups were able to demonstrate that the material activated by ultraviolet light could be found in the sterol fraction (Hess et al., 1925, 1926; Steenbock and Black, 1925). These discoveries not only led to the isolation and identification of vitamin D_2 from the plant sterol fractions in 1931–32, but most important from the medical viewpoint, they led to a complete elimination of the disease rickets in the western world for all practical purposes.

Waddell (1934) was the first to focus attention on the fact that the vitamin D which is produced by an irradiation of the animal sterol fractions is much different from the vitamin D produced by the irradiation of the plant sterol fractions. Using the chick efficacy ratio, he was able to show that the animal sterols yield a vitamin D which is much more effective in preventing rickets in chicks than is the plant sterol material, whereas both are equally effective in the treatment of rickets in rats. This finding was confirmed and led to the synthesis, isolation, and identification of vitamin D_3 by Windaus and his co-workers in 1936–37 (Windaus et al., 1936; Schenck, 1937). The search for the antirachitic substances of dietary origin ended with that discovery. It was not until 1966, when Lund and DeLuca demonstrated for the first time a highly biologically active metabolite of vitamin D_3 in the tissues of animals given radioactive vitamin D_3, that it was realized that the vitamin had actually metabolic or hormonally active forms (Lund and DeLuca, 1966).

II. VITAMIN D ACTIVE COMPOUNDS

In order to consider the hormonal role of vitamin D, it is essential to review the biologically active forms of vitamin D. Appreciable structural modification of the vitamin D molecule results in elimination of biological activity. In considering the biological activity of vitamin D, it is essential that one keep in mind that vitamin D has not only the antirachitic biological activity, but it also functions directly in stimulating intestinal calcium transport and in the mobilization of bone mineral. In most cases, only the antirachitic activity has been measured. Bone mobilization, which is a fairly recent observation in regard to the action of vitamin D, has only been rarely studied. A very good example of how the results of one test can be misleading is evident when one considers the biological activity of the DHT's. The DHT's are very poor in antirachitic activity, giving only approximately 180 IU of antirachitic activity per milligram of compound. This compares with a value of 40,000 units/mg for vitamin D_3. On the other hand, the DHT's are actually more effective in the mobilization of bone in the hypoparathyroid animal than is vitamin D_3. These deficiencies in measurement of biological activity must therefore be kept in mind in the ensuing discussion of the biologically active compounds of vitamin D. Where possible, the different activities will be indicated.

A. VITAMINS D_2 AND D_3

Figures 1 and 2 give the structure of vitamins D_2 and D_3, ergocalciferol and cholecalciferol, respectively. These two forms of vitamin D must be considered the dietary forms of the vitamin. In addition, the vitamin D_3, or cholecalciferol, should also be considered the natural form of vitamin D in the sense that it is the form most likely to have been

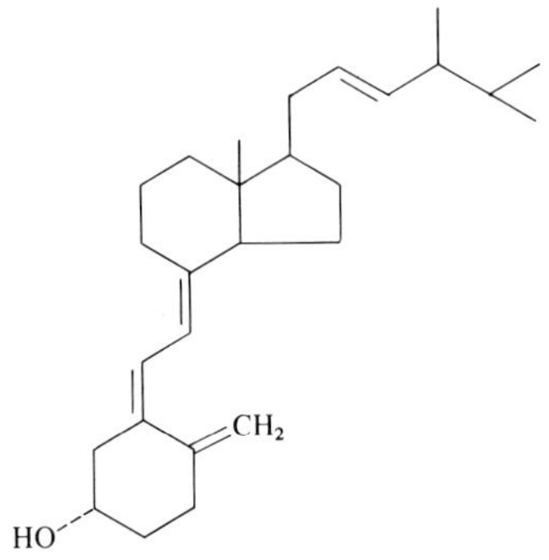

FIG. 1. Ergocalciferol (vitamin D_2).

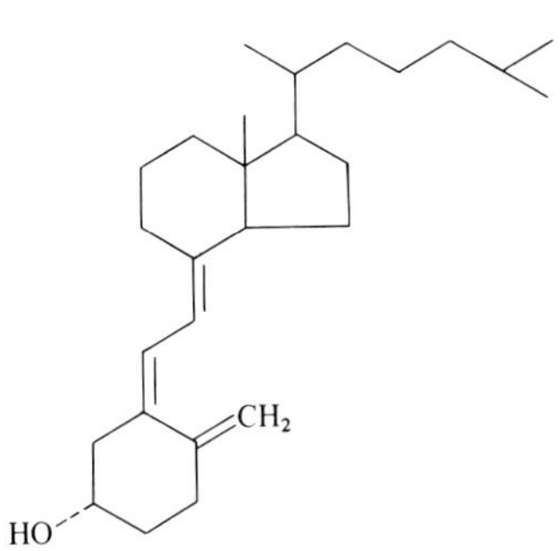

FIG. 2. Cholecalciferol (vitamin D_3).

produced in the skin by ultraviolet radiation, since 7-dehydrocholesterol is the only known provitamin to exist in that tissue. Because the intestinal calcium transport phenomenon is believed to be directly responsible for the antirachitic activity measured by line test in rats or by mineralization of bone in chicks, it seems likely that vitamins D_2 and D_3 are equally effective in this system in rats and in man, whereas in chicks vitamin D_2 is approximately one-tenth as active as vitamin D_3 (Sebrell and Harris, 1954; DeLuca, 1967; P. S. Chen and Bosmann, 1964). New world monkeys also respond poorly to vitamin D_2 as compared to D_3 (Hunt *et al.*, 1967). In bone mobilization, vitamin D_2 is only one-half as active as is vitamin D_3. Clearly then, vitamin D_3 should be the vitamin of choice to induce bone mineral mobilization in the hypoparathyroid patient or animal. However, because of cost and convenience, vitamin D_2 is generally the vitamin used to treat hypoparathyroidism in man.

B. 25-Hydroxycholecalciferol and 25-Hydroxyergocalciferol

The most biologically active forms of vitamin D known are 25-HCC and 25-HEC, recently discovered, isolated, identified, and synthesized at the University of Wisconsin (Blunt *et al.*, 1968a; Blunt and DeLuca, 1969; Suda *et al.*, 1969). Of the two, 25-HCC, or the 25-hydroxylated form of vitamin D_3, shown in Fig. 3, is the most universally effective compound. On a weight basis, it possesses approximately 60 IU of antirachitic activity per microgram in both rats and chicks, whereas vitamin D_3 possesses only 40 IU of antirachitic activity per microgram (Blunt *et al.*, 1968b). Similarly, 25-HEC (Fig. 4) possesses 60 IU of antirachitic activity per microgram in rats (Suda *et al.*, 1970a), whereas preliminary data suggest that it is virtually ineffective in chicks (Drescher *et al.*, 1969). 25-HEC has not yet been tested in purified form in either chicks

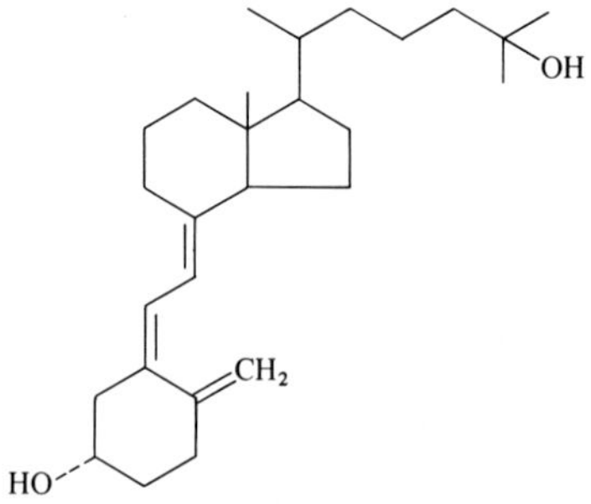

Fig. 3. 25-Hydroxycholecalciferol (25-HCC).

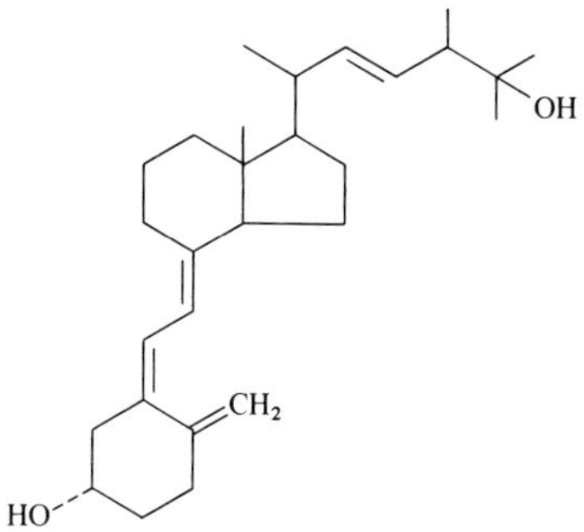

Fig. 4. 25-Hydroxyergocalciferol (25-HEC).

or new world monkeys, two species which discriminate against vitamin D_2.

25-HEC and 25-HCC are both very effective in inducing intestinal calcium transport in rats. In addition, both are effective in the induction of bone mineral mobilization in the vitamin D-deficient rat. Perhaps the most important observation is that both of these 25-hydroxylated forms of the vitamin act much more rapidly in the induction of intestinal calcium transport and in the induction of the bone mineral mobilization system. For example, 10 IU of vitamin D_3 injected intravenously into vitamin D-deficient rats on a normal calcium, normal phosphorus diet will bring about a rise in intestinal calcium transport in about 10–12 hours. In contrast, both 25-HCC and 25-HEC bring about a rise in intestinal calcium transport at the same dosage level in about 3 hours (Blunt *et al.*, 1968b; Suda *et al.*, 1970a). Thus, it appears that approximately 6 hours of the 10-hour lag in the action of 10 IU vitamin D_3 is required for hydroxylation.

The 25-hydroxylated D vitamins are infinitely more effective in isolated organ systems as compared with the dietary forms or the nonhydroxylated vitamins D_2 and D_3 (Trummel *et al.*, 1969; Olson and DeLuca, 1969). For example, in intestinal calcium transport in the vascularly perfused intestine, 25-HCC brings about a very rapid rise in intestinal calcium transport with a dosage of 2.5 μg, whereas massive doses of vitamin D_3 in this system are ineffective. Undoubtedly, in some disease states of vitamin D resistance, it will be found that the 25-hydroxy derivatives may be 100 to 1000 times more effective than vitamin D_3 in their treatment. Such an example has already been demonstrated in the case of the vitamin D-resistant hypoparathyroid patients in which as little as 2000–5000 IU of 25-HCC can bring about a rise in plasma calcium in patients who are not responding to even as much as 600,000 IU of vitamin D_2 or 4 mg of

DHT (Pak *et al.*, 1970). The exact reason for the vitamin D resistance and the great effectiveness of the 25-hydroxylated derivatives is one which merits further investigation.

C. DIHYDROTACHYSTEROLS

A discussion of vitamin D active compounds would be incomplete without mentioning the DHT series. Von Werder (1939) first demonstrated that reduction of tachysterol produces a substance which is very effective in the elevation of plasma calcium concentration. The effective substance proved to be DHT_2. A group at the Philips–Duphar Company (Westerhof and Keverling Buisman, 1956, 1957) developed reduction methods which yield as much as 40% DHT from tachysterol, the vitamin D-like compound isolated from the irradiation mixture of the corresponding 5,7-diene sterol. The DHT_2 and DHT_3 derived from the ergosterol irradiation mixture and the 7-dehydrocholesterol irradiation mixtures, respectively, are shown in Figs. 5 and 6. Note that the structures of the

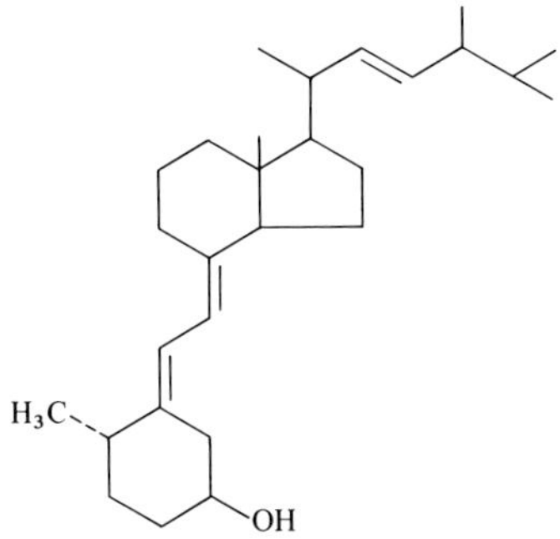

FIG. 5. Dihydrotachysterol$_2$ (DHT_2).

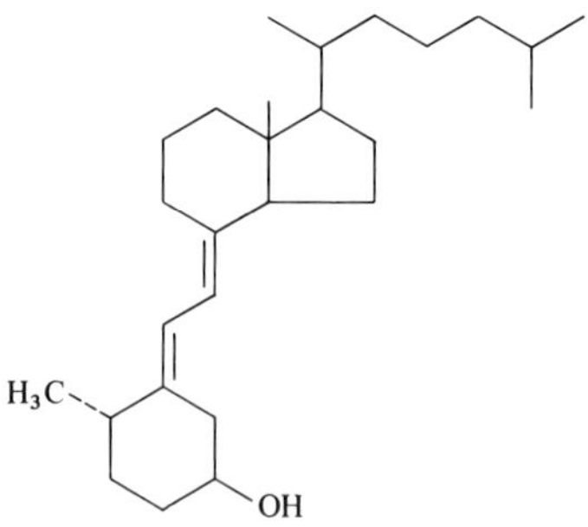

FIG. 6. Dihydrotachysterol$_3$ (DHT_3).

DHT's differ significantly from those of vitamins D_2 and D_3. First of all, the C_{19} methylene has become a methyl on reduction and ring A is now in a different conformation from that seen in the vitamin D series. [It should be noted parenthetically that the conformation of the D vitamins was clearly established by the work of Crowfoot and Dunitz (1948).] The DHT's have very characteristic ultraviolet absorption spectra, giving a λ_{max} at 242, 251 and 265 mμ. Of the DHT's, DHT_2 is the substance used clinically because it is much less expensive to make than the corresponding DHT_3. DHT_3 and DHT_2 are extremely effective in inducing bone mineral mobilization, both in the vitamin D-deficient animal and in the thyroparathyroidectomized animal. It is much more effective than the D vitamins in the thyroparathyroidectomized animals, but less effective in mobilizing bone in vitamin D-deficient animals (Harrison *et al.*, 1968). It is not yet clear, although it is likely, that DHT_3 is more effective than DHT_2. DHT's are, on the other hand, both relatively ineffective in curing rickets, having only 180 IU of antirachitic activity per milligram of compound. This falls far below the 40,000 IU/mg for vitamin D_2 and D_3 in rats. Thus, DHT's are synthetic materials which preferentially act on the bone mineral mobilization system. This curious selection for one action of vitamin D by the DHT compound is not at all understood on a biochemical basis at the present time.

Another question of great interest is the fact that the DHTs are much more effective than the vitamin Ds in inducing bone mobilization in the thyroparathyroidectomized animals when high doses are required (Harrison *et al.*, 1968). Although several explanations have been offered, the most likely explanation is that the DHTs are hydroxylated in the 25 position very rapidly and in an uncontrolled fashion by the 25-hydroxylase of liver whereas vitamins D_2 and D_3 are hydroxylated slowly and are very strongly inhibited by the 25-HCC product. On the other hand, 25-OHDHT does not exert this type of inhibitory action at least not at the same concentration ranges (Horsting, 1970). Thus it would appear that the 25-hydroxylation of the DHT's is not limited by its product and hence when large amounts are fed, large amounts of the 25-hydroxylated derivative are formed, thus accounting for its greater effectiveness than vitamin D_3 whose conversion to the 25-hydroxy derivative is very strongly product inhibited.

Recently, Suda *et al.* have synthesized 25-OHDHT$_3$ (Suda *et al.*, 1970b) (Fig. 7). This compound is more effective than DHT_3 in all respects. It is more effective than DHT_3 in curing rickets (800 IU/μg) and about two times more effective in bone mineral mobilization in both thyroparathyroidectomized and vitamin D-deficient rats (Suda *et al.*, 1970b). These results are consistent with the above suggestion that DHT's

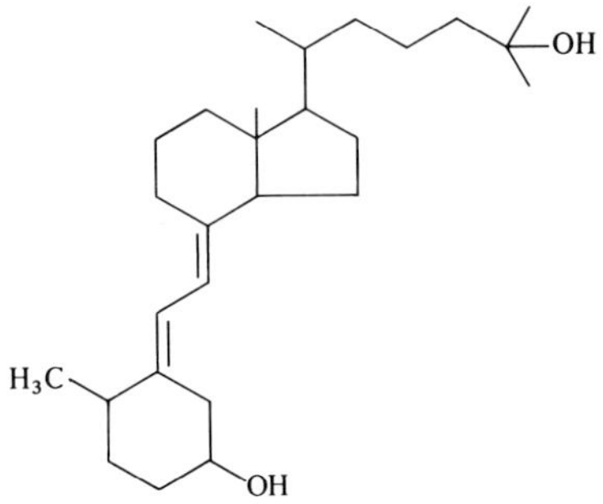

FIG. 7. 25-Hydroxydihydrotachysterol₃ (25-OHDHT₃).

are more effective in large doses than vitamin D because of the lack of product inhibition of the 25-hydroxylation of DHT's. However, hydroxylation of DHT's has not yet been demonstrated *in vivo*. Finally, it must be emphasized that 25-HCC is, nevertheless, the most active form of vitamin D known for all systems, including bone mineral mobilization in the hypoparathyroid state.

D. OTHER FORMS OF VITAMIN D

Besides the biologically active forms of vitamin D mentioned above, there are many other vitamin D active substances that have been reported. Of particular note is the 22,23-dihydrovitamin D_2, or vitamin D_4, which mimics vitamin D_2 action almost exactly, except that it is not as effective as D_2 in rats. These substances are all of academic interest and are discussed thoroughly elsewhere (Sebrell and Harris, 1954; Fieser and Fieser, 1959).

III. METABOLISM OF THE D VITAMINS

A. HISTORY

The first attempt to study the metabolism of the vitamin D molecule was by Kodicek and his co-workers, who by means of biological assay attempted to learn how rapidly the vitamin D_2 is inactivated when administered to animals (Kodicek, 1960). In the early work, a large dose of vitamin D was given to rats and 24 hours later their tissues were removed and assayed for antirachitic activity following chemical manipulation. Kodicek and his co-workers could account for only 20% of the originally administered vitamin D as biologically active material. Kodicek and co-workers continued their investigation by preparing ^{14}C-labeled vitamin D_2 of very low specific activity (Kodicek, 1955). By administering this substance and measuring the radioactivity, he could account for all of the radioactivity from the vitamin but only 20% of it was biologically active, providing clear evidence that vitamin D is metabolized to inactive products (Kodicek, 1957).

Unfortunately, because of inadequate chromatographic methods and because of the low specific activity of the radioactive vitamin D_2 preparation used, Kodicek reported that he could find no biologically active metabolites of vitamin D (Kodicek, 1957), a conclusion which was later to be negated by more refined methods. Kodicek (1957), Blumberg *et al.* (1960), and Norman and DeLuca (1963) carried out studies with radioactive vitamin D_3 on the distribution of radioactivity among the tissues following the oral feeding or intravenous injection of the radioactive vitamin D. The liver, skeleton, and muscle were found to contain most of the radioactivity following administration of 100–40,000 units of radioactive vitamin D. Of particular interest was the large initial accumulation of radioactivity in the liver which appeared at first to confirm the belief that the liver is the major storage organ for vitamin D (Kodicek, 1960). However, accumulation of radioactivity in the liver following the injection of vitamins D_2 or D_3 has now been quite clearly related to the metabolism of the vitamin to the 25-hydroxy forms as will be described below.

B. Synthesis of Radioactive Vitamin D

Significant progress in the understanding of the functional metabolism of vitamin D was not made until radioactive vitamin D of high specific activity was prepared. Neville and DeLuca (1966) prepared 1,2-labeled vitamin D_3 with sufficient radioactivity that 10 IU (0.25 μg) given to each animal would allow detection of metabolic products as well as tissue distribution. This synthesis of the vitamin D_3-1,2-^{3}H is shown in Fig. 8. This synthesis was followed very closely by the preparation of carbon-14 labeled vitamin D_2 by Imrie *et al.* (1967). In addition, vitamin D_4 labeled in the 22,23 position of extremely high specific activity was prepared by DeLuca *et al.* (1968a). Although Callow *et al.* (1966)

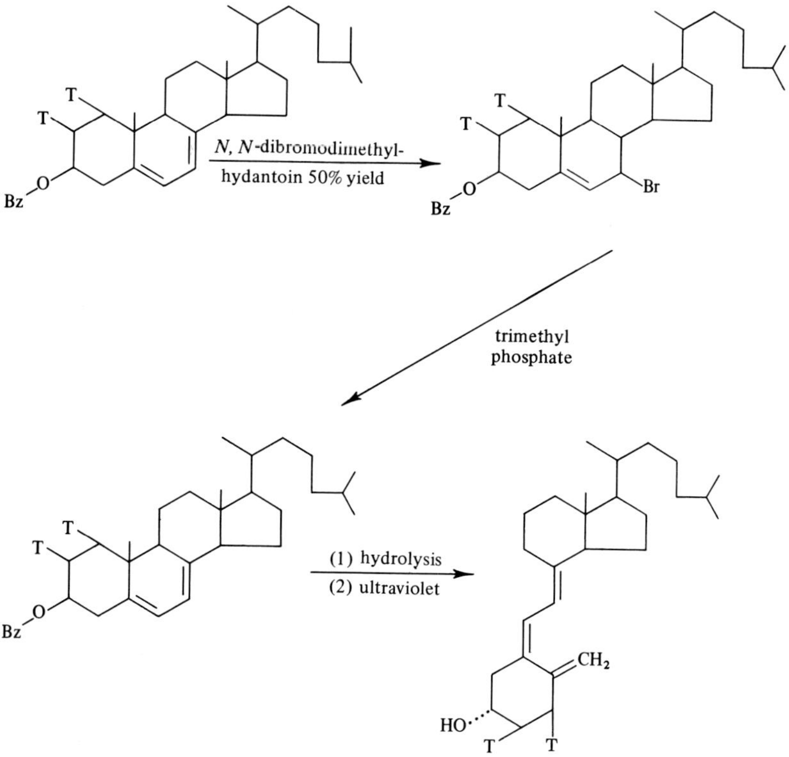

FIG. 8. Synthesis of vitamin D_3-1,2-^{3}H.

prepared a number of radioactive vitamin D's, until recently they were of a very low specific activity but higher than had been used previously.

C. Demonstration of Biologically Active Metabolites

With the synthesis of the radioactive vitamins D's of high specific activity came the first clear-cut demonstration that vitamin D was in fact converted to biologically active metabolites. Lund and DeLuca (1966) presented the first convincing evidence that there exists a metabolite of vitamin D possessing biological activity equivalent to that of the parent vitamin. This conversion to the biologically active forms of the vitamin was found to take place even before the first physiological action of the vitamin could be demonstrated. Besides the very potent peak IV metabolite shown in Fig. 9, two other biologically active metabolites were demonstrated. The first biologically active metabolite, peak I, was clearly

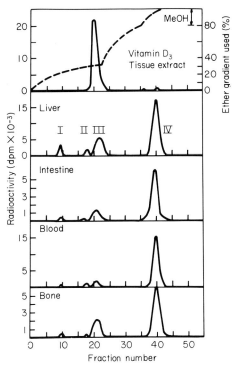

Fig. 9. Silicic acid column profiles of chloroform extracts of tissues from rats given 10 IU vitamin D_3-1,2-^{3}H 12 hours earlier. Peak III is unchanged vitamin D_3. ——, radioactivity; ———, solvent gradient (right-hand ordinate).

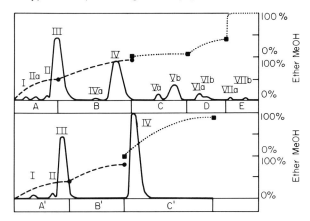

Fig. 10. Metabolites of vitamin D_3 separated by improved gradient elution from silicic acid columns from plasma 24 hours after intravenous injection of 10 IU vitamin D_3-1,2-^{3}H to vitamin D-deficient rats. ——, ^{3}H; · · · and ———, solvent gradient generated to elute the metabolites. A–E, elution regions with new gradual solvent gradient; A'–C', elution regions generated by the old solvent gradients. (Ponchon and DeLuca, 1969a.)

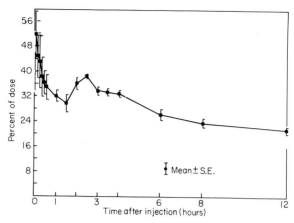

Fig. 11. Disappearance of ^{3}H from the plasma of rats given 10 IU vitamin D$_3$-1,2-^{3}H. (Ponchon and DeLuca, 1969b.)

cochromatography. Homogenates of other tissues were inactive in making the 25-hydroxy vitamin D under the same conditions (Horsting, 1970). Confirmation of the observation of Horsting and DeLuca (1969) was provided by the experiments of Ponchon and co-workers (1969) in which hepatectomy eliminated the ability of the animal to make not only 25-hydroxy vitamin D, but other metabolites as well.

The vitamin D 25-hydroxylase of liver is not found in nuclei obtained from 2.3 M sucrose or other nuclear preparations which are essentially homogenous (Horsting, 1970). The reaction requires a cytoplasmic protein. The cytoplasm from kidney or other tissues does not contain this factor. In addition to the cytoplasmic factor the reaction requires or takes place in the mitochondria. Although some activity is obtained in the microsomal fraction, it is apparently due to mitochondrial fragment contamination. Thus far, the 25-hydroxylase system has not been solubilized and thus is apparently very tightly bound to the membranous components of the mitochondria. The 25-hydroxylase system is not inhibited by carbon monoxide–oxygen mixtures or other hydroxylation inhibitors and is not inhibited by lipid peroxidation inhibitors such as diphenylparaphenylenediamine. Thus, this reacton appears to be quite unique in that it produces a tertiary hydroxylation, and that it does not appear to be inhibited by the usual hydroxylase inhibitors. It is not inhibited by any of the cytochrome inhibitors such as antimycin A, cyanide, or azide, thus eliminating the electron transport chain as participating in the hydroxylation reaction. Chicken liver also contains the hydroxylation enzyme.

F. 25-HCC Inhibition of the Vitamin D 25-Hydroxylase System:
    An Important Physiological Control Mechanism

Of great interest was the observation that rats predosed with vitamin
D failed to reveal any of the 25-hydroxylase activity in their livers
(Horsting, 1970). 25-HCC is a very potent inhibitor of the hydroxylase
reaction, presumably by competing with the substrate for the enzyme.
Injection of 25-HCC *in vivo* failed to inhibit to any marked degree the
in vivo production of 25-HCC, suggesting that the plasma levels of 25-
HCC do not play a role in regulating the amount of 25-HCC by direct
inhibition. If the animals are predosed with vitamin D 15 or 30 minutes
prior to examination, the hydroxylation reaction is not inhibited. Thus,
it appears that the liver level of 25-HCC exhibits a product inhibition
on the 25-hydroxylation reaction. The rate at which 25-HCC is transferred
from the liver into the blood stream then becomes a very critical reaction. It is clear that product inhibition by the 25-HCC plus the rate
of transferal of this substance into the blood stream is a very important
controlling reaction for vitamin D function and for vitamin D metabolism. The liver then acts as a synthetic and secretory organ for the
active form of vitamin D, 25-HCC. 25-HCC can be considered the
hormonal form of vitamin D and the liver can be considered the secretory organ. It is clear that much remains to be learned in regard to the
control of 25-HCC secretion or synthesis by the liver. At our present
stage of knowledge, however, a very good case can be made for 25-HCC
as a hormone derived from vitamin D.

Of great interest is the fact that 25-OHDHT does not inhibit the
vitamin D hydroxylation reaction (Horsting, 1970). This very important
observation can mean two things. First, it is apparent that the recognition
by the enzyme of 25-HCC is a highly specific one. Second, it perhaps
provides the answer as to why DHT is much more effective at higher
doses than is vitamin D (Harrison *et al.*, 1968). These results suggest
that DHT is hydroxylated in an uncontrolled fashion to completion and
hence provides very large supplies of the active form of DHT. Vitamin
D on the other hand is hydroxylated in a very slow and controlled
process, perhaps by product inhibition, thus limiting the amount of
active vitamin D that can be made. Administration of large amounts
of DHT results in large amounts of 25-OHDHT, which can produce
massive effects on bone mineral mobilization. In this regard, it is
important to note that Suda *et al.* (1970b) have synthesized the 25-
OHDHT, and although they find it very active in the bone mineral
mobilization assay, it is not as active as 25-HCC in any system. It is
interesting, however, that it has very minor effects on intestinal calcium

transport and on the cure of rickets in rats. These results, then, are
consistent with the above advanced hypothesis regarding why DHT's
are more effective in the bone mineral mobilization system.

G. Further Metabolism of 25-HCC to Peak V Materials (Tissue Active Forms?)

25-HCC has recently been synthesized with tritium in the 26 and 27
positions such that a very high specific activity can be obtained. The
synthesis of this substance is shown in Fig. 12. 25-Ketonorcholestryl
acetate is reacted with methyl magnesium iodide labeled with tritium
by a Grignard reaction followed by acetylation with acetic anhydride
and pyridine at which time the Δ^7 double bond is introduced by means

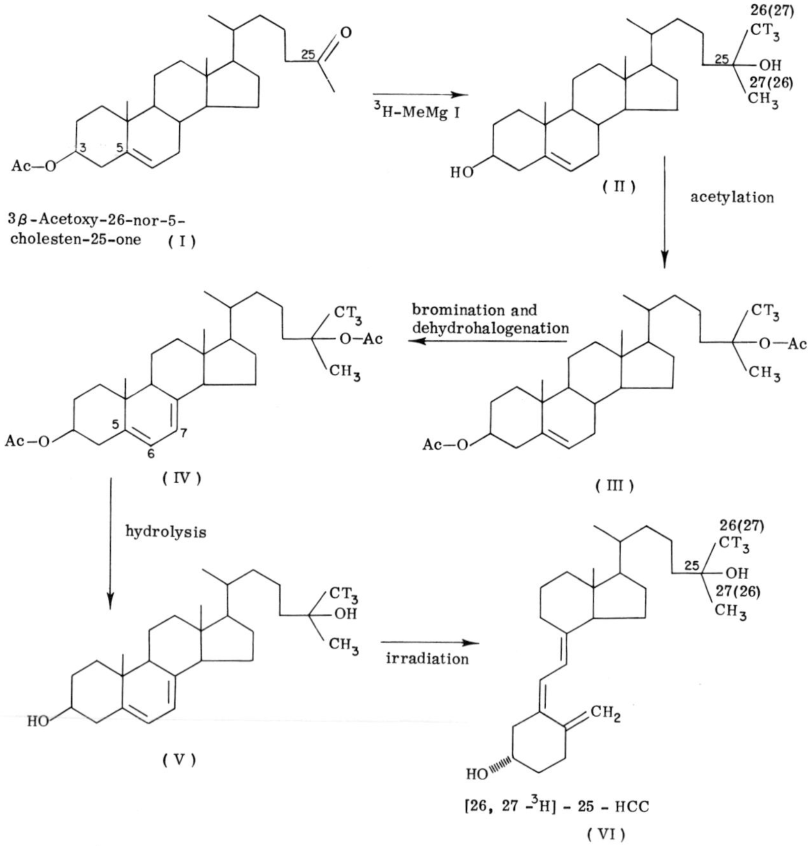

Fig. 12. Synthesis of radioactive 25-HCC from 25-keto-26-norcholesteryl acetate.

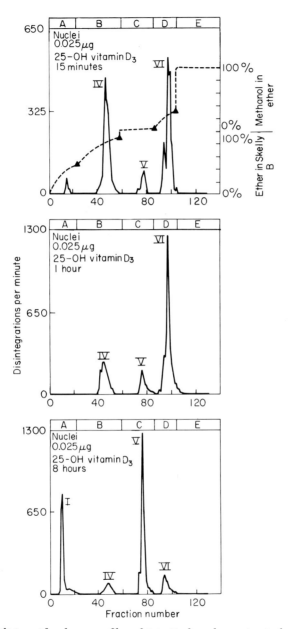

Fig. 13. Silicic acid column profiles of intestinal nuclear extracts from rats given 0.25 μg 25-HCC-26,27-³H.— — —, the solvent gradient used to elute the metabolites (see right-hand ordinate). A–E represent elution regions brought about by solvent changes. (Cousins *et al.*, 1970a.)

of an allylic brominating agent followed by dehydrohalogenation with trimethyl phosphite. The resulting 5,7-diene diacetate is treated with lithium aluminum hydride very briefly to eliminate the diacetate, and the 5,7-diene is irradiated with untraviolet light to yield ultimately tritium-labeled 25-HCC.

When 25-HCC is injected into vitamin D-deficient rats or chicks, it is rapidly converted to more polar metabolites in the intestine, bone, kidney, and liver (Cousins et al., 1970a,b). Figure 13 shows the type of chromatographic profile obtained in the case of intestine, while Fig. 14 demonstrates the type of profile obtained in the case of bone. In the case of intestine, a very polar metabolite is first observed, followed by polar peak V metabolite, which in turn is more polar than 25-HCC. The peak V metabolite in intestine and bone represents the terminal metabolism steps. In the chicken, the peak V material appears to be formed well in advance of the intestinal calcium transport mechanism in response to vitamin D or 25-HCC. The polar metabolite, peak V, of intestine corresponds with the peak 4b of Haussler et al. (1968) and to the peak P of Lawson et al. (1969). Thus it is clear, as shown in Fig. 15, that vitamin D_3 can be considered the storage form of vitamin D, while 25-HCC can at least be considered a hormonal or circulating active form of vitamin D. The peak V material may then be the tissue active forms.

Two new metabolites of vitamin D have recently been isolated and identified at the University of Wisconsin. Their origin is not known, but one is 21,25-dihydroxycholecalciferol (Suda et al., 1970c), a metabolite which has a major effect on bone mineral mobilization and a minor

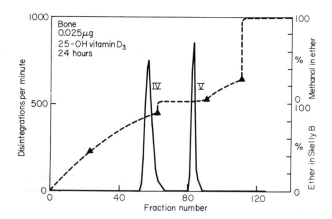

Fig. 14. Silicic acid column profiles of bone extracts from rats given 0.25 μg 25-HCC-26,27-³H. — — —, solvent gradient used to elute the metabolites (right-hand ordinate). (Cousins et al., 1970b.)

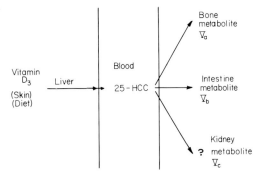

Fig. 15. Diagrammatic representations of vitamin D metabolites.

effect on intestinal calcium transport, and the other is 25,26-dihydroxy-cholecalciferol (Suda *et al.*, 1970d), a metabolite which has preferential activity on the intestine. Exactly where these metabolites fit in from a functional point of view is not entirely clear. It must be recognized, however, that they originate neither from bone nor intestine. It is nevertheless clear that the peak V metabolites from intestine and bone are of major importance in understanding the function of vitamin D at the molecular level. For this reason, a knowledge of their structures remains an important problem in the study of vitamin D whether they are inactivation regulatory products or whether they are metabolically active forms.

H. Discrimination by Chicks and New World Monkeys against Vitamin D_2

An intriguing metabolic problem in the area of vitamin D made its appearance when it was noted that the irradiated ergosterol was much less effective in the prevention of rickets in fowls than was irradiated 7-dehydrocholesterol. Waddell (1934) was the first to suggest that there was a new form of vitamin D which was later identified by Windaus and his collaborators as vitamin D_3 (Schenck, 1937; Windaus *et al.*, 1936). The problem has been examined many times, yielding much information in regard to the relative effectiveness of vitamin D_2 versus vitamin D_3 in chicks. Recently, a similar observation was made in regard to new world monkeys in which it could be shown that vitamin D_2 was relatively ineffective in the prevention of bone disease in these monkeys, while vitamin D_3 was completely effective (Hunt *et al.*, 1967). This curious discrimination by chicks has remained an intriguing problem among nutritionists now for some 30 years. Parenthetically, it might be stated that chicks and other fowls discriminate against vitamin D_4 as well as vitamin D_2. In a recent estimate by Chen and co-workers (P. S. Chen and Bosmann, 1964), it appeared that vitamin D_3 is ten times more effective in prevention of rickets and other rachitic lesions in chicks than is vitamin D_2. Insight into this very interesting problem was obtained when Imrie *et al.* (1967) compared the metabolism of vitamin D_2 labeled with carbon-14 with that of vitamin D_3 labeled with tritium. Both preparations were of high enough specific activity so that a mere 10 units per chicken could be administered to allow a study of metabolism. All tissues took up the carbon-14 from the vitamin D_2 and the tritium from the vitamin D_3 equally well initially. However, it was soon noted that the carbon-14 from vitamin D_2 disappeared very rapidly from the blood and other tissues of chicks as compared with the tritium from vitamin D_3. The carbon-14 which disappeared from the blood and other tissues made its appearance in the bile and fecal excretions. Closer examination revealed that the chicks could make the 25-hydroxy derivatives of both vitamin D_2 and of vitamin D_3, but the 25-hydroxy derivative of vitamin D_2 was biologically inactive in chickens, whereas the 25-hydroxy vitamin D_3 was very active (Drescher *et al.*, 1969). These results suggested that the chicken is fully capable of making 25-HEC, but that it is rapidly degraded and metabolized to excretion products that are immediately eliminated into the bile. Continuing work has revealed that this radioactivity appears as a biliary conjugate which is currently under study for chemical identification. Thus, the discrimination, at least in chicks, against vitamin D_2 appears to be a metabolic one directed against the 25-hydroxy derivative of vitamin D_2.

I. Absorption and Blood Transport of Vitamin D

Very little is understood concerning the mode of absorption of vitamin D from the intestinal tract since there appears to be only uniform agreement that bile is necessary for the absorption of the vitamin (Schachter *et al.*, 1964). There is considerable disagreement as to the site of vitamin D absorption in the intestine. Schachter and co-workers (Schachter *et al.*, 1964) have concluded that the duodenum is the site of vitamin D absorption, while Kodicek (1960) and Norman and DeLuca (1963) conclude that the distal segments of the small intestine are the sites of vitamin D absorption. The work of Schachter and co-workers was carried out with isolated loops of intestine in which the vitamin D was dissolved in ethanol, whereas the work of Kodicek and of Norman and DeLuca was carried out with oil solutions of the vitamin. It is possible that both conclusions are correct in that the free form of the vitamin might be absorbed more rapidly from the upper tract from the vehicle supplied by Schachter and co-workers, whereas when the vitamin is dissolved in oil it is absorbed more rapidly in the distal tract. This interesting area warrants further attention. There is some evidence that vitamin D is esterified at least partially during absorption (Bell and Bryan, 1965). Both of these suggestions are only tentative and require additional investigation.

Several investigators have considered how vitamin D is carried in the plasma. Although it has been clear that it is primarily protein bound, some differences in regard to the conclusions as to how they are carried have appeared. Kodicek's group considered it bound primarily to albumin, but more recent evidence obtained *in vivo* suggests that an α_2-globulin carries both the vitamin D_3 and the 25-HCC (Rikkers and DeLuca, 1967; DeCrousaz *et al.*, 1965). The plasma protein which carries the vitamin D and the 25-HCC has not yet been purified and is currently under intensive investigation by several groups. It appears likely that this may well yield a competitive binding assay for vitamin D and 25-HCC.

Other studies have revealed that initially, following absorption, the vitamin D is associated with the chylomicron fraction and the β-lipo-proteins, but following some incubation *in vivo* or *in vitro*, the vitamin D becomes associated with the α_2-globulin. The 25-HCC is bound more tightly to the α_2-globulin than is the vitamin D_3. This area represents a very fruitful area for investigation since there is a possibility that some disease states may be the result of a defective supply of vitamin D carrier protein. In addition, the possibility of assaying vitamin D by competitive binding represents a very useful clinical approach.

J. Excretion of Vitamin D

Vitamin D and its metabolites are excreted primarily through the bile. Less than 2% of radioactivity derived from vitamin D appears in the urine. In the 24 hours following injection of vitamin D, approximately 30% of the radioactivity will appear in the bile of bile duct cannulated rats. Little or no enterohepatic circulation appears to occur, since bile duct cannulated rats or chicks show similar disappearance curves for the radioactivity derived from vitamin D. The nature of the excretory products has not yet been determined, although there appears to be very little free vitamin D_3 and much more in the way of metabolites conjugated with glucuronic acid. Again this represents a relatively unknown and fruitful area of investigation.

IV. PHYSIOLOGICAL ACTION OF VITAMIN D

Having considered the metabolism of vitamin D to 25-HCC and further to other possible biologically active metabolites, it now seems appropriate to consider how these active forms of vitamin D might work. A brief review of the physiological actions of vitamin D appears to be in order, although the subject has been adequately reviewed several times in the past few years (DeLuca, 1967, 1969, 1970).

A. GENERAL REMARKS

Because the end effect of vitamin D is the prevention of the disease rickets or osteomalacia, it appeared for many years that the vitamin might function in the actual mineralization process at the bone site. However, some 40 years later, following many attempts at demonstrating such a function, the weight of evidence appears against this hypothesis, although all the evidence must be considered negative in nature and not absolutely exclusive of such a mechanism. The defect in rickets and osteomalacia appears by and large to be an inadequate supply of calcium and phosphate to the calcification sites rather than a defect in the calcification process per se. It had been recognized from the early days of Shipley and co-workers (1925) that rachitic bone slices will calcify normally when placed either in normal serum or in reconstituted inorganic solutions approximating normal serum, whereas they fail to calcify either in rachitic serum or inorganic salt solutions which were made to resemble rachitic serum. This observation remained essentially unnoticed despite the fact that the calcium–phosphorus product of the plasma has long been used as a diagnostic test for vitamin D deficiency. However, following the revelation by Neuman and Neuman (1958) that plasma is normally supersaturated with regard to bone mineral and that in rickets the plasma is undersaturated (Neuman, 1958), the concept that in vitamin D-deficiency there is a defective supply of calcium and phosphorus to the calcification site gained acceptance. Vitamin D must function, then, by elevating plasma calcium and phosphorus levels, which are in turn necessary for normal mineralization for bone.

The elevation of plasma calcium and phosphorus in response to vitamin D results from at least two basic mechanisms. First, vitamin D markedly increases intestinal calcium absorption and secondarily phosphorus, and second, it increases bone mineral mobilization by means of a cellular mechanism which is augmented further by parathyroid hormone. These two mechanisms then bring about a rise in plasma calcium and phosphorus product to supersaturation levels with regard to bone mineral.

B. CALCIUM ABSORPTION

In 1923, Orr first suggested (Orr *et al.*, 1923) that vitamin D increases intestinal calcium absorption. He noted this as a result of balance studies in which there was a large fecal loss of calcium in deficiency. This large fecal loss of calcium was also observed by others, but the concept that vitamin D increases intestinal calcium absorption fell into disfavor when it became generally believed that the effect was due to an increased excretion of calcium into the intestinal tract in vitamin D deficiency. However, the work of Nicolaysen and his collaborators (Nicolaysen, 1934, 1937a,b,c; Nicolaysen and Eeg-Larsen, 1953) clearly placed on a firm experimental basis the fact that vitamin D markedly increases intestinal calcium absorption. He was able to demonstrate this by many techniques, including isolated loop experiments as well as *in vivo* whole animal studies. The fact was confirmed many times using radiocalcium and other techniques, but little new additional information was obtained (Greenberg, 1945; Harrison and Harrison, 1951; Lindquist, 1952; Migicovsky and Nielson, 1951). As will be shown below, this process is a cation-oriented active transport system which is induced by vitamin D.

C. BONE MINERAL MOBILIZATION

It was not until 1951 that Bauer, Lindquist, and Carlsson (Bauer *et al.*, 1955) first brought forth the suggestion that vitamin D increases bone mineral mobilization. It had been recognized prior to this that massive amounts of vitamin D do in fact bring about extensive bone mineral mobilization or reduced ash content (Nicolaysen and Eeg-Larsen, 1957), but that was considered to be a pharmacological action of the vitamin rather than its normal physiological function. However, the experiments of Carlsson, Bauer, and Lindquist placed on a firm basis the idea that physiological amounts of vitamin D bring about bone mineral mobilization. More recently, Harrison and Harrison (1964) and Rasmussen *et al.*

(1963) have shown conclusively that parathyroid hormone is unable to induce bone mineral mobilization unless the animals are pretreated with vitamin D. These observations show conclusively that vitamin D brings about mobilization of calcium and phosphate from preformed bone into blood. This acting in concert with the intestinal absorption mechanism brings about the rise in plasma calcium phosphorus to supersaturation levels which are in turn necessary for normal bone mineralization.

D. KIDNEY EFFECTS

Although investigated as early as 1941 (Harrison and Harrison, 1941), it is still not known whether vitamin D has a direct effect on kidney metabolism of calcium and phosphate. It is clear that the kidney is able to reabsorb most of the filtered calcium, even in the absence of vitamin D. However, there is a report of increased tubular reabsorption of calcium in response to vitamin D (Gran, 1960). This limited study requires additional verification and would add another very basic function at the physiological level of vitamin D. Harrison and Harrison in 1941 reported that vitamin D increased tubular reabsorption of phosphate. Unfortunately, the animals were not parathyroidectomized and their experiments now raise the question of whether these changes are due to a secondary effect on the parathyroid glands. It seems reasonable that vitamin D produces slight hypercalcemia, which would shut down parathyroid secretion. The reduced secretion of parathyroid hormone would reduce the renal excretion of phosphate characteristic of parathyroid hormone action. Thus, the increased phosphate excretion in vitamin D deficiency may well be secondary to secondary hyperparathyroidism. In any case, these experiments should be reexamined so that some definite conclusion may be reached in regard to possible function of vitamin D on renal tubular reabsorption of calcium and phosphate. Until such time, however, this must remain an open question.

V. BIOCHEMISTRY OF VITAMIN D ACTION

A. INTESTINAL TRANSPORT MECHANISM

Little is known concerning the biochemistry of vitamin D action on bone mineral mobilization. Technically, bone tissue is extremely difficult to work with and hence has remained relatively uninvestigated in regard to the function of vitamin D. On the other hand, much work has been carried out on the intestinal transport mechanism, and thus our primary remarks will be confined to the intestinal transport mechanism with only an occasional reference to the bone mineral mobilization system. It was primarily through the efforts of Schachter and his co-workers (Schachter, 1963; Schachter and Rosen, 1959; Schachter *et al.*, 1960, 1961, 1966) that the initial understanding of calcium transport mechanism in the intestine in response to vitamin D was obtained. By employing the Wilson and Wiseman (1954) technique for glucose transport, Schachter and Rosen (1959) were able to demonstrate for the first time that vitamin D increases the transport of calcium against the concentration gradient. This transport system was blocked by metabolic inhibitors and was studied very extensively in the Columbia laboratory. Schachter and his collaborators came to the conclusion that vitamin D increases the rate of entry of calcium into the mucosal brush border surfaces as well as the rate of exit of calcium into the serosal fluid (Schachter *et al.*, 1966). They were further able to demonstrate that the calcium transported across intestinal sac membrane was done so against an electrochemical potential gradient, verifying that it was an active transport process (Schachter, 1963). Harrison and Harrison (1960, 1963b, 1965) also studied this system and have confirmed the results of Schachter but came to the conclusion that vitamin D changes the permeability of intestinal membrane to calcium and does not affect directly the active transport mechanism. Wasserman and co-workers (Wasserman, 1962, 1963; Wasserman and Kallfelz, 1962; Wasserman *et al.*, 1966) have done extensive investigation in the *in vivo* transport of calcium in chick intestine and have shown that the calcium is actively transported against an electrochemical potential gradient and that vitamin D increases the rate of transfer both from the gut to blood as well as from blood to the lumen (Wasserman and Kallfelz, 1962). Wasserman and co-workers believe that calcium transport is an active process but that vitamin D facilitates the calcium flux in both directions. Saltman and his co-workers (Helbock *et al.*, 1966) came to the conclusion that calcium is transported secondarily to phosphate and that phosphate is transported against an electrochemical potential gradient. Harrison and Harrison (1961), on the other hand, have found a phosphate transporting system which is increased following vitamin D but which requires the presence of calcium.

Sodium ions have been conclusively shown to participate in the calcium transport mechanism (Martin and DeLuca, 1969a; Harrison and Harrison, 1963a). Martin (1968) attempted to simplify the reaction medium for everted gut sac calcium transport so that definite conclusions might eventually be made in regard to the transport mechanism. He was able to demonstrate that calcium could be transported against an electrochemical potential gradient provided there was an oxidizable substrate, in agreement with previous observations, magnesium ions, choline chloride, and surprisingly, sodium ions. The sodium ions were required not for the uptake of calcium into the mucosal surface but rather for the expulsion of calcium across the serosal surface into the serosal medium. Vitamin D was involved in at least the initial uptake process. Martin and DeLuca (1969b) investigated more thoroughly the transport mechanism and found that vitamin D does not appear to have much effect on the flux ratios determined by Ussing's method (1949), and their results are in agreement with those reported by Wasserman and his collaborators (Wasserman *et al.*, 1960). On the other hand, calcium uptake across brush border surface was very markedly affected by vitamin D, but this uptake was affected neither by sodium nor by phosphate and was inhibited by lack of oxygen. This appeared to confirm the belief that vitamin D must be involved in the initial uptake of calcium across the brush border surface. Adams *et al.* (1969), using polyene antibiotics, have come to a similar conclusion with chicks. Holdsworth and his colleagues, on the other hand, have come to quite different conclusions on the basis of iodoacetate inhibition and other studies (Sallis and Holdsworth, 1962). Clearly, the transport mechanism is far from defined, except that there appears to be uniform agreement that vitamin D induces the formation of a substance which plays at least one role at the brush border site and that there may be an additional substance which affects the serosal membrane exit of calcium.

Wasserman and his colleagues have isolated a calcium-binding protein from supernatant fractions of homogenates from intestinal mucosa of chicks given vitamin D (Taylor and Wasserman, 1967; Wasserman and Taylor, 1966, 1968; Wasserman *et al.*, 1968; Ebel *et al.*, 1969). This binding protein appears only after vitamin D administration. Its very potent calcium binding ability suggests that it may well be involved in the transport mechanism. This substance has a molecular weight of 24,000–28,000 and binds one mole of calcium per mole of protein. Thus, it must be a carrier and must have very rapid turnover rates. Harmeyer and DeLuca (1969) have measured the calcium-binding protein in chicks on various diets, before and after vitamin D administration, and have demonstrated that vitamin D brings about a rise in intestinal calcium transport long before a measurable rise in calcium binding protein. However, Ebel *et al.* (1969), using immunoassay for the calcium-binding protein, have shown that small amounts of the binding protein appear at a time consistent with its possible involvement in intestinal absorption. In any case, it is quite clear that the amount of calcium-binding protein bears no quantitative relationship to intestinal calcium transport. If it does play a role, a small amount must play a very marked role and the additional amount of calcium-binding protein must have some other role.

Martin *et al.* (1969) have found, on the other hand, a calcium-stimulated adenosine triphosphatase in the brush borders of rats and chicks (Melancon and DeLuca, 1970) given vitamin D. This ATPase has been very thoroughly studied, and it appears at the same time that calcium absorption is increased in response to vitamin D. Nagode *et al.* (1970) consider this enzyme to be identical with brush border alkaline phosphatase. In any case, they have confirmed the observations of Melancon and DeLuca (1970), and thus it appears that at least part of the vitamin D-induced system is a calcium-dependent ATPase in the brush border which appears to function in the initial transfer of calcium from the lumen to the mucosal cell. On the other hand, Wasserman and co-workers and Cohn and his collaborators consider the calcium-binding protein as the transport protein (MacGregor *et al.*, 1970). Only additional investigation will be able to verify the mechanism of calcium absorption in response to vitamin D and the relative roles played by these two components.

Thus far, only the calcium-binding protein that was originally discovered by Wasserman and Taylor (1966) has been studied in regard to its biosynthesis following the administration of vitamin D. This work has been carried out by Cohn and co-workers (MacGregor *et al.*, 1970) and reveals that if chicks are made severely vitamin D deficient there is a very great lag in the appearance of radioactivity from radioactive amino acids in the calcium-binding protein. However, if the chicks are maintained at a borderline deficiency state by the daily administration of approximately 4 units of vitamin D_3 and then the incorporation following a large dose of vitamin D is studied, very rapid appearance of carbon-14-labeled amino acids into calcium-binding protein can be observed. Exactly what the correct interpretation is for these experiments is not entirely clear at the present time. An argument for *de novo* synthesis might be made; on the other hand, this may be a very sensitive method of detecting calcium-binding protein turnover. Clearly, much additional work must be carried out before the question of synthesis of calcium binding protein in response to vitamin D administration can be resolved.

There is no question that vitamin D brings about the production of protein components of the calcium transport system of small intestine.

There is little agreement in regard to the nature of the substance made
in response to vitamin D and how it might participate in the calcium
transport process. There seems to be little doubt that the calcium transport process of small intestine is a cation-oriented active transport
mechanism. Whether vitamin D is involved in the synthesis of the active
transport system must at this stage remain controversial. Harrison and
Harrison (1960, 1963b, 1965), with their observations in regard to
intestinal permeability to calcium in response to vitamin D, have concluded that vitamin D contributes a substance which does not directly
participate in the active transport process. On the other hand, Martin
and DeLuca (1969b) and Schachter and his colleagues (Schachter and
Rosen, 1959; Schachter et al., 1961) have considered that the vitamin
D-induced substance participates in the active transport mechanism.
It is likely that both conclusions are correct and that vitamin D influences the transport of calcium both actively and passively, and thus,
the component which is induced by vitamin D may function in an active
transport manner or may act in a passive manner depending upon
conditions.

It seems clear that sodium is required for the calcium transport
process. However, in contrast to the situation with amino acids and
sugars, the sodium appears to be required for the extrusion of calcium
into the serosal fluid (Martin and DeLuca, 1969a). There appears to
be increasing agreement, including the calcium-binding protein studies
of Wasserman, that the vitamin D-induced substance participates in
some reaction at the brush border membrane. Using the fluorescent
antibody technique, Wasserman and co-workers (Taylor and Wasserman, 1969) have demonstrated that the calcium-binding protein is found
predominately in the goblet cells and at the mucosal membrane surface.
Thus, its appearance in the cytoplasm is an artifact of the homogenization technique. Some questions can be raised in regard to the fluorescent
antibody technique, but the conclusions of the Wasserman group seem
to be well founded. It is evident that much new information has been
generated on the calcium transport system in the past 10 years, but
thus far a unified hypothesis encompassing all observations is not yet
forthcoming.

B. Lag in Vitamin D Action

Since the work of Carlsson and Hollunger in 1951 (Carlsson, 1952),
it has been recognized that vitamin D does not act immediately to
induce its well known physiological responses. In short, there is a marked

lag in time following the administration of vitamin D before the appearance of any of its physiological or biochemical effects. This observation
is best illustrated in Fig. 16, which shows that the intestinal calcium
transport system of rats fails to make its appearance following 10 IU
of vitamin D_3 intravenously until some 10–12 hours later. At Wisconsin,
investigation first centered around the fate of the vitamin D molecule
during this lag period. Following the synthesis of radioactive D vitamins
of very high specific activity, the question of whether the lag might
be due to a lack of transport of the vitamin to the target tissues was
examined. It was very quickly demonstrated that the radioactivity from
radioactive vitamin D appeared in the target tissues within minutes
after its intravenous administration, eliminating this as a contributing
factor to the lag in vitamin D action. On the other hand, the next
question—whether vitamin D might be converted to a metabolically
active form before it could act—produced very striking results already
discussed in a prior section. It was demonstrated that at least a fraction
of the lag in vitamin D action is due to the necessity to convert vitamin
D to the 25-hydroxy analog. In the case of rats and 10 units of vitamin
D_3, approximately 5–6 hours are required for the hydroxylation step.
However, as shown in Fig. 17, it is evident that even with 25-HCC
administered intravenously, an approximately 3 hour lag is required
before 10 IU of this active form of vitamin D can produce a rise in
intestinal calcium transport. Thus, either the 25-HCC must be converted further to a metabolically active form or some additional factor
must be involved. In results described earlier, it is evident that the
metabolism of 25-HCC to further metabolites is a very rapid process
in rats, and if the further metabolites represent metabolically active

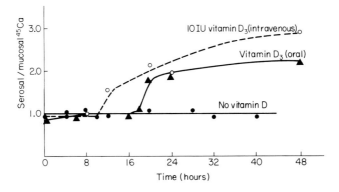

Fig. 16. Lag in intestinal calcium transport response to 0.25 μg vitamin D_3. The
transport measurements were by the everted sac technique. (DeLuca, 1969.)

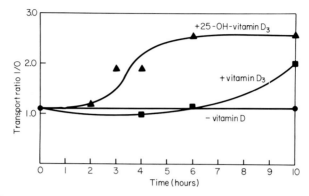

Fɪɢ. 17. Lag in intestinal calcium transport response to 0.25 μg 25-HCC. The transport measurements were by the everted sac technique. (DeLuca, 1969.)

forms, it is clear that their production does not contribute significantly to the 3 or 4 hour lag in the action of 25-HCC.

One of the most fundamental observations in recent years has been that of Zull and co-workers (1965, 1966), who demonstrated very conclusively that actinomycin D given prior to vitamin D blocks completely both the intestinal transport response and the bone mineral mobilization response (Fig. 18). In continued investigation, it could be shown that actinomycin D was acting in the expected fashion, since administration of it following vitamin D could no longer prevent its response. In addition, it could be shown that the metabolism of vitamin D to the polar metabolites was not blocked by actinomycin D nor was the transport of the radioactive substances to the target tissues significantly affected. In addition, histological examination of intestinal mucosa showed these cells to be approximately normal during these experiments. Furthermore, administration of other RNA and protein synthesis inhibitors produced partial inhibition of vitamin D action. Norman (1965) reported that the prior administration of actinomycin D to chicks also prevents the intestinal calcium absorption response to vitamin D. The overall conclusion from these results is that the expression of vitamin D action must involve RNA and protein synthesis.

In confirmation of these results, Stohs et al. (1967) and Stohs and DeLuca (1967) were able to demonstrate that vitamin D induces the synthesis of tritium-labeled RNA of intestinal nuclei from orotic acid-[3]H. Experiments were carried out by giving vitamin D-deficient rats either vehicle or 2000 units of vitamin D_3 intraperitoneally, and 1 hour before the animals were killed they were injected with a pulse of tritiated orotic acid. The ribonucleic acid from the intestinal nuclei was isolated, purified, and counted. It could be shown that 3 hours after this dose of

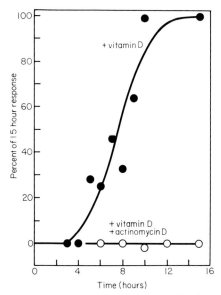

F_IG. 18. Prevention of vitamin D-induced intestinal calcium transport response by actinomycin D. (Zull *et al.*, 1965. Copyright 1965 by the American Association for the Advancement of Science.)

vitamin D_3 there was a rise in the nuclear RNA labeling which diminished at about 8 hours following vitamin D dosage. This pulse labeling of RNA has been confirmed many times and has been found in response to 25-HCC. Pulse labeling of RNA in this case appears within 30 minutes following 25-HCC administration. These results confirm the conclusion from the actinomycin D experiments.

Additional evidence for the vitamin D action in intestinal nuclei was obtained when chromatin was isolated by the method of Marushige and Bonner (1966) from animals deficient in vitamin D and from those given vitamin D at various times prior to the isolation of the intestinal chromatin. Chromatin obtained in this manner could then be incubated with excess RNA polymerase from *E. coli*, nucleoside triphosphates containing ^{14}C-labeled ATP, and other components of the reaction mixture to examine the rate of synthesis of RNA (Hallick and DeLuca, 1969). With this experimental format, it could be shown that at times exactly corresponding to *in vivo* RNA labeling in response to vitamin D, there is an increased template activity of the chromatin isolated from the vitamin D-treated animals. These results suggest that vitamin D in some way brings about the "unmasking" of genetic information which can then be transcribed by RNA polymerase. At the present time, the nature of the RNA generated both *in vivo* or by means of the *E. coli* RNA polymerase experiments has not been identified. Other evidence by investigators concerned with hormonal action has demonstrated that the RNA generated in similar experiments not only includes messenger but ribosomal and all types of RNA. Thus, the RNA which has been measured must not be considered as solely messenger, although it perhaps contains messenger RNA. Thus far, the evidence indicates that 25-HCC or perhaps a further metabolite of it interacts with the nuclei and in some way brings about the unmasking and consequent transcribing of genetic information which probably codes for the calcium transport substance.

Of major interest is the subcellular location of 25-HCC and the further metabolites of vitamin D. Haussler and Norman (1967) as well as Stohs and DeLuca (1967) concluded that the nuclear fraction and the cytoplasmic fraction contain the major amounts of radioactivity of intestinal cells following radioactive vitamin D administration. The nuclear sites appear saturable, since prior administration with nonradioactive vitamin D reduces the appearance of radioactive vitamin D metabolites in the nuclei. Haussler and Norman, however, concluded that the form of vitamin D in the nuclei is unchanged vitamin D, a position which was later reversed. Stohs and DeLuca carried out experiments using nuclear preparations prepared by different methods and found that citric acid preparations yielded nuclei with very small amounts of radioactive vitamin D metabolites. Similarly, deoxyribonucleoproteins were very low in the amounts of radioactivity observable. On the other hand, nuclei prepared in 2.3 M sucrose according to the method of Chaveau (1952) contained all of the radioactivity found originally in the crude nuclear fraction. When the 2.3 M sucrose nuclei from rats given radioactive vitamin D were treated with either 1% citric acid or 1% Triton X-100, the radioactive vitamin D metabolites were removed from the nuclear pellet. These treatments are known to remove the outer nuclear membrane (Blobel and Potter, 1966; Gurr *et al.*, 1963). By means of electron microscopy these conclusions were confirmed by Stohs and DeLuca, and it was tentatively concluded that a major functional site of vitamin D metabolites might be the nuclear membrane. On the other hand, Haussler *et al.* (1968) concluded that chromatin isolated by a procedure they had devised as a modification of the Marushige and Bonner (1966) procedure yielded chromatin which contained the nuclear radioactivity derived from radioactive vitamin D_3. In this laboratory, repeated attempts in both rats and chicks to duplicate these observations using the procedure of Marushige and Bonner met with uniform failure. However, continued investigations revealed that the method of Haussler and Norman yielded very impure chromatin containing many cell organ-elles and membranes (T. Chen *et al.,* 1970). These contaminants were not observed in the Marushige and Bonner procedure and hence the conclusion that vitamin D or its metabolites is bound to the chromatin has little experimental evidence in its support. However, it must be emphasized that these experiments cannot exclude the possibility that the metabolites of vitamin D might be associated with chromatin in the intact tissue. Perhaps autoradiography will be able to resolve this very important question. At present it can only be stated that the metabolites of vitamin D appear in the nuclei, probably the nuclear membrane, and in some fashion bring about the unmasking of genetic information which codes for the calcium transport material.

Figure 19 demonstrates the current working hypothesis in regard to the action of vitamin D on the small intestine. We must consider the liver as the secretory organ of 25-HCC and that it produces this sub-stance in a controlled fashion sensitive to the amount of liver 25-HCC, which in turn must be in some way related to the plasma circulating 25-HCC. This hydroxylation step probably represents a major control point for vitamin D action. The 25-HCC goes to the nuclei of the small intestine and presumably bone where it in some unknown fashion either directly or following further metabolism unmasks genetic in-formation which codes for the calcium transport protein(s). These proteins make their appearance at the brush border site either as a calcium-dependent ATPase or as calcium-binding protein or both, whereupon they facilitate the transfer of calcium into the mucosal cell from the lumen of intestine. The calcium, probably via the mitochondria, is transferred across the mucosal cell and is finally extruded at the serosal surface by a downhill sodium gradient. The sodium gradient is

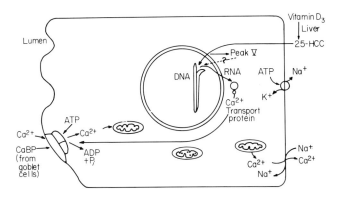

Fig. 19. Model of working hypothesis of vitamin D action in intestine.

presumably maintained by the sodium–potassium pump system. We consider that a mechanism very similar to this may well be taking place in the bone in which the brush border surfaces of the osteoclasts, or the plasma membrane nearest the bone surface in the case of the osteocytes, carry out this transfer function. Obviously, much remains to be learned, but it is evident from the ensuing discussion that within the last 10 years much has been learned in regard to vitamin D action.

The case for vitamin D as a hormone certainly merits discussion here. If man were to bathe in the sun sufficiently by wearing brief clothing and by not spending most of his time inside dwellings, he would generate in his skin sufficient amounts of vitamin D to meet his needs. The vitamin D then no longer is a vitamin in the sense that it would not be required in the diet. The vitamin D would then appear in the liver where upon it would be utilized by the 25-hydroxylation system. This system, being very sensitive to the amount of 25-HCC in the liver, would be a very important control site for the production of active vitamin D. The secretion of the 25-HCC in the blood must be a very slow and perhaps rate limiting process, which would in turn bring about feedback shut down of the 25-hydroxylase system by product inhibition. The 25-HCC would then find its way via the α_2-globulin or specific protein in the plasma to the intestine, bone, and perhaps kidney sites, where it would induce, by mechanisms very similar to other steroid hormones, proteins which carry out then the specific function of vitamin D. The major lacking feature in demonstrating the 25-HCC as a hormone is the feedback control by the product of its action. This has not been tested, and it may well be that the circulating calcium level may affect the 25-hydroxylation system or the secretion of 25-HCC in the plasma. Only additional investigation can bring about a firm conclusion that the 25-HCC represents, in fact, a hormone derived from a dietary or skin-produced substance.

VI. VITAMIN D AND BONE DISEASE

A number of diseases have appeared in the human population in which there is a failure of calcification or a hypocalcemia which are resistant to treatment with even massive amounts of vitamin D. These diseases include familial hypophosphatemia, pseudo vitamin D deficiency disease, sporatic vitamin D-resistant rickets, renal osteodystrophy, Fanconi syndrome, renal rickets. The nature of these diseases and their etiology are quite diverse. Most of them, however, are treatable with massive amounts of vitamin D or its analog DHT. It had been attractive to consider that at least one of these diseases might well be a block in the conversion of vitamin D to the 25-HCC. This, however, has not yet proved to be the case, since none of these diseases thus far treated with 25-HCC respond to physiological doses. However, Pak *et al.* (1970) have reported that 25-HCC is effective in hypoparathyroidism at doses of about 2000–5000 IU per day. These cases included at least one vitamin D-resistant patient. Some successful treatment of familial hypophosphatemia has been obtained with doses of 5000–10,000 IU per day. Fanconi syndrome has been treatable with approximately 5000 IU per day. Pseudo vitamin D deficiency disease, which is completely curable with 50,000–100,000 IU of vitamin D_3 per day, responds to about 5000–10,000 IU of 25-HCC per day. All of these investigations are in their preliminary stages, but the outlook at the present time is that 25-HCC will be a much more effective and safer treatment for patients requiring large doses of vitamin D_3. The reason that the 25-HCC would be safer than vitamin D_3 is that it is turned over more rapidly, and hence, if toxicity is experienced, one can more readily remove the patient from danger by merely removing the 25-HCC, and within a few days toxicity should have subsided, which is in clear contrast to the experience with vitamin D.

VII. ROLE OF VITAMIN D IN CALCIUM AND PHOSPHATE HOMEOSTASIS

Animals that possess adequate amounts of vitamin D and functional parathyroid and thyroid glands maintain a fine control of serum calcium levels. This is accomplished by the abilities of vitamin D, PTH, and CT to influence the handling of calcium and/or phosphate by bone, intestine, and kidney. Thus, in the normal animal, these three agents function to (1) facilitate the absorption of dietary calcium and phosphate, (2) control the mobilization of bone, and (3) prevent the loss of excessive calcium in the urine and increase the urinary excretion of phosphate.

A. ROLE OF PARATHYROID HORMONE AND CALCITONIN IN INTESTINAL CALCIUM TRANSPORT

The effect of vitamin D on intestinal absorption of calcium is readily demonstrated by *in vivo* and *in vitro* techniques. The effect of vitamin D on calcium transport as measured by the everted gut sac technique has been described above. PTH has also been shown to increase calcium transport, by this method (Harrison *et al.*, 1968; Lifshitz *et al.*, 1969) and by *in vitro* techniques (Cramer, 1963; Shah and Draper, 1966). It should be noted, however, that whereas gut sacs prepared from parathyroid-ectomized rats possessing normal amounts of vitamin D demonstrate considerable active transport of calcium, active transport of calcium is very low or completely lacking in gut sacs prepared from vitamin D-deficient animals in spite of the high circulating levels of PTH present in these animals (Harrison *et al.*, 1968; Lifshitz *et al.*, 1969).

In vivo studies of the possibility that CT might reduce the intestinal absorption of calcium have been equivocal (Care and Keynes, 1964; Krawitt, 1967; Cramer *et al.*, 1969). Using the isolated perfused rat small intestine described above, it has been possible to demonstrate that CT reduces the absorption of calcium (Olson and DeLuca, 1970).

B. Role of Vitamin D, Calcitonin, and Parathyroid Hormone in Bone

Vitamin D, as described earlier, requires protein synthesis to produce its physiological response and therefore is relatively slow acting. Even 25-HCC, the "hormonal" form of vitamin D, requires several hours to induce bone mobilization. PTH and CT are more rapid acting, showing changes in bone in less than 1 hour (Tashjian, 1965; Pechet *et al.*, 1967). In fact, common assay for CT is done at 50–60 minutes, at which time the response is maximum. There are also long-term effects of these hormones on bone, but it is not known whether they are direct effects of the hormone or secondary effects due to changes in intracellular calcium. Talmage has shown that there are similar changes in bone RNA following PTH or calcium administration (Park and Talmage, 1968).

In the absence of vitamin D, bone is refractory to normal or even greatly elevated levels of PTH. This is evidenced by (1) the low serum calcium levels observed in a number of species during vitamin D deficiency, (2) a condition in which parathyroid activity is increased, and (3) the inability of all except extremely high doses of PTH to induce an elevation of serum calcium in vitamin D deficiency (Rasmussen *et al.*, 1963).

CT, however, has been shown to be active even in vitamin D-deficient animals (Morii and DeLuca, 1967; Gudmundsson *et al.*, 1966). Of great interest was the fact that Morii and DeLuca found that the serum calcium remained depressed in thyroparathyroidectomized vitamin D-deficient rats given CT, but returned to preinjection levels in intact vitamin

D-deficient rats. This suggested that endogenous PTH was counteracting the hypocalcemic effect of CT even in these vitamin D-deficient animals. The ability of exogenous PTH to block the hypocalcemic effect of CT in thyroparathyroidectomized vitamin D-deficient rats supported this proposition. These vitamin D-deficient rats were otherwise unresponsive to PTH as demonstrated by the lack of (1) a fall in serum calcium following thyroparathyroidectomization and (2) an increase in serum calcium above control levels following injection with PTH. These observations led to the model of bone mobilization proposed by DeLuca *et al.* (1968b) (Fig. 20).

Another approach to the action of PTH in the vitamin D-deficient rat involved maintenance of serum calcium levels by means of high levels of dietary lactose and calcium injections (Au and Raisz, 1967). In the case of dietary lactose, the serum calcium values approached normal. Parathyroidectomization of these animals resulted in a significant drop in serum calcium levels. Subsequent PTH injections restored serum calcium to near presurgical levels in animals possessing normal amounts of vitamin D and in vitamin D-deficient animals receiving dietary lactose or calcium injections, but was without effect on those rats on the standard vitamin D-deficient diet. As an explanation of this PTH responsiveness of vitamin D-deficient rats, these investigators suggested that an early step in PTH action may involve the entrance of calcium into bone cells, and that in vitamin D deficiency with uncalcified osteoid and low serum calcium, this first step may not be possible. These observations, however, are in conflict with a previous report of Arnaud *et al.* (1966). In this study, vitamin D-deficient rats maintained on a high calcium ration and

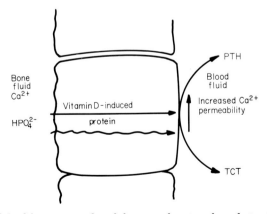

FIG. 20. Model of bone mineral mobilization showing the relationship of vitamin D, PTH, and TCT. (DeLuca *et al.*, 1968b.)

exhibiting near normal serum calcium values did not respond with a serum calcium increase when PTH was given subsequent to parathyroidectomy.

CT is able to reduce the high levels of bone mobilization caused by doses of 10^5–10^6 IU of vitamin D as evidenced by the drop in serum calcium following CT administration to vitamin D-dosed animals (Gudmundsson *et al.*, 1966; Mittleman *et al.*, 1967; Melancon and DeLuca, 1969) and the rise in serum calcium and phosphate following thyroid removal in rats previously dosed with vitamin D (Melancon and DeLuca, 1969; Melancon *et al.*, 1970).

C. Role of Vitamin D, Calcitonin, and Parathyroid Hormone in Kidney

PTH, CT, and vitamin D have all been implicated in the handling of calcium and/or phosphate by the kidney. PTH has been shown to increase phosphate excretion and decrease calcium excretion both in the presence and absence of vitamin D. These are less readily observable in vitamin D-deficient animals than in normal animals. Several of the reasons for this are: (1) intact vitamin D-deficient animals have high circulating levels of PTH which are stimulating these systems to maximal or near maximal levels; (2) at low serum calcium levels, calcium excretion is already low even in parathyroidectomized vitamin D-deficient animals; and (3) the effects of serum calcium levels on phosphate diuresis (Eisenberg, 1968). The ability of PTH to cause phosphate diuresis in vitamin D deficiency is shown by the increase in serum phosphate following parathyroidectomy of such animals. In agreement with this observation, exogenous PTH has been shown to increase urinary phosphate in vitamin D-deficient rats (Arnaud *et al.*, 1966). The ability of PTH to decrease calcium excretion in vitamin D deficiency has been demonstrated most clearly by these workers in studies in which parathyroidectomized vitamin D-deficient rats were perfused with calcium so as to have near normal serum calcium levels. Even under these circumstances, however, the response was less than that observed in parathyroidectomized vitamin D-fed animals. The ability of PTH to increase urine phosphate and decrease urine calcium has also been demonstrated in rats possessing high levels of vitamin D (Melancon *et al.*, 1970).

The effect of PTH on kidney, particularly as measured by phosphate diuresis, is very rapid, being measurable in less than 10 minutes (Beutner and Munson, 1960; Chase and Aurbach, 1967; Sallis *et al.*, 1967). While this appears to be much more rapid than the effect on bone, it may be that changes in urine composition are more readily measurable than changes in bone mobilization. There does appear to be a basic difference in PTH effects on bone and kidney, however, because preadministration of actinomycin D prevents the bone mobilization effect of PTH (Eisenstein and Passavoy, 1964; Tashjian *et al.*, 1964) but not the diuretic effect (Tashjian *et al.*, 1964). Because actinomycin D blocks the effect of vitamin D on bone and intestine (as described above) it has been suggested that actinomycin D prevents a vitamin D-induced system in bone which is required for PTH-induced bone mobilization (Zull *et al.*, 1966), but that vitamin D is not required for PTH action on kidney, and therefore, phosphate diuresis is unaffected by actinomycin D. In fact, the data of Rasmussen *et al.* (1964) are completely consistent with this viewpoint. It is interesting to note, however, that the initial (up to 6 hours) bone mobilization effects of PTH are not blocked by the prior administration of actinomycin D.

Large amounts of vitamin D itself have been shown to increase urine phosphate in the absence of PTH in dogs (Ney *et al.*, 1965, 1968), but Bernstein and co-workers (1963) did not find this in the hypoparathyroid cases which they examined. In any case, the question of whether physiological quantities of vitamin D have a renal effect has not been adequately investigated.

Initial studies of the effect of CT on the kidney seemed to show a CT-induced phosphate diuresis; however, CT-induced hypocalcemia would cause the release of PTH, and the phosphate diuresis observed might well be PTH-induced. More recent studies utilizing parathyroidectomized animals demonstrate a phosphaturia following CT injection (Robinson *et al.*, 1966; Rasmussen *et al.*, 1967), although Rasmussen attributes this to the CT-induced hypocalcemia rather than to CT directly.

D. Summary

The calcium homeostatic mechanisms of vitamin D, PTH, and CT present divergent interrelations depending on the organ tested. Bone mobilization is minimal in the vitamin D-deficient state as after parathyroidectomy. CT and PTH appear to act in an antagonistic fashion to each other and both actions do not appear to require protein synthesis, while that of vitamin D does. At the intestinal absorption site, vitamin D has the major effect with small effects elicited by PTH and CT, with PTH stimulating and CT inhibiting calcium transport. In the kidney, the PTH brings about a massive phosphate diuresis more or less independent of vitamin and CT. It also increases calcium reabsorption. Renal effects of vitamin D and CT are small, if present at all. Clearly the interrelation-ships of these three agents are complex, but they have been substantially clarified in recent years.

VIII. SUMMARY

It has now been clearly demonstrated that vitamin D, which can be taken in the diet or generated in the skin by ultraviolet irradiation, is converted in the liver by means of a specific enzyme system to 25-hydroxy vitamin D. The amount of this conversion is under very tight product inhibition control resulting in an important control site in the production of active vitamin D. The 25-HCC in the plasma is bound to a specific carrier protein and carried to the intestine, bone, and perhaps kidney, the presumed targets of vitamin D action. In the intestine, at least, this metabolite or a further metabolite thereof appears in the nuclei, probably in the nuclear membrane, where it somehow unmasks specific DNA's which are transcribed by RNA polymerase to produce an RNA which codes for the calcium transport component or components. These make their appearance at the brush border surface either as calcium-binding protein or as a calcium-dependent ATPase or both, and they there facili-tate the transfer of calcium from the lumen to the intestinal cell. The calcium is transferred across the intestinal cell by unknown mechanisms, presumably involving mitochondria, and the calcium is excluded at the serosal surface in exchange for sodium ions, whereupon sodium gradient is maintained by the sodium–potassium pump system. Clearly, the 25-HCC functions in almost every regard as a hormonal substance derived from vitamin D_3, and in conjunction with PTH and CT, it contributes to the maintenance of normal serum calcium and phosphate levels and consequently of normal bone.

REFERENCES

Adams, T. H., Wong, R. G., and Norman, A. W. (1969). *Federation Proc.* **28**, 759.

Arnaud, H., Rasmussen, H., and Anast, C. (1966). *J. Clin. Invest.* **45**, 1955.

Au, W. Y. W., and Raisz, L. G. (1967). *J. Clin. Invest.* **46**, 10.

Avioli, L., McDonald, J., Lund, J., and DeLuca, H. F. (1967). *J. Clin. Invest.* **46**, 983.

Bauer, G. C. H., Carlsson, A., and Lindquist, B. (1955). *Kgl. Fysiograf. Sallskap. Lund, Forh.* **25**, 3.

Bell, N., and Bryan, P. (1965). *J. Lab. Clin. Med.* **66**, 852.

Bernstein, D., Kleeman, C. R., and Maxwell, M. H. (1963). *Proc. Soc. Exptl. Biol. Med.* **112**, 353.

Beutner, E. H., and Munson, P. L. (1960). *Endocrinology* **66**, 610.

Blobel, G., and Potter, V. R. (1966). *Science* **154**, 1622.

Blumberg, A., Aebi, H., Hurni, H., and Schonholzer, G. (1960). *Helv. Phys. Acta* **18**, 56.

Blunt, J. W., and DeLuca, H. F. (1969). *Biochemistry* **8**, 671.

Blunt, J. W., DeLuca, H. F., and Schnoes, H. K. (1968a). *Biochemistry* **7**, 3317.

Blunt, J. W., Tanaka, Y., and DeLuca, H. F. (1968b). *Proc. Natl. Acad. Sci. U. S.* **61**, 1503.

Callow, R. K., Kodicek, E., and Thompson, G. A. (1966). *Proc. Roy. Soc.* **B164**, 1.

Care, A. D., and Keynes, W. M. (1964). *Proc. Roy. Soc. Med.* **57**, 867.

Carlsson, A. (1952). *Acta Physiol. Scand.* **26**, 212.

Chase, R., and Aurbach, G. D. (1967). *Proc. Natl. Acad. Sci. U. S.* **58**, 518.

Chaveau, J. (1952). *Compt. Rend.* **235**, 902.

Chen, P. S., Jr., and Bosmann, H. B. (1964). *J. Nutr.* **83**, 133.

Chen, T., Weber, J., and DeLuca, H. F. (1970). *J. Biol. Chem.* **245**, 3776.

Cousins, R. J., DeLuca, H. F., Suda, T., Chen, T., and Tanaka, Y. (1970a). *Biochemistry* **9**, 1453.

Cousins, R. J., DeLuca, H. F., and Gray, R. (1970b). *Biochemistry* **9**, 3649.

Cramer, C. F. (1963). *Endocrinology* **72**, 192.

Cramer, C. F., Parkes, C. O., and Copp, D. H. (1969). *Can. J. Physiol. Pharmacol.* **47**, 181.

Crowfoot, D., and Dunitz, J. D. (1948). *Nature* **162**, 609.

DeCrousaz, B., Blanc, B., and Antener, I. (1965). *Helv. Odontol. Acta* **9**, 151.

DeLuca, H. F. (1967). *Vitamins Hormones* **25**, 315.

DeLuca, H. F. (1969). *Federation Proc.* **28**, 1678.

DeLuca, H. F. (1970). *In* "International Encyclopedia of Pharmacology and Therapeutics" (H. Rasmussen, ed.), pp. 101-329. Pergamon Press, Oxford.

DeLuca, H. F., Weller, M., Blunt, J. W., and Neville, P. F. (1968a). *Arch. Biochem. Biophys.* **124**, 122.

DeLuca, H. F., Morii, H., and Melancon, M. J., Jr. (1968b). *In* "Parathyroid Hormone and Thyrocalcitonin (Calcitonin)" (R. V. Talmage and L. F. Belanger, eds.), p. 448. Excerpta Med. Found., Amsterdam.

Drescher, D., Imrie, M. H., and DeLuca, H. F. (1969). *Arch. Biochem. Biophys.* **130**, 657.

Ebel, J. E., Taylor, A. N., and Wasserman, R. H. (1969). *Am. J. Clin. Nutr.* **22**, 431.

Eisenberg, E. (1968). *In* "Parathyroid Hormone and Thyrocalcitonin (Calcitonin)" (R. V. Talmage and L. F. Belanger, eds.), p. 458. Excerpta Med. Found., Amsterdam.

Eisenstein, R., and Passavoy, M. (1964). *Proc. Soc. Exptl. Biol. Med.* **117**, 77.

Fieser, L. F., and Fieser, M. (1959). *In* "Steroids," pp. 90–169. Reinhold, New York.

Fraser, D. R., and Kodicek, E. (1965). *Biochem. J.* **96**, 59P.

Fraser, D. R., and Kodicek, E. (1966). *Biochem. J.* **100**, 67.

Fraser, D. R., and Kodicek, E. (1968). *Biochem. J.* **106**, 485.

Goldblatt, H., and Soames, K. M. (1923). *Biochem. J.* **17**, 446.

Gran, F. C. (1960). *Acta Physiol. Scand.* **50**, 132.

Greenberg, D. M. (1945). *J. Biol. Chem.* **157**, 99.

Griffenhagen, G. (1952). *Bull. Natl. Inst. Nutr.* **2**, No. 9, 8.

Gudmundsson, T. V., MacIntyre, I., and Soliman, H. A. (1966). *Proc. Roy. Soc.* **B164**, 460.

Gurr, M. I., Finean, J. B., and Hawthorne, J. N. (1963). *Biochim. Biophys. Acta* **70**, 406.

Hallick, R. B., and DeLuca, H. F. (1969). *Proc. Natl. Acad. Sci. U. S.* **63**, 528.

Harmeyer, J., and DeLuca, H. F. (1969). *Arch. Biochem. Biophys.* **133**, 247.

Harrison, H. E., and Harrison, H. C. (1941). *J. Clin. Invest.* **20**, 27.

Harrison, H. E., and Harrison, H. C. (1951). *J. Biol. Chem.* **188**, 83.

Harrison, H. E., and Harrison, H. C. (1960). *Am. J. Physiol.* **199**, 265.

Harrison, H. E., and Harrison, H. C. (1961). *Am. J. Physiol.* **201**, 1007.

Harrison, H. E., and Harrison, H. C. (1963a). *Am. J. Physiol.* **205**, 107.

Harrison, H. E., and Harrison, H. C. (1963b). *In* "The Transfer of Calcium and Strontium Across Biological Membranes" (R. H. Wasserman, ed.), pp. 229–235. Academic Press, New York.

Harrison, H. E., and Harrison, H. C. (1964). *Metab., Clin. Exptl.* **13**, 952.

Harrison, H. E., and Harrison, H. C. (1965). *Am. J. Physiol.* **208**, 370.

Harrison, H. E., Harrison, H. C., and Lifshitz, F. (1968). *In* "Parathyroid Hormone and Thyrocalcitonin (Calcitonin)" (R. V. Talmage and L. F. Belanger, eds.), p. 458. Excerpta Med. Found., Amsterdam.

Haussler, M. R., and Norman, A. W. (1967). *Arch. Biochem. Biophys.* **118**, 145.

Haussler, M. R., Myrtle, J. F., and Norman, A. W. (1968). *J. Biol. Chem.* **243**, 4055.

Helbock, H. J., Forte, J. G., and Saltman, P. (1966). *Biochim. Biophys. Acta* **126**, 81.

Hess, A. F., and Weinstock, M. (1924a). *Proc. Soc. Exptl. Biol. Med.* **22**, 5.

Hess, A. F., and Weinstock, M. (1924b). *Proc. Soc. Exptl. Biol. Med.* **22**, 6.

Hess, A. F., Weinstock, M., and Helman, F. D. (1925). *J. Biol. Chem.* **63**, 305.

Hess, A. F., Weinstock, M., and Sherman, E. (1926). *J. Biol. Chem.* **67**, 413.

Horsting, M. (1970). Ph.D. Thesis, University of Wisconsin.

Horsting, M., and DeLuca, H. F. (1969). *Biochem. Biophys. Res. Commun.* **36**, 251.

Huldshinsky, K. (1919). *Deut. Med. Wochschr.* **45**, 712.

Hunt, R. D., Garcia, F. G., and Hegsted, D. M. (1967). *Lab. Animal Care* **17**, 222.

Imrie, M. H., Neville, P. F., Snellgrove, A. W., and DeLuca, H. F. (1967). *Arch. Biochem. Biophys.* **120**, 525.

Kodicek, E. (1955). *Biochem. J.* **60**, 25.

Kodicek, E. (1957). *Ciba Found. Symp., Bone Struct. Metab.* pp. 161–171.

Kodicek, E. (1960). *Proc. 4th Intern. Congr. Biochem., Vienna, 1958* Vol. II, pp. 198–208. Pergamon Press, Oxford.

Krawitt, E. L. (1967). *Proc. Soc. Exptl. Biol. Med.* **125**, 1084.

Lawson, D. E. M., Wilson, P. W., and Kodicek, E. (1969). *Biochem. J.* **115**, 269.

Lifshitz, F., Harrison, H. C., and Harrison, H. E. (1969). *Endocrinology* **84**, 912.

Lindquist, B. (1952). *Acta Paediat.* **41**, 86.

Loomis, W. F. (1967). *Science* **157**, 501.

Lund, J., and DeLuca, H. F. (1966). *J. Lipid Res.* **7**, 739.

Lund, J., DeLuca, H. F., and Horsting, M. (1967). *Arch. Biochem. Biophys.* **120**, 513.

McCollum, E. V., Simonds, N., Becker, J. E., and Shipley, P. G. (1922a). *Bull. Johns Hopkins Hosp.* **33**, 229.

McCollum, E. V., Simonds, N., Becker, J. E., and Shipley, P. G. (1922b). *J. Biol. Chem.* **53**, 293.

McCollum, E. V., Simonds, N., Becker, J. E., and Shipley, P. G. (1925). *J. Biol. Chem.* **65**, 97.

MacGregor, R. R., Hamilton, J. W., and Cohn, D. V. (1970). *Federation Proc.* **29,** 368.

Martin, D. L. (1968). Ph.D. Thesis, University of Wisconsin.

Martin, D. L., and DeLuca, H. F. (1969a). *Am. J. Physiol.* **216,** 1351.

Martin, D. L., and DeLuca, H. F. (1969b). *Arch. Biochem. Biophys.* **134,** 139.

Martin, D. L., Melancon, M. J., Jr., and DeLuca, H. F. (1969). *Biochem. Biophys. Res. Commun.* **35,** 819.

Marushige, K., and Bonner, J. (1966). *J. Mol. Biol.* **15,** 160.

Melancon, M. J., Jr., and DeLuca, H. F. (1969). *Endocrinology* **85,** 704.

Melancon, M. J., Jr., and DeLuca, H. F. (1970). *Biochemistry* **9,** 1658.

Melancon, M. J., Jr., Morii, H., and DeLuca, H. F. (1970). *In* "The Fat Soluble Vitamins" (H. F. DeLuca and J. W. Suttie, eds.), pp. 111–123. Univ. of Wisconsin Press, Madison, Wisconsin.

Mellanby, E. (1919a). *J. Physiol. (London)* **52,** liii.

Mellanby, E. (1919b). *Lancet* **I,** 407.

Migicovsky, B. B., and Nielson, A. M. (1951). *Arch. Biochem. Biophys.* **34,** 105.

Mittleman, R., Chausmer, A., Bellavia, J., and Wallach, S. (1967). *Endocrinology* **81,** 599.

Morii, H., and DeLuca, H. F. (1967). *Am. J. Physiol.* **213,** 358.

Morii, H., Lund, J., Neville, P. F., and DeLuca, H. F. (1967). *Arch. Biochem. Biophys.* **120,** 508.

Nagode, L. A., Haussler, M. R., Boyce, D. W., Pechet, M. M., and Rasmussen, H. (1970). *Federation Proc.* **29,** 368.

Neuman, W. F. (1958). *A.M.A. Arch. Pathol.* **66,** 204.

Neuman, W. F., and Neuman, M. W. (1958). "The Chemical Dynamics of Bone Mineral." Univ. of Chicago Press, Chicago, Illinois.

Neville, P. F., and DeLuca, H. F. (1966). *Biochemistry* **5,** 2201.

Ney, R. L., Au, W. Y. W., Kelly, G., Radde, I., and Bartter, F. C. (1965). *J. Clin. Invest.* **44,** 2003.

Ney, R. L., Kelly, G., and Bartter, F. C. (1968). *Endocrinology* **82,** 760.

Nicolaysen, R. (1934). *Skand. Arch. Physiol.* **69,** 1.

Nicolaysen, R. (1937a). *Biochem. J.* **31,** 107.

Nicolaysen, R. (1937b). *Biochem. J.* **31,** 122.

Nicolaysen, R. (1937c). *Biochem. J.* **31,** 323.

Nicolaysen, R., and Eeg-Larsen, N. (1953). *Vitamins Hormones* **11,** 29.

Nicolaysen, R., and Eeg-Larsen, N. (1957). *Ciba Found. Symp., Bone Struct. Metab.* pp. 175–184.

Norman, A. W. (1965). *Science* **149,** 185.

Norman, A. W., and DeLuca, H. F. (1963). *Biochemistry* **2,** 1160.

Olson, E. B., Jr., and DeLuca, H. F. (1969). *Science* **165,** 405.

Olson, E. B., Jr., and DeLuca, H. F. (1970). Unpublished observations.

Orr, W. J., Holt, L. E., Jr., Wilkens, L., and Boone, F. H. (1923). *Am. J. Diseases Children* **26,** 362.

Pak, C. Y. C., DeLuca, H. F., Chavez de los Rios, J. M., Suda, T., Ruskin, B., and DeLea, C. S. (1970). *Arch. Internal Med.* **126,** 239.

Park, H. Z., and Talmage, R. V. (1968). *In* "Parathyroid Hormone and Thyrocalcitonin (Calcitonin)" (R. V. Talmage and L. F. Belanger, eds.), p. 203. Excerpta Med. Found., Amsterdam.

Pechet, M. M., Bobadilla, E., Carroll, E. L., and Hesse, R. H. (1967). *Am. J. Med.* **43,** 696.

Ponchon, G., and DeLuca, H. F. (1969a). *J. Nutr.* **99**, 157.

Ponchon, G., and DeLuca, H. F. (1969b). *J. Clin. Invest.* **48**, 1273.

Ponchon, G., Kennan, A. L., and DeLuca, H. F. (1969). *J. Clin. Invest.* **48**, 2032.

Rasmussen, H., DeLuca, H. F., Arnaud, C., Hawker, C., and von Stedingk, M. (1963). *J. Clin. Invest.* **42**, 1940.

Rasmussen, H., Arnaud, C., and Hawker, C. (1964). *Science* **144**, 1019.

Rasmussen, H., Anast, C., and Arnaud, C. (1967). *J. Clin. Invest.* **46**, 746.

Rikkers, H., and DeLuca, H. F. (1967). *Am. J. Physiol.* **213**, 380.

Robinson, C. J., Martin, T. J., and MacIntyre, I. (1966). *Lancet* **II**, 83.

Sallis, J. D., and Holdsworth, E. S. (1962). *Am. J. Physiol.* **203**, 497.

Sallis, J. D., Hopcroft, S. C., and Opit, L. J. (1967). *J. Appl. Physiol.* **23**, 316.

Schachter, D. (1963). *In* "The Transfer of Calcium and Strontium Across Biological Membranes" (R. H. Wasserman, ed.), pp. 197–210. Academic Press, New York.

Schachter, D., and Rosen, S. M. (1959). *Am. J. Physiol.* **196**, 357.

Schachter, D., Dowdle, E. B., and Shenker, H. (1960). *Am. J. Physiol.* **198**, 275.

Schachter, D., Kimberg, D. V., and Shenker, H. (1961). *Am. J. Physiol.* **200**, 1263.

Schachter, D., Finkelstein, J. D., and Kowarski, S. (1964). *J. Clin. Invest.* **43**, 787.

Schachter, D., Kowarski, S., Finkelstein, J. D., and Wang Ma, R. (1966). *Am. J. Physiol.* **211**, 1131.

Schenck, F. (1937). *Naturwissenschaften* **25**, 159.

Sebrell, W. H., Jr., and Harris, R. (1954). *Vitamins* (N. Y.) **2**, 131–266.

Shah, B. G., and Draper, H. H. (1966). *Am. J. Physiol.* **211**, 963.

Shipley, P. G., Kramer, B., and Howland, J. (1925). *Am. J. Diseases Children* **30**, 37.

Steenbock, H. (1924). *Science* **60**, 224.

Steenbock, H., and Black, A. (1924). *J. Biol. Chem.* **61**, 405.

Steenbock, H., and Black, A. (1925). *J. Biol. Chem.* **64**, 263.

Steenbock, H., and Nelson, M. T. (1924). *J. Biol. Chem.* **62**, 209.

Stohs, S. J., and DeLuca, H. F. (1967). *Biochemistry* **6**, 3338.

Stohs, S. J., Zull, J. E., and DeLuca, H. F. (1967). *Biochemistry* **6**, 1304.

Suda, T., DeLuca, H. F., Schnoes, H. K., and Blunt, J. W. (1969). *Biochemistry* **8**, 3515.

Suda, T., DeLuca, H. F., and Tanaka, Y. (1970a). *J. Nutr.* **100**, 1049.

Suda, T., Hallick, R. B., DeLuca, H. F., and Schnoes, H. K. (1970b). *Biochemistry* **9**, 1651.

Suda, T., DeLuca, H. F., Schnoes, H. K., Ponchon, G., Tanaka, Y., and Holick, M. F. (1970c). *Biochemistry* **9**, 2917.

Suda, T., DeLuca, H. F., Schnoes, H., Tanaka, Y., and Holick, M. F. (1970d). *Biochemistry* **9**, 4776.

Tashjian, A. H., Jr. (1965). *Endocrinology* **77**, 375.

Tashjian, A. H., Jr., Ontjes, D. A., and Goodfriend, T. L. (1964). *Biochem. Biophys. Res. Commun.* **16**, 209.

Taylor, A. N., and Wasserman, R. H. (1967). *Arch. Biochem. Biophys.* **119**, 536.

Taylor, A. N., and Wasserman, R. H. (1969). *Federation Proc.* **28**, 759.

Trummel, C., Raisz, L. G., Blunt, J. W., and DeLuca, H. F. (1969). *Science* **163**, 1450.

Ussing, H. H. (1949). *Acta Physiol. Scand.* **19**, 43.

von Werder, F. (1939). *Z. Physiol. Chem.* **260**, 119.

Waddell, J. (1934). *J. Biol. Chem.* **105**, 711.

Wasserman, R. H. (1962). *J. Nutr.* **77**, 69.

Wasserman, R. H. (1963). *In* "The Transfer of Calcium and Strontium Across

Biological Membranes" (R. H. Wasserman, ed.), pp. 211–228. Academic Press, New York.

Wasserman, R. H., and Kallfelz, F. A. (1962). *Am. J. Physiol.* **203**, 221.

Wasserman, R. H., and Taylor, A. N. (1966). *Science* **152**, 791.

Wasserman, R. H., and Taylor, A. N. (1968). *J. Biol. Chem.* **243**, 3987.

Wasserman, R. H., Kallfelz, F. A., and Comar, C. L. (1960). *Science* **133**, 883.

Wasserman, R. H., Taylor, A. N., and Kallfelz, F. A. (1966). *Am. J. Physiol.* **211**, 419.

Wasserman, R. H., Corradino, R. A., and Taylor, A. N. (1968). *J. Biol. Chem.* **243**, 3978.

Westerhof, P., and Keverling Buisman, J. A. (1956). *Rec. Trav. Chim.* **75**, 453.

Westerhof, P., and Keverling Buisman, J. A. (1957). *Rec. Trav. Chim.* **76**, 680.

Wilson, T. H., and Wiseman, G. (1954). *J. Physiol. (London)* **123**, 116.

Windaus, A., Schenck, F., and von Werder, F. (1936). *Z. Physiol. Chem.* **241**, 100.

Zull, J. E., Czarnowska-Misztal, E., and DeLuca, H. F. (1965). *Science* **149**, 182.

Zull, J. E., Czarnowska-Misztal, and DeLuca, H. F. (1966). *Proc. Natl. Acad. Sci. U. S.* **55**, 177.

CHAPTER 12

Insect Hormones

G. R. Wyatt

I. INTRODUCTION

Research on the hormones of insects has followed a course influenced by the special opportunities—and problems—for experimental analysis offered by this group of animals. Because they lack specific immune mechanisms and because of their relatively decentralized circulatory, respiratory, and nervous systems, insects show remarkable tolerance to operations such as ligation, decapitation, grafting together of individuals, or removal of the brain, to which vertebrates would quickly succumb. Such approaches have been resourcefully exploited for many years and have led to a large body of literature establishing hormonal regulatory systems in insect development and cellular activity. Although the main framework of the insect neuroendocrine system is now clear, research of this kind continues to bring new features to light.

For chemical studies, on the other hand, the small size of insects is a serious disadvantage, and because of difficulty in obtaining sufficient material, the first insect hormone to be isolated in pure form (ecdysone) was not so obtained until 1954, and its chemical structure as a steroid was reported only in 1965. For studies on the subcellular mode of action on hormones, insects exhibit certain unique advantages, notably the polytene chromosomes of certain flies which permit gene activity to be seen with the microscope. But this is offset by the difficulty of biochemical investigation; although many biochemical experiments have been performed with homogenates of whole insects, this must be avoided whenever possible, for insects contain tissues as distinct in their functions as those of mammals. Hence, biochemical experiments with insects must often use inadequate amounts of material obtained by tedious dissection, and knowledge of the biochemistry of hormone action as well as other aspects of biochemistry in insects has lagged behind that in vertebrate animals. Another point that has complicated the development of a coherent picture of insect endocrinology is the vast number and remarkable diversity of species in the group. Greater physiological diversity has evolved within the class Insecta than among all the classes of the subphylum Vertebrata, and one cannot assume, for example, that the chemical source of flight energy or the endocrine control of yolk deposition will be similar in a locust, a mosquito, and a moth.

Since 1966, the two chief hormones that control insect development and metamorphosis (ecdysone and juvenile hormone) and highly active analogs of them have become available in pure form. This, together with technical advances such as the culture of insect tissues *in vitro*, has accelerated insect hormone research to an uncomfortably rapid flux at the time of writing. Another stimulus is the encouraging practical possibility that the use of hormone analogs to distort insect development may provide specific, nontoxic means for control of species harmful to man (Williams and Robbins, 1968; Williams, 1970).

This chapter will emphasize recent studies that contribute, or indicate experimental approaches likely to contribute, to understanding the biochemical actions of hormones in insects. The biological background, as well as the extensive recent work on the chemistry of ecdysone and juvenile hormone analogs, will be presented in mere outline, and the reader wishing more detailed information should turn elsewhere. The extensive earlier work on the physiology of insect development and metamorphosis is assembled in two monographs (Wigglesworth, 1954; Pflugfelder, 1958), while a review (Karlson, 1956a) covers the earlier work on the biochemistry of insect hormones. Among many reviews on the role of hormones in insect development, the most comprehensive are those of L. I. Gilbert (1964a,b), Wigglesworth (1964), and Doane (1972), who gives contemporary coverage of subjects omitted or skimped in the present chapter. Another general review on insect hormones is by Highnam (1967). Siddall (1970) emphasizes chemical aspects of ecdysones and juvenile hormones. Three books on insect hormones have appeared (Novák, 1966; Joly, 1968; Wigglesworth, 1970). Finally, there are several review articles on the biochemistry of insect metamorphosis, including discussion of hormone action (Karlson and Sekeris, 1964; L. I. Gilbert, 1967a; G. R. Wyatt, 1968a).

A. OUTLINE OF INSECT DEVELOPMENT

The central process in the postembryonic development of insects (Fig. 1) is molting, the periodic shedding of the exoskeleton, or cuticle, to permit growth (Fig. 2) (described in detail by Locke, 1964; see also Jenkin, 1966). Molting is a function of the epidermis, a simple epithelium that lines the cuticle. In molting, the epidermis retracts (apolysis) from the cuticle, undergoes mitosis, lays down the first protective layers of a new cuticle, and then secretes into the space between old and new cuticles (ecdysial space) hydrolytic enzymes which digest most of the protein and chitin of the old cuticle for resorption and reuse. Finally, the thin remnant of the old cuticle splits open and is cast off (ecdysis), and the insect expands in its temporarily elastic new skin. Frequently, within a few hours the new cuticle is hardened by quinone cross-linking of the protein (sclerotization). In addition, the epidermis

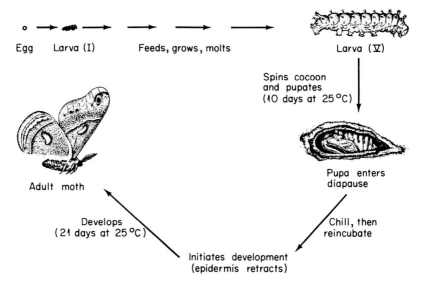

Egg   Larva (I)   Feeds, grows, molts   Larva (Ⅴ)

Spins cocoon
and pupates
(10 days at 25 °C)

Pupa enters
diapause

Adult moth

Develops
(21 days at 25 °C)

Chill, then
reincubate

Initiates development
(epidermis retracts)

Fig. 1. An insect life cycle with complete metamorphosis and pupal diapause, illustrated by the cecropia silkworm (*Hyalophora cecropia*). In nature, there is one generation per year. The larva feeds on foliage and passes through five stages (instars) separated by molting. The pupa is the overwintering stage and requires prolonged chilling to activate the brain neurosecretory cells and reinitiate development. The moth mates and lays eggs, completing the cycle. Rearranged from G. R. Wyatt (1963).

continues after ecdysis to deposit protein and chitin to bring the new cuticle to its full thickness. The activity cycle involves marked changes in form and structure of the epidermal cells.

During larval molts, the new cuticle is essentially similar to the old, and there is relatively little change in the internal organs. Metamorphosis, on the other hand, comprises one (in the more primitive Exopterygota) or two [in the more highly evolved Endopterygota (Fig. 1)] special molts in which cuticle of different character (form, texture, pigmentation, bristles, and scales fitting the pupa or adult stage of the species) is deposited, and there is more or less extensive reconstruction of the internal organs. The latter process involves histolysis of organs no longer needed (for example intersegmental muscles in a caterpillar) and the growth of new organs for the adult (such as flight muscles and gonads). New integumentary structures of the adult develop from special groups of cells (imaginal disks) destined for this role. These cells have been carried through the larval stage invaginated from the epidermis and thus freed from the constraint of the cuticle and from participation in molting.

A versatile and characteristically insectan organ with important roles

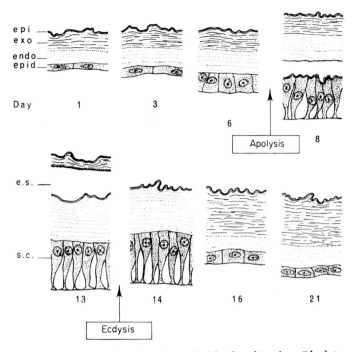

epi
exo
endo
epid

Day   1   3

6

Apolysis   8

e.s.

s.c.

13   14   16   21

Ecdysis

Fig. 2. Steps in insect molting, based on the blood-sucking bug *Rhodnius prolixus.* Time is shown in days after taking a blood meal, which initiates the molting cycle. Layers of the cuticle differing in structure: epi, epicuticle; exo, exocuticle; endo, endocuticle. epid, epidermis; e.s., ecdysial space; s.c., secreting cells. From Jenkin (1966) after Wigglesworth (1959).

in the biochemistry of development is the fat body (discussed by Kilby, 1963). This organ is distributed in the hemocoel and consists of numerous lobes or strings of large cells bathed in the hemolymph for efficient exchange of metabolites. It is a center for intermediary metabolism of carbohydrates (G. R. Wyatt, 1967), lipids (L. I. Gilbert, 1967b), and amino acids (Chen, 1966), as well as being the site of synthesis of most of the blood proteins. It is also the chief site of storage of reserves—fat, glycogen, and, during metamorphosis, granules which apparently constitute reserves of protein. It may also accumulate end products, and during metamorphosis, it may become loaded with crystals of uric acid.

B. Endocrine Control of Insect Development

The processes just described are controlled by the coordinated activity of a neuroendocrine system (Fig. 3). The invariable requisite for molting is tissue stimulation by the molting hormone ecdysone or

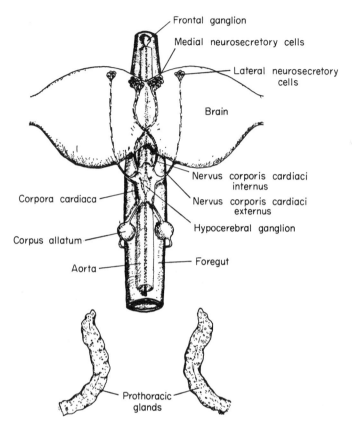

FIG. 3. The chief components of the insect neuroendocrine system. In this view, the ventral nerve cord and the subesophageal ganglion are not shown. From Highnam (1967).

an active analog. The source of molting hormone was first demonstrated by Fukuda (1940, 1944), who showed, in a series of experiments with silkworms, that larval abdomens isolated by ligature would molt if implanted with a group of large cells from the thorax known as the prothoracic gland.[1] Similar results have since been obtained with other insects. In different groups of insects and other arthropods, the homologous organ varies greatly in form and location, and to avoid the consequent multiple terminology, the general name "ecdysial gland" is recommended (Gorbman and Bern, 1962; Herman, 1967), though

[1] The question has recently been raised, and is unresolved at the time of writing, whether ecdysone is actually synthesized in the ecdysial gland (see Section II,C,2). That this gland has some essential role in ecdysone production *in vivo*, however, is not disputed.

"prothoracic gland" is common in the literature. In the developing insect, the ecdysial gland passes through cycles of secretion and inactivity correlated with molting and metamorphosis, and in the adult it normally degenerates permanently. Its functions have recently been duplicated experimentally with pure hormones.

Control over ecdysial gland activity is normally a function of a group of neurosecretory cells in the brain, which produce ecdysiotropin (brain hormone or prothoracotropic hormone). Determination of molting by the brain was demonstrated by ligature and brain removal in gypsy moth caterpillars in some of the earliest successful insect endocrinological experiments (Kopeč, 1922). The relation between brain and ecdysial glands was established much later by Williams (1947), who showed that in isolated abdomens of diapausing cecropia silkworm pupae (which possess no known endocrine organs), implantation of active brains together with portions of prothoracic gland (but neither alone) could induce development. The brain is the receptor for various stimuli (e.g., temperature change, photoperiod, distension of the gut after feeding) which initiate molting in different insects, and it passes the signal on to the ecdysial glands in a manner analogous to the activation of thyroid, adrenal cortex, or gonads by the vertebrate anterior pituitary.

Both larval molts and metamorphic molts depend on ecdysone, and which type will occur is determined by a third hormone, that of the corpora allata. These are bodies (generally paired but sometimes fused) of ectodermal origin situated behind the brain. Their role in metamorphosis was elegantly shown by Wigglesworth (1934) in the blood-sucking bug *Rhodnius*. When the corpora allata were eliminated from an early-stage larva by decapitation (the ecdysial glands being already activated), the larva would molt to a precocious miniature adult. Conversely, when the secretion from corpora allata of an early stage was made available to a fifth (normally final) stage larva, either by grafting or gland implantation, metamorphosis was blocked, and upon molting an unnatural sixth-stage larva appeared. These results, since confirmed in other insects—e.g., the silkworm (Bounhiol, 1938; Fukuda, 1944)—indicate that in the larva the corpora allata secrete a juvenile hormone, the production of which is shut down after an appropriate duration of larval growth. Its role is to influence the character of the molt; during molting in the presence of ecdysone plus juvenile hormone, immature characteristics are retained, but molting provoked by ecdysone alone involves differentiation toward adult form and function. The functions of the corpora allata have recently been duplicated with soluble extracts and pure compounds.

The activity and inactivity of the corpora allata is again generally ruled by the brain, but in this case control depends upon direct nervous connection, and several different mechanisms seem to exist (Doane, 1972). Although the responsibilities of the corpora allata in controlling metamorphosis cease at pupation, in many (but not all) insects these glands resume activity in the adult and the juvenile hormone (paradoxically) then exerts some quite distinct functions in connection with reproductive maturation (Section III,D,2).

One further phenomenon that must be mentioned is diapause, a state of developmental arrest with the ecological purpose of tiding over the winter or other unfavorable season. It sets in at a particular stage in the life cycle, which may be egg, larva, pupa, or adult in different insect species. Diapause is characterized by exceedingly depressed metabolic activity, and is under endocrine control which differs with the stage and species. Thus, saturniid silkmoths exhibit a pupal diapause resulting from lack of ecdysone as a consequence of neurosecretory inactivity of the brain. Development resumes in nature when conditions of temperature and/or photoperiod reactivate the brain, or in the laboratory when either brain hormone or ecdysone is injected. Conversely, in species which normally undergo continuous diapauseless pupal development (such as the commercial silkworm), surgical removal of the brain produces an artificial diapause. A different example is the adult diapause of the Colorado potato beetle and some other insects, which is a consequence of inactivity of the corpora allata and may be terminated by administration of juvenile hormone.

II. THE MOLTING HORMONE—ECDYSONE

Among the hormones that regulate insect development, we shall consider ecdysone first, since it was the first to be obtained in pure form and the most is known about its action. Indeed, studies on the mode of action of ecdysone have had a significant influence on the development of hormone research as a whole.

A. Assay

Ecdysone activity is generally assayed by capacity to cause formation of the puparium in the larvae of certain flies. The puparium is formed by contraction of the mature larva, or maggot, into an ovoid form, followed by sclerotization, or phenolic tanning, of its cuticle to form a hard, dark case within which molting to the true pupa subsequently occurs. In 1935, in a paper that greatly influenced the course of insect endocrinology, Fraenkel reported that when blowfly larvae (*Calliphora erythrocephala*) were ligated behind the thoracic region shortly before the onset of puparium formation, only the anterior portion formed a puparium; but the process could be induced in a certain proportion of the isolated posterior portions by injection of blood from individuals about to pupate. This experiment was developed by E. Becker and Plagge (1939) and Karlson (1956a) into the quantitative *Calliphora* test, the assay which guided the isolation of ecdysone. More recently, similar assays have been carried out with *C. stygia* (Thomson *et al.*, 1970a), the fleshfly (*Sarcophaga peregrina*) (Ohtaki *et al.*, 1967), and the housefly (*Musca domestica*) (Kaplanis *et al.*, 1966a; Kobayashi *et al.*, 1967a; Staal, 1967; Adelung and Karlson, 1969) which gives greater sensitivity and precision. Variables in the test have been studied by Fraenkel and Zdarek (1970).

Demonstration of cuticular darkening in *Calliphora* or other fly larvae is, however, not entirely specific for ecdysones. Ohtaki *et al.* (1968) have challenged Fraenkel's results (1935) in view of evidence that at no stage does larval hemolymph accumulate sufficient ecdysone to bring about pupariation in test abdomens, and, in confirming the original observations, Zdarek and Fraenkel (1969) have shown that a neurohormone is also involved. Tyrosine and certain other phenols can also enhance cuticular tanning (Karlson and Hanser, 1953). True molting hormone activity of a preparation can be confirmed by induction of adult development in the pupae of Lepidoptera such as silkworms (*Bombyx mori*) (Kobayashi *et al.*, 1967a; *Samia cynthia*, Williams, 1968). Natural development in test pupae can be prevented by removal of the brain, but since brainless pupae can also be caused to develop by activation of their ecdysial glands, unequivocal proof of molting hormone activity requires the use of isolated abdomens, which lack all known endocrine glands (Williams, 1954, 1968). The assay by adult development in Lepidoptera, while more definitive, is much less sensitive than that by puparium formation in Diptera (Table I).

B. CHEMISTRY

1. Isolation and Identification

The formidable task of isolation of insect molting hormone in pure form, first undertaken by E. Becker and Plagge (1939), was achieved after many years of work by Butenandt and Karlson (1954). From 500

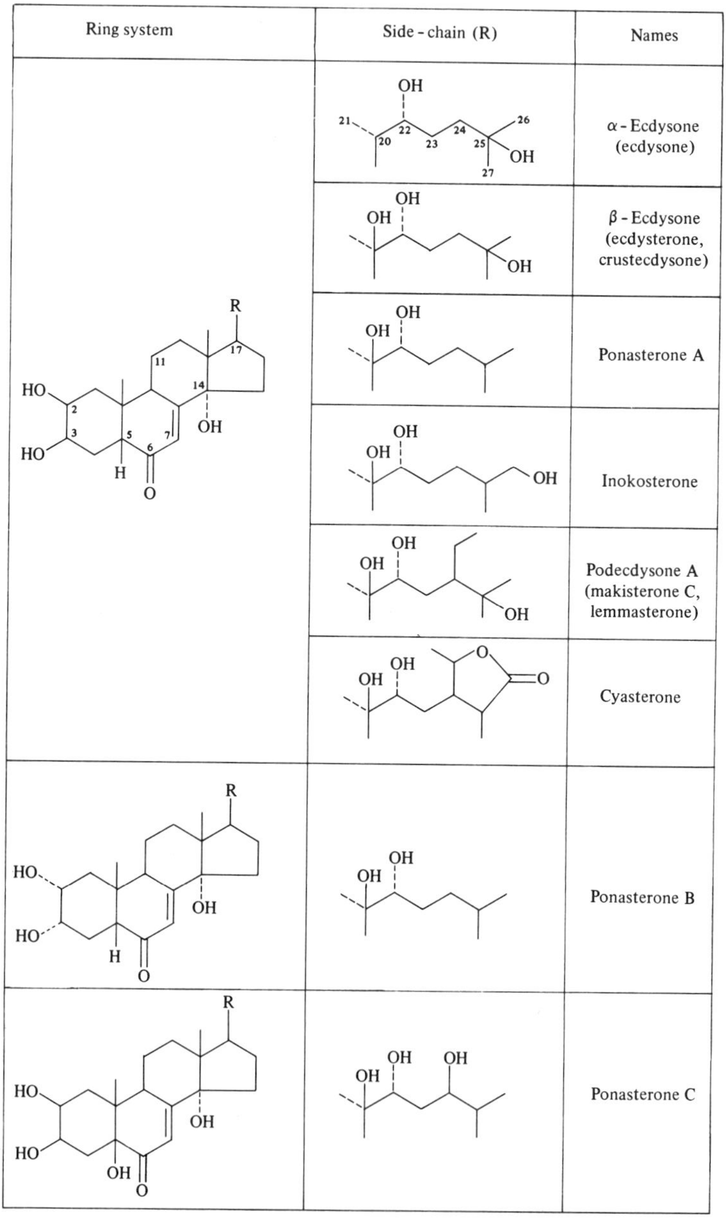

FIG. 4. Structures of ecdysones and some selected phytoecdysones.

kg of *Bombyx* silkworm pupae, guided by the *Calliphora* assay, they recovered 25 mg of recrystallized hormone, to which the name ecdysone (signifying its role in molting) was subsequently given (Karlson, 1956a). A second biologically active substance was separated by countercurrent distribution and obtained pure in still smaller amounts; the two were designated α-ecdysone (the more abundant and less polar) and β-ecdysone, respectively. Attention was then concentrated on α-ecdysone (thereafter often simply called ecdysone) (Hocks *et al.*, 1967), and after improvement of the procedure, 250 mg were obtained from 1000 kg dry pupae (Karlson *et al.*, 1963). In 1965, through extensive chemical studies followed by X-ray crystallographic analysis, the structure was established (Huber and Hoppe, 1965). This was confirmed by synthesis in three different laboratories (Kerb *et al.*, 1966; Siddall *et al.*, 1966; Mori *et al.*, 1968). α-Ecdysone is a C_{27} sterol of exceptionally polar character as a consequence of its multiple hydroxyl groups (Fig. 4). The pure substance is moderately soluble in water and readily soluble in dilute organic solvents such as 10% ethanol. The α,β-unsaturated ketone function confers ultraviolet absorption (λ_{max} in ethanol = 242 nm).

From the later large-scale fractionations from *Bombyx* pupae, the more polar component (β-ecdysone) was obtained in amounts sufficient for assignment of structure. It was recognized as 20-hydroxyecdysone (Hocks and Wiechert, 1966) and named ecdysterone (Hoffmeister, 1966). The same compound (Galbraith *et al.*, 1967) has also been isolated from Crustacea ("crustecdysone") (Hampshire and Horn, 1966) and from various plants (with further synonymy) and has been synthesized (Hüppi and Siddall, 1967; Kerb *et al.*, 1968). Since this substance now appears to be the molting hormone most generally found in insects, and is readily available and likely to be used in future studies on ecdysone action, it seems appropriate to retain for it Karlson's original term "β-ecdysone." If "α-ecdysone" is used for the hormone first identified, the unqualified term "ecdysone" can then be used in a generic sense for steroidal substances with arthropod molting hormone activity.

2. Phytoecdysones

An unanticipated development that set off a recent burst of work on the chemistry of molting hormones was the discovery that a number of active ecdysone analogs occur in astonishing concentrations in certain plants. Nakanishi *et al.* (1966) found four compounds (ponasterones) chemically related to ecdysone and possessing high molting hormone activity in leaves of the Japanese gymnosperm tree *Podocarpus nakaii* (the yield of crystalline products from 4.8 kg of dried leaves was more than 2.5 gm). Takemoto *et al.* (1967) independently found β-ecdysone plus additional related substances (inokosterones) in a drug derived from roots of *Achyranthes fauriei*. This was quickly followed by reports from other laboratories. Jizba *et al.* (1967) in Prague established that a substance first isolated in 1933 from fern rhizomes (*Polypodium vulgare*) was identical with β-ecdysone, and Kaplanis *et al.* (1967) found both α- and β-ecdysone in the bracken fern. Leaves, bark, and wood of the Australian *Podocarpus elatus* and the European yew (*Taxus baccata*) are rich in β-ecdysone (Galbraith and Horn, 1969; Staal, 1967; Hoffmeister *et al.*, 1967a). An energetic survey of plant sources in Japan has resulted in descriptions and structural identification of many new "phytoecdysones." In 1968, 40 out of 1056 plant species tested were stated to yield active extracts (Takemoto, in Williams and Robbins, 1968). At the time of writing, more than thirty chemically distinct phytoecdysones have been described (Fig. 4). These probably have an ecological role in the protection of plants against insect depredation (Williams, 1970).

3. Structure–Activity Relationships

The chemistry of these relatives of ecdysone is reviewed elsewhere (Berkoff, 1969; Horn, 1971; Nakanishi, 1971; Doane, 1972), and only some general features, and their apparent relations to biological activity, inferred from both naturally-occurring and synthetic substances, can be outlined here (Fig. 4; Table I). In the majority of the phytoecdysones, the ring system is identical to that of α- and β-ecdysone. All the ecdysones are sterols of the 5β series (rings A and B *cis*), which contrasts with the conformation of mammalian steroid hormones, in which the A and B rings are planar, and must influence the manner of binding to receptor molecules (Grant, 1969). The importance of this structural feature is confirmed by the inactivity of a synthetic 5α isomer (Robbins *et al.*, 1970); natural 5β-hydroxy ecdysones, on the other hand, in which the ring relationship is maintained, are active (e.g., ponasterone C). The various ring hydroxyl functions seem not to be crucial for activity. Thus, a 2α,3α-hydroxy analog is quite active (ponasterone B; Fig. 4, Table I), and natural and synthetic ecdysone analogs which lack either 2-hydroxyl, 3-hydroxyl or 14-hydroxyl are active, as is a phytoecdysone with an extra hydroxyl group at C-11.

In the side chain, the one essential feature appears to be 22R-hydroxyl. All of the natural ecdysones possess this group, and synthetic 22-iso-α-ecdysone or 22-deoxy-β-ecdysone show very little or no activity (Furlenmeier *et al.*, 1967; Galbraith *et al.*, 1969a). 22-Isoecdysone has proved to be a useful control compound in demonstrating the specificity of

TABLE I

ACTIVITIES OF SEVERAL ECDYSONES IN DIFFERENT ASSAYS

	Effective dose in each assay			
Ecdysone	*Calliphora*[a]	*Musca*[b]	*Sarcophaga*[c]	*S. cynthia*[d]
α-Ecdysone	0.01	0.005	0.63	2.5
β-Ecdysone	0.005	0.005	0.32	5.0
Ponasterone A	0.02	0.005	0.20	1.3
Ponasterone B	0.15	—	0.41	1.3
Ponasterone C	0.05	—	0.45	2.5
Inokosterone	—	0.01	1.15	5.0
Cyasterone	—	0.01	0.29	0.13

[a] Dose in micrograms per animal causing 55–70% puparium formation in *Calliphora erythrocephala* larval abdomens (Hoffmeister *et al.*, 1968).

[b] Dose in micrograms per animal causing 50–60% puparium formation in *Musca domestica* larval abdomens (Robbins *et al.*, 1970).

[c] Dose in micrograms per gram live weight causing 50% puparium formation in *Sarcophaga peregrina* larval abdomens (Williams, 1968).

[d] Dose in micrograms per gram live weight causing 50% formation of normal moths in brainless *Samia cynthia* pupae (Williams, 1968).

certain effects obtained with α-ecdysone (Judy, 1969; Marks and Leopold, 1970; S. S. Wyatt and Wyatt, 1971). All of the active compounds except α-ecdysone possess 20R-hydroxyl, and since α-ecdysone is rapidly hydroxylated at C-20 in certain insects (Section II,C,2), the question may be raised whether it is, without modification, a bona fide hormone. Otherwise, various numbers and arrangements of hydroxyl groups in the side chain seem acceptable, as well as lactones and acetyl derivatives, without drastic alteration of hormone activity. Also, compounds with a C-10 side chain (C-29 sterols related to β-sitosterol) have comparable activities to those with C-8 (related to cholesterol).

In comparing the activities of different ecdysones, quantitative results may be influenced by variations in assay animals or technique. Thus, in the *Calliphora* test, β-ecdysone is reported to be two to three times as active as α-ecdysone (Hoffmeister, 1966), or of equal activity (Kaplanis *et al.*, 1966a). In different insects, relative activities vary greatly (Table I). Thus, ponasterones B and C are much less active than β-ecdysone in *Calliphora*, but are of similar activity in *Sarcophaga* and somewhat higher activity in *cynthia*. Cyasterone, which is by far the most active compound tested in *S. cynthia*, and is also highly active in *Bombyx mori* (Hikino *et al.*, 1968), is no more active than β-ecdysone when assayed in flies. These differences must reflect not only intrinsic hormonal activities but also susceptibility to metabolic modification. For example, the synthetic triol with unhydroxylated side chain (Fig. 6) has molting activity in *Manduca sexta*, but this is probably due to its efficient conversion *in vivo* to α- and β-ecdysone (Kaplanis *et al.*, 1969). On the other hand, resistance of the lactone side chain to degradation (Williams, 1970) probably accounts for the high activity of cyasterone in lepidopteran assays, for the achievement of adult development in a moth undoubtedly requires persistence of active hormone for much longer time than does puparium formation in a maggot.

C. OCCURRENCE AND METABOLISM IN INSECTS

1. Identity and Titer of Ecdysones

Several insect species have now been analyzed for specific ecdysones. The Moroccan locust, *Dociostaurus maroccanus*, yielded rather more β- than α-ecdysones, both being much higher than in *Bombyx* (Stamm, 1958, 1959). Among Lepidopteran pupae, *Antheraea pernyi* yielded β-ecdysone and only minute amounts of α- (Horn *et al.*, 1966), while from the tobacco hornworm (*Manduca sexta*) α-ecdysone, β-ecdysone, and 20,26-dihydroxyecdysone were isolated, β- being the major component (Kaplanis *et al.*, 1966b; Thompson *et al.*, 1967). Among Diptera, pupae of *Calliphora erythrocephala* yielded both α- and β-ecdysone (α- reported to be the chief component; Karlson, 1956a,b), whereas in prepupae of *Calliphora stygia* and *Calliphora vicina* β-ecdysone was the only hormone detectable in significant amounts (Galbraith *et al.*, 1969b). These data are too few to support confident generalization, but β-ecdysone now appears to be the most generally distributed molting hormone in insects, and Karlson's original report of predominantly α-ecdysone in *Bombyx mori* stands out as an exception.

Also of interest are the changes in endogenous ecdysone titer during molting and metamorphosis of a species. This can be determined by extraction from batches of insects, concentration of the hormone, and bioassay (Karlson and Shaaya, 1964). In the blowflies *Calliphora* and *Lucilia*, there is a sharp peak of ecdysone activity close to the time of puparium formation, followed by a second peak which may be related to the development of the adult tissues; samples were not taken during larval development (Fig. 5) (Shaaya and Karlson, 1965a; Barritt and Birt, 1970). In the silkworm, *Bombyx mori*, both the last larval molt and the larval–pupal molt are preceded by peaks of ecdysone activity, and during the pupal period and adult development there is continued high titer, with two apparent maxima (Shaaya and Karlson, 1965b; cf.

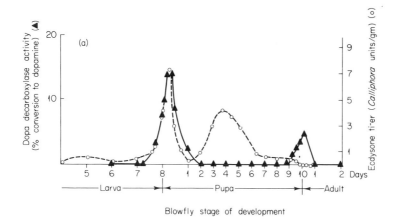

FIG. 5. Changes in ecdysone titer during insect development. (a) Ecdysone titer and activity of dopa decarboxylase in the blowfly *Calliphora erythrocephala*. (b) Ecdysone titer and body weight in the silkworm *Bombyx mori*. Redrawn from Shaaya and Sekeris (1965) and Shaaya and Karlson (1965b).

Burdette, 1962). Assays on the tobacco hornworm, *Manduca sexta* (Kaplanis *et al.,* 1966b), show a single peak during the pupal stage, which, surprisingly, is tenfold higher (per gram live weight) than the maximum observed in *Bombyx.* In adult insects, which have completed their development and lost their ecdysial glands, no ecdysone activity would be expected, and this was observed in *Calliphora;* in several other species, however—locusts (Karlson and Stamm-Menéndez, 1956),

Bombyx (Shaaya and Karlson, 1965b), the milkweed bug (Feir and Winkler, 1969)—significant levels of ecdysone activity were detected in adults, a finding not at present understood.

For further understanding of these differences and of the relations between α- and β-ecdysone, it will be important to discover how the levels of the individual compounds change in hemolymph and tissues during developmental cycles. With improved chromatographic procedures for separation of ecdysones (Hori, 1969), this should now be possible.

2. Biosynthesis

Insects are incapable of steroid biosynthesis *de novo* and fulfill their requirements by utilization of dietary plant or animal sterols. Present information concerning production and degradation of ecdysones in insects is summarized in Fig. 6. Plant sterols are efficiently converted to cholesterol (in the tobacco hornworm, *Manduca sexta;* Svoboda and Robbins, 1968), which can serve as a precursor for ecdysones—demonstrated in the blowfly, *Calliphora* (Karlson and Hoffmeister, 1963; Galbraith *et al.*, 1970) and the silkworm, *Bombyx* (Moriyama *et al.*, 1970). That the triol shown in the scheme is a normal intermediate in conversion of cholesterol to ecdysone is not proven, but the high efficiency with which it is converted in *Manduca* suggests this role (Kaplanis *et al.*, 1969). The side-chain hydroxylations would then occur after completion of the ecdysone tetracycle. Efficient conversion of labeled α-ecdysone to β-ecdysone has been demonstrated in several insect species (King and Siddall, 1969; Galbraith *et al.*, 1969a; Moriyama *et al.*, 1970; Cherbas and Cherbas, 1970). In silkworms at the sixth day of the fifth stage, 15 minutes after injection of α-ecdysone, more than half of the radioactivity recovered was in the form of β-ecdysone. Nevertheless, 24 hours after administration of cholesterol-^{14}C, more activity was found in α-ecdysone than in β-, which suggests that endogenous α-ecdysone, in contrast to exogenous, is protected by some form of binding (Moriyama *et al.*, 1970).

The tissue site of ecdysone synthesis has long been assumed to be the ecdysial gland on the basis of many experiments showing that molting can be induced either by transplanted portions of this gland (Section I,A) or by purified ecdysone (Table II). The gland exhibits cycles of cytological change correlated with molting (Herman and Gilbert, 1966), but direct proof that it produces ecdysone is lacking (cf. Bern, 1967; Herman, 1967, 1968). Its suitability for steroid synthesis has been questioned on fine-structural grounds (Locke, 1969), but this comment is inconclusive, since only modification, and not synthesis, of steroids is

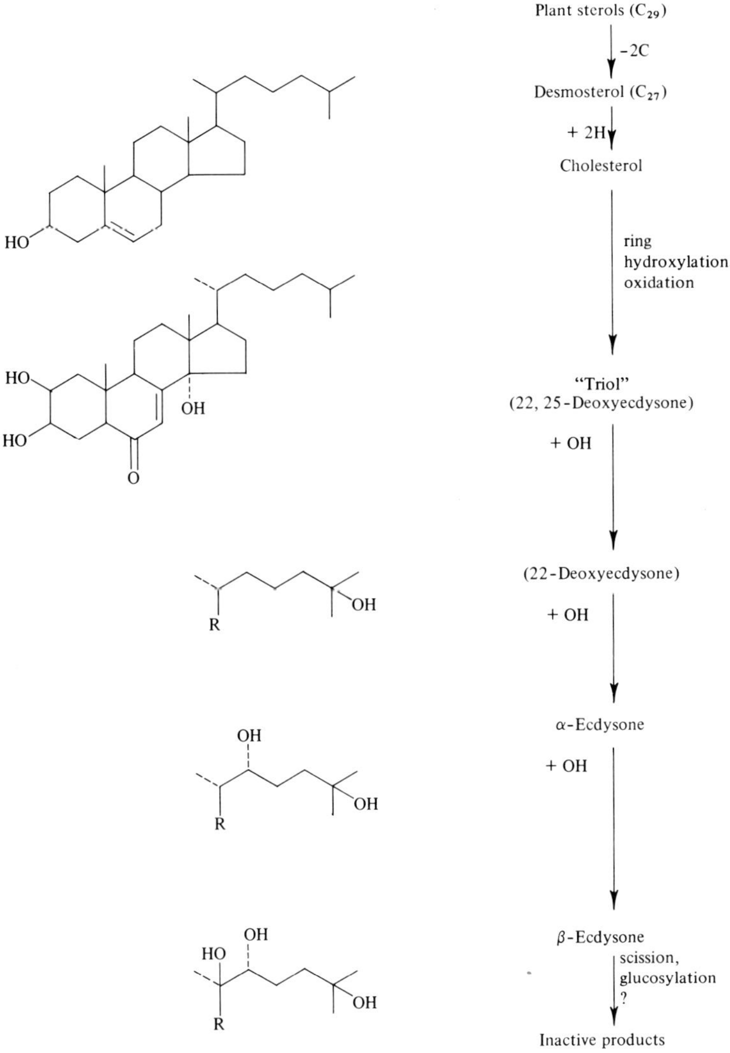

Plant sterols (C_{29})

$\downarrow$ -2C

Desmosterol (C_{27})

+ 2H $\downarrow$

Cholesterol

ring
hydroxylation,
oxidation

$\downarrow$

"Triol"
(22, 25-Deoxyecdysone)

+ OH

$\downarrow$

(22-Deoxyecdysone)

+ OH

$\downarrow$

α-Ecdysone

+ OH

$\downarrow$

β-Ecdysone

scission,
glucosylation
?

$\downarrow$

Inactive products

FIG. 6. Outline of biosynthesis and metabolism of ecdysones.

required of the ecdysone-producing cells. The question must now be raised on biochemical evidence. Efficient conversion of α-ecdysone to β- has been obtained in ligated isolated abdomens of *Calliphora* and *Bombyx* larvae (King and Siddall, 1969: Moriyama *et al.*, 1970), and recently, *Manduca* larval fat body *in vitro* has been shown capable of the necessary hydroxylation (King, 1970). There is now also evidence that earlier steps in ecdysone biosynthesis may be accomplished outside of the ecdysial gland. King (1970) has shown conversion of 22-deoxyecdysone to α- and β-ecdysones in isolated fat body. Nakanishi *et al.* (1971) have obtained evidence for some conversion of cholesterol-^{14}C to α-ecdysone in ligated abdomens of *Bombyx* silkworms. If these last results, which imply the entire synthesis of ecdysone from dietary sterols in tissue other than ecdysial gland, are confirmed, the biochemical role of the ecdysial gland is thrown into question. Recently, the oenocytes have been proposed as a source of ecdysone (Weir, 1970) and shown to contain assayable activity (Romer, 1971). On the other hand, the view that ecdysial gland does indeed make ecdysone is supported by Kambysellis and Williams (1971) who found that explants of this gland could replace pure ecdysone in inducing spermiogenesis in S. *cynthia* silkmoth testes *in vitro*. Clearly, these interrelations will be unambiguously sorted out only when the biochemical capabilities of each tissue and how they are regulated are established by experiments with isolated tissues.

The biosynthesis of β-ecdysone in plants has also been demonstrated; from cholesterol in *Podocarpus elata* (Sauer *et al.*, 1968) and from mevalonate in *Taxus baccata* (de Souza *et al.*, 1969).

3. Degradation

Ecdysones undergo further metabolism resulting in biological inactivation. The rate of this process has been assessed by the decline in activity that can be detected by extraction and bioassay. In mature *Sarcophaga* larvae, injected α-ecdysone has a half-life of 1 hour or less, and the inactivation process is prevented by cold or exclusion of oxygen (Ohtaki *et al.*, 1968). In *Calliphora* larvae, the half-life of exogenous ecdysone is similarly 1–3 hours, and the tissue responsible for inactivation is the fat body, in which an enzyme system capable of inactivating α-ecdysone could be demonstrated (Karlson and Bode, 1969; Shaaya, 1969). Fat body is also the site of ecdysone catabolism in *Manduca* (King, 1970).

The degradative metabolism of ecdysones appears to involve more than one pathway, including side-chain scission to release a carboxylic acid (Galbraith *et al.*, 1969b) and glucoside formation (Heinrich and Hoffmeister, 1970). Several polar degradation products have been recognized chromatographically (Cherbas and Cherbas, 1970). Because of changes in the rate of ecdysone catabolism, it is suggested that regulation of this process may have a role in determining ecdysone titer in an insect (Moriyama *et al.*, 1970a). Like its inactive products, however, α-ecdysone itself may pass into the gut and be excreted (Hoffmeister *et al.*, 1965; Moriyama *et al.*, 1970a).

D. Effects of Ecdysone Action

Some of the observed consequences of administration of purified ecdysones to insects *in vivo* are compiled in Table II, and those observed after addition to tissues isolated *in vitro* are in Table III. Many earlier studies were accomplished by transplantation of tissue, grafting, or stimulation of the endogenous endocrine system.

1. Molting

The principal event brought about by ecdysone is molting. When ecdysone is administered to an insect which is prepared to molt but lacks endogenous hormone, such as a brainless or ligated larva or pupa, molting follows promptly. At a stage when molting does not normally occur (e.g., soon after completion of a molt or in an adult), the insect may be less responsive to ecdysone, either because of rapid inactivation of the hormone or possibly some unpreparedness of the epidermal tissue. It appears, however, that ecdysone can bring about molting at any stage. Silkworm larval abdomens molted even when isolated by ligation and injected with ecdysone immediately after the previous molt (Morohoshi and Iijima, 1969). Adult *Rhodnius* (Wigglesworth, 1940) and cecropia abdomens (Williams, 1963; Krishnakumaran and Schneiderman, 1964) molted in synchrony with immature forms of the same species to which they were grafted. Molting of adult insects as a consequence of injected ecdysone has not yet been reported; possibly the grafting technique is more effective in maintaining the level of hormone for the requisite length of time.

The first visible event in arthropod molting and that most directly associated with ecdysone action is apolysis (also termed "retraction"), the separation of the epidermal cell layer from the old cuticle (see Section I,A; Fig. 2). Apolysis can be detected by dissection within 18 hours after injection of ecdysone into cecropia silkmoth pupae (G. R. Wyatt, 1970), and observed externally in cecropia or cynthia within 2–4 days after administering the hormone (Williams, 1968). Low doses of ecdysone may produce incipient apolysis but failure to complete the molt. The biochemical mechanism of apolysis is, unfortunately, quite unknown, though it is reasonable to suggest the enzymatic hydrolysis of protein or mucopolysaccharide which might be responsible for attachment of the epidermis to the cuticle (cf. Taylor and Richards, 1965). In cecropia pupae, apolysis is prevented by administration of actinomycin D or puromycin together with ecdysone, which shows that synthesis of RNA and protein are required (G. R. Wyatt, 1971).

The major biochemical process in molting is deposition of a new exo-

TABLE II

EFFECTS OF PURIFIED ECDYSONES IN INSECTS *in Vivo*

Order, species, stage, and preparation[a]	Observed effects	Ecdysone dose[b]	Reference
Isoptera			
Kalotermes flavicollis	Molting	α, 0.025 μg[c]; 12 μg by feeding	Lüscher and Karlson (1958)
Hemiptera			
Rhodnius prolixus			
L, decapitated	Muscle regeneration	α, 0.25 μg	Wigglesworth (1957)
	Molting	α, 0.75 μg	Wigglesworth (1955)
Lepidoptera			
Anagasta kühniella			
L, ligated	"Pupation" (localized)	α, 0.4 μg	Karlson (1956a)
Antheraea pernyi			
L	RNA and protein synthesis	α, 12 μg/gm	Sahota and Mansingh (1970)
Bombyx mori			
L	Silk fibroin synthesis	β, 2 μg	Shigematsu and Moriyama (1970)
P, brainless	Development to moths[d]	β, 1 μg (crude)	Kobayashi *et al.* (1967b)
	Trehalose synthesis		Kobayashi and Kimura (1967)
Calpodes ethlius			
L, ligated	Fat body protein granule formation	α, 40 μg	Collins (1969)
Chilo suppressalis			
L, ligated	Sclerotization, apolysis[d]	β, 2.5 μg externally by dipping	Sato *et al.* (1968)
Dicranura vinula			
L, ligated	Pigmentation (ommochromes)	α, 0.1–3 μg[c]	Bückmann (1959)
	Pupation	α, 10–60 μg[c]	Bückmann (1959)

Galleria mellonella			
L, wing disks	RNA synthesis	α, 3 μg/gm	Patel and Madhavan (1969)
P, brainless and isolated abdomens	Nerve connective shortening	α, 0.03–0.06 μg	Pipa (1969)
Hyalophora cecropia			
P, brainless	Adult development	α, 10 μg	Williams (1954)
P, various tissues	Protein synthesis	α, 40 μg	Skinner (1963)
	RNA synthesis	(crude)	G. R. Wyatt and Linzen (1965)
	Respiration, protein and RNA synthesis	α or β, 2–10 μg	G. R. Wyatt (1971)
Ostrinia nubilalis			
L, diapause	Apolysis	α or β, 2–4 μg	Beck and Shane (1969)
Samia cynthia			
P, diapause	Adult development[a]	α, 2.5–5 μg; β, 5–10 μg	Williams (1968a)
P, isolated abdomens	Development	α, 20 μg	Williams (1968a)
P, brainless	Trehalose synthesis	(crude)	Kobayashi *et al.* (1967c)
Hymenoptera			
Cimbex americana			
L, diapause	Development	α, <5 μg	Williams, in Karlson (1956a)
Diptera			
Calliphora erythrocephala			
L, ligated	Puparium formation[a]	α, 0.01 μg[c]	Karlson (1956a)
		β, 0.005 μg	Hoffmeister (1966)
	Dopa decarboxylase induction	α, 0.02 μg[c]	Karlson and Sekeris (1962)
		β, 0.01 μg	Hoffmeister *et al.* (1967b)
	RNA synthesis	α, 0.05 μg[c]	Sekeris *et al.* (1965a)
	Protein synthesis	α, 0.15 μg	Arking and Shaaya (1969)
	Phagocyte activity	β, 4 μg (?)	Crossley (1968)
L, ring gland cauterized	RNA synthesis	α, 0.2 μg	Karlson and Peters (1965)
	Phenol oxidase activator induction	α, 0.1 μg	Karlson and Schweiger (1961)

TABLE II (Continued)

Order, species, stage, and preparation[a]	Observed effects	Ecdysone dose[b]	Reference
L, ring gland removed	Puparial contraction, tanning, pupation	α, 2 × 0.6 μg	Berreur and Fraenkel (1969)
Calliphora stygia			
L	Puparium formation RNA and protein synthesis	α or β, 0.2 μg, α or β, 0.002–0.2 μg	Thomson and Horn (1969); Neufeld et al. (1968)
Chironomus tentans			
L	Pupation; Polytene chromosome puffing; Salivary protein synthesis	α, 0.4 μg; α, 2 × 10^{-6} μg; α, 0.1 μg	Clever (1961); Clever (1961, 1963b); Clever et al. (1969)
Drosophila hydei			
L	Polytene chromosome puffing; Puffing, glue secretion, pigmentation	α, 10^{-5} μg; β, 0.25–2.5 μg/gm	Berendes (1967); Poels (1970)
Drosophila melanogaster			
L	Polytene chromosome puffing	α, 0.02 μg	Ashburner (1970)
L, starved	Molting, puparium formation	α, by feeding 2 mg/100 ml medium	Fourche (1967)
L imaginal disks implanted in adult	Growth; Metamorphosis	β, 7.2 μg/gm in 6 doses; β, 1.2 mg/gm in 3 doses	Postlethwait and Schneiderman (1970); Postlethwait and Schneiderman (1970)

Musca autumnalis L, ligated	Puparium formation, calcification	α, 0.0016 μg	Fraenkel and Hsiao (1967)
Musca domestica L, ligated	Puparium formation, tanning[d]	α, 0.006 μg	Kaplanis *et al.* (1966a)
Sarcophaga argyrostoma P, diapause	Initiation of adult development	α, 0.06–0.3 μg	Fraenkel and Hsiao (1968)
Sarcophaga bullata L, ligated	Puparium formation	α, 0.35 μg	Zdarek and Fraenkel (1969)
Sarcophaga peregrina L, ligated	Puparium formation[d]	α, 0.035 μg; β, 0.018 μg	Ohtaki *et al.* (1967)

[a] L = larva, P = pupa.

[b] α = α-ecdysone; β = β-ecdysone (20-hydroxy-ecdysone or ecdysterone). The dose given is generally the smallest amount per animal, administered by injection, that produced the response in more than 50% of individuals.

[c] Assuming 1 *Calliphora* unit = 0.01 μg.

[d] Response used as ecdysone assay.

TABLE III

EFFECTS OF ECDYSONES ON INSECT TISSUES *in Vitro*

Order, species, stage, and preparation[a]	Observed effects	Ecdysone concentration, time[b]	Reference
Orthoptera			
Periplaneta americana			
L, regenerating legs	Secretion of cuticle and chitin	β, 2.5 μg/ml, 7 days	Marks and Leopold (1970)
Lepidoptera			
Antheraea pernyi			
Ovarian cell line	Increased cell division	β, 0.1 μg/ml, 2–4 days	Mitsuhashi and Grace (1970)
Ovarian cell line	Cell growth, metabolism	β, > 0.1 μg/ml, 2–5 days	Reinecke and Robbins (1971)
Chilo suppressalis			
L, diapause integument	Apolysis, secretion of cuticle	β, 3 μg/ml, 2 days	Agui et al. (1969a)
L, wing disks	Growth	β, 3 μg/ml, 2 days	Agui et al. (1969b)
L, diapause testes	Growth, spermatogenesis	β, 200 μg/ml, few days	Yagi et al. (1969)
Galleria mellonella			
L, wing disks	Growth, morphogenesis	α or β, 3 μg/ml, 3–10 days	Oberlander (1969a)
	DNA synthesis	α, 3 μg/ml, 24 hours	Oberlander (1969b)
Hyalophora cecropia			
P, diapause wings	RNA and protein synthesis	β, 5 μg/ml, 20 hours	S. S. Wyatt and Wyatt (1971)
Manduca sexta			
P, diapause hindgut and fat body	Cell movement	β, 2.5 μg/ml, 8–20 hours	Judy (1969)
Samia cynthia			
P, diapause testis	Spermiogenesis	α, 0.1 μg/ml	Williams and Kambysellis (1969); Kambysellis and Williams (1971)
Coleoptera			
Tenebrio molitor			
P, ovary	Growth, oogenesis	α, 3 μg/ml, 5–10 days	Laverdure (1970)

Diptera			
Chironomus tentans			
L, salivary gland	Polytene chromosome puffing	α, 5 μg/ml, 2 hours	Clever (1965)
Chironomus thummi			
L, salivary gland	Puffing, potential difference	α, 150 μg/ml,[c] 15 minutes	Kroeger (1966)
Drosophila hydei			
L, salivary gland	Chromosome puffing	α, 330 μg/ml,[c] 30 minutes	Berendes (1967)
Drosophila melanogaster			
L, imaginal disks	Differentiation	β, 10 μg/ml, and phyto-ecdysones, 1 day	Kuroda (1969)
L, complex with imaginal disks	Development, differentiation, ecdysis	α, 3–30 μg/ml, 15 days	Mandaron (1970)

[a] L = larva, P = pupa.
[b] Generally, the minimal values for clear-cut effects are given.
[c] Assuming 1 *Calliphora* unit = 0.01 μg.

skeleton, which requires substantial synthesis of cuticular protein, chitin and lipid components by the epidermal cells. This may involve massive intracellular reconstruction, particularly if ecdysone is made available to an insect in a state of diapause or arrested development, when the epidermal cells are attenuated and inactive. When ecdysone was administered to starved *Rhodnius* larvae, Wigglesworth (1957) noted nuclear enlargement and cytological evidence of RNA synthesis within 4–6 hours, followed by proliferation of mitochondria and endoplasmic reticulum, cell growth, cell division, and, after several days, synthesis of cuticular material. In diapause pupae of the silkmoth, *Hyalophora cecropia,* the sequential response of the epidermis to ecdysone is similar— increased RNA and protein synthesis are demonstrable by biochemical analysis within about 6 hours and build up thereafter (see Section II,E,3). Study of fine structure in this tissue shows increased nuclear activity and production of endoplasmic reticulum, polysomes, and mitochondria within the first 2 days, and the deposition of new cuticle begins about the fifth day of ecdysone-induced development (Willis, 1966; Greenstein, 1971). Apolysis, RNA synthesis and cuticular synthesis have all been induced by ecdysone added to epidermal structures *in vitro,* which demonstrates the direct action of the hormone on this tissue (Table III).

Ecdysones induce molting also in arthropods other than insects. β-Ecdysone was found to be effective in several Crustacea, spiders, and the horseshoe crab, which, with the insects, represent four different classes of the phylum (Lowe *et al.,* 1968; Krishnakumaran and Schneiderman, 1968, 1969). In the crayfish *Procambarus,* α-ecdysone, inokosterone, and ponasterone A were also tested and all induced molting. In a tick, larval diapause can be terminated by administration of α-ecdysone, 22,25-deoxy-ecdysone, and (apparently less active) β-ecdysone (Wright, 1969). These results imply that ecdysones were in use to regulate molting before the divergence of the major arthropod groups, which is believed to have occurred before the Cambrian period, at least 200 million years before the emergence of the vertebrates.

2. Puparium Formation

One of the most investigated ecdysone-induced processes is the formation of the puparium of flies. This process provides the basis of the usual assay for ecdysone activity (Section II,A). Both the initial contraction of the larva into puparial form and the cuticular sclerotization that follows are dependent upon the hormone (Berreur and Fraenkel, 1969). After injection of ecdysone into ligated larvae of *Sarcophaga peregrina,* a minimum of 8.5 hours is required before the puparium forms (Ohtaki *et al.,* 1968). In most fly species, the hardening and darkening of the puparium are brought about by phenolic tanning of cuticular protein, the biochemistry of which, and relation to ecdysone action, have been intensively studied (see Section II,E,3). In the facefly, *Musca autumnalis,* the puparium is hardened not by phenolic tanning but by calcification, yet here too the process is controlled by ecdysone (Fraenkel and Hsiao, 1967).

Puparium formation is a specialized process unique to the higher Diptera. In the usual insect molt, sclerotization is a relatively late event, which affects the new cuticle after ecdysis, and thus may be separated by several days from the initial actions of ecdysone. Thus, the sequence of specific enzyme syntheses consequent to ecdysone action must differ greatly with species and stage of insect.

3. Pigmentation

In certain insects, integumentary color changes have been associated with ecdysone action. The best documented example is the prepupal coloration of the European puss moth, *Dicranura vinula* (Bückmann, 1959). The green larvae normally turn dark red just before cocoon spinning as a consequence of ommochrome production. This change can be prevented in the abdomen by ligation at the thorax, and injection of small doses of ecdysone into such abdomens is followed by the normal reddening within 1–3 days.

4. Growth and Metamorphosis of Imaginal Disks

Imaginal disks are groups of cells of epidermal origin which, though apparently undifferentiated during larval growth, are destined to transform at metamorphosis into specialized adult structures (Section I,A). Recently, they have gained much attention as material for the study of cell determination (review, Gehring, 1972). The relationship of their growth and metamorphosis to ecdysone is therefore of much interest.

When disks were extirpated from the metathorax of flour moth larvae (*Anagasta kühniella*) ligated so as to isolate this segment from the ecdysial glands, regeneration occurred nevertheless, suggesting hormone-independent growth (Pohley, 1961). But recent experiments with wax moth larvae (*Galleria mellonella*) showed that when disk removal is delayed for more than 6 days after ligation, few regenerate unless ecdysone is injected (Madhavan and Schneiderman, 1969), and the earlier result is attributed to persistence of some ecdysone after ligature.

Transplantation of disks from larvae of *Drosophila* into the abdomens of adult flies is followed by rapid growth but no further differentiation; development into adult organs then takes place after they are transplanted back into a larva and allowed to metamorphose with it (Hadorn, 1966). Metamorphosis of the disk in the adult abdomen can also be induced by implantation of ecdysial gland tissue (Bodenstein, 1943) or by injection of large amounts of ecdysone (Table II). These results suggest that ecdysone is not essential for growth and cell division in disks, but only for their metamorphosis. Similar experiments in the mosquito *Culex pipiens* gave somewhat different results, however (Spinner, 1969).

During culture of *Galleria* wing disks *in vitro*, some differentiation dependent on ecdysone was obtained. Most impressive are the recent experiments of Mandaron (1970) with *Drosophila* disks, which achieved extensive differentiation and formation of adult cuticular structures in response to ecdysone *in vitro* (Table III).

From these results, it is clear that imaginal disks are very sensitive to ecdysone, and that their metamorphosis (which involves secretion of cuticle) requires it. Whether they can grow in the absence of ecdysone cannot be taken as settled. The experiments which suggest that they can do so may have to be reinterpreted in the light of recent evidence that ecdysone may possibly be synthesized outside of the ecdysial gland (Section II,C,2) and that some ecdysone can persist in adult insects (Section II,C,1).

5. Nonepidermal Tissues

We have emphasized actions of ecdysone on the epidermis. As source of the exoskeleton, the arthropod epidermis has a special role in the determination of body form (Wigglesworth, 1959), and it is unmistakably a target tissue of ecdysone. In ecdysone-initiated molting and metamorphosis, other tissues undergo either growth and differentiation or histolysis, and it is important to determine which processes result from direct action of the hormone and which from secondary interactions in the animal. The development of a saturniid silkmoth from pupa to adult takes about 21 days at 25°C, but can be brought about by a single initial injection of ecdysone into a brainless pupa or isolated abdomen. In view of the short life of ecdysone *in vivo*, none should persist during the latter part of this period. By isolation of abdomens from the thorax at different times, Williams (1952) has inferred that the ecdysial gland hormone is required only for the first 7 days of adult development. Hence, developmental processes which take place later than this, such as flight muscle growth and ovarian maturation, are presumably independent of ecdysone.

The fat body, which is responsible for much of the intermediary metabolism, nutrient storage, and blood protein synthesis in insects, is a tissue of particular interest. In *Calliphora* larvae, stimulation of synthesis of RNA and protein in fat body is observed within 1–4 hours after injection of ecdysone, and the kinetics of the effect are quite similar to those of ecdysone action on body wall (Neufeld *et al.*, 1968; Arking and Shaaya, 1969). After administration of ecdysone to diapause silkmoth pupae, changes in protein and nucleic acid synthesis appear in the fat body with similar timing to those in the epidermis (G. R. Wyatt, 1971). These results suggest direct action of the hormone on fat body cells. In *Rhodnius,* on the other hand, whereas epidermis and intersegmental muscles (which atrophy after each molt) respond quickly to ecdysone, cytologically similar changes in fat body which were at first attributed to ecdysone (Wigglesworth, 1957) were later evoked by nutrition in the apparent absence of the hormone (Wigglesworth, 1963a).

An effect (though not necessarily a direct one) of ecdysone on metabolism in fat body is shown by experiments on utilization of glucose-^{14}C in brainless pupae of *Bombyx mori* and *Samia cynthia* (Kobayashi and Kimura, 1967; Kobayashi *et al.*, 1967c). Eighteen to twenty-four hours after administration, ecdysone greatly increased incorporation of glucose into blood trehalose (which is chiefly synthesized in the fat body), and decreased incorporation into fat body glycogen. In *S. cynthia,* the hormone also stimulated incorporation into fat body lipid and blood protein. In brainless *Hyalophora cecropia* pupae, ecdysone stimulated incorporation of radioactive glucose into both trehalose and glycogen (G. R. Wyatt, 1970). In the *Calpodes* larva, formation of protein granules in fat body from absorbed blood protein is dependent on ecdysone (Collins, 1969).

The hemocytes continue to synthesize DNA during silkmoth pupal diapause and therefore are believed to divide independently of ecdysone (B. Bowers and Williams, 1964; Krishnakumaran *et al.*, 1967). Phagocytic activity by *Calliphora* hemocytes, however, is stimulated by ecdysone (Crossley, 1968).

Clearly, the direct action of a hormone on a tissue can be definitely established only by an effect demonstrated *in vitro*. Since the recent availability of pure ecdysone and of technical improvements in insect tissue culture, experiments of this type have been proceeding apace (Table III). Effects of ecdysone have been shown on gonads, salivary glands, and intestinal tissue, as well as epidermal structures. As yet, there seem to be no published reports of direct effects of ecdysone on isolated insect fat body. A cell line from *Antheraea pernyi* ovaries which grows continuously in culture without hormone is nevertheless stimulated by added ecdysone. In summary, it appears at present that while certain insect tissues can grow in the absence of ecdysone, most are stimulated by the hormone and some may depend on it for growth. The actions of ecdysone demonstrated *in vitro* have been reviewed by Marks (1970).

6. *Abnormalities Produced by High Doses*

Some abnormalities produced by high experimental doses of ecdysones may give clues to the nature of ecdysone action. In *Calliphora stygia* (Thomson and Horn, 1969) and *Drosophila* (Poels, 1970), high doses cause cuticular sclerotization without contraction of the larva to puparial form. In *Dicranura vinula,* high doses cause early apolysis and outward signs of pupation without the normal red pigmentation by ommochromes (which are chiefly synthesized in the fat body) (Bückmann, 1959). Most interesting are the effects in silkmoth pupae induced to initiate adult development by massive injections of ecdysones (Kobayashi *et al.,* 1967a,b; Williams, 1968). These undergo apolysis and rapidly deposit pupal-type cuticle (tanned and lacking the normal scales of the moth), so that the resulting animal much resembles the "second pupae" which can be produced by administration of juvenile hormone (Section III,D). In each of these cases, it appears that the epidermis was forced to molt with such rapidity that certain normal events (perhaps requiring genetic reprogramming) were by-passed. These observations support the concept that apolysis and cuticular synthesis are under rather immediate control of ecdysone and can be quickly induced by high doses, whereas the normal developmental sequence, involving an ordered progression of effects in the epidermis and elsewhere, depends on continued presence of lower titers of the hormone (cf. Wigglesworth, 1963a; Ohtaki *et al.,* 1968).

7. *Respiratory Metabolism*

The mobilization of quiescent tissue for biosynthetic activity requires increased energy supply, and the stimulation of tissue by ecdysone may be accompanied by spectacular increases in respiratory rate and by new synthesis of cytochromes. After injection of β-ecdysone into brainless *H. cecropia* pupae, enhanced respiration can be detected in about 6 hours and the rise continues thereafter (G. R. Wyatt, 1971). Attention was early directed to the respiratory enzyme system of silkmoths by the discovery that pupae in diapause are highly resistant to the cytochrome oxidase inhibitors cyanide and carbon monoxide (Schneiderman and Williams, 1954). It seemed possible that respiration during diapause might be mediated by a noncytochrome pathway, and the suggestion was made that the resynthesis of cytochromes might be especially closely linked to the action of ecdysone (Williams, 1951; Shappirio and Williams, 1957). From further analysis with attention to the kinetics of respiratory metabolism, however, it became clear that the resistance of diapause respiration to inhibitors of cytochrome oxidase could be explained by the excess of that enzyme above the normal flux of the system, which is limited by control steps elsewhere (Harvey and Williams, 1958; Kurland and Schneiderman, 1959). The synthesis of cytochromes, though essential for renewed development from diapause, is not the cause of this, for stimulation of diapause pupae by experimental injury is followed by cytochrome synthesis but not development (Shappirio, 1960).

In *Rhodnius,* also, the molting cycle is accompanied by impressive changes in respiratory rate and tissue cytochrome levels, but again the evidence suggests that respiratory activity is secondary to energy demand, chiefly for protein synthesis, and that control of the latter process is closer to the action of the molting hormone (Wigglesworth, 1957).

8. Interrelations with Steroid Hormones of Vertebrates

Only a few experiments have been done on the important questions whether the steroid hormones of vertebrates can affect insects, and what effects the ecdysones may have on tissues of vertebrates. Hydrocortisone can apparently retard insect growth, without disturbing the molting cycle or differentiation. This was reported for mealworms and locusts with low steroid doses (Mordue, 1967), and for the fungus gnat *Sciara coprophila* with massive dietary supplementation (Crouse, 1968). This effect deserves further study. The reported induction of polytene chromosome puffs (see Section II,E,4) by hydrocortisone phosphate (E. F. Gilbert and Pistey, 1966), however, may be dismissed as nonspecific because of the high concentration used, and the reported blocking of puffing by hydrocortisone (Goodman et al., 1967) could not be confirmed (Crouse, 1968).

Reports of inhibition of mammalian tumor cell and fibroblast growth *in vitro* by ecdysone (Burdette and Richards, 1961) may be discounted due to the use of a crude preparation of the hormone. Pure ecdysones had no visible effect on the growth of vertebrate tumor or normal cells (Hoffmeister and Lang, 1964; Hirono et al., 1969). Ecdysones do appear to be capable of some physiological effects on mammalian cells, however. α-Ecdysone injected into mice has a definite mineralcorticoid effect, including sodium retention and potassium excretion (Siddall, in Williams and Robbins, 1968). Furthermore, various phytoecdysones have recently been shown to stimulate protein and RNA synthesis in mouse liver (Okui et al., 1968; Otaka et al., 1968, 1969a,b; Otaka and Uchiyama, 1969).

E. Biochemistry of Ecdysone Action

1. Ecdysone and DNA Synthesis

The pattern of DNA synthesis during the developmental cycle has been examined in saturniid silkmoths by autoradiography of various tissues after injection of thymidine-^{3}H (Bowers and Williams, 1964; Krishnakumaran *et al.*, 1967). At the beginning of the pupal diapause, DNA synthesis shuts down throughout the animal except in the hemocytes and a few cells of other tissues; in the epidermis, there is no trace of it. Early in post-diapause development, DNA synthesis recommences in almost all tissues and is especially intense in the epidermis. Furthermore, inhibition of DNA synthesis by injection of 5-fluorodeoxyuridine or mitomycin C, which has no obvious effect upon pupae in diapause, prevents their initiating development toward the adult (Williams, 1965; Krishnakumaran and Schneiderman, 1964). Therefore, DNA synthesis is an essential part of the normal ecdysone-induced molting cycle.

The use of pure ecdysone has permitted more analytical experiments. Following injection of ecdysone into brainless cecropia pupae, a rise in DNA synthesis was observed only at 48 hours, distinctly later than the effects upon synthesis of RNA and protein (G. R. Wyatt, 1968b, 1971). Injection of high doses of ecdysone into pupae or ligated adult abdomens together with sufficient mitomycin C to block synthesis is reported to bring about apolysis but no deposition of new cuticle by the epidermis (Madhavan and Schneiderman, 1968). Hence, the earliest events in ecdysone action appear to be independent of DNA synthesis.

The striking changes in DNA synthesis during ecdysone-induced development encouraged investigation of enzymes associated with production of DNA precursors. In wing epidermis of the silkmoth, *Antheraea pernyi*, thymidine kinase activity increases 25-fold at the initiation of adult development (Brookes and Williams, 1965). In cecropia, deoxycytidylate and thymidylate kinases rise from essentially zero levels in diapause to maxima at an early stage of adult development, and changes in other kinases in epidermis and other tissues have also been documented (Berry and Firshein, 1967). Deoxycytidine deaminase, deoxyguanosine deaminase, and thymidylate synthetase also rise sharply in the transition from diapause to development (Firshein *et al.*, 1967). There is no evidence that any of these enzymes regulates DNA synthesis *in vivo;* indeed, for the kinases there is contrary evidence, for increased enzyme activity without concomitant DNA synthesis is observed after injury to pupae (Berry and Firshein, 1967). Unfortunately, when these experiments were carried out, pure ecdysone was not available so the time sequence of enzyme changes in relation to hormone action was not determined.

In explanted larval wing discs of *Galleria*, it is reported that α-ecdysone stimulated DNA synthesis but β-ecdysone did not, an apparent difference difficult to reconcile with their similar morphogenetic effects (Oberlander, 1969b).

2. *Ecdysone and Enzyme Induction; Dopa Decarboxylase*

In addition to the stimulation of DNA synthesis, many examples have been given (Section II,D) in which the action of ecdysone must be accompanied by increased enzyme activity. In molting, in addition to the unknown enzymatic basis of apolysis, digestion of the old cuticle requires hydrolytic enzymes, and production of the new cuticle requires activity in synthesis of proteins, chitin, and certain lipids. Increases in respiration and respiratory enzymes early in ecdysone action have been demonstrated. The induction of these processes, as well as production of new blood protein during ecdysone action, is blocked by inhibitors of RNA and protein synthesis. The changes in pigmentation and carbohydrate metabolism discussed above probably also depend on enzyme synthesis, though this has not been shown. In none of these cases, however, has either the temporal or causal relationship between the action of the hormone and the production of a specific enzyme been analyzed. An example that has been studied with this objective is that of certain enzymes concerned with puparial tanning in the blowfly *Calliphora*.

The hardening and darkening of the blowfly puparium, like the sclerotization of insect cuticles generally (Brunet, 1966), is accomplished by phenolic tanning of cuticular protein. The biochemistry of the process in *Calliphora* has been extensively investigated by Karlson, Sekeris, and their colleagues (review, Sekeris and Karlson, 1966). The chief tanning agent is the *o*-quinone derived by oxidation of *N*-acetyldopamine, which is produced in turn from tyrosine by oxidation, decarboxylation, and acetylation. Experiments with tyrosine-^{14}C showed a change in its metabolic fate at a critical stage of larval development: in young larvae it is metabolized chiefly by transamination and degradation to several phenolic acids, but just before puparium formation tyrosine is converted instead to the tanning agents (Sekeris and Karlson, 1962). This shift is dependent on the action of ecdysone; in ligated larvae, incorporation of tyrosine into the cuticle occurs only if ecdysone is injected, whereas incorporation of leucine into cuticular protein is unaffected by the hormone (Karlson, 1960). Two enzymes in the pathway which appear to be important in regulation have been particularly studied: (1) a phenol oxidase, which is converted from an inactive proenzyme by an activator enzyme (Schweiger and Karlson, 1962; Karlson *et al.*, 1964a); and (2) dopa decarboxylase (Sekeris, 1963).

The phenol oxidase and its activator rise in concentration during the third instar of larval life. In larvae with cauterized ring-glands they disappear and can then be restored by injection of ecdysone; the activator enzyme is back to its normal level about 30 hours after administration of the hormone (Karlson and Schweiger, 1961). Because of the complexity of the phenol oxidase system, however, it has not been further studied.

The dopa decarboxylase normally rises sharply in activity during the day before puparium formation, in coordination with elevated ecdysone titer (Fig. 5a). In larvae ligated as for the assay of ecdysone, induction by the hormone can be demonstrated; during 20 hours after injection of α-ecdysone, enzyme activity rises about tenfold (Karlson and Sekeris, 1962). In later experiments with β-ecdysone, significant elevation was shown by 4 hours (Hoffmeister *et al.*, 1967b). A certain level of activity apparently exists even before hormone treatment. The rise in enzyme activity (and puparium formation) in intact larvae is much retarded by various inhibitors of nucleic acid and protein synthesis, so that synthesis *de novo* is implied, though the interactions of inhibitors and hormone have not been analyzed in detail (Sekeris and Karlson, 1964).

Another enzyme, 5-hydroxytryptophan decarboxylase, whose function is not related to cuticular tanning, shows somewhat inverse changes, exhibiting high activity at developmental stages when ecdysone titer is low and declining after administration of the hormone (Marmaras *et al.*, 1966).

To seek the basis for the induction of dopa decarboxylase, the effect of ecdysone on RNA synthesis in *Calliphora* larvae was investigated. The incorporation of ^{32}P *in vivo* into RNA extractable from whole larvae by cold phenol (chiefly cytoplasmic RNA) showed up to 85% elevation 4–7 hours after administration of α-ecdysone (Karlson and Peters, 1965). When a cell fraction representing larval epidermal nuclei was prepared and RNA was extracted with the aid of heat and detergent, enhanced incorporation could be shown during the first hour after injection of hormone (Sekeris *et al.*, 1965a). By 3 hours, increased radioactivity appeared in the microsomes. Similar rapid responses have been confirmed with β-ecdysone (Neufeld *et al.*, 1968).

The activity of *Calliphora* RNA in cell-free protein-synthesizing systems was then examined. When added to microsomal preparations from either *Calliphora* epidermis or rat liver, the RNA extracted at 65°C from epidermal nuclei gave strong stimulation of leucine incorporation, suggesting messenger activity; RNA from incipient puparia, in which ecdysone would be active, was more effective than that from an earlier larval stage (Sekeris *et al.,* 1965a). In a further crucial experiment, the development of dopa decarboxylase activity was reported during incubation of a rat liver microsomal system, dependent upon addition of RNA from the appropriate developmental stage of *Calliphora* (Sekeris and Lang, 1964; Sekeris, 1967). This was interpreted as demonstrating the specific messenger activity of the RNA. Unfortunately, despite the important implications of this experiment and much discussion aroused by it, no more extensive publication has appeared since the preliminary report, which included few experimental data. The presumptive enzyme product was characterized only by its catalytic activity; amino acid incorporation into a specifically identified protein was not shown. No tests with inhibitors were described. Rat liver normally contains dopa decarboxylase, and mechanisms for its activation during incubation are conceivable. Therefore, although it is quite likely that template RNA for dopa decarboxylase may be produced during the action of ecdysone, direct experimental demonstration of this cannot be taken as established. In other recent work with eukaryote systems, cell-free synthesis of specific proteins has been established only in certain favorable cases where a particular protein makes up a high proportion of the production of a tissue, and unambiguous identification of the product has been stressed. More conclusive demonstration of messenger activity in the *Calliphora* epidermal system may be very difficult.

Further experiments with the *Calliphora* system were directed toward demonstrating direct effects of ecdysone added to cell nuclei *in vitro*. It was reported that the presence of α-ecdysone (1 μg/ml) strongly stimulated incorporation of uracil-^{14}C (uridine triphosphate was apparently not tested) into *Calliphora* epidermal nuclei during 15 or 60 minutes (Sekeris *et al.,* 1965b) and that RNA extracted from nuclei thus treated stimulated leucine incorporation in a rat liver ribosomal system more than RNA from control nuclei (Dukes *et al.,* 1966). It is difficult to assess these experiments, since characterization of the insect nuclei or the effects of steroids other than ecdysone were not reported.

From another tissue of *Calliphora* larvae, the fat body, nuclei have been isolated and direct stimulation of RNA synthesis (UTP-^{14}C incorporation) by ecdysone has been reported (Congote *et al.,* 1969). Further, it is claimed on the basis of RNA–DNA hybridization experiments that the RNA produced in nuclei treated with ecdysone (or juvenile hormone) is qualitatively different from that of controls (Congote *et al.,* 1970). These results may be of the highest importance, but support with further data is needed.

These studies on enzyme induction by ecdysone have been summarized by Sekeris (1967) and, together with cytological observations on induction of chromosome puffs by ecdysone (Section II,E,5), presented in support of a general theory of hormone action by specific gene derepression (see Section II,E,8).

3. Biosynthesis in the Development of Saturniid Silkmoths

For the study of hormone action in insect development, the spectacular saturniid silkmoths have several virtues (Williams, 1951). Their size permits dissection of individual tissues in quantities sufficient for biochemical analysis, and their developmental cycle includes a well defined pupal diapause (Fig. 1). Recently, a rapid response of RNA and protein synthesis after injection of ecdysone into silkmoth larvae has been reported (Sahota and Mansingh, 1970). Changing rates of RNA synthesis in several tissues of the cecropia silkmoth (*Hyalophora cecropia*) have been followed by autoradiography (Berry *et al.*, 1967) and especially striking increases were shown at the ecdysone-induced termination of diapause. At this time, enhanced RNA synthesis concomitant with ecdysone action is demonstrable also by biochemical measurement of precursor incorporation in wings and fat body (G. R. Wyatt and Linzen, 1965; Barth *et al.*, 1964). A distinct rise in total RNA content can be detected in the pupal wings, though not in the fat body (G. R. Wyatt, 1959; Linzen and Wyatt, 1964); the massive increases reported for both tissues by Barth *et al.* (1964) are probably attributable to an inadequate method of extraction.

The pupal wings were selected for study of the pattern of macromolecular synthesis in the early phases of ecdysone-induced development toward the adult wings (G. R. Wyatt, 1968b, 1971). After injection of ecdysone, the rate of RNA synthesis is elevated significantly at 6 hours, attains a maximum (about tenfold over the diapause level) at 18–20 hours, and then falls off again. This decline might be attributed to inactivation of the hormone, but it occurs even when the dose is sufficient to ensure continued development to the moth. Furthermore, a similar pattern, with an early peak of RNA synthesis followed by a sharp decline and a later, more diffuse second peak, is observed during development of intact animals under the influence of endogenous hormone. Therefore, a burst of RNA synthesis appears to be a characteristic early consequence of ecdysone action in this system (Fig. 7).

The synthesis of protein, measured by similar *in vivo* labeling experiments, begins to rise at about the same time as RNA (or slightly later), attains rates manyfold above the low initial level, and remains at a continuous high rate for some days thereafter. Unfortunately, we have as yet no information as to what specific proteins are being produced by the wing tissue.

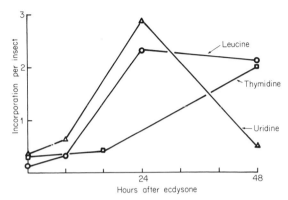

FIG. 7. Effects of ecdysone on macromolecular synthesis in wing tissue of cecropia silkmoth pupae. Ecdysone was injected into brainless diapause pupae; then, at different times, radioactive leucine (for protein), uridine (for RNA), and thymidine (for DNA) were injected and incorporation was measured after 4 hours of incubation. Results are in arbitrary units per insect. From G. R. Wyatt (1968). *In* "Metamorphosis" (W. Etkin and L. I. Gilbert, eds.). Appleton, New York. Copyright 1968 by Meredith Corporation.

The RNA produced in cecropia wing tissue during this response to ecdysone has been characterized with respect to base composition by pulse incorporation of ^{32}P, and has been shown to be clearly different from the bulk (chiefly ribosomal) RNA of the tissue (G. R. Wyatt and Linzen, 1965). After 2 hours of labeling, it contains 44% guanine + cytosine, which could be accounted for by a mixture of about half ribosomal RNA (55% guanine + cytosine) (Applebaum *et al.*, 1966) and half RNA reflecting the overall composition of the DNA (35% guanine + cytosine); this composition, however, was no different after ecdysone stimulation than in control animals. Fractionation by sucrose gradient centrifugation indicated enhanced synthesis of all classes of RNA, none being distinctively responsive (G. R. Wyatt, 1968b). The stimulatory effect of cecropia wing RNA on amino acid incorporation by *Escherichia coli* ribosomes was tested, and a marked rise in such activity was found early in ecdysone-induced development (Howells and Wyatt, 1969). However, difficulty in interpreting the role of animal RNA when added to bacterial ribosomal systems leaves it uncertain to what extent this reflects true template activity in protein synthesis. Evidence for specificity in the RNA made during ecdysone action has also been sought by competition in RNA–DNA hybridization (Lucas and Wyatt, 1971). When RNA labeled 18 hours after administration of ecdysone was used

for hybridization, RNA from tissue at the same stage competed significantly better than that from other stages, indicating that certain species
of RNA were more abundant during early hormone action than at other
times (Fig. 8). But the difference was small, and, surprisingly, RNA
from diapause and several developmental stages was indistinguishable
by this test. It is now recognized that with complex eukaryote nucleic
acids the technique as carried out would not be expected to detect
limited amounts of messenger RNA transcribed from unique DNA
sequences (Bishop, 1969).

In the related silkmoth *Antheraea pernyi*, a 12 S RNA component
observed in sucrose gradients, which showed rapid labeling in injured
and early developing pupae, was tentatively dubbed messenger RNA
(Barth *et al.*, 1964).

Another aspect of cecropia wing development concerns ribosomes
and polysomes (Ebstein and Wyatt, 1971). In diapause, there are
abundant 80 S monosomes but virtually no polysomes. Within a few
hours of ecdysone-induced development, polysomes active in protein
synthesis begin to be formed; these appear to incorporate both preexisting ribosomes and new ones produced under the hormonal stimulus.
These findings are in accord with changes observed in the fine structure
of the tissue (Greenstein, 1971).

To summarize, these studies show that during roughly the first 24

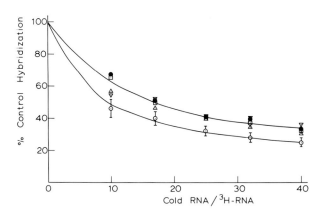

Fig. 8. Characterization of RNA from cecropia pupal and developing wings by
competition in RNA–DNA hybridization. RNA was pulse-labeled by incubating
wings with cytidine-³H 18 hours after injection of ecdysone into diapause pupae,
and was hybridized with DNA immobilized on membrane filters. Nonradioactive
RNA for competition, added in the proportions indicated, was prepared from wings
at the following developmental stages: □, diapause; ○, 18 hours after ecdysone
(homologous); △, 2 days; ▽, 5 days; ●, 13 days. From Lucas and Wyatt (1971).

hours after stimulating diapause wing tissue with ecdysones, there is massive new synthesis of a wide variety of RNA and build up of the protein-synthesizing system. The assays for template activity and RNA–DNA hybridization suggest that, among this RNA output, there is selective derepression of new genes. One must recognize that such a tissue awakening from diapause and undergoing general biochemical reconstruction may not be the most advantageous for seeking specific messenger RNA's; also, the time used in most of these studies, which was that of maximal RNA output in response to the hormone, may be too late for detecting initial specific syntheses.

4. Polytene Chromosomes and Puffing

A unique contribution of certain insects to the analysis of hormone-induced development results from their possession of giant chromosomes in which evidence of gene activity can be perceived directly with the microscope. The extensive experimental work on these has been covered in several reviews (Beermann, 1962, 1967; Kroeger and Lezzi, 1966; Clever, 1968; Ashburner, 1970a) and will here merely be summarized in its relation to hormone action.

During larval growth of Diptera, ordinary cell division is replaced by endomitosis, in which the DNA replicates but does not separate, so that a polytene chromosome is built up consisting of a bundle of fibers each genetically equivalent to a normal chromatid. The number of such replications varies with species and tissue; for example, in *Drosophila melanogaster* salivary glands, nine doublings result in chromosomes with 1024 times the haploid amount of DNA. The numerous bands visible in squash preparations, which are characteristic of the species and correlated with the genetic map, are attributed to different degrees of coiling of the DNA down the length of the strand. At certain times, many of the bands produce puffs—enlargements in both length and diameter, which are believed to be indicative of localized genetic activity (Beermann, 1965, 1967). Puffing involves RNA synthesis, shown by incorporation of uridine-^{3}H (Pelling, 1964). The RNA's from different chromosome regions marked by large puffs (Balbiani rings) have distinctive compositions (Edström and Beermann, 1962). The RNA produced in puffing probably includes messenger RNA, but direct evidence is lacking. In a special cell type in the salivary glands of *Chironomus palliduvitatus* and in hybrids with *Ch. tentans*, the production of cytoplasmic protein granules and of a particular electrophoretic protein component is correlated with the presence of a particular Balbiani ring in the chromosomes (Grossbach, 1968). It has been estimated, however, that the DNA of an average chromosome band in the *Ch. tentans* salivary gland is of the order of 10^{-16} gm per haploid unit, which is enough to code for 30,000 amino acids (Daneholt and Edström, 1968). This suggests that more is involved than coding the structure of one or a few proteins. Beermann (1967) has discussed the nature of the bands (chromomeres) as "operational units of higher order."

Puffing also involves the accumulation of acidic protein (stainable with fast green at acid pH), but this does not rapidly incorporate labeled amino acids and is not blocked by inhibitors of protein synthesis; hence it appears to be drawn from preformed reserves in the cell. The puff protein includes ribonucleoprotein granules which are tentatively implicated in the transport of RNA from chromosome to cytoplasm.

Puffing in different tissues exhibits characteristic patterns in relation to the progress of development. The larval salivary gland is the tissue that has been most studied. In the midge, *Ch. tentans* (Clever, 1962, 1963a), in *Drosophila hydei* (Berendes, 1967), and in *D. melanogaster* (Ashburner, 1970a), a proportion of the puffs, which apparently varies with the species, may appear at any stage of larval development, but another group is correlated with molting. The latter are produced in a regular sequence, and some are formed during both larval and pupal molts while others are specific for pupation. Another tissue recently examined is the developing adult foot pad of the fleshfly *Sarcophaga bullata* (Whitten, 1969; Bultmann and Clever, 1969). In this epidermal structure, the detailed study of 71 puff loci in a sample chromosome region during 8 days of pupal and adult development showed that all of them appear and disappear in a specific sequence. Bultmann and Clever suggest that this specificity reflects the sequence of synthetic activities required for the development of a complex differentiated organ, in contrast to the more continuous secretory function of the salivary gland.

Ecdysone causes specific changes in the puff patterns. Ligation of *Drosophila* larvae before the critical time for molting hormone secretion prevents the formation, in the portion of the gland posterior to the ligature, of puffs characteristic of the pupal molt (H. J. Becker, 1962). Injection of α-ecdysone into early last instar larvae of *Ch. tentans* evokes the rapid production of puffs characteristic of pupation (Fig. 9) (Clever and Karlson, 1960; Clever, 1961). Puff I-18-C appears within 15–30 minutes after administration of the hormone, IV-2-B within 30–60 minutes, and a number of other puffs at later times ranging from 5 to 72 hours. The two puffs that are induced early by the hormone are also the first to appear in the natural molting sequence and are ones whose appearance is normally restricted to times of molting. Of the

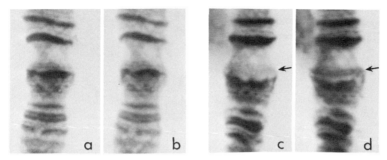

Fig. 9. Induction of a polytene chromosome puff in *Chironomus tentans* by ecdysone. (a and b) Section of chromosome I of untreated larva, photographed with green and red filters, respectively. (c and d) The same from a larva injected with 0.45 μg α-ecdysone. The arrows indicate the ecdysone-responsive puff I-18-C. From Clever (1961).

later-forming puffs, some are normally confined to molting times, and others are enlargements of puffs that may appear at any time. The two early puffs become maximal after about 2 hours from injection of the hormone, and their size and duration depend on the dose; puff I-18-C appears to be the more sensitive, having a response threshold to ecdysone at less than 10^{-3} μg per gram larval weight (Clever, 1963b).

Further evidence on the sequential relationships between ecdysone action and puff formation has been obtained with the use of inhibitors (Clever, 1964; Clever and Romball, 1966). When *Ch. tentans* larvae were treated with actinomycin D (0.2 μg/ml) for 6 hours, RNA synthesis was almost totally blocked, but it began to resume 15–20 hours after the larvae were put in fresh medium without inhibitor. When ecdysone was injected after the actinomycin treatment, the production of all new puffs was delayed for a length of time equal to the duration of inhibition of RNA synthesis; then, specific puffs appeared in their normal sequence and temporal relationship, starting with I-18-C and IV-4-B. Treatment of larvae with cycloheximide or puromycin sufficient to block protein synthesis, on the other hand, had no inhibitory effect on the production of the two early puffs by ecdysone, nor on the incorporation of uridine-^{3}H into them, but did prevent the puffs that normally follow. It is concluded that the early specific puffs are induced by ecdysone by a mechanism independent of protein synthesis, but that protein synthesis, presumably using RNA from the early puffs, is prerequisite for the puffs that follow. This is presented thus (Clever and Romball, 1966):

Ecdysone → (?) → activation of specific genes → mRNA → protein
→ (?) ⇌ further gene activation(s).

The authors confess ignorance of the link between ecdysone and the initial gene activation, and recognize that RNA other than messenger RNA may be involved.

The induction of puffs by ecdysone has also been examined in salivary glands of *Drosophila*, where the picture is more complex than in *Chironomus*. In third instar larvae of *D. hydei*, Berendes (1967) reports that within 15–20 minutes after injection of 0.3 μg α-ecdysone, 3 puffs arise newly (Fig. 10), 18 puffs show increased activity to varying degrees, and 12 puffs show decreased activity; 4–6 hours later another 5 puffs form. Six selected puffs showed the same changes in midgut and Malphighian tubules after injection of ecdysone as in salivary gland, and this pattern of change was said to be the same as occurs during normal puparium formation. Maximal responses were obtained with 3×10^{-4} μg ecdysone per larva, and some puffs gave some response with doses less than 3×10^{-7} μg. For two selected puffs, the relations between β-ecdysone dose, age of larva, and puff size have been described (Poels, 1970). In *D. melanogaster*, Ashburner (1970a) has studied the changes in puff pattern that follow injection of ecdysone and found the sequence beginning within 15 minutes to be identical to that which normally occurs before puparium formation. With a low dose of ecdysone, however, the gross developmental physiology did not keep up with the chromosomal changes, so that prepupal puff patterns were produced in morphological larvae. β-Ecdysone, tested in both species of *Drosophila*, gave the same results as α-ecdysone (Berendes, 1968; Ashburner, 1971).

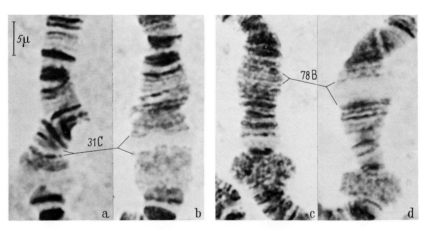

FIG. 10. Induction of chromosome puffs in *Drosophila hydei* by ecdysone. (a and c) Chromosomes from control larvae. (b and d) The same regions in larvae 15–20 minutes after injection of 0.33 μg α-ecdysone. 31C and 78B are ecdysone-responsive puffs. From Berendes (1967).

The puffs in *Drosophila,* like those in *Chironomus,* incorporate radioactive uridine and accumulate protein from an intracellular source. With regard to the causal sequence, however, Berendes' (1968) conclusions differ somewhat from Clever's. He reports that, in *D. hydei,* although the application of sufficient actinomycin D to block RNA synthesis (0.02 μg per larva) does greatly reduce the size of new puffs in specific response to ecdysone or thermal shock, and it does not entirely block their formation nor the accumulation of acidic protein in them. Berendes concludes that puff formation, marked by protein deposition and uncoiling of DNA, is the prerequisite for, rather than the consequence of, new synthesis of RNA. It is difficult at present to reconcile these conflicting viewpoints, based on results obtained in different laboratories with different species.

In the fungus gnat *Sciara coprophila,* production of the unusual DNA-containing puffs, as well as DNA synthesis throughout the polytene chromosomes, are elicited by ecdysone within 24 hours (Crouse, 1968).

When evidence was first obtained for ecdysone control over puff formation during molting, it was suggested that the sequential appearance of puffs might be a consequence of their differing sensitivity to ecdysone, whose titer was gradually rising (H. J. Becker, 1962). The results with pure hormone and inhibitors, however, conflict with such a simple correlation and show that the connection of some puffs with hormone action is much more direct than that of others. It is noteworthy that when puff IV-2-B, which is evoked rapidly in *Ch. tentans* larval salivary glands, has regressed in the prepupa, it cannot be restored by injection of ecdysone (Clever, 1966). A detailed study by Bultmann and Clever (1969) on *Sarcophaga* foot pad chromosomes showed further that the timing of the sequential appearance of 71 puffs differs significantly in cells in different positions in the foot pad and in different pairs of legs of the insect. Since the hormonal titer is presumably uniform, it is inferred that superimposed on the endocrine regulation of puffing is a strong degree of intracellular programming of some kind.

Induction of specific puffs by ecdysone can be achieved by adding the hormone to larval salivary glands explanted *in vitro* (Table III), but not as yet to isolated nuclei (Berendes and Boyd, 1969). The response in tissue *in vitro* is sensitive to the conditions. Clever (1965) found that various organic additives to the medium facilitate the effect; Kroeger (1966) reports that the gland must be isolated with extreme care to avoid wounding, and that oxygen is essential. It is recently reported that in *D. hydei* salivary glands with β-ecdysone in a Ringer solution the sensitivity of an early puff to the hormone is enhanced by the simultaneous presence of cyclic adenosine 3′,5′-monophosphate (Leenders *et al.,* 1970).

Puffing patterns in polytene chromosomes may be modified by various nonendocrine treatments applied to whole larvae, isolated glands, or cell nuclei (listed by Kroeger and Lezzi, 1966). These include, among others, temperature shock; dinitrophenol, azide, and other metabolic inhibitors; ribonuclease; trypsin; and certain inorganic ions. This may be interpreted as indicating that the unfolding of the chromomeres can be brought about by various nonspecific agents as well as by stimulation of RNA synthesis (Beermann, 1965). That certain of the loci thus affected are the same as respond to ecdysones presumably means that these loci are in some way more sensitive than others. Kroeger, on the other hand, argues that the observed effects of inorganic ions are significant in revealing the normal chain of events between hormone action and gene activation.

Kroeger's theory (Kroeger and Lezzi, 1966; Kroeger, 1967, 1968) states that the primary action of ecdysone is a membrane effect leading to increased uptake of K^+ into the cell and nucleus, possibly via stimulation of the outward Na^+ pump, and that the elevated intranuclear K^+ in turn activates certain genes, possibly by some selective effect on histone–DNA binding, which results in RNA synthesis. In addition, a regulatory role for Mg^{2+} is proposed (Lezzi, 1967). The evidence for the K^+–Na^+ mechanism, derived chiefly from experiments with *Chironomus thummi*, may be summarized as follows: (1) When salivary glands are explanted into solutions of progressively differing K^+/Na^+ ratio, the puff activity at five loci in chromosome III differs progressively from larval pattern in high Na^+ to prepupal pattern in high K^+ (Kroeger, 1963). (2) Isolated gland nuclei of *Ch. thummi* or *Ch. tentans*, made permeable by freezing and thawing, respond in a certain percentage of cases to potassium chloride (1.0–1.1%) by forming a puff characteristic of pupation and to sodium chloride (0.7–1.1%) by a puff characteristic of the larva (Lezzi, 1966). Similar effects are now reported with isolated chromosomes (Lezzi and Gilbert, 1970). (3) The resting potential measured across the plasma membrane of explanted salivary glands increased in correlation with advancing puff pattern and in response to ecdysone added to glands *in vitro* (Kroeger, 1966).

In criticism of this evidence, one may note that the number of puffs recorded was extremely small, and their response to varied K^+/Na^+ ratios, reported in a brief note (Kroeger, 1963) has never been substantiated with fuller data. The response of the puff pattern *in vivo* to ecdysone injected into *Ch. thummi* has never been described (the reaction to ecdysone was inferred from the changes when larval glands were transplanted into prepupae) (Kroeger, 1964). Clever (1965), in experiments with salivary glands of *Ch. tentans*, could find no specific differences in the responses to potassium chloride and sodium chloride of equal molarity and attributed the effects of both to high ionic strength, which is known to stimulate RNA polymerase in chromatin. Further, Clever obtained a puffing response to ecdysone with glands in simple sodium chloride solution (lacking K$^+$). In the experiments with isolated nuclei (Lezzi, 1966), the nuclei for potassium chloride tests were obtained from early last instar larvae, and those for the sodium chloride tests from prepupae; the reciprocal tests are not reported. In the experiments with ecdysone *in vitro*, the level used was high (150 μg/ml), and the purity of the hormone preparations is not stated, so that nonspecific effects on membrane potential must be considered. Ito and Loewenstein (1965) could find no significant changes in resting potential across cell or nuclear membranes of *Ch. thummi* salivary glands during development or treatment with moderate levels of ecdysone, although they did observe a gradual increase in nuclear membrane resistance, implying decreased ion permeability. In summary, there is insufficient evidence that polytene chromosomes respond to inorganic ions with the sensitivity and specificity that would be required of intermediaries in the action of ecdysone.

5. Binding of Labeled Ecdysone

Provided that detection is sufficiently sensitive, demonstration of the sites of binding of a radioactive hormone in an organism can give evidence on the steps in its action. With ecdysone, this approach was first attempted with hormone of low specific activity (catalytically tritiated) by Karlson *et al.* (1964b). They injected ecdysone-^{3}H into full grown *Calliphora* larvae and, after several time intervals, measured the radioactivity in hemolymph, epidermis, and fat body, and in subcellular fractions prepared by centrifugation from the two latter tissues. Epidermis took up the hormone relatively quickly (maximal label at 1 hour), and fat body more gradually (label still increasing from 4 to 7 hours); the epidermis bound relatively more label in a crude nuclear fraction and fat body more in microsomes. These results are reminiscent of the binding pattern of estradiol-^{3}H in rat uterus and liver, respectively (Jensen and Jacobson, 1962), and are consistent with the epidermis being a target organ and the fat body a site of destructive metabolism of the hormone.

Synthetic ecdysone of high ^{3}H specific activity has made it realistic to seek binding by the autoradiographic method. Weirich and Karlson (1969) made squash preparations of salivary glands of *Ch. tentans* and several tissues of *Rhynchosciara* sp. after ecdysone-^{3}H uptake *in vivo*, but could find no significant localization of label over nuclei or chromosomes relative to the cytoplasm. In these experiments, loosely bound steroid may have been lost during the ethanol–acetic acid fixation. Emmerich (1969) incubated *D. hydei* salivary glands with ecdysone-^{3}H *in vitro* for 10 minutes and then prepared sections after freeze-drying and osmium fixation. Glands taken 10 hours before pupation showed a distinct concentration of label in the nuclei—about threefold higher grain count than the cytoplasm—whereas at 1 hour before pupation, the nuclei showed less activity than the cytoplasm. These results appear to demonstrate concentration of ecdysone in the nucleus at the appropriate stage. Thomson *et al.* (1970b), on the other hand, using β-ecdysone-^{3}H and *Calliphora,* could find no localized intracellular concentration of the hormone in salivary glands or imaginal disks, though fat body nuclei did concentrate it strongly just prior to puparium formation.

By biochemical methods of protein fractionation, binding of ecdysone to hemolymph components has been shown in *Pyrrhocoris* and *Drosophila* (Emmerich, 1970a,b), though the possible role of these proteins as biological hormone carriers remains to be demonstrated. In the silkmoth *Samia cynthia,* Chino *et al.* (1970) find no hemolymph binding of ecdysone-^{3}H, and suggest that the hormone may be transported in the free state. Emmerich (1970b) has recently published interesting data on the binding of α-ecdysone-^{3}H to protein fractions from salivary glands of larval *D. hydei.* After incubation of glands from larvae of a specific age with labeled hormone for 30–60 minutes, activity was bound to two protein fractions of about 3.6 S and 2 S. When the incubation was at 0°C, these components were in the cytoplasmic fraction, whereas at 25°C they appeared in the nuclear extract, which suggests a metabolic transport. Evidence of binding proteins was also found by Sephadex chromatography and electrophoresis. There was very little conversion of ecdysone to other metabolites, a point which is crucial to the interpretation of such experiments. Selective binding of ecdysone to developing antennae in polyphemus silkmoths has also recently been reported (Cherbas and Cherbas, 1970).

6. Ecdysone and Spermiogenesis

A new suggestion of a role for ecdysone comes from recent experiments of Williams and Kambysellis (1969) on the control of spermiogenesis in diapause silkmoth testes studied in culture as described earlier by Schmidt and Williams (1953). Intact testes *in vitro* require for spermiogenesis both ecdysone and a macromolecular factor from silkmoth blood, whereas exposed spermatocytes respond to the macromolecular factor alone but not to the steroid. It is inferred that the role of ecdysone is to facilitate penetration of the macromolecular factor through the testis wall. The testis wall, however, is a cellular layer and it is not ruled out that changes in its permeability may be secondary to effects of ecdysone at the nuclear level. Assessment of the significance of this intriguing system must await further evidence. Yagi *et al.* (1969) have reported spermiogenesis in rice stem borer testes *in vitro* in response to ecdysone in the absence of insect blood, but their medium contained fetal bovine serum, which is found to have macromolecular factor activity (Kambysellis and Williams, 1971).

7. *Mechanism of Ecdysone Action—Present Status*

The observations on ecdysone and insect development have provided Karlson with the basis for a theory of hormone action by selective gene derepression, causing the production of messenger RNA for specific protein synthesis. In early presentations (Karlson, 1963), the suggestion was that the hormone might interact directly with DNA in the chromosomes, but more recently (Karlson, 1965, 1966, 1967, 1968; Karlson and Sekeris 1966a,b), combination of the hormone with a repressor protein has been favored, by analogy with the Jacob-Monod scheme for bacterial enzyme induction. The most compelling established evidence underlying such speculation is the rapid (10–30 minutes) evocation of specific polytene chromosome puffs in certain dipterous larvae by very low levels of ecdysone. This is impressive, but it tells nothing about the primary action of the hormone, for much can happen in a cell in 10 minutes. Further, there is as yet no evidence to link the ecdysone-induced puffs with any specified kind of RNA or the coding of any particular protein. The biochemical studies show that ecdysone, after a somewhat longer interval of time, stimulates the broad-spectrum synthesis of RNA. The experiments which have been cited as showing the production of specific RNA in early response to the hormone with isolated nuclei need the substantiation of further data. Thus, the relation of hormone action to RNA synthesis is no clearer for ecdysone than for the steroid hormones of vertebrates.

Another theory of ecdysone action—that it acts on a membrane to modify the transport of ions which in turn activate genes (Kroeger, 1967)—has been criticized above as lacking experimental evidence. On the contrary, the experiments with radioactive ecdysone do suggest some concentration of the hormone within the nucleus, as has been shown for certain mammalian steroids. It is probable that there is unity of mechanism of action of steroid hormones in different systems, and the analysis of ecdysone action must be pursued with isolated responsive tissues and the gamut of techniques of molecular biology.

III. JUVENILE HORMONE

The most intriguing of insect hormones in its biological effects is the juvenile hormone.[2] In immature insects it has the morphogenetic role of preventing metamorphosis, and in the adults of many species the same substance regulates a second, quite distinct, set of processes connected with reproductive maturation and activity. Although the existence of a juvenile hormone was predicted from surgical experiments 35 years ago (Wigglesworth, 1934), soluble active extracts were not obtained until 1956 (Williams, 1956), and pure hormone not until 1965 (Röller and Bjerke, 1965). The spectacular effects of juvenile hormone have stimulated speculation on its mechanism of action, but there is, as yet, rather little experimental evidence. Some aspects of the juvenile hormone have been reviewed (Wigglesworth, 1965; Röller and Dahm, 1968; Trost, 1970; Williams, 1970).

A. Assay

Juvenile hormone activity can be demonstrated by application of a test substance to insects which are about to undergo a metamorphic molt. Since the corpora allata possess reduced activity at this life stage (cf. Fig. 14), no operation is needed to eliminate endogenous hormone. In the ensuing molt, instead of a normal adult, a supernumerary larval or pupal form or an abnormal intermediate between immature and adult is produced (Figs. 11 and 12). The first quantitative assay to be developed involves injection of hormone dissolved in oil into pupae of the polyphemus silkmoth which have been chilled for several months so that the ecdysial glands are activated (L. I. Gilbert and Schneiderman, 1960; Williams, 1961; Williams and Law, 1965). After about three weeks for development and molting, they are scored for degree of juvenilization—retention in the new cuticle of pupal texture and body form. Depending on hormone activity, all intergrades are seen from almost perfect second pupae to normal moths (Fig. 12).

Juvenile hormone may be assayed by topical application to insects

---

[2] In this chapter, the term "juvenile hormone" will be applied generically to substances active in appropriate bioassays (cf. Berkoff, 1970). The C_{18} cecropia hormone of Röller et al. (1967) and the C_{17} compound of Meyer et al. (1968) will be referred to as JH-I and JH-II, respectively (Fig. 13). The name "neotonin" (Wigglesworth, 1954) was not applied to any particular compound, and the terminology based on "juvenate" (Meyer et al., 1968), though systematic, has not been widely used.

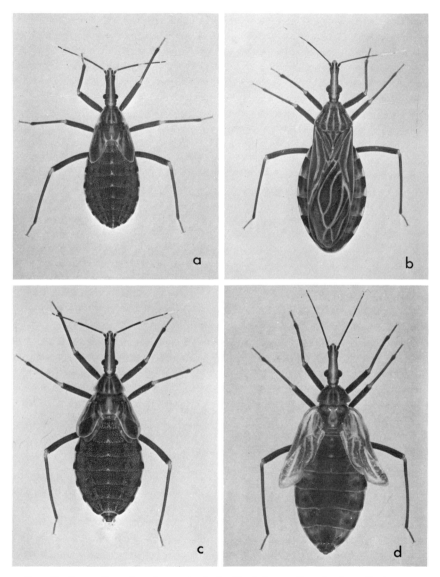

Fig. 11. Prevention of metamorphosis in *Rhodnius prolixus* by juvenile hormone. (a) Normal fifth-stage larva; (b) normal adult; (c) supernumerary (sixth-stage) larva produced after administration of pure juvenile hormone to a fifth-stage larva; (d) intermediate form resulting from a lower dose of juvenile hormone. From Wigglesworth (1969).

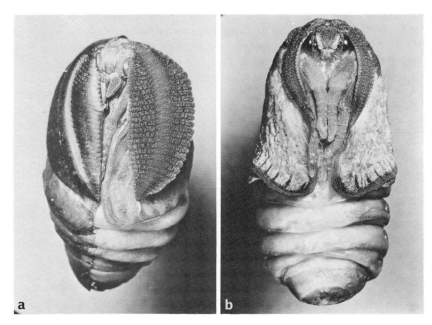

Fig. 12. Prevention of metamorphosis in silkmoths by juvenile hormone. (a) A pupa of *Antheraea polyphemus* transformed into a second pupa as a result of the implantation of three pairs of corpora allata from adult cecropia moths. The left side shows the original pupal cuticle; on the right side, this has been trimmed away to reveal the second pupa. (b) A pupal-adult intermediate of *Hyalophora cecropia* produced after implantation of adult corpora allata into a pupa. From Williams (1959).

instead of injection. Because of their lipophilic character, the active substances can be absorbed directly through the intact cuticle (Williams, 1956; Wigglesworth, 1969). After molting, the response to topical application of hormone ranges from a local patch of juvenile cuticle to general juvenilization. Sensitivity may be increased by light abrasion of the cuticle (Wigglesworth, 1958), or by puncturing it. In the wax test, a mixture containing the hormone in oil and paraffin is used to seal a cuticular wound (L. I. Gilbert and Schneiderman, 1960; Schneiderman *et al.*, 1965). The sensitivity of topical assays can be many times greater than that obtained by injection in the same insects (W. S. Bowers *et al.*, 1965).

The solvent used in juvenile hormone assay is important. For topical application, one can use either oil or a volatile organic solvent such as octane or acetone. For injection, oils (either plant or mineral) are best, and hormone injected in aqueous emulsion or in water-miscible solvents, such as 1,2-propanediol, exhibits very little activity (Wigglesworth, 1963b, 1969; Röller and Dahm, 1968). The effect of a given amount of hormone may vary with the volume of oil in which it is injected. This suggests that the role of the oil is to sequester the hormone in droplets in which it is protected from degradation and gradually released (L. I. Gilbert and Schneiderman, 1960; Wigglesworth, 1963b; cf. Grässmann *et al.*, 1968). The precise developmental stage of the insects used is also important (see Section III,D,1).

Smaller and more readily available insects have advantages over polyphemus pupae for juvenile hormone assays. Pupae of the mealworm, *Tenebrio molitor*, injected with low doses of juvenile hormone retain white patches of pupal cuticle after the adult molt (Wigglesworth, 1958). This has been made a quantitative test (Karlson and Nachtigall, 1961) and has provided the basis for the first isolation of pure juvenile hormone (Röller *et al.*, 1965; Röller and Dahm, 1968). In other assays with *Tenebrio*, by using higher doses, pupal–adult intermediates are obtained (W. S. Bowers *et al.*, 1965; Rose *et al.*, 1968). With pupae of the wax moth *Galleria mellonella*, the topical wax test has been made into a quantitative assay (Schneiderman *et al.*, 1965), which has been used to guide the isolation of two pure compounds (Meyer *et al.*, 1970). The response of the blood-sucking bug *Rhodnius* to juvenile hormone has been intensively studied and graded quantitatively (Fig. 11) (Wigglesworth, 1958, 1969). This insect lacks a pupal stage and the test is applied to the last stage larva.

Juvenile hormone activity may also be assessed quantitatively on the basis of the gonadotropic response. This has been done with adults of the cockroach (*Periplaneta americana*) in which the source of endogenous hormone has been removed either by allatectomy or by ligation at the neck. The response has been measured by the growth of terminal oocytes (W. S. Bowers *et al.*, 1965) or by the secretory activity of the colleterial gland (Bodenstein and Shaaya, 1968).

B. Chemistry of Juvenile Hormones

1. Cecropia Juvenile Hormone

Attempts to obtain active juvenile hormone by extraction of corpora allata having failed, an unexpected source was discovered in the abdomens of adult male cecropia moths (Williams, 1956). This crucial finding was the outcome of experiments in which adult moths or abdomens were fused in parabiosis with pupae; the pupae developed into pupal–adult intermediates, indicating that the adults to which they were grafted

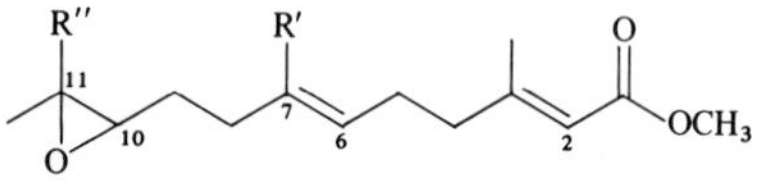

(Ia) R' = R" = CH₃   Methyl 10, 11-epoxyfarnesoate
(methyl juvenate)

(Ib) R' = CH₃ ; R" = C₂H₅ Cecropia JH-II
(methyl 12-homojuvenate)

(Ic) R' = R" = C₂H₅   Cecropia JH-I
(methyl 12, 14-dihomojuvenate)

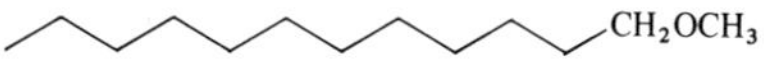

Dodecyl methyl ether
(II)

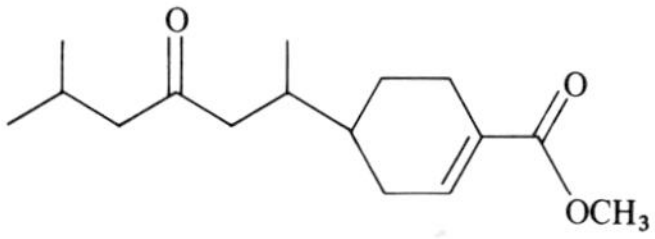

Juvabione
(III)

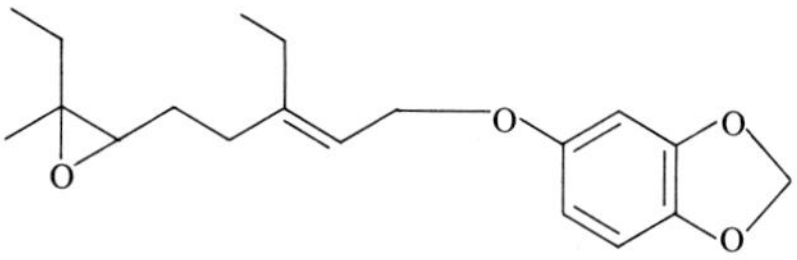

6, 7-Epoxydihomogeranyl-
methylenedioxyphenyl ether
(IV)

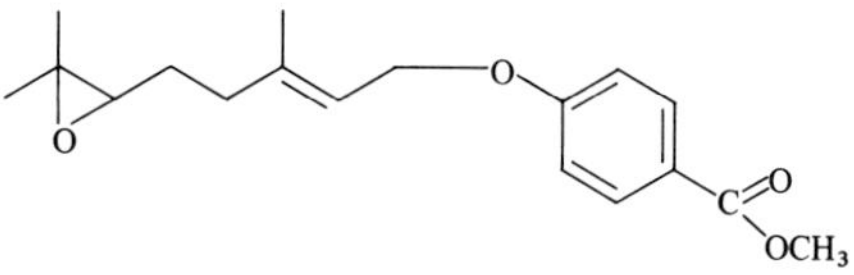

6, 7-Epoxygeranyl *p*-benzoyl
ether methyl ester
(V)

FIG. 13. Some compounds possessing juvenile hormone activity.

contained reserves of juvenile hormone (Williams, 1963). The hormone was then shown to be localized in the abdomens and extractable with ether, yielding an oily concentrate with high activity that provided a rich source for experimentation.

Although the isolation of the pure cecropia juvenile hormone was then pursued with competitive vigor in several laboratories, guided by the assays described above, the problem proved difficult. By 1965, procedures involving solvent extraction and column, thin-layer, and gas chromatography had been developed for the isolation of highly purified fractions (Williams and Law, 1965; Meyer *et al.*, 1965; Röller *et al.*, 1965). From their most active fraction, Williams and Law isolated methyl-9,10-epoxyhexadecanoate which, however, when prepared synthetically, proved to be quite inert. Pure hormone in amounts sufficient for structural determination was reported shortly thereafter (Röller *et al.*, 1967, 1969; Meyer *et al.*, 1968, 1970). One obstacle in this isolation was the proneness of the hormone to decompose in contact with hot metal surfaces or impurities in the solvents (Meyer *et al.*, 1970).

Before the cecropia juvenile hormone was obtained pure, certain natural and synthetic derivatives of the acyclic sesquiterpene farnesol had been found to exhibit such high activity as to engender the prediction that the natural hormone would be very similar to 10,11-epoxyfarnesoic acid methyl ester (Fig. 13, Ia) (W. S. Bowers *et al.*, 1965). This proved quite correct. The hormone obtained by Röller *et al.* (1967) was methyl-10-epoxy 7-ethyl-3,11-dimethyl-2,6-tridecadienoate (JH-I) (Fig. 13, Ic). Meyer *et al.* (1968, 1970) confirmed this identification and obtained also, in about one-fifth of the yield, an active homolog having methyl instead of ethyl at C-7 (JH-II) (Fig. 13, Ib). These compounds differ by only two and one carbon atom, respectively, from the farnesol derivative prepared by Bowers and co-workers, for which the name methyl juvenate has been proposed (Meyer *et al.*, 1968).

In these terpenoid structures, the *dl* pairs of eight geometrical isomers are possible: both the natural hormones are trans,trans,cis (Dahm *et al.*, 1968; Meyer *et al.*, 1968) and the mixture of them is dextrorotatory (Meyer and Hanzmann, 1970). The stereochemistry has been confirmed by synthesis of juvenile hormone by different routes in four laboratories (Dahm *et al.*, 1967; Corey *et al.*, 1968; W. S. Johnson *et al.*, 1968; Zurflüh *et al.*, 1968) and recently the two enantiomers have been prepared (Loew and Johnson, 1971). Yet other simpler routes of synthesis have been described (Braun *et al.*, 1968; Findlay and MacKay, 1969; Van Tamelen and McCormick, 1970; and others).

2. Other Active Substances

The first compound of known identity to be shown to possess juvenile hormone activity was the acyclic sesquiterpene alcohol farnesol, isolated from feces of the mealworm *Tenebrio molitor* (Schmialek, 1961). Although quite large amounts are required, farnesol exhibits distinct juvenile hormone activity in several different assays (Table IV). Certain

TABLE IV

ACTIVITIES OF SOME JUVENILE HORMONE-ACTIVE COMPOUNDS IN DIFFERENT ASSAYS

Substance	Effective dose (μg/individual)							
	Rhodnius prolixus[a]	Pyrrhocoris apterus[b]	Tenebrio molitor[c]	Tenebrio molitor[d]	Galleria mellonella[e]	Galleria mellonella[f]	Antheraea polyphemus[g]	Periplaneta americana[h]
dl-JH-I	0.5	—	0.0002	0.5	0.3	—	0.01–0.1	1
Methyl dl-trans, trans-10-epoxyfarnesoate	—	3	5	10	500	—	>50	1
Ethyl trans-dihydrochlorofarnesoate[i]	18	0.0005	0.01	100	15	—	25–50	10
Farnesyl methyl ether	1.9	30	0.06	10	—	1.6	—	—
Farnesyldiethylamine	>50	—	—	—	—	1.0	—	—
Farnesol	180	>100	4	100	—	17	—	—
Dodecyl methyl ether	(>250)	—	20	—	—	1	—	—
Juvabione	(>100)	3	20	>1000	8	—	8	—

[a] Dose producing half larval, half adult intermediates after topical application. Parentheses indicate only a weak response at the given level (Wigglesworth, 1969).

[b] Dose producing half larval, half adult intermediates after topical application (Sláma et al., 1969).

[c] Dose producing a spot of pupal cuticle at the site of injection (Röller and Dahm, 1968).

[d] Dose producing half pupal, half adult intermediates after injection (Sláma et al., 1969).

[e] Dose producing larval–pupal intermediates after injection (Röller and Dahm, 1968).

[f] Weight of one Galleria unit (referred to standard cecropia oil) by topical application (Sc'neiderman et al., 1965).

[g] Dose producing 3+ pupal–adult intermediates after injection into chilled A. polyphemus pupae (Law et al., 1966; Sláma and Williams, 1966a; Röller and Dahm, 1968; Williams, 1970).

[h] Dose producing egg maturation after topical application to allatectomized adult females (W. S. Bowers et al., 1965; Röller and Dahm, 1968).

[i] In assays described in footnotes c, e, g, and h, crude preparations (Law et al., 1966) containing other active substances were used.

synthetic derivatives of farnesol have proved to be vastly more active, approaching the potency of the subsequently isolated cecropia hormone. A highly active product, containing the ethyl ester of dihydrochlorofarnesoate and other components, can be prepared simply by bubbling hydrogen chloride through a solution of farnesoic acid in ethanol (Law et al., 1966; Romaňuk et al., 1967).

The activity of farnesol derivatives is understandable in view of their structural relationship to the natural cecropia hormone. But quite unexpected was the high activity possessed by a number of other substances. Among several straight-chain aliphatic ethers assayed in Tenebrio and Galleria, dodecyl methyl ether (Fig. 13, II) and dodecyl ethyl ether have as great activity as the corresponding farnesyl ethers (W. S. Bowers and Thompson, 1963; Schneiderman et al., 1965). A remarkable discovery was made as a result of investigating why the bug Pyrrhocoris apterus failed to mature in cages with paper towelling in them (Sláma and Williams, 1966a). The "paper factor" was extracted and traced to wood pulp of certain species (notably balsam fir). From the latter source an active substance was then isolated, named juvabione, and identified as the methyl ester of todomatuic acid, a monocyclic sesquiterpene (Fig. 13, III) (W. S. Bowers et al., 1966). A second active substance, dehydrojuvabione, has also been obtained from fir wood (Černý et al., 1967), and several synthetic aromatic analogs have been shown to possess still higher juvenilizing activity in Pyrrhocoris and related bugs (Sláma et al., 1968). Some peptides with similar molecular features are also active (Zaoral and Sláma, 1970).

A further series of synthetic compounds with astonishingly high juvenile hormone activity has been developed by W. S. Bowers (1968, 1969). This began with the observation that certain substances used commercially as insecticide synergists, such as sesoxane and piperonyl butoxide, were active at the 1 μg level in blocking metamorphosis of Tenebrio and the milkweed bug Oncopeltus fasciatus. Bowers then synthesized ethers of the methylenedioxyphenyl group characteristic of these synergists together with terpenoid moieties similar to that in the cecropia juvenile hormone and found activity to be enormously enhanced. One of the most active of these products (Fig. 13, IV) gives a strong response when 1 ng is applied topically to Tenebrio pupae, which is two orders of magnitude less than the amount of cecropia JH-I active in the same assay. Another substance (V), which is much less active in Tenebrio, is active at the 1 ng level in Oncopeltus. Since synergists fortify the action of organic insecticides by inhibiting detoxifying enzymes, the possibility must be considered that these compounds might exert their effect in metamorphosis by protecting endogenous juvenile hormone from biological inactivation. This is unlikely, however, since sesoxane has a juvenilizing effect in isolated *Tenebrio* abdomens, which have no known source of hormone (W. S. Bowers, 1968).

3. Structure–Activity Relationships and Receptor Specificity

In attempting to analyze structure–activity relationships for the juvenile hormones, one is confronted with a perplexing picture. On the one hand, there is evidence of quite specific structural requirements, while, on the other hand, some very diverse compounds can exert high hormonal activity.

In the compounds related to farnesol, the geometrical isomerism is important. In analogs of the cecropia juvenile hormone, assayed in *Tenebrio,* the trans configuration at the Δ^2 double bond is essential for activity, and conversion of the Δ^6 double bond from trans to cis lowers the activity to less than one-tenth, but the cis–trans configuration at the oxirane ring is of minor importance (Röller and Dahm, 1968). Somewhat different conclusions as to the importance of geometrical isomerism were reached by Westermann *et al.* (1969). Natural farnesol (from plant sources) is trans,trans, and for juvenile hormone activity in *Tenebrio,* farnesol must be trans at Δ^6 but is nonspecific at Δ^2 (Yamamoto and Jacobson, 1962). With respect to optical configuration, the natural *d* form is 10R, 11S (Nakanishi *et al.,* 1971) and is approximately nine times more active than the *l* form by topical test in pupae of *Galleria mellonella* (Siddall and Staal, 1971). The racemate has lower activity than the *d* isomer in this assay.

In a series of methyl esters related to cecropia juvenile hormone, assayed in *Tenebrio,* removal of the alkyl side chains, saturation of double bonds, chain cyclization, or replacement of the epoxy by an alkoxy group all led to drastic lowering of activity (Wakabayashi, 1969; Sonnet *et al.,* 1969; Wakabayashi *et al.,* 1969). Among a series of 42 compounds, many of them structurally related to farnesol, assayed quantitatively in *Rhodnius,* none was more active than cecropia JH-I (Wigglesworth, 1969). The importance of the trans,trans configuration, the location of the oxirane ring, and a suitable balance of polar and apolar properties became evident.

The most remarkable feature of juvenile hormone structural specificity is how greatly it differs in different test insects. Whereas cecropia JH-I and JH-II are about equally active when assayed in Lepidoptera (*Galleria* and *Antheraea polyphemus*), JH-II has only one-fifth or less the activity of JH-I in *Tenebrio,* which may well account for JH-II having been missed in the isolation based on the *Tenebrio* assay

(Schwarz *et al.*, 1969; W. S. Johnson *et al.*, 1969). The synthetic ethyl ester analog of JH-I is, surprisingly, about eight times more active than the natural methyl ester in *Tenebrio*, but of no greater activity in *Rhodnius* (Röller and Dahm, 1968; Wigglesworth, 1969). Methyl-epoxyfarnesoate is quite active in *Pyrrhocoris*, *Tenebrio*, and *Periplaneta*, but inert in Lepidoptera (Table IV). Among a series of farnesane derivatives, some are more active in *Galleria* larvae and others in pupae of the same species (Jarolím *et al.*, 1969). Most astonishing is the high sensitivity of *Pyrrhocoris* (and other bugs of the same family; Sláma *et al.*, 1969) to the ethylfarnesoate hydrochloride product and to juvabione. The latter substance has been termed "little short of a pyrrhocoricide" (Sláma and Williams, 1966a)!

Various preparations active in other insects failed to produce morphogenetic effects in higher Diptera (flies), so that it seemed possible that this order might have a distinctive juvenile hormone. Lethal disturbances of development have been obtained in mosquitoes (Spielman and Williams, 1966; Spielman and Skaff, 1967; Nair, 1967) and *Drosophila* (Bryant and Sang, 1968; Ashburner, 1970b), however. Recently, using pure JH-I and several other compounds at high doses, Srivastava and Gilbert (1968, 1969) have obtained clear evidence of juvenilization in the fleshfly *Sarcophaga bullata*.

Variations in penetration and in rates of inactivation undoubtedly contribute to these discrepancies, but the differences in hormonal potency of certain compounds in different insect groups are so great as very strongly to imply differences in the specificity of the receptor sites (Williams, 1970). Williams suggests further that the compounds used as juvenile hormones may themselves have evolved during the millions of years of insect evolution. It is noteworthy, however, that all the insects tested are sensitive to cecropia JH-I. Also, corpora allata are active when transplanted between donor and recipient insects belonging to different families or orders (see Wigglesworth, 1954, p. 63).

While it is easy to make comparisons of the activities of two related structures in a given assay, not many conclusions can be drawn as to general structural requirements for juvenile hormone activity (cf. Schneiderman *et al.*, 1965; Wigglesworth, 1969; Stowe and Hudson, 1969). There appears to be a critical molecular size, corresponding to a chain length of 13 to 15 carbon and oxygen atoms, or about 20 Å (Stowe, 1971). The trans configuration at double bonds, which favors extended conformation of the molecule, is generally important for activity. Nevertheless, certain saturated compounds, such as dodecyl methyl ether, can also be active. A certain balance of polar and apolar functions is important; compounds that carry a net charge (farnesoate, farnesylamine) are inactive, but the presence of some less strongly polar groups is essential.

C. Distribution and Metabolism

1. Occurrence in Insects

Among insect materials tested, the abdomens of adult male cecropia moths are unique in their high content of juvenile hormone. The content per individual abdomen has been estimated as about 1 μg of juvenile hormone (Röller *et al.*, 1969; Meyer *et al.*, 1970). By extracting with ether, evaporating the solvent, and assaying the oil, L. I. Gilbert and Schneiderman (1961) detected activity in both sexes of all of twenty-three species of adult Lepidoptera. The hormone content was invariably greater in males than in females (the total lipid content was also much greater). The specific activity of the oil from *Samia cynthia* was two-thirds of that from cecropia, but in other species the activity did not exceed one-third that of cecropia and was generally much less. The closely related species *Hyalophora gloveri* contains JH-I and JH-II at levels substantially lower than those in *H. cecropia* (Dahm and Röller, 1970). It was indeed fortunate that Williams (1956) picked the cecropia silkmoth for his pioneering experiments!

Considering the respective roles of juvenile hormone in (a) keeping the larva juvenile and (b) regulating reproductive maturation in the adult of certain insects, one might expect to find its titer higher in larvae, low or absent during pupation and development of the adult, and high again in the mature adult. This is precisely the pattern observed in cecropia, both by extraction and assay of soluble hormone (L. I. Gilbert and Schneiderman, 1961; Krishnakumaran and Schneiderman, in Patel and Madhavan, 1969) and by transplantation of corpora allata from different stages into test *A. polyphemus* pupae (Fig. 14) (Williams, 1961). Both methods also agree in showing juvenile hormone to be high early in a larval instar and to fall off as the next molt is approached. Thus, in the immature stages, accumulation of hormone is correlated with secretory activity of the corpora allata. A similar pattern is observed in earwigs (Ozeki, 1965).

Cecropia and related moths, however, in contrast to many other insects, do not require juvenile hormone for reproductive maturation (Section III,D,2). The biological reason for accumulation of the hormone in adult male cecropia is thus an enigma; Williams suggests that it may be an evolutionary carry-over from an earlier requirement for reproduction. Physiologically, the extent of accumulation in the adult seems to be

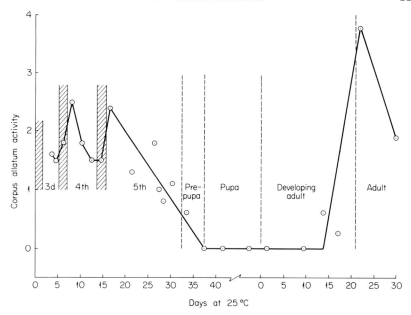

Fig. 14. Changes in the endocrine activity of the corpora allata of the cecropia silkmoth during the third, fourth, and fifth larval stages and during metamorphosis. Activity was assayed by transplanting corpora allata from cecropia at each stage into test polyphemus pupae. The break in the time scale represents storage of the donor pupae at 6°C for 10–20 weeks to break diapause; the cross-hatched zones represent larval molting. From Williams (1961).

largely determined by the capacity for inactivation of the hormone. The corpora allata of female moths, which do not accumulate juvenile hormone, are active when assayed by transplantation (Williams, 1959). Implantation of ovaries into castrate males, moreover, lowers their content of the hormone, presumably by providing tissue which destroys it (L. I. Gilbert and Schneiderman, 1961).

Assays of extracts from larvae or adults of a number of insect species belonging to different orders yielded positive results in certain instances and negative in others (Wigglesworth, 1958; Schneiderman and Gilbert, 1958). It appears that the juvenile hormone can control insect development without accumulating to any great extent in the body. No quantitative study, nor chemical characterization of the hormone, has yet been reported from any insect other than the silkmoths discussed above.

2. Other Biological Materials

A diversity of biological materials have yielded some juvenile hormone activity when oil extracted from them was assayed in the sensitive wax test. These include some bacteria (notably culture medium from *Escherichia coli*), yeasts, protozoa, and soy bean meal, but not various commercial plant oils (Schneiderman *et al.*, 1960); some but not all, of a series of invertebrates belonging to different phyla (Schneiderman and Gilbert, 1958); and all of an extensive series of mammalian tissues, of which thymus and adrenal cortex were the most active (L. I. Gilbert and Schneiderman, 1958; Williams *et al.*, 1959). The insect-parasitic protozoan *Nosema* produces a diffusible substance which can block metamorphosis of its host by juvenile hormone action (Fisher and Sanborn, 1964). From none of these sources was the active principle isolated or characterized. In view of the diversity of chemical compounds that are now known to possess some juvenile hormone activity, these initially intriguing observations may have little significance.

3. Biosynthesis and Degradation

Since the pioneering work of Wigglesworth (1936), a multitude of surgical experiments have implicated the corpora allata in the production of juvenile hormone. The fine structure of these glands from several insect species shows abundant mitochondria and elaborate smooth endoplasmic reticulum, features appropriate for lipoid biosynthesis (Scharrer, 1964; Waku and Gilbert, 1964; Odhiambo, 1966a; Fukuda *et al.*, 1966). Recently, JH-I has been identified from cecropia corpora allata cultured for 7 days *in vitro*, whereas freshly excised glands did not contain hormone (Röller and Dahm, 1970).

Lower terpenoids, unlike steroids, are synthesized from simple precursors by insects. Schmialek (1963) indicated incorporation of mevalonate-^{14}C in cynthia moths into compounds migrating chromatographically with farnesol and farnesal. Happ and Meinwald (1965) showed incorporation of acetate-^{14}C and mevalonate-2-^{14}C in an ant into the monoterpenes citronellal and citral, which this insect produces for defensive purposes. Mevalonate-1-^{14}C was not incorporated, indicating decarboxylation as in the mammalian synthetic pathway. Mevalonate kinase, a key enzyme in the pathway, has been demonstrated and characterized in the fleshfly *Sarcophaga bullata* (Barnes and Goodfellow, 1968, 1969). The enzymatic oxidation of farnesol to farnesal and farnesoate, which has been detected in *Tenebrio* larvae (Emmerich *et al.*, 1965a), might be on the route of juvenile hormone biosynthesis.

The existence of mechanisms for biological inactivation of juvenile hormone has already been inferred from the protective effect of oil as a solvent in assays and from the disappearance of juvenile hormone in female adult silkmoths. Rapid destruction of farnesyl-^{14}C methyl ether in *Tenebrio* has been shown (Grässmann *et al.*, 1968), but nothing has yet been published on the catabolism of juvenile hormone itself.

D. Effects of Juvenile Hormone

1. Control of Metamorphosis

The juvenile hormone controls metamorphosis in all kinds of insects. In those with simple metamorphosis (Exopterygota), such as *Rhodnius,* it prevents the change from larva to adult; in those with complex metamorphosis (Endopterygota), such as the silkworm, it can block the change from larva to pupa or from pupa to adult. Experimental administration of the hormone, depending on the dose and time, can lead to either a repetition of the immature stage (supernumerary larva or second pupa), or an abnormal intermediate. In insect groups which exhibit specialized polymorphism, such as termites, aphids, and locusts, juvenile hormone is involved in morph determinism (see Doane, 1972). The most remarkable example is perhaps the production of termite soldiers by juvenile hormone. The manifestation of these morphogenetic effects (juvenilizing and other) requires molting induced by ecdysone and cannot be achieved by exposure of tissue to juvenile hormone alone.

The time in the molting cycle at which the hormone is supplied is crucial—if too early, it is inactivated and lost, if too late, the tissues are no longer sensitive. Röller and Dahm (1968) concluded from experiments with *Galleria* that juvenile hormone must act prior to ecdysone to exert its morphogenetic activity, but it is not clear that this is always the case. In *Rhodnius,* during the 20 day fifth larval stage, juvenile hormone must be injected before day 12 to have any effect, and the effect is maximal at day 8, when mitosis in the epidermis is beginning (Wigglesworth, 1963b). In the wax moth (*Galleria mellonella*), when the final larval stage lasts 9 days, juvenile hormone is effective only if injected between days 3 and 6; following treatment at day 3, the result is either a perfect superlarva or a normal pupa, but after treatment on later days, intermediates are produced with larval cuticle on the abdomen and pupal cuticle on the thorax (Sehnal and Meyer, 1968). This demonstrates that the developmental fate of different body parts is determined at different times (cf. Geyer *et al.,* 1968a). Similarly, in polyphemus pupae, hormone must be administered before the fourth day of adult development to achieve the retention of pupal features (Williams, 1956). Even when pupae are treated before the beginning of visible development, adultoid eyes are invariably produced (L. I. Gilbert and Schneiderman, 1960). But when hormone is injected into the nondiapausing relative *Samia ricini* within 12 hours after pupation, eyeless second pupae are formed (Tsao *et al.,* 1963), which suggests that the apparent resistance of the eyes of polyphemus is simply a result of their fate being determined earlier than that of other structures (Willis, 1969).

Despite the ineffectiveness of juvenile hormone applied to larvae too early in the molt cycle, remarkable effects can follow treatment of embryos. Both in bugs and in silkworms, hormone applied to undeveloped eggs or early embryos blocks their development (Sláma and Williams, 1966b; Riddiford and Williams, 1967; Riddiford, 1970). When later embryos are treated, however, the eggs hatch and larvae develop, but abnormalities appear during growth or at metamorphosis. These may include the production of supernumerary larval stages. In the milkweed bug (*Oncopeltus fasciatus*), this has been shown to result from persistent activity of the corpora allata in the full grown larva, as a delayed effect of some hormonal influence in the embryo (Riddiford, 1970; cf. Willis and Lawrence, 1970).

How is the successive differentiation of larva, pupa and adult in holometabolous insects brought about? This might be a rigorously programmed sequence, progress in which can merely be blocked by juvenile hormone. However, the program can be shortcut, with the omission of steps. Patches of larval cuticle grafted onto pupae can molt directly to adult cuticle with scales when the pupa molts (Nayar, 1954). Cecropia larvae deprived of juvenile hormone by allatectomy develop (in a certain proportion of cases) into pupae with some adult features, and larval wing disks implanted into pupae can produce adult cuticle, bypassing the pupal stage (Williams, 1961). These observations suggest that the hormone can oppose developmental progress to a degree proportional to its concentration, so that the normal sequence of metamorphic stages is determined by successively lower levels of juvenile hormone in the presence of ecdysone (Williams, 1961; cf. Fig. 14).

Can the developmental program be reversed by endocrine control? When adult *Rhodnius* is induced to molt (by ecdysone from larvae grafted to it) in the presence of sufficient juvenile hormone, some reversion to larval-type cuticle is achieved (Wigglesworth, 1940, 1958). However, despite a few other instances (e.g., Lawrence, 1966) such partial reversal of metamorphosis is exceptional. Forced adult molting in cecropia produces adult cuticle (Williams, 1963). No matter how much hormone is administered, pupae have never been seen to revert to larvae. Thus, the degree of plasticity of the developmental program appears to be quite limited, and the effect of juvenile hormone in metamorphosis can generally be described as favoring maintenance of the *status quo* (Willis, 1969).

Juvenile hormone acts directly on the epidermal cells. This is shown by the local response to topical application of small amounts of hormone. The result is modification of growth and form (e.g., suppression of wings and genitalia), and alteration of the character (e.g., thickness, surface texture, sclerotization, pigmentation) of the cuticle that is deposited during molting. While most attention has been given to epidermal structures, which determine the external form of an insect, Sehnal (1968) has documented the changes undergone by the internal organs of *Galleria* in the last stage larva developing to a pupa. Administration of juvenile hormone blocks these changes, each organ retaining its form almost as at the time when the hormone was applied. Evidence is lacking, however, to prove that the hormone acts directly on the cells of each tissue.

Another experimentally demonstrable action of juvenile hormone in insect development is the prothoracotropic effect. Brainless silkmoth pupae can be caused to develop by administering juvenile hormone (including pure JH-I), which is believed to stimulate the ecdysial gland in lieu of brain hormone (Kobayashi, 1960; Williams, 1963; Krishnakumaran and Schneiderman, 1965; Röller and Dahm, 1968). The significance of this phenomenon is not clear.

Rather surprisingly, there are very few data on effects of juvenile hormone added to insect tissue isolated *in vitro* (see, however, Section III,E,2 and 5). One difficulty in carrying out such experiments arises from the insolubility of the hormone in aqueous media.

2. Reproductive Maturation and Activity

In insects, development of the external genitalia and secondary sexual characters is generally under direct genetic control, independent of hormonal influence (see, however, Section V,A). Maturation of the gonads and some other processes related to reproductive activity, on the other hand, frequently are controlled by hormones. This permits reproduction to be coordinated with such influences as nutrition, season of the year, or the completion of a previous reproductive cycle. The control mechanisms, which involve interactions between neural activity, brain neurosecretion, corpora cardiaca, corpora allata, and gonads have evolved differently in different groups of insects and are not easy to disentangle. The resultant rather confusing literature has been reviewed elsewhere (Wigglesworth, 1964; De Wilde, 1964; Highnam, 1967; Engelmann, 1968, 1970; Doane, 1972), and in this section we shall emphasize the involvement of the corpora allata and their product, the juvenile hormone.

Dependence of reproduction on the corpora allata was discovered by Wigglesworth (1936) in *Rhodnius*. Soon after adult bugs were fed, their corpora allata showed signs of renewed activity (following inactivity during metamorphosis). If the glands were then removed by decapitation, the oocytes of the female failed to develop beyond the point at which deposition of yolk should begin, and the accessory glands of the male did not fill with secretion. Implantation of active corpora allata into

TABLE V

Effects of Corpora Allata and Juvenile Hormone on Vitellogenic Protein Production in Female Insects

Order and species	Endocrine treatment	Method of analysis[a]	Reference
Dictyoptera			
Blattella germanica	Ligation, injection of *dl*-JH-I and analogs	Acrylamide gel electrophoresis	Kunkel (1970)
Leucophaea maderae	Allatectomy	Cellulose acetate electrophoresis; immunoelectrophoresis	Engelmann and Penney (1966)
	Decapitation, corpus allatum implantation, farnesyl methyl ether treatment	Acrylamide gel electrophoresis	Scheurer and Lüscher (1968); Scheurer (1969a)
	Isolated abdomens treated with *t,t,t*-JH-I	Immunoelectrophoresis	Engelmann (1969a)
	Isolated abdomens treated with farnesoate–HCl product	Leucine-^{14}C incorporation; ultracentrifugation	Brookes (1969a)
Periplaneta americana	Allatectomy, implantation	Paper electrophoresis	Menon (1965a)
	Allatectomy	Cellulose acetate electrophoresis	Thomas and Nation (1966a)
	Cardiac allatectomy	Acrylamide gel electrophoresis	Adiyodi and Nayar (1967)
	Allatectomy, implantation; farnesyl methyl ether injection	Acrylamide gel electrophoresis; immunodiffusion	Bell (1969, 1970)
Orthoptera			
Locusta migratoria	Allatectomy, implantation	Agar gel electrophoresis; amino acid-^{14}C incorporation	Minks (1967)
	Allatectomy	Acrylamide gel electrophoresis of ovary proteins	Bentz and Girardie (1969)
Heteroptera			
Rhodnius prolixus	Decapitation	Starch gel electrophoresis	Coles (1965a,b)

Coleoptera			
Leptinotarsa decemlineata	Allatectomy	Agar gel, cellulose acetate electrophoresis	de Loof (1969); de Loof and de Wilde (1970b)
Lepidoptera			
Pieris brassicae	Neck ligature, corpus allatum implantation	Cellulose acetate electrophoresis	Karlinsky (1967a,b); Lamy (1967)
Danaus plexippus	Neck ligature, injection of JH-I	Immunodiffusion, electrophoresis, gradient centrifugation	Pan and Wyatt (1971)
Diptera			
Sarcophaga bullata	Allatectomy (variable effect)	Immunoelectrophoresis	Wilkens (1969)

[a] Generally applied to hemolymph.

the abdomen remedied the endocrine defect, and was followed by normal maturation of eggs. Later experiments, transplanting corpora allata between immature and adult stages, indicated that their respective roles in larval development and in reproduction might depend on the same hormone (Wigglesworth, 1948), a conjecture recently proven correct by tests with pure compounds (Section III,B).

In *Rhodnius,* cockroaches, and some other insects, ovarian development requires only the juvenile hormone. In the woodroach *Leucophaea maderae,* for example, after allatectomy, decapitation, or even severing the abdomen from the remainder of the body, egg development can be induced by implantation of corpora allata or application of juvenile hormone compounds (Scharrer, 1946; Chambers and Brookes, 1967; Brookes, 1969b; Engelmann, 1969a). In many other insects which have been tested by microsurgical procedures (for example, locusts and various flies), both the corpora allata and the medial neurosecretory cells of the brain, or possibly in some cases the latter alone, influence egg development. In still another group, which includes the silkmoths, neither source of hormone is needed; viable eggs are produced in moths developing under the influence of ecdysone alone, brain and corpora allata having been removed (Williams, 1959). In these moths, the adults take no food, and gametogenesis is largely completed before their emergence, but in certain other Lepidoptera in which the adult does feed before oocyte maturation—the cabbage butterfly *Pieris brassicae* (Karlinsky, 1967a,b), the armyworm *Leucania separata* (Wu and Quo, 1963), the cotton leafworm *Spodoptera littoralis* (El-Ibrashy and Boctor, 1970) and the monarch butterfly *Danaus plexippus* (Pan and Wyatt, 1971)—corpus allatum activity is required for vitellogenesis. Thus, the variations in endocrine participation appear to be adaptations to way of life rather than characteristics of taxonomic groups.

When juvenile hormone is required for reproduction, it can be shown to activate several essential processes. The production and uptake of yolk proteins are discussed below. Secretion in accessory glands of both male and female may be controlled; in the left colleterial gland of the cockroach *Periplaneta americana,* the production of a protein that forms the ootheca and of protocatechuic acid glucoside to tan it are dependent on juvenile hormone (Willis and Brunet, 1966; Adiyodi, 1968; Shaaya and Bodenstein, 1969; Shaaya and Sekeris, 1970). In some species, juvenile hormone is required for the production of sex pheromones (Barth, 1968; Borden *et al.,* 1969; Menon, 1970) or for female receptivity in mating (Barth, 1968). In desert locusts, body coloration, and development of the accessory glands and sexual behavior in the male are dependent on juvenile hormone (Odhiambo, 1966b; Joly, 1968).

The most thoroughly investigated aspect of juvenile hormone action in insect reproduction, especially from the biochemical viewpoint, concerns yolk deposition. This depends upon vitellogenins, specific proteins synthesized in the fat body and transported in the blood (Telfer, 1965; Pan *et al.*, 1969). Telfer (1954) first demonstrated by immunological analysis of cecropia silkmoth hemolymph a protein component which was present only in female pupae and adults and was selectively taken up and accumulated in the developing oocytes. Although, as mentioned above, egg development in the cecropia silkmoth is independent of corpus allatum control, this work laid the basis for subsequent studies on analogous hormonally controlled processes in other insects.

Vitellogenins have been detected, generally by electrophoretic or immunochemical techniques, in a number of species, and examples where there is evidence for regulation by corpus allatum hormone are listed in Table V. In the usual conditions of zone electrophoresis (pH 8–9), the vitellogenins generally form one or two anodally migrating bands (Fig. 15). Generally, vitellogenins occur in significant amounts in the hemolymph of only post-larval females of a species (in *Rhodnius*, however, they appear in adult males also) (Coles, 1965a). They are normally not the most abundant of the hemolymph proteins, but after ovariectomy accumulate until they may account for more than 50% of the total blood protein. In the mature ovary of *Leucophaea*, some 80% of the total protein is vitellogenin (Dejmal and Brookes, 1968), and in *Periplaneta*, two vitellogenins make up almost 90% of the yolk protein (Bell, 1970). In several respects, there is parallelism with the vitellogenic proteins produced by the livers of amphibians and birds (Heald and McLachlan, 1965; Wallace and Dumont, 1968).

Vitellogenins may be prepared by fractionation from hemolymph or from eggs. In the roach *Leucophaea maderae*, the bulk of the protein of mature eggs is extractable only at high ionic strength (NaCl 0.4 *M* or above), and precipitates upon dilution (Dejmal and Brookes, 1968). Such aggregation may perhaps account for immobility in agar gel electrophoresis (Engelmann, 1969a). Vitellogenins have recently been purified and characterized from the cecropia silkmoth and the German cockroach (*Blattella germanica*) (Kunkel and Pan, 1971). Both are soluble at low ionic strength, have very similar sedimentation coefficients (close to 16 S, corresponding to molecular weights of about 500,000) and dissociate in sodium dodecyl sulfate into subunits (molecular weight about 140,000). They are somewhat acidic proteins, rich in aspartic and glutamic acids and their amides (as is the vitellogenin of the Colorado beetle *Leptinotarsa decemlineata*) (de Loof and de Wilde, 1970a). The vitellogenins of several species give staining reactions for lipid and carbohydrate

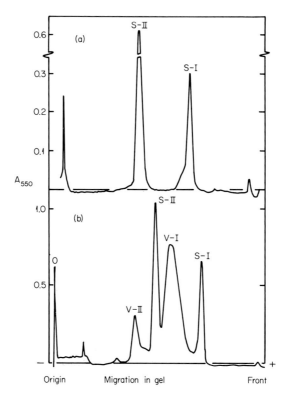

FIG. 15. Induction of vitellogenin in the cockroach *Blattella germanica* by juvenile hormone. Ovariectomized female adults were fed at 0 hours, ligated at the neck at 48 hours, injected with 0.66 µg *dl*-JH-I (gift of Dr. H. Röller) in olive oil (or with pure olive oil controls) at 60 hours, and bled at 108 hours. The serum was analyzed by electrophoresis in 4% acrylamide gel, stained with Coomassie blue, and scanned in the Gilford spectrophotometer. (a) Control; (b) juvenile hormone-treated. S-I, S-II, serum proteins; V-1, V-II, vitellogenin components I and II. From Kunkel (1970).

(Adiyodi and Nayar, 1967; Dejmal and Brookes, 1968; de Loof and de Wilde, 1970a; Thomas and Gilbert, 1969), and that of cecropia contains about 10% lipid (Pan, 1970).

From much experimental work, it appears that the synthesis of insect blood proteins can be influenced both by juvenile hormone (from the corpora allata) and by brain neurosecretion (cf. Section IV,F). The literature on the roles of the two hormones is highly confusing, but recent work, recognizing the variation in regulatory systems in different insect species and the necessity to distinguish specific proteins, is beginning to clear up the picture. In the roach *Leucophaea*, Scheurer (1969a) has shown that, after decapitation, implantation of brains or corpora cardiaca as sources of neurohormone can stimulate synthesis of certain electrophoretic protein components, whereas the vitellogenic component responds strongly and specifically to corpus allatum hormone.

Synthesis of vitellogenin in fat body incubated *in vitro* has been demonstrated in both cecropia and cockroaches by incorporation of labeled amino acid into protein identified immunochemically (Pan *et al.*, 1969) or by precipitation and centrifugation (Brookes, 1969a). This is consistent with earlier evidence that the insect fat body produces blood proteins (Shigematsu, 1958) and fails to support the suggestion, based on cellular fine structure in the mosquito, that vitellogenin might arise in the midgut (Roth and Porter, 1964).

Data are beginning to accumulate on hormonal effects on biosynthesis in the fat body of adult insects. Allatectomy is followed by decreased rates of incorporation of labeled precursors into protein and/or RNA of fat body in locusts (Hill, 1965; Minks, 1967), cockroaches (Thomas and Nation, 1966b), *Rhodnius* (Vanderberg, 1963), and houseflies (Bhaskaran and Nair, 1966). In decapitated roaches (*Nauphoeta cinerea*), incorporation of alanine-^{14}C is stimulated after implantation of corpora allata (Lüscher, 1968).

Hormonal induction of vitellogenin synthesis has been studied recently in *Leucophaea maderae*. Brookes (1969a) showed, 40 hours after treatment of isolated abdomens with synthetic methyl farnesoate hydrochloride product, strong stimulation of amino acid incorporation into a component that precipitates and sediments as vitellogenin. Engelmann (1969a) showed, after treatment of isolated abdomens with synthetic juvenile hormone, stimulation of synthesis of immunochemically identified vitellogenin, as well as possibly enhanced incorporation into other protein. The quantitative response of specific synthesis to several hormone compounds is shown in Fig. 16. This system appears advantageous for investigation of the mechanism of induction of specific protein synthesis, a question which will be considered later (Section III,E,3).

The uptake of vitellogenic proteins from the hemolymph into yolk spheres in the oocyte is also of interest as a possible site of hormonal regulation (review, Telfer, 1965). The mechanism involves permeation between the cells of the ovariole wall and the follicular epithelium, followed by pinocytotic entry into the oocyte. The process is selective, yet not entirely exclusive; in silkmoths the specific vitellogenins are concentrated in the eggs to more than twenty times their level in the blood (Telfer, 1960), and in a cockroach to almost one hundred times (Bell, 1970), while other proteins (both endogenous and foreign) may be found in the eggs at levels similar to or less than those in the sur-

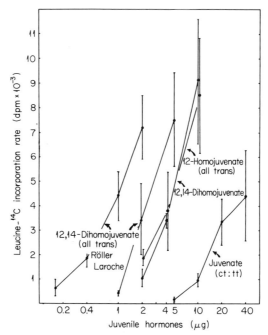

Fɪɢ. 16. Induction of vitellogenin synthesis in the woodroach *Leucophaea maderae* by the two cecropia juvenile hormones and a lower homolog (juvenate). Isolated abdomens of previously allatectomized female adults were treated topically with the hormones in olive oil. Five days later, leucine-¹⁴C was injected, and after 4 hours for incorporation, blood was collected and vitellogenin was isolated by precipitation with specific antibody and counted. Vertical limits are standard errors. From Engelmann (1971).

rounding fluid (cf. Scheurer, 1969b). The specificity of the uptake mechanism has recently been directly demonstrated with radioactive cecropia and *Blattella germanica* vitellogenins, from which the oocytes of each species clearly selected their own kind (Kunkel and Pan, 1971).

An influence of corpus allatum hormone on vitellogenin uptake has been proposed. Joly (1945) implanted corpora allata directly into ovaries of the diving beetle *Dytiscus* and reported that oocytes in contact with the implants grew before any others (cf. de Loof and de Wilde, 1970b). In allatectomized desert locusts, yolk deposition is blocked while hemolymph protein builds up to levels higher than normal, which was interpreted as indicating that the corpus allatum hormone is required for protein uptake by the oocytes and not for protein synthesis (Highnam *et al.*, 1963), but whether the accumulated blood protein contained vitellogenin was not determined. Recently, it has been shown that yolk protein injected into allatectomized or ligated cockroaches is not deposited in the oocytes unless juvenile hormone is administered simultaneously (Bell, 1969; Bell and Barth, 1971), which strongly indicates an action of the hormone on the process of uptake into the ovary. On the basis of experiments with the fleshfly *Sarcophaga*, on the other hand, Wilkens (1969) has proposed that neurosecretion from the pars intercerebralis of the brain has the role of gonadotropin, controlling ovarian protein uptake.

3. Adult Diapause

In certain insects, the juvenile hormone acts in the regulation of diapause in the adult. Colorado potato beetles (*Leptinotarsa decemlineata*) feed and reproduce if kept in long-day (18 hours of light) conditions, but under short-day (10 hours) illumination, they burrow into the soil and enter the quiescent state of diapause (de Wilde and de Boer, 1961). If long-day beetles are allatectomized, the changes characteristic of diapause ensue and can then be reversed by implantation of corpora allata. The onset and termination of diapause is correlated with changes in the titer of juvenile hormone in the hemolymph (de Wilde *et al.*, 1968). Implantation of allata into short-day beetles does not arouse them, however, since the glands require activation by neurosecretion dependent on photoperiod. Most interesting is the demonstration that a synthetic juvenile hormone analog (methylepoxyfarnesoate) is capable of breaking adult diapause, both in the Colorado beetle (de Wilde and de Boer, 1969) and in the alfalfa weevil (W. S. Bowers and Blickenstaff, 1966).

Diapause in the adult Colorado beetle is accompanied by extensive degeneration of the flight muscles and storage of lipid in the fat body, processes which are reversed with the resumption of activity (Stegwee *et al.*, 1963; de Kort, 1969). Profound changes in muscle structure, as well as the levels of a number of enzymes involved in muscle energy conversion, are correlated with juvenile hormone action. It is concluded that the hormone plays an important part in maintaining the biochemical integrity of flight muscle in the Colorado beetle and probably in other adult-diapausing insects. These effects are reminiscent of some of the actions of ecdysone in immature insects—the stimulation of intersegmental muscle regeneration in *Rhodnius* and the breaking of diapause in various species (Section II,C; Table I).

In insects lacking adult diapause, allatectomy does not cause degeneration of flight muscle (*Tenebrio molitor*, El-Ibrashy, 1965; *Locusta*, Minks, 1967). The pine bark beetle (*Ips confusus*) even shows an opposite effect, for the reproductive adult tunnels under bark and has no further need of flight muscle, and juvenile hormone causes muscle degeneration (Borden and Slater, 1968). Again, the remarkable diversity of hormonal adaptations in insects is illustrated.

E. Biochemistry of Juvenile Hormone Action

1. Respiration

The observation of Thomsen (1949) that the oxygen consumption of blowflies (*Calliphora erythrocephala*) was lowered after allatectomy and restored by implantation of corpora allata has been followed by many reports on relations between juvenile hormone and respiration. In most circumstances, the respiration of insects is greater in the presence of active corpora allata or juvenile hormone than in their absence, but how closely respiratory metabolism is linked to action of the hormone is debatable.

In larval insects, elimination of juvenile hormone by allatectomy can induce precocious metamorphosis, while metamorphosis can be delayed by implantation of active allata or administration of juvenile hormone. The larval and pupal molt cycles of a species exhibit characteristic patterns of respiratory change, and when the developmental sequence is modified by such manipulation, respiration is influenced accordingly. Measurements of oxygen uptake during experimentally modified development of the bug *Pyrrhocoris apterus* and the wax moth *Galleria mellonella* suggest that the effects of juvenile hormone on respiratory metabolism are secondary to its morphogenetic actions (Sláma, 1965; Sehnal, 1966; Sehnal and Sláma, 1966). Similarly, when pupal–adult development of *Tenebrio molitor* is inhibited by implantation of active corpora allata or by administration of farnesyl methyl ether, the U-shaped curve of oxygen uptake that normally characterizes the pupal stage is flattened (Schmialek and Drews, 1965; Geyer *et al.*, 1968b).

Adult insects, in which juvenile hormone can regulate reproduction and diapause, provide a somewhat less complex situation. In *Pyrrhocoris* female adults, the reproductive cycles are accompanied by peaks of oxygen uptake, which are eliminated after allatectomy (Sláma, 1964a), while in the male, the respiratory rate is lower, noncyclic, and virtually unaffected by removal of the allata (Sláma, 1964b). This suggests that respiration rises in support of the energy demand of ovarian development. In stick insects (Neugebauer, 1961) and locusts (Roussel, 1963), on the other hand, corpus allatum-stimulated respiration does not obviously coincide with the period of maximal ovarian growth. In the woodroach (*Leucophaea maderae*), implantation of allata was followed by elevated respiration in female adults even when they were previously deprived of ovaries and accessory glands (Sägesser, 1960). These observations seemed to indicate that the hormone could stimulate respiration independently of ovarian development. A consistent picture emerges now that it is known that much of the hormone-induced protein synthesis associated with egg development, which must require substantial energy, takes place in the fat body and continues after ovariectomy (Section III,D,2). In support of this interpretation, the respiration of isolated cockroach fat body tissue has been shown to depend on the presence of active corpora allata in the animal from which the tissue was taken (Lüscher, 1968)—but addition of allata to fat body *in vitro* was ineffective (Lüscher and Leuthold, 1965). More extreme respiratory change associated with juvenile hormone activity is observed in the adult diapause of the Colorado potato beetle, involving breakdown of the thoracic muscles as well as cessation of egg development (de Wilde and Stegwee, 1958, Stegwee, 1964).

There are several reports of effects of hormonal preparations on activities of isolated insect mitochondria, chiefly the giant mitochondria (sarcosomes) of flight muscle. Sarcosome preparations from Colorado potato beetles showed substantial increases in both oxygen uptake and P/O ratio of oxidative phosphorylation in the presence of low concentrations of cecropia oil (Stegwee, 1960). Experiments with mitochondria from adult locusts indicated some stimulation of respiration when crushed corpora allata were added (Clarke and Baldwin, 1960). Effects on locust mitochondria have been investigated more thoroughly by Minks (1967). With mitochondria from either flight muscle or fat body, P/O was significantly elevated by addition of homogenized corpora allata, and the extract also caused some reversal of uncoupling by dinitrophenol and inhibition of DNP-stimulated mitochondrial ATPase. Cecropia oil, added in emulsion at low levels, also raised P/O, but farnesol and farnesyl methyl ether were ineffective. These intriguing results are interpreted as showing an effect of juvenile hormone on oxidative phosphorylation, but such a conclusion seems premature since the observations could be due to unknown components of the crude extracts that were used.

From the data at hand, it seems most probable that the physiological influences of juvenile hormone on mitochondrial activity are secondary to the stimulation of other anabolic processes. The story is reminiscent of that of thyroxine in vertebrates. Thyroxine, incidentally, at 10^{-5} M fully uncouples insect mitochondria, although it is not a hormone in insects (Karlson and Schulz-Enders, 1963).

2. Lipid Metabolism

There is considerable evidence to indicate a rather close relationship between juvenile hormone action and the metabolism of lipids. Pfeiffer (1945), investigating the basis of the hormonal control of egg production in the grasshopper *Melanoplus differentialis*, observed that in allatectomized female adults the fat reserves, which normally attain a steady state level, instead continued to accumulate up to three times the normal amount. Ovariectomy had little effect, and it was proposed that a primary function of the corpus allatum hormone is to facilitate the mobilization of materials needed for egg growth, including lipids. Subsequently, on the basis of either biochemical analyses or histological examination of the fat body, abnormal accumulation of lipid in this tissue after allatectomy has been reported in cockroaches (*Periplaneta americana*) (Bodenstein, 1953; Vroman *et al.*, 1965; Mills *et al.*, 1966), locusts (Odhiambo, 1966c; Beenakkers, 1969), bugs (Janda and Sláma, 1965; Janda, 1970), blowflies (*Calliphora erythrocephala*) (Thomsen, 1952), and noctuid moths (El-Ibrashy and Boctor, 1970). In *Drosophila hydei*, consistent with the general picture, removal of the allata is followed by increased lipid in the fat body (Vogt, 1949), yet in *Drosophila melanogaster*, implantation of corpora allata from females into adult males or treatment of the latter with synthetic juvenile hormone also led to accumulation of fat (Butterworth and Bodenstein, 1969); the resolution of this paradox, in which withdrawal of a hormone and increasing the supply of it appear to have the same effect, is not obvious. Genetic differences may be important; the abnormally high lipid in fat body of *D. melanogaster adp* homozygous females is not diminished by implantation of wild-type corpora allata or administration of juvenile hormone preparations (Doane, 1961, 1963).

In most of the experiments cited, the deposition of lipid was an accompaniment of cellular hypertrophy in the fat body. Among lipids, the greatest change is in triglycerides (Vroman *et al.*, 1965). In some cases, accumulation of glycogen was also observed (e.g., Janda and Sláma, 1965; Odhiambo, 1966c; Butterworth and Bodenstein, 1969). Indirect mechanisms have been proposed; e.g., that the nutrient reserves are depleted as a consequence of increased muscular activity due to the allatum hormone (Odhiambo, 1966d). But a direct effect of juvenile hormone on fat body metabolism seems likely, since accumulation of fat after allatectomy has been observed in male and female insects and in the absence of corpora cardiaca and of gonads, and since a direct action of this hormone on the fat body in regulating vitellogenic protein production has been established (Section III,D,2). As would be expected if juvenile hormone is required for mobilization from fat body, allatectomy of cockroaches is followed by decreased serum lipid (Menon, 1965a,b).

Recently, investigation of the biochemical basis of these effects has begun. Vroman *et al.* (1965) measured the incorporation of acetate-^{14}C into lipids in cockroaches, and found that allatectomy was followed by a markedly altered pattern, which was described as showing decreased rate of turnover, but which from the data appears more indicative of accelerated synthesis of triglycerides. Thus, juvenile hormone may retard lipid synthesis. L. I. Gilbert (1967c), by balance studies *in vivo* and by incubation of prelabeled tissue *in vitro*, has demonstrated transfer of fat from fat body to ovaries in the cockroach *Leucophaea maderae*. He also measured the incorporation of palmitate-^{14}C into lipids in organs *in vitro* and observed an effect of juvenile hormone, supplied either by added corpora allata or by emulsified juvenile hormone substances; in the presence of the hormone, incorporation into ovarian lipids was elevated while incorporation into fat body lipids was depressed.

As the outcome of lipid analyses of cecropia silkmoths at several stages of development, Stephen and Gilbert (1970) arrive at two correlations—an inverse relationship between juvenile hormone titer and rate of fat synthesis, and a direct correlation of hormone titer with the proportion of saturated fatty acids in the lipids. To explain these observations, they propose that juvenile hormone acts to block desaturation of palmitic and stearic acids. This, it is suggested, would retard the synthesis of storage triglycerides (which in cecropia are rich in unsaturated fatty acids), and divert saturated fatty acids into diglycerides, which are the chief blood transport form of lipid. According to this theory, the role of the enigmatically high titer of juvenile hormone found in adult male cecropia moths (Section III,C,1), is to facilitate lipid transport for flight energy. As a test of the hypothesis, it would be interesting to know the lipid pattern in male cecropia moths allatectomized as pupae.

3. Enzyme Levels

The levels of several enzymes in insect tissues have been shown to change in relation to juvenile hormone titer. After allatectomy of larval or adult cockroaches (*P. americana*), aspartate transaminase activity in thoracic muscle was lower than in controls; measurements were made 50–90 days after the operation, and the effect was greatest in female adults (Wang and Dixon, 1960). In mealworm pupae (*T. molitor*) treated with farnesyl methyl ether, activities of glucose-6-phosphate dehydrogenase, aldolase, and aspartate transaminase were elevated significantly over controls at times ranging from 2 to 7 days after treatment, while malate dehydrogenase and lactate dehydrogenase also showed indications of a positive effect (Emmerich et al., 1965b). When adult Colorado potato beetles are kept in diapause by allatectomy, the rise in several enzymes of carbohydrate metabolism which would accompany normal muscular development is blocked (de Kort, 1969). Rapid and selective response to administration or withdrawal of juvenile hormone, however, has not yet been demonstrated for any enzyme.

4. Nucleic Acids and Protein Synthesis

Evidence for induction by juvenile hormone of synthesis of vitellogenins (proteins destined for deposition in egg yolk) in the fat body of female adult insects has been reviewed in Section III,D,2. In several cases, elevated RNA synthesis associated with hormone action was also demonstrated. In view of the substantial output of an identified protein under clear hormonal regulation, this system should be favorable for biochemical analysis, and experiments in this direction have recently begun. Engelmann (1969b) has shown that the induction of vitellogenin synthesis in cockroach fat body is blocked by actinomycin D, and suggests on this basis that the hormone is involved in the synthesis of specific messenger RNA.

Relations between RNA and protein synthesis have also been examined in the colleterial gland of the cockroach Blattella germanica, in which the production of oothecal protein is controlled by juvenile hormone (Zalokar, 1968). Initiation of hormone release is followed within 1 hour by sharply increased uridine incorporation, and somewhat later by new protein synthesis. By 48 hours, the rate of incorporation into RNA had returned to the preinduction level, while protein synthesis continued to rise. The observations are consistent with gene derepression by the hormone, but it was noted that uptake of uridine into the nucleotide pool also rose early, so that mechanisms connected with nucleotide synthesis cannot be ruled out.

The biochemical analysis of juvenile hormone action in insect metamorphosis is complicated because molting, under the simultaneous influence of ecdysone, is necessary for manifestation of the morphogenetic effects, and these do not appear in the initial phases of the molt. Furthermore, in experiments in vivo, juvenile hormone may activate the ecdysial gland and so increase the availability of ecdysone. Thus, when enhanced RNA synthesis was observed in several tissues of silkmoth pupae developing after injection of juvenile hormone, it was impossible to know which hormone was immediately responsible (Oberlander and Schneiderman, 1966).

In some recent experiments, direct effects of juvenile hormone on RNA synthesis in isolated nuclei are claimed. Nuclei from fat body of *Calliphora* larvae were assayed for RNA polymerase, and it is reported that activity was significantly stimulated after 10 minutes exposure *in vitro* to either ecdysone (1 μg/ml) or juvenile hormone (JH-I, 0.1 μg/ml), but not when both hormones were present together (Congote *et al.*, 1969). As the larvae approached maturity, their fat body nuclei lost sensitivity to juvenile hormone. It is further reported that RNA from hormone-treated nuclei (either ecdysone or juvenile hormone) hybridized with DNA more efficiently than that from control nuclei, and that qualitative differences in the RNA could be shown by competition in hybridization (Congote *et al.*, 1970). These potentially exciting findings are difficult to assess because of scanty data in the publications.

In the mealworm *Tenebrio molitor*, when farnesyl methyl ether was injected into fresh pupae, significantly increased rates of RNA and protein synthesis were found in fat body taken 4–6 days later and incubated *in vitro* (Geyer *et al.*, 1968b). Using whole pupae and developing adults of the same species, Ilan (1968) has developed a system for cell-free amino acid incorporation and has analyzed the regulation of protein synthesis (Ilan *et al.*, 1970). The system prepared from 7-day-old "pupae" (pharate adults) incorporates a much higher ratio of tyrosine to leucine than that from 1-day-old pupae; this situation is believed to reflect partial synthesis of cuticular protein rich in tyrosine. The pattern of tryptic peptides from the product of the 7-day preparation corresponds to that from cuticular protein synthesized *in vivo*. Control of synthesis at the translational level was demonstrated by combining washed ribosomes from days 1 and 7 with tRNA and an enzyme fraction from each stage. High tyrosine incorporation could be catalyzed by ribosomes (with endogenous mRNA) from either stage, but required both tRNA and enzyme from day 7. This supported previous experiments with actinomycin D (Ilan *et al.*, 1966) in indicating that some template RNA for cuticular protein was present from the beginning of the pupal period. Other experiments indicated that the specificity depends on competition for synthetases by multiple tRNA's for a given amino acid, whose codons might occur selectively in the templates for different proteins. When pupae were treated on day 1 with the hormone analog dodecyl methyl ether, they were juvenilized and developed to second pupae instead of adults, and such animals did not produce the specific tRNA and enzymes necessary for cuticular protein synthesis, though their ribosomes were active. It is inferred that the control of specific protein synthesis by juvenile hormone is mediated by the production or activation of certain tRNA's and amino acyl-tRNA synthetases, rather than by specific messenger RNA. The biochemical analysis appears satisfactory. But the regulation of protein synthesis 7 days after administration of the hormone in an animal profoundly modified by its action may be only remotely linked to its primary effects.

Recent work in two laboratories reports effects of juvenile hormone on puffing of polytene chromosomes in salivary glands of *Chironomus* species—a phenomenon which has been intensively studied in relation to ecdysone action (Section II,E,4) and can serve as an indicator of gene activity. Application of synthetic JH-I and other compounds to prepupae of *Chironomus tentans* was followed within 2–4 hours by formation of one new puff and regression of a puff and a Balbiani ring (Lezzi and Gilbert, 1969). At the same loci, treatment with ecdysone induced the reverse effects, and an antagonistic action of the two hormones is inferred—via altered Na^+/K^+ ratio, in the view of these authors. In tests on *Chironomus thummi* by Laufer and Holt (1970), after synthetic juvenile hormone analogs were present in the culture water for 1 day or more, metamorphosis was blocked at the larval–pupal molt and the puff pattern was altered—puffs decreased in size at nine loci, and one Balbiani ring increased. In similar experiments with JH-I, changes in seven loci were observed within 6 hours (Laufer and Greenwood, 1969). The inhibited puffs were characteristic of pupation, but a puff which appears to be ecdysone-specific was not blocked by juvenile hormone, so that an action in concert with, rather than antagonistic to, that of ecdysone is postulated. The latter interpretation is based on a greater number of loci and seems more consistent with the action of juvenile hormone in controlling insect development (cf. Clever, 1963a). But neither study establishes the immediacy of puffing changes that has been shown with ecdysone.

5. Juvenile Hormone and Biological Membranes

Wigglesworth (1957) suggested that juvenile hormone might be concerned with regulation of permeability relations within cells, and more recently (Wigglesworth, 1969), he has discussed this concept again in the light of new evidence on the structural requirements for juvenile hormone activity. Direct evidence for an effect of juvenile hormone on properties of biological and synthetic membranes has recently been presented by Baumann (1968). With intracellular microelectrodes in excised larval salivary glands of the wax moth (*Galleria mellonella*), lowered membrane potential was found in the presence of juvenile hormone. The effect was obtained with cecropia oil from male adults, but not with oil from previously allatectomized cecropia moths used as a control. Lowered membrane resistance was also demonstrated within 3 minutes after addition of hormone extract and is believed to underlie the observed depolarization. Several synthetic hormonal analogs were also active, but there was no clear relationship between effectiveness in membrane depolarization and the concentration or hormonal potency of different substances. Subsequently, increased conductance has been shown within a few seconds after addition of juvenile hormone compounds to artificial lipid bilayers modified by addition of gating ion translocators (Baumann, 1969). The possible relationship of these observations to the biological action of juvenile hormone is intriguing.

6. Mechanism of Juvenile Hormone Action—Present Status

As reviewed above, different workers have claimed direct actions of juvenile hormone on plasma membrane, mitochondria, and cell nuclei. Especially close linkage has been suggested between juvenile hormone action and the enzyme systems of fatty acid metabolism. Specificity in induction of protein synthesis has been attributed to messenger RNA or to transfer RNA and enzymes. While the hormone does not necessarily have a single primary site of action, it is unlikely that all of these diverse suggestions are valid. Further evidence must be sought with different systems, pure hormonal substances, and adequate controls.

The best-established biochemically identifiable action of juvenile hormone is the induction of synthesis of yolk proteins in adult fat body. In view of the time lag, the concurrent synthesis of RNA, and the blockage by actinomycin, it is probable that this induction is controlled at the genetic level. A framework for action of juvenile hormone similar to that of steroid hormones is thus suggested, perhaps involving penetration along with binding proteins to the nucleus, though in neither case is the eventual mechanism of gene derepression yet known. The action of juvenile hormone in insect development is probably similar in principle to that in vitellogenesis, but modified by different competence of the immature tissues and by the concurrent action of ecdysone.

IV. NEUROHORMONES

A. NEUROSECRETION IN INSECTS

Neurosecretion, the production of hormones within the nervous system, provides the link between neural communication and biochemical regulation. Neurosecretion is highly developed in insects (reviews, Raabe, 1959; van der Kloot, 1960; Highnam, 1965; Bern and Hagadorn, 1965), and while certain common features are now well established, the complexity and diversity of the system becomes increasingly evident. Neuro-

TABLE VI

Some Insect Neurohormones

Hormone	Source	Action	References
Ecdysiotropin (brain, activation or prothoracotropic hormone)	Brain medial neurosecretory cells (probably all insects)	Stimulation of ecdysial gland, leading to ecdysone production	See Section IV,B
Bursicon	Brain or ganglia (flies, cockroaches)	Tanning of exocuticle, deposition of endocuticle	See Section IV,C
Diapause hormone	Subesophageal ganglion (*Bombyx mori*)	Production of diapause eggs; deposition of glycogen in ovary	See Section IV,D
Pupariation hormone	Brain, corpus cardiacum (blow-flies)	Acceleration of formation and tanning of puparium	Zdarek and Fraenkel (1969)
Neurotropic ecdysis hormone	Brain (saturniid silkmoths)	Release of adult ecdysis	Truman and Riddiford (1970)
Hyperglycemic hormone	Corpus cardiacum (various insects, but not Lepidoptera)	Glycogenolysis in fat body; elevation of blood trehalose	See Section IV,F
Adipokinetic hormone	Corpus cardiacum (locusts)	Release of diglycerides from fat body	Mayer and Candy (1969), Beenakkers (1969)
Cardiac accelerator	Corpus cardiacum (cockroach, locusts)	Acceleration of heart beat	Davey (1964), Brown (1965), Mordue and Goldsworthy (1969), Natalizi et al. (1970)
Diuretic hormone	Brain neurosecretory cells (various insects), thoracic ganglion (*Rhodnius*)	Stimulation of Malpighian tubule excretion, inhibition of rectal absorption	Maddrell (1963), Berridge (1966), Cazal and Girardie (1968), Mordue (1969a)
Antidiuretic hormone	Brain, corpus cardiacum, ganglia (cockroach, locusts)	Stimulation of rectal absorption, inhibition of Malpighian tubule excretion (?)	Wall (1967), Cazal and Girardie (1968), Mordue (1970)

secretory cells are present in the brain and all of the other major ganglia, as recognized cytochemically and, in an increasing number of instances, by demonstrated activity of extracts. The corpora cardiaca (review, Joly and Cazal, 1969), paired bodies behind the brain connected to it by nerve tracts, are one focal point of the neurosecretory system. They contain cells which produce their own active secretions and they also function as neurohemal organs, sites of release into the blood of neuro-secretion transported from the brain cells. Brain hormone can be released directly in the absence of corpora cardiaca, however, and transport of neurosecretion through axons to other tissues has also been documented (B. Johnson and Bowers, 1963; Thomsen, 1969).

Neurosecretory cells accumulate material with characteristic staining properties, and this material is released under appropriate stimulation (Highnam, 1965; Scharrer and Kater, 1969). The relation between this cytologically recognizable neurosecretory material and the soluble hormones is not clear, but biologically active extracts have frequently been obtained from such cells without great difficulty. The active principles, when characterized, generally have the properties of polypeptide or protein. This contrasts with the developmental hormones of non-neural origin (ecdysone and juvenile hormone), which are lipoidal in nature and have not been shown to accumulate in the endocrine glands. Although further generalization is distinctly risky at this stage, a tentative distinction in relation to mode of action will also be offered: the neuro-hormones act, at least in certain instances, relatively rapidly (during minutes or a few hours) on processes which are interpretable in terms of activation of preexisting enzymes, whereas the non-neural develop-mental hormones act during many hours or days on processes requiring synthesis of nucleic acids and proteins.

Some neurohormones whose role has been demonstrated in more than one species of insect both by extirpation and reimplantation of the active center (or injection of extract from it) are listed in Table VI. Others have been omitted, either because of the provisional state of knowledge of them, or because their roles appear to be specialized in certain insect species. The latter include various examples of the control of pigmenta-tion, either by the deposition of pigment during development or by the reversible migration of pigment granules in response to ambient illumination (see Joly, 1968).

B. Ecdysiotropin (Brain Hormone)

The hormone by which the brain stimulates the ecdysial glands to activity resulting in molting is of central importance in the control of insect development (review, Doane, 1972). Since it is now clear that the neurosecretory cells of the insect brain are of several kinds and produce a number of hormones, the term "ecdysiotropin" (Gorbman and Bern, 1962; Herman, 1968) is recommended as more specific and precise than other names in current use (brain hormone, activation hormone, prothoracotropic hormone).

Heroic efforts have been made to isolate and characterize this hormone. Notwithstanding the isolation from silkworm brains of cholesterol having apparent ecdysiotropic activity (Kobayashi et al., 1962; cf. L. I. Gilbert and Goodfellow, 1965), it is now agreed that the brain hormone is water soluble and of high molecular weight. From the extract of 118,000 excised silkworm brains, Ishizaki and Ichikawa (1967) achieved some 8000-fold purification. The hormone was heat stable, precipitable by ammonium sulfate, and separable on Sephadex G-100 into three active fractions of molecular weights about 9,000, 12,000 and 30,000, respectively, which appear to be proteins. Activity was destroyed by subtilisin and Pronase, but not by trypsin or chymotrypsin (Ichikawa and Ishizaki, 1963). Purification of a possibly different component having ecdysiotropic activity and some characteristics of a glycoprotein has been reported by Yamazaki and Kobayashi (1969). Starting with brains of the saturniid silkmoth *Antheraea pernyi*, Williams (1967) obtained an active fraction similar to that of Ishizaki and Ichikawa, but because of its resistance to trypsin, chymotrypsin, heat and to denaturation by chloroform, he suggested that it may be mucopolysaccharide. From cockroach brains, Gersch and Stürzebecher (1968) obtained three fractions with ecdysiotropic activity and some characteristics suggestive of protein. Ishizaki (1969) has assayed the titer of brain hormone in silkworm pupae and adults of different ages, and found unexpectedly high activity close to the time of adult emergence. This may facilitate obtaining sufficient material for chemical analysis.

Inasmuch as the insect brain can induce molting only in the presence of ecdysial glands, the role of the brain hormone is presumably to induce these glands to secrete ecdysone (Williams, 1952) (see, however, Section II,C,2). The chief biochemical correlate of this activation so far reported is elevated RNA synthesis in the ecdysial gland, shown in silkworms by autoradiographic measurement of incorporation of uridine-^{3}H (Oberlander et al., 1965; Kobayashi et al., 1968). In cockroaches, the RNA level in the gland is significantly elevated 8 hours after implantation of brains or administration of "activation hormone," and the tissue also produces a complex lipid fraction of unknown function (Gersch and Stürzebecher, 1970). If RNA synthesis does prove to be an essential step in the action of ecdysiotropin, this would contrast with the mode of action of some other protein neurohormones.

C. BURSICON

An interesting recent development, as a result of independent work in two laboratories (Cottrell, 1962a,b; Fraenkel and Hsiao, 1962, 1963), has been the recognition of a hormone that controls tanning of the cuticle in newly molted insects. When blowflies emerge from puparia buried in the soil, the cuticle remains soft and white until the fly has dug itself to the surface, whereupon a neuroendocrine stimulus releases cuticular expansion and tanning. Tanning is prevented by ligature at the neck, and the·appearance of a hormone in the blood of normal flies soon after emergence can be demonstrated by tanning after transfusion into such ligated individuals. Similar endocrine control of cuticular tanning has been demonstrated in cockroaches (*Periplaneta americana*) (Mills *et al.*, 1965). The hormone has been termed "bursicon" (Fraenkel and Hsiao, 1965).

In flies, bursicon is produced by the medial neurosecretory cells of the brain. Though the brain is clearly the site of control, active hormone can be extracted both from it and from the thoracic compound ganglion (Fraenkel and Hsiao, 1965). In the cockroach, ligation experiments show the terminal abdominal ganglion to be the site of release, but activity can be found by extraction from all parts of the central nervous system (Mills, 1965). Activity may be assayed by injection into appropriately ligated specimens of either insect, or by incubation of extracts with disks of untanned integument *in vitro* [Mills (1965); but this assay has been criticized by Fogal and Fraenkel (1969) and Vincent (1969)]. Hormonal activity is nonspecific among insects, and blood from species of five other orders was active in flies, but only when taken immediately after a molt normally followed by tanning (Fraenkel and Hsiao, 1965).

Bursicon has been partially purified and has the general properties of a protein. The hormone from flies is nondialysable; precipitable by ammonium sulfate; inactivated by trichloroacetic acid, alcohol, trypsin, Pronase, and subtilisin; but relatively stable to heat (Cottrell, 1962b; Fraenkel and Hsiao, 1965; Fraenkel *et al.*, 1966). The molecular weight is estimated by gel filtration as about 40,000. The hormone from cockroaches is generally very similar, though more heat sensitive (Mills and Lake, 1966; Mills and Nielsen, 1967).

The biochemistry of tanning of the post-ecdysial insect cuticle involves

N-acetyldopamine derived from tyrosine (Sekeris, 1964) and is essentially similar to that of the fly puparium, which is controlled by ecdysone (Section II,E,2), but the mode of action of bursicon in releasing the process is quite distinct. Bursicon-induced tanning is not blocked by actinomycin or puromycin and is thus presumably linked to the action, rather than the synthesis, of enzymes (Fogal and Fraenkel, 1969). In flies, the utilization of tyrosine, as well as its turnover from tyrosine O-phosphate and an apparent additional pool, is accelerated in the presence of bursicon (Seligman et al., 1969), and in cockroaches, hormone preparations stimulate the incorporation of tyrosine-^{14}C into epidermis and cuticle (Whitehead, 1969). Several enzymes of this pathway were not stimulated by addition of hormone preparations to homogenates (Mills et al., 1967), and there is no close temporal correlation of phenol oxidase activity with bursicon titer during a molt (Mills et al., 1968). However, it has recently been claimed that bursicon may stimulate the penetration of tyrosine into hemocytes and decarboxylation there to tyramine on the pathway to the tanning quinone (Whitehead, 1969; Mills and Whitehead, 1970). This provocative suggestion of a hormonal effect on membrane permeability merits further study.

In addition to tanning of the exocuticle, the post-molt deposition of endocuticle (Section I,A) in flies and cockroaches has been shown to require bursicon (Fogal and Fraenkel, 1969; Vincent, 1969). The hormone stimulates the incorporation of leucine, and in contrast to tanning, this biosynthetic process is inhibited by actinomycin and puromycin.

D. Silkworm Diapause Hormone

The mulberry silkworm (*Bombyx mori*) possesses a facultative diapause in the egg, the occurrence of which is determined by the conditions of light and temperature to which the maternal insect was exposed as an embryo, a full generation previously. This influence is expressed during oogenesis by a neurohormone from the subesophageal ganglion, the release of which is controlled via connectives from the brain (Fukuda, 1963). Implantation of subesophageal ganglia from diapause pupae (i.e., those that would produce diapause eggs) into nondiapause pupae induces production of diapause eggs in the latter. Subesophageal ganglia, or silkmoth heads (from either female or male moths of various ages) (Hasegawa, 1964), yield active extracts. The hormone has been purified to some extent (Hasegawa, 1957), but no details of purification and characterization have been published. The preparations are water soluble, and 0.2–1.0 mg is required for activity.

Diapause eggs contain more glycogen than nondiapause eggs, and the role of the hormone in bringing this about has been investigated in Hasegawa's laboratory. The greater glycogen content of the ovaries in diapause pupae is accompanied by lower hemolymph trehalose and fat body glycogen. These differences can be induced by injection of diapause hormone into nondiapause pupae, or reversed by extirpation of sub-esophageal ganglia from diapause pupae (Yamashita and Hasegawa, 1964). Implantation of ovaries causes depletion of fat body glycogen in male pupae (provided that the hormone is present), showing that the effects on fat body are secondary to action on the ovaries (Hasegawa and Yamashita, 1965). Subesophageal ganglia or extracts from them stimulate incorporation of glucose-^{14}C into ovarian glycogen, but the level of glycogen synthetase is apparently unaffected (Yamashita and Hasegawa, 1967, 1970). In the conversion from trehalose to glycogen, a controlling step is believed to be the initial cleavage catalyzed by trehalase, the level of which reflects the presence or absence of diapause hormone. Trehalase activity in the ovaries rises within 3 hours after injection of the hormone, and by 24 hours is elevated 75% above controls, hence induction of ovarian trehalase synthesis by the hormone is suggested (Yamashita and Hasegawa, 1967; Yamashita, 1969).

Another consequence of the action of diapause hormone, related to the production of ommochrome pigments in diapause eggs, is increased content of 3-hydroxykynurenine in the ovaries (Yamashita and Hasegawa, 1966). Further elements in the picture are influences of the hormone on ovarian lipid content and molecular weight distribution of RNA (Hasegawa and Yamashita, 1967). How the hormone determines the onset of diapause in the eggs, however, is not known, nor is the mechanism responsible for the biochemical differences just described.

E. HYPERGLYCEMIC HORMONE

An insect hormone comparable to the glucagon of vertebrates was first demonstrated by Steele (1961, 1963). Injection of fresh or boiled aqueous extracts of corpora cardiaca into adult cockroaches (*Periplaneta americana*) was followed by elevation of blood trehalose (which is the predominant sugar in most insects) (G. R. Wyatt, 1967). Blood glucose (present at a low level) was little affected. Effects were obtained in as short a time as 30 minutes and with as little extract as the equivalent of 0.002 pair of corpora cardiaca; the maximal effect was about 2.5-fold elevation of blood trehalose lasting for several hours. The phenomenon was confirmed and extended to other species of cockroach (W. S. Bowers and Friedman, 1963; Ralph and McCarthy, 1964; Wiens and Gilbert, 1965), and more recently to other insects—the stick insect (Dutrieu and Gourdoux, 1967), locusts (Goldsworthy, 1969) and blowflies (Friedman, 1967; Normann and Duve, 1969). Hormone extracted from locusts, flies, and bees (Natalizi and Frontali, 1966) is active when assayed in cockroaches. In certain Lepidoptera, however, neither production nor action of hyperglycemic hormone could be shown (*Manduca sexta,* W. S. Bowers, 1963; *Hyalophora cecropia,* Wiens and Gilbert, 1967b).

The hyperglycemic hormone accumulates in the corpus cardiacum and is released from it under electrical stimulation (Normann and Duve, 1969). The cardiacum is probably also the site of production since greater activity is found in the glandular lobe than in the storage lobe of this gland in *Locusta* (Mordue and Goldsworthy, 1969). The presence of some activity in extracts of brain and of cardiacum storage lobe, however, raises the possibility that the hormone (or perhaps a second one) may originate in the brain neurosecretory cells and be released via the cardiaca (Ralph and McCarthy, 1964; Mordue and Goldsworthy, 1969).

The factor from cockroach cardiaca is stable to brief boiling in 0.06 N HCl but is inactivated by incubation with trypsin (Natalizi and Frontali, 1966). Two active fractions may apparently be resolved by chromatography on paper (Brown, 1965; Mordue and Goldsworthy, 1969) or SE-Sephadex C-50 (Natalizi and Frontali, 1966). Sephadex G-25 or G-15 gives a homogeneous peak of activity separated partially from the cardiacum heart-stimulating factor and completely from 5-hydroxytryptamine, but because of chromatographic effects, the molecular weight cannot be deduced (Natalizi and Frontali, 1966; Natalizi *et al.,* 1970). In all probability, the hormone is a polypeptide.

The source of the sugar released is glycogen in the fat body, as shown by depletion of this reserve both *in vivo* (Steele, 1963) and during action of the hormone on fat body tissue *in vitro* (Ralph, 1962; Wiens and Gilbert, 1967a; Friedman, 1967). Glycogen of muscle and gut tissue are not mobilized. As anticipated from analogy with vertebrate systems, fat body phosphorylase shows increased activity during action of the insect hormone (Steele, 1963; Mordue and Goldsworthy, 1969). In the roach *Leucophaea maderae,* phosphorylase is converted from an inactive to an active form maximally during 10 minutes of hormone action, and some preliminary results suggest that there may also be activation of trehalose-6-phosphate synthetase, the enzyme controlling trehalose synthesis (Wiens and Gilbert, 1967a).

Decreased glycogen synthesis from glucose-^{14}C accompanied increased glycogenolysis in hormone-treated roach fat body (Wiens and Gilbert, 1967a), as in the mammalian cyclic nucleotide-regulated system. Suppression of glycogen synthesis (and stimulation of fat synthesis) is also brought about in mosquitos by a hormone from the median neurosecretory cells of the brain, but this system differs in that glycogenolysis is not affected (Lea and Van Handel, 1970; Van Handel and Lea, 1970).

F. Neurosecretion and Protein Synthesis

1. Hemolymph Proteins

Ever since Bodenstein (1953) observed that elimination of the corpora cardiaca from cockroaches prevented the normal accumulation of uric acid in the fat body, some participation of neurosecretion in the regulation of protein metabolism has repeatedly been suggested. In the course of experiments on the endocrine control of ovarian maturation (see Section III,D,2) in locusts (Hill, 1962; Highnam *et al.,* 1963) and in *Tenebrio* (Mordue, 1965), ablation of brain neurosecretory cells was found to lower the blood protein level. In locusts, the incorporation of glycine-^{14}C into fat body protein was also decreased (Hill, 1965), and these results were taken to indicate neurosecretory control over blood protein synthesis. Engelmann and Penney (1966), however, showed that in the roach *Leucophaea maderae* lowered blood protein after medial neurosecretory cell cautery could be attributed to decreased feeding by the operated animals, and suggested that the earlier observations might be explained in a similar way. The criticism is valid, but is circumvented in more recent work in which implantation of brains or corpora cardiaca into decapitated roaches (*Leucophaea*) led to elevation of total hemolymph protein as well as certain electrophoretic components (Scheurer, 1969a). Some stimulation of incorporation of alanine-^{14}C into protein of isolated fat body from *Leucophaea* in the presence of corpora cardiaca has also been reported (Wyss-Huber and Lüscher, 1966), and some effect on specific blood proteins in locusts is suggested by changes in the electrophoretic pattern after medial neurosecretory cell cautery (Minks, 1967; Bentz and Girardie, 1969). On the other hand, neurosecretory cell ablation in the fleshfly (*Sarcophaga*) does not lead to lowered blood protein level (Wilkens, 1969), and implantation of cardiaca into the roach *Nauphoeta cinerea* (in contrast to the related *Leucophaea*) did not stimulate protein synthesis (Lüscher, 1968).

Thus, the possible participation of neurosecretion in regulation of fat body protein synthesis and hemolymph protein levels is as yet by no means clear. Further experiments with isolated tissues and specific proteins are needed.

2. Digestive Enzymes

In many insects, the level of digestive enzymes rises during maturation of the adult and after food intake (review, Waterhouse, 1957), and the regulatory processes have been investigated with somewhat conflicting results. In the blowfly *Calliphora erythrocephala*, midgut protease activity rises after feeding on meat, but not after ingestion of sugar. The rise is abolished in flies from which the brain medial neurosecretory cells have been removed and is partially restored by implantation of corpora cardiaca–allata, from which neurosecretory control over gut protease production has been inferred (Thomsen and Møller, 1963). Similar observations were made subsequently in relation to midgut esterase (Thomsen, 1966). It is also recorded that meat feeding causes release of neurosecretory material from the medial neurosecretory cells in this species (Thomsen and Lea, 1968), but in view of the involvement of these cells in ovarian maturation (Section III,D,2), this does not necessarily imply a connection with digestive enzyme synthesis.

In the mealworm beetle *Tenebrio molitor*, direct evidence for a blood-borne factor has been obtained by elevation of gut protease following transfusion of hemolymph from fed beetles into starved beetles, and the consequences of neck ligation indicated a hormonal source in the head (Dadd, 1961). In the tsetse fly (*Glossina morsitans*), a blood meal is required for the development of midgut protease, the level of enzyme produced being correlated with the degree of crop distension, not with the amount of blood ingested, and, there being no nervous connection between crop and midgut, neuroendocrine regulation is postulated (Langley, 1966). Further experiments indicated some elevation of midgut protease after injection of brain extract into neck-ligated flies (Langley, 1967).

An alternative mechanism would be digestive enzyme induction by direct action of dietary components on intestinal cells. Engelmann (1969c) has shown that in *Leucophaea maderae*, midgut protease is synthesized after ingestion of certain proteins (but not others); the level of enzyme activity attained is correlated with the amount of food passing into the midgut, and this correlation is unaffected by extirpation of brain, corpora cardiaca, or corpora allata. Similar results have been obtained with the fleshfly *Sarcophaga bullata* (Englemann and Wilkens, 1969). These authors believe digestive enzyme production to be induced by substances ("secretagogues") in the food and reinterpret Thomsen's results on the basis of decreased food intake in operated flies. In line with this viewpoint, Gordon (1970) found no effect of medial neurosecretory cell cautery on the activities of various midgut digestive enzymes in the roach *Blatta orientalis*.

Clearly, the mechanisms responsible for regulation of insect digestive enzymes are by no means settled and may differ in different species.

G. Neurohormones and Respiration

There are a number of reports showing an influence of neurohormones on respiration of insect tissues. Whole-animal respiration is lowered after cardiatectomy of adult females of the bug *Pyrrhocoris apterus* (Sláma, 1964a) and the roach *Blaberus discoidalis* (Keeley and Friedman, 1967), and after removal of brain neurosecretory cells from milkweed bugs (Conradi-Larsen, 1970). The effect appears to be due in part to influences on fat body metabolism, for respiration of isolated fat body is stimulated by addition of corpora cardiaca or extracts of them *in vitro* (Lüscher and Leuthold, 1965; Wiens and Gilbert, 1965; Müller and Engelmann, 1968). Ralph and Matta (1965) have claimed effects on oxygen uptake when hormonal extracts were added to fat body homogenates. These phenomena are difficult to interpret in view of the variety of metabolic and physiological processes in the fat body and other insect organs known to be influenced by neurohormones, many of which could affect respiration.

After long-term cardiatectomy of roaches, Keeley and Friedman (1969) have shown lowered respiratory activity in isolated fat body mitochondria not reversible by added hormone. This suggests some endocrine requirement for maintenance of mitochondrial integrity or enzyme content and recalls the effect of thyroxine in vertebrates.

H. Cyclic Nucleotides in Insects

In view of the role of 3′,5′-cyclic adenosine monophosphate as a second messenger in the action of many hormones of vertebrates, it is worth summarizing the present evidence concerning cyclic nucleotides in insects. The conversion of glycogen phosphorylase from an inactive to an active form in the cockroach fat body under the influence of hyperglycemic hormone (Section IV,E) and in silkmoth fat body in response to injury (Section V,C) suggests a cyclic nucleotide-mediated system. Addition of cyclic AMP caused activation of phosphorylase in intact *Periplaneta* fat body but not in homogenates (Steele, 1964). In homogenates of cecropia silkmoth fat body, added cyclic AMP gave no stimulation of phosphorylase kinase activity (Wiens and Gilbert, 1967b). Some observations with respect to lipolysis are similar—cyclic AMP stimulates fatty acid release from *Periplaneta* fat body *in vitro*, but with cecropia tissue no effect was obtained (Bhakthan and Gilbert, 1968).

In a survey of cyclic nucleotide levels in animal tissues, Ishikawa *et al.* (1969) discovered that crickets, in contrast to tissues of vertebrates, contain more 3′,5′-cyclic guanosine monophosphate than cyclic AMP. The content of cyclic GMP in whole crickets was 2–4 nmoles/gm, in comparison with 0.01–0.07 nmoles/gm in various tissues of the rat. Provoked by this observation and by the discovery of cyclic GMP-dependent protein kinase in an arthropod, the lobster (Kuo and Greengard, 1969), Kuo *et al.* (1971) have recently examined a series of insect tissues for cyclic nucleotide-dependent protein kinases. Both cyclic AMP-dependent and cyclic GMP-dependent kinases were found, and several lepidopteran tissues, including cecropia fat body, showed almost exclusively the latter activity. It appears that cyclic GMP may be important in biochemical regulation in insects, and may possibly perform in lepidopteran fat body some of the functions exercised by cyclic AMP elsewhere.

Secretion by isolated *Calliphora* salivary glands (Berridge and Patel, 1968) and by locust Malpighian tubules (Mordue, 1969b) are both stimulated by added cyclic AMP. An apparent synergism of cyclic AMP and ecdysone in evoking chromosome puffs has been mentioned above (Section II,D,4) (Leenders *et al.*, 1970).

V. OTHER HORMONES

A. GLOWWORM ANDROGENIC HORMONE

The glowworm *Lampyris noctiluca* exhibits striking sexual dimorphism, the female being wingless and equipped with a highly developed luminous organ. Young larvae of the two sexes are similar, and the secondary sexual characters as well as differentiation of the gonads themselves are determined by an androgenic hormone produced in the male, as demonstrated by grafting and transplantation experiments. The source of the androgenic hormone is a group of apical cells in the testis, and development of these in turn is determined by a secretion of brain neurosecretory cells (Naisse, 1966, 1969).

B. PROCTODONE

In the European corn borer *Ostrinia nubilalis,* breaking of diapause in the prepupal larva is reported to depend on a secretion of the hindgut cells, termed "proctodone" (Beck and Alexander, 1964). Although characteristic inclusion bodies have been observed in these cells (Alexander and Fahrenbach, 1969), their endocrine nature and role in causing pupation seem not to have been established beyond doubt.

C. Injury Factor

In silkmoth pupae in diapause, respiration is stimulated after simple injury to the integument, the magnitude and duration of the effect (up to about 3 weeks) varying in relation to the size of the wound (Schneiderman and Williams, 1953; Harvey and Williams, 1961). Further studies have shown that the injury effect includes synthesis of cytochromes (Shappirio, 1960; Shappirio and Harvey, 1965), stimulation of RNA synthesis in epidermis and fat body (G. R. Wyatt, 1963; Barth *et al.*, 1964; G. R. Wyatt and Linzen, 1965) and other tissues (Berry *et al.*, 1967), stimulation of protein synthesis (Telfer and Williams, 1960; Stevenson and Wyatt, 1962; Skinner, 1963), and stimulation of carbohydrate metabolism including activation of silkmoth fat body phosphorylase (G. R. Wyatt, 1963; Stevenson and Wyatt, 1964). The induced protein synthesis includes selective production of certain proteins which have been termed "injury protein" (Berry *et al.*, 1964).

The injury effect is most marked in developmental stages characterized by low metabolism. In adult *Rhodnius,* where the epidermal cells are normally quiescent, wounding is followed by cytological changes similar to those produced by ecdysone (Wigglesworth, 1957). In larval *Rhodnius* after development is arrested by decapitation, injury produces intensely elevated respiration (Okasha, 1970). Even in normal *Calliphora* larvae, however, at a stage responsive to ecdysone, effects on RNA and protein synthesis observed after control injections of water must be attributed to the injury of puncture (Neufeld *et al.*, 1968).

Since a localized integumentary wound induces reactions throughout an insect, a circulating messenger substance must be involved. The observed biochemical events are very similar to those induced by ecdysone, and it may be that release of some ecdysone contributes to the injury response. However, injury alone has never been observed to provoke apolysis or any other developmental event, apart from healing of the wound. Furthermore, cellular response to injury can be obtained in the absence of ecdysial glands [adult *Rhodnius* (Wigglesworth, 1957), isolated abdomens of *cynthia* pupae (Harvey and Williams, 1961)]. In any case, the stimulus must be transmitted via the hemolymph from the site of wounding. Thus, one is forced to postulate a circulating "injury factor," as yet unidentified.

ACKNOWLEDGMENTS

The preparation of this chapter and research in my laboratory were supported by grants from the Whitehall Foundation and the National Institutes of Health, U. S. Public Health Service (HD-02176). I am indebted to several authors for access to manuscripts prior to publication, and to Dr. Winifred Doane and Prof. C. M. Williams for critical reading of the text.

REFERENCES

Adelung, D., and Karlson, P. (1969). *J. Insect Physiol.* **15**, 1301.
Adiyodi, K. G. (1968). *J. Insect Physiol.* **14**, 309.
Adiyodi, K. G., and Nayar, K. K. (1967). *Biol. Bull.* **133**, 271.
Agui, N., Yagi, S., and Fukaya, M. (1969a). *Appl. Entomol. Zool.* **4**, 156.
Agui, N., Yagi, S., and Fukaya, M. (1969b). *Appl. Entomol. Zool.* **4**, 158.
Alexander, H. J., and Fahrenbach, W. H. (1969). *Z. Zellforsch. Mikroskop. Anat.* **94**, 337.
Applebaum, S. W., Ebstein, R. P., and Wyatt, G. R. (1966). *J. Mol. Biol.* **21**, 29.
Arking, R., and Shaaya, E. (1969). *J. Insect Physiol.* **15**, 287.
Ashburner, M. (1970a). *Advan. Insect. Physiol.* **7**, 1.
Ashburner, M. (1970b). *Nature* **227**, 187.
Barnes, F. J., and Goodfellow, R. D. (1968). *Am. Zoologist* **8**, 777.
Barnes, F. J., and Goodfellow, R. D. (1969). *Am. Zoologist* **9**, 1109.
Barritt, L. C., and Birt, L. M. (1970). *J. Insect Physiol.* **16**, 671.
Barth, R. H. (1968). *Advan. Reprod. Physiol.* **3**, 167.
Barth, R. H., Bunyard, P. B., and Hamilton, T. H. (1964). *Proc. Natl. Acad. Sci. U. S.* **52**, 1572.
Baumann, G. (1968). *J. Insect Physiol.* **14**, 1459.
Baumann, G. (1969). *Nature* **223**, 316.
Beck, S. D., and Alexander, N. (1964). *Biol. Bull.* **126**, 185.
Beck, S. D., and Shane, J. L. (1969). *J. Insect Physiol.* **15**, 721.
Becker, E., and Plagge, E. (1939). *Biol. Zentr.* **59**, 326.
Becker, H. J. (1962). *Chromosoma* **13**, 341.
Beenakkers, A. M. T. (1969). *Gen. Comp. Endocrinol.* **13**, 492.
Beermann, W. (1962). *Protoplasmatologia* **6 (D)**, 1.
Beermann, W. (1965). *Naturwissenschaften* **52**, 365.
Beermann, W. (1967). *In* "Heritage from Mendel" (R. A. Brink and E. D. Styles, eds.), pp. 179–201. Univ. of Wisconsin Press, Madison, Wisconsin.
Bell, W. J. (1969). *J. Insect Physiol.* **15**, 1279.
Bell, W. J. (1970). *J. Insect Physiol.* **16**, 291.
Bell, W. J., and Barth, R. H. (1971). *Nature New Biol.* **230**, 220.
Bentz, F., and Girardie, A. (1969). *Compt. Rend.* **D269**, 2014.
Berendes, H. D. (1967). *Chromosoma* **22**, 274.
Berendes, H. D. (1968). *Chromosoma* **24**, 418.
Berendes, H. D., and Boyd, J. B. (1969). *J. Cell Biol.* **41**, 591.

Berkoff, C. E. (1969). *Quart. Rev. (London)* 23, 372.

Berkoff, C. E. (1970). *Science* 168, 1607.

Bern, H. A. (1967). *Am. Zoologist* 7, 815.

Bern, H. A., and Hagadorn, I. R. (1965). *In* "Structure and Function of the Nervous Systems of Invertebrates" (T. H. Bullock and G. A. Horridge, eds.), Vol. 1, pp. 353–429. Freeman, San Francisco, California.

Berreur, P., and Fraenkel, G. (1969). *Science* 164, 1182.

Berridge, M. J. (1966). *J. Exptl. Biol.* 44, 533.

Berridge, M. J., and Patel, N. G. (1968). *Science* 162, 462.

Berry, S. J., and Firshein, W. (1967). *J. Exptl. Zool.* 166, 1.

Berry, S. J., Krishnakumaran, A., and Schneiderman, H. A. (1964). *Science* 146, 938.

Berry, S. J., Krishnakumaran, A., Oberlander, H., and Schneiderman, H. A. (1967). *J. Insect Physiol.* 13, 1511.

Bhakthan, H. M. G., and Gilbert, L. I. (1968). *Gen. Comp. Endocrinol.* 11, 186.

Bhaskaran, G., and Nair, K. K. (1966). *Proc. Seminar Intern. Cell Biol., Bombay, 1965* (K. J. Ranadive, ed.), pp. 64–66. Bombay University Press, Bombay.

Bishop, J. O. (1969). *Biochem. J.* 113, 805.

Bodenstein, D. (1943). *Biol. Bull.* 84, 34.

Bodenstein, D. (1953). *J. Exptl. Zool.* 124, 105.

Bodenstein, D., and Shaaya, E. (1968). *Proc. Natl. Acad. Sci. U. S.* 59, 1223.

Borden, J. H., and Slater, C. E. (1968). *Z. Vergleich. Physiol.* 61, 366.

Borden, J. H., Nair, K. K., and Slater, C. E. (1969). *Science* 166, 1626.

Bounhiol, J. J. (1938). *Bull. Biol. France Belg. Suppl.* 24, p. 1.

Bowers, B., and Johnson, B. (1966). *Gen. Comp. Endocrinol.* 6, 213.

Bowers, B., and Williams, C. M. (1964). *Biol. Bull.* 126, 205.

Bowers, W. S. (1963). *Dissertation Abstr.* 23, 2575.

Bowers, W. S. (1968). *Science* 161, 895.

Bowers, W. S. (1969). *Science* 164, 323.

Bowers, W. S., and Blickenstaff, C. C. (1966). *Science* 154, 1673.

Bowers, W. S., and Friedman, S. (1963). *Nature* 198, 685.

Bowers, W. S., and Thompson, M. J. (1963). *Science* 142, 1469.

Bowers, W. S., Thompson, M. J., and Uebel, E. C. (1965). *Life Sci.* 4, 2323.

Bowers, W. S., Fales, H. M., Thompson, M. J., and Uebel, E. C. (1966). *Science* 154, 1020.

Braun, B. II., Jacobson, M., Schwarz, M., Sonnet, P. E., Wakabayashi, N., and Waters, R. M. (1968). *J. Econ. Entomol.* 61, 866.

Brookes, V. J. (1969a). *Develop. Biol.* 20, 459.

Brookes, V. J. (1969b). *J. Insect Physiol.* 15, 621.

Brookes, V. J., and Williams, C. M. (1965). *Proc. Natl. Acad. Sci. U. S.* 53, 770.

Brown, B. E. (1965). *Gen. Comp. Endocrinol.* 5, 387

Brunet, P. C. J. (1966). *In* "Aspects of Insect Biochemistry" (T. W. Goodwin, ed.), pp. 49–77. Academic Press, New York.

Bryant, P. J., and Sang, J. H. (1968). *Nature* 220, 393.

Bückmann, D. (1959). *J. Insect Physiol.* 3, 159.

Bultmann, H., and Clever, U. (1969). *Chromosoma* 28, 120.

Burdette, W. J. (1962). *Science* 135, 432.

Burdette, W. J., and Richards, R. C. (1961). *Nature* 189, 666.

Butenandt, A., and Karlson, P. (1954). *Z. Naturforsch.* 9b, 389.

Butterworth, F. M., and Bodenstein, D. (1969). *Gen. Comp. Endocrinol.* 13, 68.

Cazal, M., and Girardie, A. (1968). *J. Insect Physiol.* 14, 655.

Černý, V., Dolejš, L., Lábler, L., Šorm, F., and Sláma, K. (1967). *Tetrahedron Letters* No. 12, p. 1053.

Chambers, D. L., and Brookes, V. J. (1967). *J. Insect Physiol.* **13**, 99.

Chen, P. S. (1966). *Advan. Insect Physiol.* **3**, 53.

Cherbas, L., and Cherbas, P. (1970). *Biol. Bull.* **138**, 115.

Chino, H., Gilbert, L. I., Siddall, J. B., and Hafferl, W. (1970). *J. Insect Physiol.* **16**, 2033.

Clarke, K. U., and Baldwin, R. W. (1960). *J. Insect Physiol.* **5**, 37.

Clever, U. (1961). *Chromosoma* **12**, 607.

Clever, U. (1962). *Chromosoma* **13**, 385.

Clever, U. (1963a). *Chromosoma* **14**, 651.

Clever, U. (1963b). *Develop. Biol.* **6**, 73.

Clever, U. (1964). *Science* **146**, 794.

Clever, U. (1965). *Chromosoma* **17**, 309.

Clever, U. (1966). *Develop. Biol.* **14**, 421.

Clever, U. (1968). *Ann. Rev. Genet.* **2**, 11.

Clever, U., and Karlson, P. (1960). *Exptl. Cell Res.* **20**, 623.

Clever, U., and Romball, C. (1966). *Proc. Natl. Acad. Sci. U. S.* **56**, 1470.

Clever, U., Storbeck, I., and Romball, C. G. (1969). *Exptl. Cell Res.* **55**, 306.

Coles, G. C. (1965a). *J. Exptl. Biol.* **43**, 425.

Coles, G. C. (1965b). *J. Insect Physiol.* **11**, 1325.

Collins, J. V. (1969). *J. Insect Physiol.* **15**, 341.

Congote, L. F., Sekeris, C. E., and Karlson, P. (1969). *Exptl. Cell Res.* **56**, 338.

Congote, L. F., Sekeris, C. E., and Karlson, P. (1970). *Z. Naturforsch.* **25b**, 279.

Conradi-Larsen, E. M. (1970). *J. Insect Physiol.* **16**, 471.

Corey, E. J., Katzenellenbogen, J. A., Gilman, N. W., Roman, S. A., and Erickson, B. W. (1968). *J. Am. Chem. Soc.* **90**, 5618.

Cottrell, C. B. (1962a). *J. Exptl. Biol.* **39**, 395.

Cottrell, C. B. (1962b). *J. Exptl. Biol.* **39**, 413.

Crossley, A. C. (1968). *J. Insect Physiol.* **14**, 1389.

Crouse, H. V. (1968). *Proc. Natl. Acad. Sci. U. S.* **61**, 971.

Dadd, R. H. (1961). *J. Exptl. Biol.* **38**, 259.

Dahm, K. H., and Röller, H. (1970). *Life Sci.* **9**, 1397.

Dahm, K. H., Trost, B. M., and Röller, H. (1967). *J. Am. Chem. Soc.* **89**, 5292.

Dahm, K. H., Röller, H., and Trost, B. M. (1968). *Life Sci.* **7**, 129.

Daneholt, B., and Edström, J. E. (1968). *Cytogenetics (Basel)* **6**, 350.

Davey, K. G. (1964). *Advan. Insect Physiol.* **2**, 219.

Dejmal, R., and Brookes, V. J. (1968). *J. Insect Physiol.* **14**, 371.

de Kort, C. A. D. (1969). *Mededel. Landbouwhogeschool Wageningen* **69**, No. 2, 1.

de Loof, A. (1969). *Gen. Comp. Endocrinol.* **13**, 518.

de Loof, A., and de Wilde, J. (1970a). *J. Insect Physiol.* **16**, 157.

de Loof, A., and de Wilde, J. (1970b). *J. Insect Physiol.* **16**, 1455.

de Souza, N. J., Ghisalberti, E. L., Rees, H. H., and Goodwin, T. W. (1969). *Biochem. J.* **114**, 895.

de Wilde, J. (1964). *In* "The Physiology of Insecta" (M. Rockstein, ed.), Vol. 1, pp. 59–90. Academic Press, New York.

de Wilde, J., and de Boer, J. A. (1961). *J. Insect Physiol.* **6**, 152.

de Wilde, J., and de Boer, J. A. (1969). *J. Insect Physiol.* **15**, 661.

de Wilde, J., and Stegwee, D. (1958). *Arch. Néerl. Zool.* **13**, Suppl. 1, 277.

de Wilde, J., Staal, G. B., de Kort, C. A. D., de Loof, A., and Baard, G. (1968). *Koninkl. Ned. Akad. Wetenschap., Proc.* **C71**, 321.

Doane, W. W. (1961). *J. Exptl. Zool.* **146**, 275.

Doane, W. W. (1963). *In* "Insect Physiology" (V. J. Brookes, ed.), pp. 66–86. Oregon State Univ. Press, Corvallis, Oregon.

Doane, W. W. (1972). *In* "Insects: Developmental Systems" (S. J. Counce and C. H. Waddington, eds.). Academic Press, New York (in press).

Dukes, P. P., Sekeris, C. E., and Schmid, W. (1966). *Biochim. Biophys. Acta* **123**, 126.

Dutrieu, J., and Gourdoux, L. (1967). *Compt. Rend.* **D265**, 1067.

Ebstein, R. P., and Wyatt, G. R. (1971). Unpublished data.

Edström, J. E., and Beermann, W. (1962). *J. Cell Biol.* **14**, 371.

El-Ibrashy, M. T. (1965). *Mededel. Landbouwhogeschool.Wageningen* **65**, No. 11, 1.

El-Ibrashy, M. T., and Boctor, I. Z. (1970). *Z. Vergleich. Physiol.* **68**, 111.

Emmerich, H. (1969). *Exptl. Cell Res.* **58**, 261.

Emmerich, H. (1970a). *J. Insect Physiol.* **16**, 725.

Emmerich, H. (1970b). *Z. Vergleich. Physiol.* **68**, 385.

Emmerich, H., Drews, G., Trautmann, K., and Schmialek, P. (1965a). *Z. Naturforsch.* **20b**, 211.

Emmerich, H., Zahn, A., and Schmialek, P. (1965b). *J. Insect Physiol.* **11**, 1161.

Engelmann, F. (1968). *Ann. Rev. Entomol.* **13**, 1.

Engelmann, F. (1969a). *Science* **165**, 407.

Engelmann, F. (1969b). *Gen. Comp. Endocrinol.* **13**, 503.

Engelmann, F. (1969c). *J. Insect Physiol.* **15**, 217.

Engelmann, F. (1970). "The Physiology of Insect Reproduction." Pergamon Press, Oxford.

Engelmann, F. (1971). *Arch. Biochem. Biophys.* **145**, 439.

Engelmann, F., and Penney, D. (1966). *Gen. Comp. Endocrinol.* **7**, 314.

Engelmann, F., and Wilkens, J. L. (1969). *Nature* **222**, 798.

Feir, D., and Winkler, G. (1969). *J. Insect Physiol.* **15**, 899.

Findlay, J. A., and MacKay, W. D. (1969). *Chem. Commun.* p. 733.

Firshein, W., Berry, S. J., and Swindlehurst, M. (1967). *Biochim. Biophys. Acta* **149**, 190.

Fisher, F. M., and Sanborn, R. C. (1964). *Biol. Bull.* **126**, 235.

Fogal, W., and Fraenkel, G. (1969). *J. Insect Physiol.* **15**, 1235.

Fourche, J. (1967). *Compt. Rend.* **D264**, 2398.

Fraenkel, G. (1935). *Proc. Roy. Soc.* **B118**, 1.

Fraenkel, G., and Hsiao, C. (1962). *Science* **138**, 27.

Fraenkel, G., and Hsiao, C. (1963). *Science* **141**, 1057.

Fraenkel, G., and Hsiao, C. (1965). *J. Insect Physiol.* **11**, 513.

Fraenkel, G., and Hsiao, C. (1967). *J. Insect Physiol.* **13**, 1387.

Fraenkel, G., and Hsiao, C. (1968). *J. Insect Physiol.* **14**, 707.

Fraenkel, G., and Zdarek, J. (1970). *Biol. Bull.* **139**, 138.

Fraenkel, G., Hsiao, C., and Seligman, M. (1966). *Science* **151**, 91.

Friedman, S. (1967). *J. Insect Physiol.* **13**, 397.

Fukuda, S. (1940). *Proc. Imp. Acad. Tokyo* **16**, 417.

Fukuda, S. (1944). *J. Fac. Sci., Imp. Univ. Tokyo Ser. IV* **6**, 477.

Fukuda, S. (1963). *Bull. Soc. Zool. France* **88**, 151.

Fukuda, S., Eguchi, G., and Takeuchi, S. (1966). *Embryologia (Nagoya)* **9**, 123.

Furlenmeier, A., Fürst, A., Langemann, A., Waldvogel, G., Hocks, P., Kerb, U., and Weichert, R. (1967). *Helv. Chim. Acta* **50**, 2387.

Galbraith, M. N., and Horn, D. H. S. (1969). *Australian J. Chem.* **22**, 1045.

Galbraith, M. N., Horn, D. H. S., Hocks, P., Schulz, G., and Hoffmeister, H. (1967). *Naturwissenschaften* **54**, 471.

Galbraith, M. N., Horn, D. H. S., Middleton, E. J., and Hackney, R. J. (1969a). *Australian J. Chem.* **22**, 1517.

Galbraith, M. N., Horn, D. H. S., Thomson, J. A., Neufeld, G. J., and Hackney, R. J. (1969b). *J. Insect Physiol.* **15**, 1225.

Galbraith, M. N., Horn, D. H. S., and Middleton, E. J. (1970). *Chem. Commun.* p. 179.

Gehring, W. (1972). In "Insects: Developmental Systems" (S. J. Counce and C. H. Waddington, eds.). Academic Press, New York (in press).

Gersch, M., and Stürzebecher, J. (1968). *J. Insect Physiol.* **14**, 87.

Gersch, M., and Stürzebecher, J. (1970). *J. Insect Physiol.* **16**, 1813.

Geyer, A., Herda, G., and Schmialek, P. (1968a). *Acta Entomol. Bohemoslov.* **65**, 161.

Geyer, A., Herda, G., and Schmialek, P. (1968b). *Acta Entomol. Bohemoslov.* **65**, 253.

Gilbert, E. F., and Pistey, W. R. (1966). *Proc. Soc. Exptl. Biol. Med.* **121**, 831.

Gilbert, L. I. (1964a). In "The Physiology of Insecta" (M. Rockstein, ed.), Vol. 1, pp. 149–225. Academic Press, New York.

Gilbert, L. I. (1964b). In "The Hormones" (G. Pincus, K. V. Thimann, and E. B. Astwood, eds.), Vol. 4, pp. 67–134. Academic Press, New York.

Gilbert, L. I. (1967a). *Comprehensive Biochem.* **28**, 198–252.

Gilbert, L. I. (1967b). *Advan. Insect Physiol.* **4**, 69.

Gilbert, L. I. (1967c). *Comp. Biochem. Physiol.* **21**, 237.

Gilbert, L. I., and Goodfellow, R. D. (1965). *Zool. Jahrb., Abt. Allgem. Zool. Physiol. Tiere* **8**, 718.

Gilbert, L. I., and Schneiderman, H. A. (1958). *Science* **128**, 844.

Gilbert, L. I., and Schneiderman, H. A. (1960). *Trans. Am. Microscop. Soc.* **79**, 38.

Gilbert, L. I., and Schneiderman, H. A. (1961). *Gen. Comp. Endocrinol.* **1**, 453.

Goldsworthy, G. J. (1969). *J. Insect Physiol.* **15**, 2131.

Goodman, R. M., Goidl, J. A., and Richart, R. M. (1967). *Proc. Natl. Acad. Sci. U. S.* **58**, 553.

Gorbman, A., and Bern, H. A. (1962). "A Textbook of Comparative Endocrinology." Wiley, New York.

Gordon, R. (1970). *Ann. Entomol. Soc. Am.* **63**, 416.

Grant, J. K. (1969). *Essays Biochem.* **5**, 1–58.

Grässmann, A., Geyer, A., Herda, G., and Schmialek, P. (1968). *Acta Entomol. Bohemoslov.* **65**, 92.

Greenstein, M. E. (1971). *J. Morphol.* (in press).

Grossbach, U. (1968). *Ann. Zool. Fenn.* **5**, 37.

Hadorn, E. (1966). *Develop. Biol.* **13**, 424.

Hampshire, F., and Horn, D. H. S. (1966). *Chem. Commun.* p. 37.

Happ, G. M., and Meinwald, J. (1965). *J. Am. Chem. Soc.* **87**, 2507.

Harvey, W. R., and Williams, C. M. (1958). *Biol. Bull.* **114**, 36.

Harvey, W. R., and Williams, C. M. (1961). *J. Insect Physiol.* **7**, 81.

Hasegawa, K. (1957). *Nature* **179**, 1300.

Hasegawa, K. (1964). *J. Exptl. Biol.* **41**, 855.

Hasegawa, K., and Yamashita, O. (1965). *J. Exptl. Biol.* **43**, 271.

Hasegawa, K., and Yamashita, O. (1967). *Nippon Sanshigaku Zasshi* **36**, 297.

Heald, P. J., and McLachlan, P. M. (1965). *Biochem. J.* **94**, 32.

Heinrich, G., and Hoffmeister, H. (1970). *Z. Naturforsch.* **25b**, 358.

Herman, W. S. (1967). *Intern. Rev. Cytol.* **22**, 269.

Herman, W. S. (1968). *In* "Metamorphosis" (W. Etkin and L. I. Gilbert, eds.), pp. 107–141. Appleton, New York.

Herman, W. S., and Gilbert, L. I. (1966). *Gen. Comp. Endocrinol.* **7**, 275.

Highnam, K. C. (1965). *Zool. Jahrb., Abt. Allgem. Zool. Physiol. Tiere* **71**, 558.

Highnam, K. C. (1967). *J. Endocrinol.* **39**, 123.

Highnam, K. C., Lusis, O., and Hill, L. (1963). *J. Insect Physiol.* **9**, 587.

Hikino, H., Hikino, Y., Nomoto, K., and Takemoto, T. (1968). *Tetrahedron* **24**, 4895.

Hill, L. (1962). *J. Insect Physiol.* **8**, 609.

Hill, L. (1965). *J. Insect Physiol.* **11**, 1605.

Hirono, I., Sasaoka, I., and Shimizu, M. (1969). *Gann* **60**, 341.

Hocks, P., and Wiechert, R. (1966). *Tetrahedron Letters* p. 2989.

Hocks, P., Schulz, G., Watzke, E., and Karlson, P. (1967). *Naturwissenschaften* **54**, 44.

Hoffmeister, H. (1966). *Z. Naturforsch.* **21b**, 335.

Hoffmeister, H., and Lang, N. (1964). *Naturwissenschaften* **5**, 112.

Hoffmeister, H., Rufer, C., and Ammon, H. (1965). *Z. Naturforsch.* **20b**, 130.

Hoffmeister, H., Heinrich, G., Staal, G. B., and van der Burg, W. J. (1967a). *Naturwissenschaften* **54**, 471.

Hoffmeister, H., Grutzmacher, H. F., and Dunnebeil, K. (1967b). *Z. Naturforsch.* **22b**, 66.

Hoffmeister, H., Nakanishi, K., Koreeda, M., and Hsu, H. Y. (1968). *J. Insect Physiol.* **14**, 53.

Hori, M. (1969). *Steroids* **14**, 33.

Horn, D. H. S. (1971). *In* "Naturally Occurring Insecticides" (M. Jacobson and D. G. Crosby, eds.), p. 333. Marcel Dekker, New York.

Horn, D. H. S., Middleton, E. J., Wunderlich, J. A., and Hampshire, F. (1966). *Chem. Commun.* p. 339.

Howells, A. J., and Wyatt, G. R. (1969). *Biochim. Biophys. Acta* **174**, 86.

Huber, R., and Hoppe, W. (1965). *Chem. Ber.* **98**, 2403.

Hüppi, G., and Siddall, J. B. (1967). *J. Am. Chem. Soc.* **89**, 7960.

Ichikawa, M., and Ishizaki, H. (1963). *Nature* **198**, 308.

Ilan, J. (1968). *J. Biol. Chem.* **243**, 5859.

Ilan, J., Ilan, J., and Quastel, J. H. (1966). *Biochem. J.* **100**, 441.

Ilan, J., Ilan, J., and Patel, N. (1970). *J. Biol. Chem.* **245**, 1275.

Ishikawa, E., Ishikawa, S., Davis, J. W., and Sutherland, E. W. (1969). *J. Biol. Chem.* **244**, 6371.

Ishizaki, H. (1969). *Develop. Growth Differentiation* **11**, 1.

Ishizaki, H., and Ichikawa, M. (1967). *Biol. Bull.* **133**, 355.

Ito, S., and Loewenstein, W. R. (1965). *Science* **150**, 909.

Janda, V. (1970). *Zool. Jahrb. Abt. Allgem. Zool. Physiol. Tiere* **75**, 361.

Janda, V., and Sláma, K. (1965). *Zool. Jahrb. Abt. Allgem. Zool. Physiol. Tiere* **71**, 345.

Jarolím, V., Hejno, K., Sehnal, F., and Šorm, F. (1969). *Life Sci* **8**, 83.

Jenkin, P. M. (1966). *Ann. Endocrinol. (Paris)* **27**, 331.

Jensen, E. V., and Jacobson, H. I. (1962). *Recent Progr. Hormone Res.* **18**, 387.

Jizba, J., Herout, V., and Šorm, F. (1967). *Tetrahedron Letters* p. 1689.

Johnson, B., and Bowers, B. (1963). *Science* **141**, 264.

Johnson, W. S., Li, T.-t., Faulkner, D. J., and Campbell, S. F. (1968). *J. Am. Chem. Soc.* **90**, 6225.

Johnson, W. S., Campbell, S. F., Krishnakumaran, A., and Meyer, A. S. (1969). *Proc. Natl. Acad. Sci. U. S.* **62**, 1005.

Joly, P. (1945.) *Arch. Zool. Exptl. Gen.* **84**, 49.

Joly, P. (1968). "Endocrinologie des Insects." Masson, Paris.

Joly, P., and Cazal, M. (1969). *Bull. Soc. Zool. France* **94**, 181.

Judy, K. J. (1969). *Science* **165**, 1374.

Kambysellis, M., and Williams, C. M. (1971). *Science* (in press).

Kaplanis, J. N., Tabor, L. A., Thompson, M. J., Robbins, W. E., and Shortino, T. J. (1966a). *Steroids* **8**, 625.

Kaplanis, J. N., Thompson, M. J., Yamamoto, R. T., Robbins, W. E., and Louloudes, S. J. (1966b). *Steroids* **8**, 605.

Kaplanis, J. N., Thompson, M. J., Robbins, W. E., and Bryce, B. M. (1967). *Science* **157**, 1436.

Kaplanis, J. N., Robbins, W. E., Thompson, M. J., and Baumhover, A. M. (1969). *Science* **166**, 1540.

Karlinsky, A. (1967a). *Compt. Rend.* **D264**, 1735.

Karlinsky, A. (1967b). *Compt. Rend.* **D265**, 2040.

Karlson, P. (1956a). *Vitamins Hormones* **14**, 227.

Karlson, P. (1956b). *Ann. Sci. Nat. Zool. Biol. Animale* [11] **18**, 125.

Karlson, P. (1960). *Z. Physiol. Chem.* **318**, 194.

Karlson, P. (1963). *Perspectives Biol. Med.* **6**, 203.

Karlson, P. (1965). *J. Cellular Comp. Physiol.* **66**, 69.

Karlson, P. (1966). *Naturwissenschaften* **53**, 445.

Karlson, P. (1967). *Mem. Soc. Endocrinol.* **15**, 67.

Karlson, P. (1968). *Humangenetik* **6**, 99.

Karlson, P., and Bode, C. (1969). *J. Insect. Physiol.* **15**, 111.

Karlson, P., and Hanser, G. (1953). *Z. Naturforsch.* **8b**, 91.

Karlson, P., and Hoffmeister, H. (1963). *Z. Physiol. Chem.* **331**, 298.

Karlson, P., and Nachtigall, M. (1961). *J. Insect Physiol.* **7**, 210.

Karlson, P., and Peters, G. (1965). *Gen. Comp. Endocrinol.* **5**, 257.

Karlson, P., and Schulz-Enders, A. (1963). *Gen. Comp. Endocrinol.* **3**, 111.

Karlson, P., and Schweiger, A. (1961). *Z. Physiol. Chem.* **323**, 199.

Karlson, P., and Sekeris, C. E. (1962). *Biochim. Biophys. Acta* **63**, 489.

Karlson, P., and Sekeris, C. E. (1964). *Comp. Biochem.* **6**, 221.

Karlson, P., and Sekeris, C. E. (1966a). *Recent Progr. Hormone Res.* **22**, 473.

Karlson, P., and Sekeris, C. E. (1966b). *Acta Endocrinol.* **53**, 505.

Karlson, P., and Shaaya, E. (1964). *J. Insect Physiol.* **10**, 797.

Karlson, P., and Stamm-Menéndez, M. D. (1956). *Z. Physiol. Chem.* **306**, 109.

Karlson, P., Hoffmeister, H., Hoppe, W., and Huber, R. (1963). *Ann. Chem.* **662**, 1.

Karlson, P., Mergenhagen, D., and Sekeris, C. E. (1964a). *Z. Physiol. Chem.* **338**, 42.

Karlson, P., Sekeris, C. E., and Maurer, R. (1964b). *Z. Physiol. Chem.* **336**, 100.

Keeley, L. L., and Friedman, S. (1967). *Gen. Comp. Endocrinol.* **8**, 129.

Keeley, L. L., and Friedman, S. (1969). *J. Insect Physiol.* **15**, 509.

Kerb, U., Schulz, G., Hocks, P., Wiechert, R., Furlenmeier, A., Fürst, A., Langemann, A., and Waldvogel, G. (1966). *Helv. Chim. Acta* **49**, 1601.

Kerb, U., Wiechert, R., Furlenmeier, A., and Fürst, A. (1968). *Tetrahedron Letters* p. 4277.

Kilby, B. A. (1963). *Advan. Insect Physiol.* **1,** 111.

King, D. S. (1970). Personal communication.

King, D. S., and Siddall, J. B. (1969). *Nature* **221,** 955.

Kobayashi, M. (1960). *Nature* **187,** 346.

Kobayashi, M., and Kimura, S. (1967). *J. Insect Physiol.* **13,** 545.

Kobayashi, M., Kirimura, J., and Saito, M. (1962). *Nature* **195,** 515.

Kobayashi, M., Nakanishi, K., and Koreeda, M. (1967a). *Steroids* **9,** 529.

Kobayashi, M., Takemoto, T., Ogawa, S., and Nishimoto, N. (1967b). *J. Insect Physiol.* **13,** 1395.

Kobayashi, M., Kimura, S., and Yamazaki, M. (1967c). *Appl. Entomol. Zool.* **2,** 79.

Kobayashi, M., Ishitoya, Y., and Yamazaki, M. (1968). *Appl. Entomol. Zool.* **3,** 150.

Kopeč, S. (1922). *Biol. Bull.* **42,** 323.

Krishnakumaran, A., and Schneiderman, H. A. (1964). *J. Exptl. Zool.* **157,** 293.

Krishnakumaran, A., and Schneiderman, H. A. (1965). *J. Insect Physiol.* **11,** 1517.

Krishnakumaran, A., and Schneiderman, H. A. (1968). *Nature* **220,** 601.

Krishnakumaran, A., and Schneiderman, H. A. (1969). *Gen. Comp. Endocrinol.* **12,** 515.

Krishnakumaran, A., Berry, S. J., Oberlander, H., and Schneiderman, H. A. (1967). *J. Insect Physiol.* **13,** 1.

Kroeger, H. (1963). *Nature* **200,** 1234.

Kroeger, H. (1964). *Chromosoma* **15,** 36.

Kroeger, H. (1966). *Exptl. Cell Res.* **41,** 64.

Kroeger, H. (1967). *Mem. Soc. Endocrinol.* **15,** 55.

Kroeger, H. (1968). *In* "Metamorphosis" (W. Etkin and L. I. Gilbert, eds.), pp. 185–219. Appleton, New York.

Kroeger, H., and Lezzi, M. (1966). *Ann. Rev. Entomol.* **11,** 1.

Kunkel, J. G. (1970). Personal communication.

Kunkel, J. G., and Pan, M. L. (1971). *Am. Zoologist* **10,** 513.

Kuo, J. F., and Greengard, P. (1969). *Proc. Natl. Acad. Sci. U. S.* **64,** 1349.

Kuo, J. F., Wyatt, G. R., and Greengard, P. (1971). *J. Biol. Chem.* **246,** 7159.

Kurland, C. G., and Schneiderman, H. A. (1959). *Biol. Bull.* **116,** 136.

Kuroda, Y. (1969). *Drosophila Inform. Serv.* **44,** 99.

Lamy, M. (1967). *Compt. Rend.* **D265,** 990.

Langley, P. A. (1966). *J. Insect Physiol.* **12,** 439.

Langley, P. A. (1967). *J. Insect Physiol.* **13,** 1921.

Laufer, H., and Greenwood, H. (1969). *Am. Zoologist* **9,** 603.

Laufer, H., and Holt, T. K. H. (1970). *J. Exptl. Zool.* **173,** 341.

Laverdure, A.-M. (1970). *Année Biol.* **9,** 215.

Law, J. H., Yuan, C., and Williams, C. M. (1966). *Proc. Natl. Acad. Sci. U. S.* **55,** 576.

Lawrence, P. A. (1966). *J. Exptl. Biol.* **44,** 507.

Lea, A. O., and Van Handel, E. (1970). *J. Insect Physiol.* **16,** 319.

Leenders, H. J., Wullems, G. J., and Berendes, H. D. (1970). *Exptl. Cell Res.* **63,** 159.

Lezzi, M. (1966). *Exptl. Cell Res.* **43,** 571.

Lezzi, M. (1967). *Chromosoma* **21,** 109.

Lezzi, M., and Gilbert, L. I. (1969). *Proc. Natl. Acad. Sci. U. S.* **64,** 498.

Lezzi, M., and Gilbert, L. I. (1970). *J. Cell Sci.* **6,** 615.

Linzen, B., and Wyatt, G. R. (1964). *Biochim. Biophys. Acta* **87,** 188.

Locke, M. (1964). *In* "The Physiology of Insecta" (M. Rockstein, ed.), Vol. 3, pp. 379–470. Academic Press, New York.

Locke, M. (1969). *Tissue Cell* 1, 103.

Loew, P., and Johnson, W. S. (1971). *J. Am. Chem. Soc.* 93, 3765.

Lowe, M. E., Horn, D. H. S., and Galbraith, M. N. (1968). *Experientia* 24, 518.

Lucas, K. U., and Wyatt, G. R. (1971). In preparation.

Lüscher, M. (1968). *J. Insect Physiol.* 14, 499.

Lüscher, M., and Karlson, P. (1958). *J. Insect. Physiol.* 1, 341.

Lüscher, M., and Leuthold, R. (1965). *Rev. Suisse Zool.* 72, 618.

Maddrell, S. H. P. (1963). *J. Exptl. Biol.* 40, 247.

Madhavan, K., and Schneiderman, H. A. (1968). *J. Insect Physiol.* 14, 777.

Madhavan, K., and Schneiderman, H. A. (1969). *Biol. Bull.* 137, 321.

Mandaron, P. (1970). *Develop. Biol.* 22, 298.

Marks, E. P. (1970). *Gen. Comp. Endocrinol.* 15, 289.

Marks, E. P., and Leopold, R. A. (1970). *Science* 167, 61.

Marmaras, V. J., Sekeris, C. E., and Karlson, P. (1966). *Acta Biochim. Polon.* 13, 305.

Mayer, R. J., and Candy, D. J. (1969). *J. Insect Physiol.* 15, 611.

Menon, M. (1965a). *Proc. 16th Intern. Congr. Zool., Washington, D. C., 1963* Vol. 1, p. 297. Nat. Hist. Press, Garden City, New York.

Menon, M. (1965b). *J. Animal Morphol. Physiol.* 12, 76.

Menon, M. (1970). *J. Insect Physiol.* 16, 1123.

Meyer, A. S., and Hanzmann, E. (1970). *Biochem. Biophys. Res. Commun.* 41, 891.

Meyer, A. S., Schneiderman, H. A., and Gilbert, L. I. (1965). *Nature* 206, 272.

Meyer, A. S., Schneiderman, H. A., Hanzmann, E., and Ko, J. H. (1968). *Proc. Natl. Acad. Sci. U. S.* 60, 853.

Meyer, A. S., Hanzmann, E., Schneiderman, H. A., Gilbert, L. I., and Boyette, M. (1970). *Arch. Biochem. Biophys.* 137, 190.

Mills, R. R. (1965). *J. Insect Physiol.* 11, 1269.

Mills, R. R., and Lake, C. R. (1966). *J. Insect Physiol.* 12, 1395.

Mills, R. R., and Nielsen, D. J. (1967). *J. Insect Physiol.* 13, 273.

Mills, R. R., and Whitehead, D. L. (1970). *J. Insect Physiol.* 16, 331.

Mills, R. R., Mathur, R. B., and Guerra, A. A. (1965). *J. Insect Physiol.* 11, 1047.

Mills, R. R., Greenslade, F. C., and Couch, E. F. (1966). *J. Insect Physiol.* 12, 767.

Mills, R. R., Lake, C. R., and Alworth, W. L. (1967). *J. Insect Physiol.* 13, 1539.

Mills, R. R., Androuny, S., and Fox, F. R. (1968). *J. Insect Physiol.* 14, 603.

Minks, A. K. (1967). *Arch. Néerl. Zool.* 17, 175.

Mitsuhashi, J., and Grace, T. D. C. (1970). *Appl. Entomol. Zool.* 5, 182.

Mordue, W. (1965). *J. Insect Physiol.* 11, 617.

Mordue, W. (1967). *Comp. Biochem. Physiol.* 23, 721.

Mordue, W. (1969a). *J. Insect Physiol.* 15, 273.

Mordue, W. (1969b). *Gen. Comp. Endocrinol.* 13, 521.

Mordue, W. (1970). *J. Endocrinol.* 46, 119.

Mordue, W., and Goldsworthy, G. J. (1969). *Gen. Comp. Endocrinol.* 12, 360.

Mori, H., Shibata, K., Tsuneda, K., and Sawai, M. (1968). *Chem. & Pharm. Bull. (Tokyo)* 16, 563.

Moriyama, H., Nakanishi, K., King, D. S., Okauchi, T., Siddall, J. B., and Hafferl, W. (1970). *Gen. Comp. Endocrinol.* 15, 80.

Morohoshi, S., and Iijima, T. (1969). *Proc. Japan Acad.* 45, 314.

Müller, H. P., and Engelmann, F. (1968). *Gen. Comp. Endocrinol.* 11, 43.

Nair, K. K. (1967). *Naturwissenschaften* 54, 494.

Naisse, J. (1966). *Arch. Biol. (Liege)* **77**, 139.

Naisse, J. (1969). *J. Insect Physiol.* **15**, 877.

Nakanishi, K. (1971). *Pure Appl. Chem.* **25**, 167.

Nakanishi, K., Koreeda, M., Sasaki, S., Chang, M. L., and Chu, H. Y. (1966). *Chem. Commun.* No. 24, p. 915.

Nakanishi, K., Moriyama, H., Okauchi, T., Fujioka, S., and Koreeda, M. (1971). *Chem. Commun.* (in press).

Natalizi, G. M., and Frontali, N. (1966). *J. Insect Physiol.* **12**, 1279.

Natalizi, G. M., Pansa, M. C., d'Ajello, V., Casaglia, O., Bettini, S., and Frontali, N. (1970). *J. Insect Physiol.* **16**, 1827.

Nayar, K. K. (1954). *Proc. Roy. Entomol. Soc. London* **A29**, 129.

Neufeld, G. J., Thomson, J. A., and Horn, D. S. H. (1968). *J. Insect Physiol.* **14**, 789.

Neugebauer, W. (1961). *Arch. Entwicklungsmech. Organ.* **153**, 314.

Normann, T. C., and Duve, H. (1969). *Gen. Comp. Endocrinol.* **12**, 449.

Novák, V. J. A. (1966). "Insect Hormones," English ed. Methuen, London.

Oberlander, H. (1969a). *J. Insect Physiol.* **15**, 297.

Oberlander, H. (1969b). *J. Insect Physiol.* **15**, 1803.

Oberlander, H., and Schneiderman, H. A. (1966). *J. Insect Physiol.* **12**, 37.

Oberlander, H., Berry, S. J., Krishnakumaran, A., and Schneiderman, H. A. (1965). *J. Exptl. Zool.* **159**, 15.

Odhiambo, T. R. (1966a). *J. Insect Physiol.* **12**, 819.

Odhiambo, T. R. (1966b). *Trans. Roy. Entomol. Soc. London* **118**, 393.

Odhiambo, T. R. (1966c). *J. Exptl. Biol.* **45**, 45.

Odhiambo, T. R. (1966d). *J. Exptl. Biol.* **45**, 51.

Ohtaki, T., Milkman, R. D., and Williams, C. M. (1967). *Proc. Natl. Acad. Sci. U. S.* **58**, 981.

Ohtaki, T., Milkman, R. D., and Williams, C. M. (1968). *Biol. Bull.* **135**, 322.

Okasha, A. Y. K. (1970). *J. Insect Physiol.* **16**, 1579.

Okui, S., Otaka, T., Uchiyama, M., Takemoto, T., Hikino, H., Ogawa, S., and Nishimoto, N. (1968). *Chem. & Pharm. Bull. (Tokyo)* **16**, 384.

Otaka, T., and Uchiyama, M. (1969). *Chem. & Pharm. Bull. (Tokyo)* **17**, 1883.

Otaka, T., Uchiyama, M., Okui, S., Takemoto, T., Hikino, H., Ogawa, S., and Nishimoto, N. (1968). *Chem. & Pharm. Bull. (Tokyo)* **16**, 2426.

Otaka, T., Okui, S., and Uchiyama, M. (1969a). *Chem. & Pharm. Bull. (Tokyo)* **17**, 75.

Otaka, T., Uchiyama, M., Takemoto, T., and Hikino, H. (1969b). *Chem. & Pharm. Bull. (Tokyo)* **17**, 1352.

Ozeki, K. (1965). *Zool. Jahrb., Abt. Allgem. Zool. Physiol. Tiere* **71**, 641.

Pan, M. L. (1970). Personal communication.

Pan, M. L., and Wyatt, G. R. (1971). *Science* **174**, 503.

Pan, M. L., Bell, W. J., and Telfer, W. H. (1969). *Science* **165**, 393.

Patel, N., and Madhavan, K. (1969). *J. Insect Physiol.* **15**, 2141.

Pelling, C. (1964). *Chromosoma* **15**, 71.

Pfeiffer, I. W. (1945). *J. Exptl. Zool.* **99**, 183.

Pflugfelder, O. (1958). "Entwicklungsphysiologie der Insekten," 2nd ed. Akad. Verlagsges., Leipzig.

Pipa, R. L. (1969). *J. Exptl. Zool.* **170**, 181.

Poels, C. L. M. (1970). *Develop. Biol.* **23**, 210.

Pohley, J. H. (1961). *Arch. Entwicklungsmech. Organ.* **153**, 443.

Postlethwait, J. H., and Schneiderman, H. A. (1970). *Biol. Bull.* **138**, 47.

Raabe, M. (1959). *Bull. Soc. Zool. France* **84**, 272.

Ralph, C. L. (1962). *Am. Zoologist* **2**, 550.

Ralph, C. L., and McCarthy, R. (1964). *Nature* **203**, 1195.

Ralph, C. L., and Matta, R. J. (1965). *J. Insect. Physiol.* **11**, 983.

Reinecke, J. P., and Robbins, J. D. (1971). *Exptl. Cell Res.* **64**, 335.

Riddiford, L. M. (1970). *Science* **167**, 287.

Riddiford, L. M., and Williams, C. M. (1967). *Proc. Natl. Acad. Sci. U. S.* **57**, 595.

Robbins, W. E., Kaplanis, J. N., Thompson, M. J., Shortino, T. J., and Joyner, S. C. (1970). *Steroids* **16**, 105.

Röller, H., and Bjerke, J. S. (1965). *Life Sci.* **4**, 1617.

Röller, H., and Dahm, K. H. (1968). *Recent Progr. Hormone Res.* **24**, 651.

Röller, H., and Dahm, K. H. (1970). *Naturwissenschaften* **57**, 454.

Röller, H., Bjerke, J. S., and McShan, W. H. (1965). *J. Insect Physiol.* **11**, 1185.

Röller, H., Dahm, K. H., Sweely, C. C., and Trost, B. M. (1967). *Angew, Chem. Intern. Ed. Engl.* **6**, 179.

Röller, H., Bjerke, J. S., Holthaus, L. M., Norgard, D. W., and McShan, W. H. (1969). *J. Insect Physiol.* **15**, 379.

Romaňuk, M., Sláma, K., and Šorm, F. (1967). *Proc. Natl. Acad. Sci. U. S.* **57**, 349.

Romer, F. (1971). *Naturwissenschaften* **58**, 324.

Rose, M., Westermann, J., Trautmann, H., Schmialek, P., and Klauske, J. (1968). *Z. Naturforsch.* **23b**, 1245.

Roth, T. F., and Porter, K. R. (1964). *J. Cell Biol.* **20**, 313.

Roussel, J. P. (1963). *J. Insect Physiol.* **9**, 721.

Sägesser, H. (1960). *J. Insect Physiol.* **5**, 264.

Sahota, T. S., and Mansingh, A. (1970). *J. Insect Physiol.* **16**, 1649.

Sato, Y., Sakai, M., Imai, S., and Fujioka, S. (1968). *Appl. Entomol. Zool.* (*Tokyo*) **3**, 49.

Sauer, H. H., Bennett, R. D., and Heftmann, E. (1968). *Phytochemistry* **7**, 2027.

Scharrer, B. (1946). *Endocrinology* **38**, 46.

Scharrer, B. (1964). *Z. Zellforsch. Mikroskop. Anat.* **62**, 125.

Scharrer, B., and Kater, S. B. (1969). *Z. Zellforsch. Mikroskop. Anat.* **95**, 177.

Scheurer, R. (1969a). *J. Insect Physiol.* **15**, 1411.

Scheurer, R. (1969b). *J. Insect Physiol.* **15**, 1673.

Scheurer, R., and Lüscher, M. (1968). *Rev. Suisse Zool.* **75**, 715.

Schmialek, P. (1961). *Z. Naturforsch.* **16b**, 461.

Schmialek, P. (1963). *Z. Naturforsch.* **18b**, 462.

Schmialek, P., and Drews, G. (1965). *Z. Naturforsch.* **20b**, 214.

Schmidt, E. L., and Williams, C. M. (1953). *Biol. Bull.* **105**, 174.

Schneiderman, H. A., and Gilbert, L. I. (1958). *Biol. Bull.* **115**, 530.

Schneiderman, H. A., and Williams, C. M. (1953). *Biol. Bull.* **105**, 320.

Schneiderman, H. A., and Williams, C. M. (1954). *Biol. Bull.* **106**, 210.

Schneiderman, H. A., Gilbert, L. I., and Weinstein, M. (1960). *Nature* **188**, 1041.

Scheiderman, H. A., Krishnakumaran, A., Kulkarni, V. G., and Friedman, L. (1965). *J. Insect Physiol.* **11**, 1641.

Schwarz, M., Braun, B. H., Law, M. W., Sonnet, P. E., Wakabayashi, N., Waters, R. M., and Jacobson, M. (1969). *Ann. Entomol. Soc. Am.* **62**, 668.

Schweiger, A., and Karlson, P. (1962). *Z. Physiol. Chem.* **329**, 210.

Sehnal, F. (1966). *Acta Entomol. Bohemoslov.* **63**, 258.

Sehnal, F. (1968). *J. Insect Physiol.* **14**, 73.

Sehnal, F., and Meyer, A. S. (1968). *Science* **159**, 981.

Sehnal, F., and Sláma, K. (1966). *J. Insect Physiol.* **12**, 1333.

Sekeris, C. E. (1963). *Z. Physiol. Chem.* **332**, 70.

Sekeris, C. E. (1964). *Science* **144**, 419.

Sekeris, C. E. (1967). *In* "Regulation of Nucleic Acid and Protein Biosynthesis" (V. V. Koningsberger and L. Bosch, eds.), pp. 388–394. Elsevier, Amsterdam.

Sekeris, C. E., and Karlson, P. (1962). *Biochim. Biophys. Acta* **62**, 103.

Sekeris, C. E., and Karlson, P. (1964). *Arch. Biochem. Biophys.* **105**, 483.

Sekeris, C. E., and Karlson, P. (1966). *Pharmacol. Rev.* **18**, 89.

Sekeris, C. E., and Lang, N. (1964). *Life Sci.* **3**, 625.

Sekeris, C. E., Lang, N., and Karlson, P. (1965a). *Life Sci.* **3**, 169. .

Sekeris, C. E., Dukes, P. P., and Schmid, H. (1965b). *Z. Physiol. Chem.* **341**, 152.

Seligman, M., Friedman, S., and Fraenkel, G. (1969). *J. Insect Physiol.* **15**, 1085.

Shaaya, E. (1969). *Z. Naturforsch.* **24b**, 718.

Shaaya, E., and Bodenstein, D. (1969). *J. Exptl. Zool.* **170**, 281.

Shaaya, E., and Karlson, P. (1965a). *J. Insect Physiol.* **11**, 65.

Shaaya, E., and Karlson, P. (1965b). *Develop. Biol.* **11**, 424.

Shaaya, E., and Sekeris, C. E. (1965). *Gen. Comp. Endocrinol.* **5**, 35.

Shaaya, E., and Sekeris, C. E. (1970). *J. Insect Physiol.* **16**, 323.

Shappirio, D. G. (1960). *Ann. N. Y. Acad. Sci.* **89**, 537.

Shappirio, D. G., and Harvey, W. R. (1965). *J. Insect Physiol.* **11**, 305.

Shappirio, D. G., and Williams, C. M. (1957). *Proc. Roy. Soc.* **B147**, 233.

Shigematsu, H. (1958). *Nature* **182**, 880.

Shigematsu, H., and Moriyama, H. (1970). *J. Insect Physiol.* **16**, 2015.

Siddall, J. B. (1970). *In* "Chemical Ecology" (E. Sondheimer and J. B. Simeone, eds.), pp. 281–306. Academic Press, New York.

Siddall, J. B., and Staal, G. B. (1971). Personal communication.

Siddall, J. B., Cross, A. D., and Fried, J. H. (1966). *J. Am. Chem. Soc.* **88**, 862.

Skinner, D. M. (1963). *Biol. Bull.* **125**, 165.

Sláma, K. (1964a). *J. Insect Physiol.* **10**, 283.

Sláma, K. (1964b). *Biol. Bull.* **127**, 499.

Sláma, K. (1965). *J. Insect Physiol.* **11**, 1121.

Sláma, K., and Williams, C. M. (1966a). *Biol. Bull.* **130**, 235.

Sláma, K., and Williams, C. M. (1966b). *Nature* **210**, 329.

Sláma, K., Suchý, M., and Šorm, F. (1968). *Biol. Bull.* **134**, 154.

Sláma, K., Romaňuk, M., and Šorm, F. (1969). *Biol. Bull.* **136**, 91.

Sonnet, P. E., Braun, B. H., Law, M. W., Schwarz, M., Wakabayashi, N., Waters, R. M., and Jacobson, M. (1969). *Ann. Entomol. Soc. Am.* **62**, 667.

Spielman, A., and Skaff, V. (1967). *J. Insect Physiol.* **13**, 1087.

Spielman, A., and Williams, C. M. (1966). *Science* **154**, 1043.

Spinner, W. (1969). *Arch. Entwicklungsmech. Organ.* **163**, 259.

Srivastava, U. S., and Gilbert, L. I. (1968). *Science* **161**, 61.

Srivastava, U. S., and Gilbert, L. I. (1969). *J. Insect Physiol.* **15**, 177.

Staal, G. B. (1967). *Kon. Ned. Akad. Wetenschap., Proc.* **70**, 409.

Stamm, M. D. (1958). *Rev. Espan. Fisiol.* **14**, 263.

Stamm, M. D. (1959). *Anales Real Soc. Espan. Fis. Quim.* (*Madrid*) **B55**, 171.

Steele, J. E. (1961). *Nature* **192**, 680.

Steele, J. E. (1963). *Gen. Comp. Endocrinol.* **3**, 46.

Steele, J. E. (1964). *Am. Zoologist* **4**, 328.

Stegwee, D. (1960). *Proc. 11th Intern. Congr. Entomol., Vienna 1960* Vol. 3, p. 218.

Stegwee, D. (1964). *J. Insect Physiol.* **10**, 97.

Stegwee, D., Kimmel, E. C., de Boer, J. A., and Henstra, S. (1963). *J. Cell Biol.* **19**, 519.

Stephen, W. F., and Gilbert, L. I. (1970). *J. Insect Physiol.* **16**, 851.

Stevenson, E., and Wyatt, G. R. (1962). *Arch. Biochem. Biophys.* **99**, 65.

Stevenson, E., and Wyatt, G. R. (1964). *Arch. Biochem. Biophys.* **108**, 420.

Stowe, B. B. (1971). *Proc. 7th Intern. Conf. Plant Growth Substances, Canberra, 1970* (in press).

Stowe, B. B., and Hudson, V. W. (1969). *Plant Physiol.* **44**, 1051.

Svoboda, J. A., and Robbins, W. E. (1968). *Experientia* **24**, 1131.

Takemoto, T., Ogawa, S., Nishimoto, N., and Hoffmeister, H. (1967). *Z. Naturforsch.* **22b**, 681.

Taylor, R. L., and Richards, A. G. (1965). *J. Morphol.* **116**, 1.

Telfer, W. H. (1954). *J. Gen. Physiol.* **37**, 539.

Telfer, W. H. (1960). *Biol. Bull.* **118**, 338.

Telfer, W. H. (1965). *Ann. Rev. Entomol.* **10**, 161.

Telfer, W. H., and Williams, C. M. (1960). *J. Insect Physiol.* **5**, 61.

Thomas, K. K., and Gilbert, L. I. (1969). *Physiol. Chem. Phys.* **1**, 293.

Thomas, K. K., and Nation, J. L. (1966a). *Biol. Bull.* **130**, 254.

Thomas, K. K., and Nation, J. L. (1966b). *Biol. Bull.* **130**, 442.

Thompson, M. J., Kaplanis, J. N., Robbins, W. E., and Yamamoto, R. T. (1967). *Chem. Commun.* p. 650.

Thomsen, E. (1949). *J. Exptl. Biol.* **26**, 137.

Thomsen, E. (1952). *J. Exptl. Biol.* **29**, 137.

Thomsen, E. (1966). *Z. Zellforsch. Mikroskop. Anat.* **75**, 281.

Thomsen, E. (1969). *Z. Zellforsch. Mikroskop. Anat.* **94**, 205.

Thomsen, E., and Lea, A. O. (1968). *Gen. Comp. Endocrinol.* **12**, 51.

Thomsen, E., and Møller, I. (1963). *J. Exptl. Biol.* **40**, 301.

Thomson, J. A., and Horn, D. H. S. (1969). *Australian J. Biol. Sci.* **22**, 761.

Thomson, J. A., Imray, F. P., and Horn, D. H. S. (1970a). *Australian J. Exptl. Biol. Med. Sci.* **48**, 321.

Thomson, J. A., Rogers, D. C., Gunson, M. M., and Horn, D. H. S. (1970b). *Cytobios* **6**, 79.

Trost, B. M. (1970). *Accounts Chem. Res.* **3**, 120.

Truman, J. W., and Riddiford, L. M. (1970). *Science* **167**, 1624.

Tsao, M., Jou, G., and Chiang, T. (1963). *Acta Biol. Exptl. Sinica* **8**, 538.

Vanderberg, J. P. (1963). *Biol. Bull.* **125**, 576.

van der Kloot, W. G. (1960). *Ann. Rev. Entomol.* **5**, 35.

Van Handel, E., and Lea, A. O. (1970). *Gen. Comp. Endocrinol.* **14**, 381.

Van Tamelen, E. E., and McCormick, J. P. (1970). *J. Am. Chem. Soc.* **92**, 737.

Vincent, J. F. (1969). *Gen. Comp. Endocrinol.* **13**, 538.

Vogt, M. (1949). *Z. Zellforsch. Mikroskop. Anat.* **34**, 160.

Vroman, H. E., Kaplanis, J. N., and Robbins, W. E. (1965). *J. Insect Physiol.* **11**, 897.

Wakabayashi, N. (1969). *J. Med. Chem.* **12**, 191.

Wakabayashi, N., Sonnet, P. E., and Law, M. W. (1969). *J. Med. Chem.* **12**, 911.

Waku, Y., and Gilbert, L. I. (1964). *J. Morphol.* **115**, 69.

Wall, B. J. (1967). *J. Insect Physiol.* **13**, 565.

Wallace, R. A., and Dumont, J. H. (1968). *J. Cellular Physiol.* **72**, 73.

Wang, S., and Dixon, S. E. (1960). *Can. J. Zool.* **38**, 275.

Waterhouse, D. F. (1957). *Ann. Rev. Entomol.* **2**, 1.
Weir, S. B. (1970). *Nature* **228**, 580.
Weirich, G., and Karlson, P. (1969). *Arch. Entwicklungsmech. Organ.* **164**, 170.
Westermann, J., Rose, M., Trautmann, H., and Klauske, J. (1969). *Z. Naturforsch.* **24b**, 378.
Whitehead, D. L. (1969). *Nature* **224**, 721.
Whitten, J. M. (1969). *Chromosoma* **26**, 215.
Wiens, A. W., and Gilbert, L. I. (1965). *Science* **150**, 614.
Wiens, A. W., and Gilbert, L. I. (1967a). *J. Insect Physiol.* **13**, 779.
Wiens, A. W., and Gilbert, L. I. (1967b). *Comp. Biochem. Physiol.* **21**, 145.
Wigglesworth, V. B. (1934). *Quart. J. Microscop. Sci.* **77**, 191.
Wigglesworth, V. B. (1936). *Quart. J. Microscop. Sci.* **79**, 91.
Wigglesworth, V. B. (1940). *J. Exptl. Biol.* **17**, 201.
Wigglesworth, V. B. (1948). *J. Exptl. Biol.* **25**, 1.
Wigglesworth, V. B. (1954). "The Physiology of Insect Metamorphosis." Cambridge Univ. Press, London and New York.
Wigglesworth, V. B. (1955). *J. Exptl. Biol.* **32**, 649.
Wigglesworth, V. B. (1957). *Symp. Soc. Exptl. Biol.* **11**, 204.
Wigglesworth, V. B. (1958). *J. Insect Physiol.* **2**, 73.
Wigglesworth, V. B. (1959). "The Control of Growth and Form." Cornell Univ. Press, Ithaca, New York.
Wigglesworth, V. B. (1963a). *J. Exptl. Biol.* **40**, 231.
Wigglesworth, V. B. (1963b). *J. Insect Physiol.* **9**, 105.
Wigglesworth, V. B. (1964). *Advan. Insect Physiol.* **2**, 243.
Wigglesworth, V. B. (1965). *Nature* **208**, 522.
Wigglesworth, V. B. (1969). *J. Insect Physiol.* **15**, 73.
Wigglesworth, V. B. (1970). "Insect Hormones." Oliver & Boyd, Edinburgh and London.
Wilkens, J. L. (1969). *J. Insect Physiol.* **15**, 1015.
Williams, C. M. (1947). *Biol. Bull.* **93**, 89.
Williams, C. M. (1951). *Federation Proc.* **10**, 546.
Williams, C. M. (1952). *Biol. Bull.* **103**, 120.
Williams, C. M. (1954). *Anat. Record* **120**, 743.
Williams, C. M. (1956). *Nature* **178**, 212.
Williams, C. M. (1959). *Biol. Bull.* **116**, 323.
Williams, C. M. (1961). *Biol. Bull.* **121**, 572.
Williams, C. M. (1963). *Biol. Bull.* **124**, 355.
Williams, C. M. (1965). *Science* **148**, 670.
Williams, C. M. (1967). *In* "Insects and Physiology" (J. W. L. Beament and J. E. Treherne, eds.), pp. 133–139. Oliver & Boyd, Edinburgh and London.
Williams, C. M. (1968). *Biol. Bull.* **134**, 344.
Williams, C. M. (1970). *In* "Chemical Ecology" (E. Sondheimer and J. B. Simeone, eds.), pp. 103–132. Academic Press, New York.
Williams, C. M., and Kambysellis, M. (1969). *Proc. Natl. Acad. Sci. U. S.* **63**, 231.
Williams, C. M., and Law, J. H. (1965). *J. Insect Physiol.* **11**, 569.
Williams, C. M., and Robbins, W. E. (1968). *BioScience* **18**, 791.
Williams, C. M., Moorhead, L. V., and Pulis, J. F. (1959). *Nature* **183**, 405.
Willis, J. H. (1966). *J. Insect. Physiol.* **12**, 933.
Willis, J. H. (1969). *J. Embryol. Exptl. Morphol.* **22**, 27.
Willis, J. H., and Brunet, P. C. J. (1966). *J. Exptl. Biol.* **44**, 363.

Willis, J. H., and Lawrence, P. A. (1970). *Nature* **225**, 81.

Wright, J. E. (1969). *Science* **163**, 390.

Wu, T. H., and Quo, F. (1963). *Acta Entomol. Sinica* **12**, 402.

Wyatt, G. R. (1959). *Proc. 4th Intern. Congr. Biochem., Vienna, 1958* Vol. 12, p. 161. Pergamon Press, Oxford.

Wyatt, G. R. (1963). *In* "Insect Physiology" (V. J. Brookes, ed.), pp. 23–41. Oregon State Univ. Press, Corvallis, Oregon.

Wyatt, G. R. (1967). *Advan. Insect Physiol.* **4**, 287.

Wyatt, G. R. (1968a). *In* "Metamorphosis" (W. Etkin and L. I. Gilbert, eds.), pp. 143–184. Appleton, New York.

Wyatt, G. R. (1968b). *Abstr. 7th Intern. Congr. Biochem., Tokyo, 1967* Vol. 2, p. 389. Sci. Council Japan, Tokyo.

Wyatt, G. R. (1970). Unpublished data.

Wyatt, G. R. (1971). In preparation.

Wyatt, G. R., and Linzen, B. (1965). *Biochim. Biophys. Acta* **103**, 588.

Wyatt, S. S., and Wyatt, G. R. (1971). *Gen. Comp. Endocrinol.* **16**, 369.

Wyss-Huber, M., and Lüscher, M. (1966). *Rev. Suisse Zool.* **73**, 517.

Yagi, S., Kondo, E., and Fukaya, M. (1969). *Appl. Entomol. Zool.* **4**, 70.

Yamamoto, R. T., and Jacobson, M. (1962). *Nature* **196**, 908.

Yamashita, O. (1969). *Nippon Sanshigaku Zasshi* **38**, 329.

Yamashita, O., and Hasegawa, K. (1964). *Nippon Sanshigaku Zasshi* **33**, 407.

Yamashita, O., and Hasegawa, K. (1966). *J. Insect Physiol.* **12**, 957.

Yamashita, O., and Hasegawa, K. (1967). *Proc. Japan Acad.* **43**, 547.

Yamashita, O., and Hasegawa, K. (1970). *J. Insect Physiol.* **16**, 2377.

Yamazaki, M., and Kobayashi, M. (1969). *J. Insect Physiol.* **15**, 1981.

Zalokar, M. (1968). *J. Insect Physiol.* **14**, 1177.

Zaoral, M., and Sláma, K. (1970). *Science* **170**, 92.

Zdarek, J., and Fraenkel, G. (1969). *Proc. Natl. Acad. Sci. U. S.* **64**, 565.

Zurflüh, R., Wall, E. N., Siddall, J. B., and Edwards, J. A. (1968). *J. Am. Chem. Soc.* **90**, 6224.

AUTHOR INDEX

Numbers in italics refer to the pages on which the complete references are listed.

SUBJECT INDEX

A

Acetate, 168, 191, 297, 298, 304–305, 324
Acetylaminofluorene, 135
N-Acetyldopamine, 468
  oxidation of, 417
Achyranthes fauriei, 396
Acid phosphatase, 148, 274
Acinar cells, 173–174, 206
ACTH, 40, 43, 186, 188, 194, 272, 306, 310–312, 318, 320, 322–324, 326, 328, 330–331
  adenyl cyclase and, 33
  "basic core" in, 318
  effects of, 325
  functional specificity, 318
  molecule, 318
  release, inhibition of, 10
  responsiveness, 329
    macromolecules in, 328
  -sensitive cyclase, 326
  site of action of, 319
  steroidogenic effect of, 319
ACTH-^{125}I, binding of to adrenal adenyl cyclase, 32
Actinomycin, 138, 329, 468
Actinomycin D, 14–16, 67, 146–147, 149–150, 168, 219–222, 226, 276, 278, 280–281, 284–285, 368–369, 377, 427, 461
  binding, 281
  inhibition of hormonal enzyme induction by, 12
Acrylamide gel electrophoresis, 220
Adenine 1-methylase, 73
Adenine N^6-methylase, 73
Adenohypophysis, 48
Adenosine, 44
Adenosine 5′-monophosphate, *see* 5′-AMP
Adenosinetriphosphate, *see* ATP
Adenosinetriphosphatase, *see* ATPase
S-Adenosyl-L-methionine decarboxylase, putrescine-dependent, 273
Adenyl cyclase, 10, 23, 28, 33, 38–39, 41,

86–87, 94–95, 101, 105–106, 156, 191–195, 198–199, 201–202, 249, 272, 307, 325, *see also* hormones affecting
  bacteria, 6
  bacterial, 32
  brain, 31
  epinephrine sensitive, 43
  of fat cells, 40
  hepatic, 88
  inhibition of, 89
  localization of, 30–31
  in nerve endings, 30
  PGE$_1$-sensitive, 43
  of pineal gland, 99
  platelet, 101
  stimulation of, 97
  storage of, 32, 39
  system(s), 181
    distribution and hormonal sensitivity, 28
Adipocyte(s), 98, 168, 170, 182–188, 190, 192–194, 196, 199, 203, 207
  ghosts, 194
Adipokinetic hormone, 464
Adipose cells, 145
Adipose tissue, 90, 145, 169–171, 176–178, 193–194, 196, 200, 202, 204, 206–207
  brown, 92, 97
  cells, 190
  effects of insulin on, 167
  perirenal, 169
  white, 92, 168
Adrenal, 311
Adrenal cell, 319, 325
Adrenal cortex, 318, 324–325
  effect of ACTH on, 317
Adrenal glands, 46
Adrenal hormone, as pleiotypic effectors, 13
Adrenal medulla, 82
Adrenal slices, 306
Adrenal tissue, 297

-dependent ion translocating enzymes, 277
in enzyme degradation, 152
inhibition of phosphodiesterase, 41
levels, 129
production, by mammalian cell nuclei, 276
ATPase, 31
activity, 132
of microsomes, 277
calcium-dependent, 365, 371, 378
mitochondrial, 457
Avenaciolide, 184
Avidin synthesis, 222
Azide, 352, 428

B

Bacteria, stringent control in, 8
Balbiani rings, 423, 462, *see also*
Chromosome puffs
Bile, 359
acids, 146
Binder I, 119–121, 135
Binder II, 118, 121, 136
Binder III, 119, 121
Binder IV, 118
Binding assay, 38
Binding proteins
corticosteroids, 117
for estradiol, 10
for progesterone, 10
Blaberus discoidalis, 473
Blatella germanica, 460
Blatta orientalis, 472
Bleeding time, 100
Blood, 100
circulation, 128
flow, 100
glucose, 93
lactate, 93
stream, 116
sugar levels, 170
supply, 132
Blowfly, 417
larvae, 393
Bombyx, 399–400, 402
silkworm pupae, 395
Bombyx mori, 397, 399, 468
Bone, 46, 196
fetal, 48

mineral mobilization, 350, 356
assay, 353
mobilization, 375, 377
Brain, 132, 196
hormone, 391
characterization of, in insects, 466
neurosecretory cells, 388
slices, 104
guinea pig, 44
Breast cancers, 230
Brevibacterium liquefaciens, 32
adenyl cyclase from, 28
Bursicon, 464, 467–468
characterization of, 467
Butanol, 122

C

Caffeine, 33, 47
level of cyclic AMP and, 91
Calcification, 360
Calcitonin, 373–378
Calcium, 33, 90, 360, 362–363, 376
absorption, 361, 374
binding protein, 364–365
turnover, 365
complexing agents, 325
intestinal absorption of, 368, 373
ions, 94, 236
levels, serum, 373
transport, 363, 366–367, 369, 371
intestinal, 343, 350, 357, 364, 368
lag in, 367
tubular reabsorption of, 362
Callantine, 226
Calliphora, 399–400, 413, 417–419, 429–430
assay, 395
test, 397
Calliphora erythrocephala, 393, 398–399, 456, 458, 472
Calliphora stygia, 393, 398
Calliphora vicina, 398
Calorigenic effect, 96–97
Calpodes, 413
Cancer, *see* specific types
Carbohydrate(s)
availability, 145
lipid metabolism, 165
metabolic pathways, 167
metabolism, 183, 207

Etiocholanolone, 146
European puss moth, 411
Evolution, 208
Exocuticle, 389, 468
Exocytosis, 101
Exopterygota, 388
Exoskeleton, 387

F

Facefly, 411
Factor ρ, 2
Factor ψR, 4
Fanconi syndrome, 372
Farnesoate, 441
Farnesol, 437, 439–440
Farnesyl methyl ether, 444, 461
Fasting, 137
 levels of insulin during, 177
Fat body, 413
Fat cells, 188
 isolated, 27
Fatty acid(s), 168–169, 171–173, 176,
  179, 191, 200, 350
 biosynthesis, 203
 free, *see* Free fatty acids
 metabolism, 182–183, 207
 mobilization, 145
 oxidation, 177–178, 197, 201
 synthesis, 178, 181, 205
Fetal calves, 170
Fetus, 119
Fibroblast(s), 8, 10, 196
 culture, 122
Ficin, 184
Filipin, 184
Flour moth larvae, 411
Fluoride, 39
Fluorocorticosteroids, 157
5-Fluorodeoxyuridine, 416
9α-Fluoroprednisolone, 130–131
Follicle stimulating hormone, *see* FSH
Foot pad chromosomes, *Sarcophaga*, 427
Free fatty acids (FFA), 97
 mobilization of, 91
 release, and cyclic AMP, 27
Frog skin, 99–100
Fructose diphosphate, 139
Fructose-1,6-diphosphatase, 204

Fruiting body, 175
FSH, 296, 298, 307, 312–313
 influence of, 301
Fungi, 6
Fungus gnat, 415

G

Galactose, 168, 194
Galactosyltransferase, 63, 66–67, 75
Galleria, 412, 417
Galleria mellonella, 411, 440, 456
Gastrin, 171–172
Gel filtration, 266
Gene(s), 2
 activity, flies, 386
 activation, 426
 expression, 272, 278
  regulation of, 16, 278
   by steroids, 12
 regulatory, 2
 repression, 1
 transcription, 59
  regulation of, 12
Genetic code, 5, 11
Genetic information
 flow of, 275
 unmasking, 371
Genetic recombination, 6
Genetic regulation, 1
Genital tract structures, 259
Genome, 116, 125, 148, 282–283
 activation, 217
 transcription of, 11
Gestagens, 257
Glass, powdered, 235
α₂-Globulin, 359, 372
Glossina morsitans, 472
Glucagon, 7, 22, 25, 27, 40, 56, 88–89,
  94, 98, 144, 155–156, 171–173, 192,
  194, 198–199, 201, 272
Glucocorticoid(s), 89, 113–114, 128–129,
  133–134, 136–137, 141, 144–146,
  148, 151, 153, 223, *see also* specific
  hormones
 binding (of), 115, 121, 129, 134
 fate of, 115
 fluorinated, 130, 134
 hormones, 56
 induction, 153
Glucokinase, 205